The Chemistry
of Organic
Medicinal Products

FOURTH EDITION

Glenn L. Jenkins

*Professor of Pharmaceutical Chemistry
and Dean of the School of Pharmacy
Purdue University*

Walter H. Hartung

*Professor of Pharmaceutical Chemistry
Medical College of Virginia*

Kenneth E. Hamlin, Jr.

*Assistant Director of Chemical Research
Abbott Laboratories*

John B. Data

*Associate Professor of Pharmaceutical Chemistry
The School of Pharmacy
Purdue University*

The Chemistry
of Organic
Medicinal Products

9161

New York · JOHN WILEY & SONS, Inc.

London · CHAPMAN & HALL, Ltd.

Library of Congress Catalog Card Number: 57–8889

PRINTED IN THE UNITED STATES OF AMERICA

Preface
to the Fourth Edition

Medicinal chemistry tends to become more and more the study of the chemical reactions between therapeutic agents and living tissues. In 1940 practically nothing was known about the processes by which drugs produce their effect, how they react with protoplasm and how they are in turn modified, detoxified, metabolized, or eliminated by the living organism. Appreciable progress in this direction is being made, and a book on medicinal chemistry must, perforce, take cognizance of these stimulating developments.

Medicinal chemistry viewed in this newer light becomes complex and extensive. In order to keep this volume within reasonable limits and cost, the authors struggled with a conflicting desire to produce a book that is yet essentially complete and up to date. The compromise, regrettably, makes it necessary to limit the discussion of even the most important topics. It is anticipated, however, that where the book is used in the class room the text will be amplified and expanded by the instructor, and that where it is used for reference purposes the literature citations may lead the student or investigator to additional sources of information.

This edition is completely revised, and all the type has been set anew. The chemical classification of medicinal agents has been retained. Elementary organic chemistry has been eliminated, but typical syntheses of important medicinal agents have been included, along with a description of properties. Correlations between chemical structure and physiological activities are pointed out. Wherever possible, protoplasmic reactions are indicated. With very few exceptions, the text does not refer to literature after April, 1956.

The separate chapter on antibiotics may appear to contradict the objectives announced above. It is felt, however, that such a heterogeneous group of chemical compounds, having in common antimicroorganic activity and genesis from molds, may advantageously be grouped together at the present stage of antibiotic history.

Friends too numerous to mention have helped with criticisms, suggestions, and encouragement, and to them all our sincere thanks. Especial appreciation is expressed to Dr. R. D. Coghill for his assistance with the chapter on antibiotics and to Messrs. John Andrako and L. Neelakantan for reading the manuscript during its production.

GLENN L. JENKINS
WALTER H. HARTUNG
KENNETH E. HAMLIN, JR.
JOHN B. DATA

June, 1957

Contents

Chapter

Compounds Composed
of Carbon and Hydrogen

SATURATED HYDROCARBONS

The saturated hydrocarbon compounds are not used extensively as medicinal agents. The lower members of the alkane series which are volatile and relatively soluble in water give rise to the characteristic narcotic effects of hydrocarbon groups on inhalation, and larger amounts cause asphyxiation. Simple aliphatic compounds cause a reversible depression of activity in living tissues; their action depends on their general physical properties which cause them to concentrate on surfaces and in lipids. Methane is weakly anesthetic, the effective dose being but little less than the toxic dose. The narcotic activity increases with increase in molecular weight; the toxicity also increases but probably less rapidly. The maximum activity is reported for heptane, octane being less active. It has been reported that the branched-chain compounds are more narcotic than their straight-chain isomers; later work has not supported these conclusions.[1] The liquid members of this group are irritants to the nerve endings in the skin and mucous membranes, increasing in activity up to heptane and then declining in activity.

The following quantities of hydrocarbons were found to produce the same toxic effects on mice:[2]

> 0.377 gram pentane
> 0.147 gram hexane
> 0.064 gram heptane
> 0.037 gram octane

Octane has about the same toxic effect as benzene.

[1] Stoughton and Lamson, *J. Pharmacol.*, **58,** 74 (1936); *C.A.*, **31,** 465 (1937).
[2] Liesegang, *Angew. Chem.*, **45,** 329 (1932); *C.A.*, **26,** 3898 (1932).

The nonvolatile, water-insoluble alkanes are not active physiologically since they are not absorbed. It thus appears that the physiological activity of the saturated hydrocarbons is dependent chiefly upon their physical properties.

Bacteria isolated from oil-bearing soil, from abscesses, and from mastitis are reported capable of metabolizing all the higher fractions of petroleum hydrocarbons, even paraffin wax; the organisms show no diminution of growth after 15 transfers under kerosene. Respiration studies indicate that long-chain organic acids and unsaturated hydrocarbons are formed by such bacterial decomposition.[3]

The most important natural source of saturated hydrocarbons is petroleum. The low-boiling compounds, up to butane, are found in natural gas; the pentane and hexane fractions are known as petroleum ether or petroleum benzin; frequently the heptane fraction is included in ligroin; fractions beginning with pentane and boiling up to about 150° are used as gasoline; the product distilling at 150–300° is compositely known as kerosene; the higher-boiling fractions may be blended for various lubricating oils or greases, or they may be "cracked" by pyrolytic methods for the purpose of augmenting the supply of gasoline.

The great abundance and economic importance of the petroleum hydrocarbons tend to overshadow the natural but limited occurrence elsewhere of the paraffin hydrocarbons. Methane is known to result from the metabolic processes of lower organisms. It has been obtained by the action of microorganisms upon cellulose and other polysaccharides. n-Heptane has been isolated from *Pinus sabiniana* var. Douglas, *Pinus jeffreyi*, and *Pittosporum resiniferum;* n-nonane from pineweed (false St. John's wort); n-undecane from *Pinus excelsa* and *Pinus monticola;* n-tetradecane from *Chrysanthemum cinerariae-folium;* n-pentadecane in *Kaempferia galanga;* n-hexadecane in rose oil; and n-octadecane in *Solanum sodomaeum.* Many other hydrocarbons have been reported in plants. Many of them are of uncertain composition because of difficulty of exact analysis. The compounds $C_{22}H_{46}$, $C_{24}H_{50}$, $C_{26}H_{54}$, and $C_{28}H_{58}$ are found in the wax from the chrysalis; the last is also found in the chrysaloids of the silkworm. Plants also produce long-chain hydrocarbons; in tobacco were found compounds melting from 58° to 70°, from which have been isolated and identified $C_{31}H_{64}$ and $C_{27}H_{56}$; from the cabbage leaf was isolated $C_{29}H_{60}$; from the fruit of the *Pittosporum undulatum* could be identified $C_{35}H_{72}$; from birch buds was obtained $C_{25}H_{52}$; the waxlike coating of the pear yields a small amount of paraffins in which $C_{29}H_{60}$ predominates; among the nonsaponifiable products of the nonvolatile constituents of the cotton plant was found $C_{35}H_{72}$; rose wax consists more than half of saturated aliphatic compounds, the following having been identified and isolated: $C_{18}H_{38}$, 0.5 per cent; $C_{20}H_{42}$, 8 per cent; $C_{21}H_{44}$, 2 per cent; $C_{22}H_{46}$, 6 per cent; $C_{23}H_{48}$, 6 per cent; $C_{26}H_{54}$, 8 per cent; $C_{27}H_{56}$, 15 per cent; $C_{30}H_{62}$, 6 per cent.[4]

The function of these paraffin hydrocarbons in plants is probably a protective one. The fact which often is particularly striking is the presence of compounds with uneven-numbered carbon chains; this is quite out of harmony with the observations as to the natural occurrence of aliphatic alcohols or of the fatty acids, which are found predominantly, if not exclusively, as chains with even-numbered carbon atoms. This suggests that the hydrocarbons must be formed from precursors other than the alcohol or the acid. The presence, for example, of the ketone $(C_{14}H_{29})_2CO$ in cabbage suggests the common origin of the ketone and of its companion paraffin $C_{29}H_{60}$.

[3] Bushnell and Haas, *J. Bact.,* **41,** 653 (1941).

[4] For a more complete survey of the hydrocarbons occurring in plants see: Edward Kremers, "Phytochemistry III. The Methane Series of Hydrocarbons," *Bulletin of the University of Wisconsin,* Madison, 1934.

It is of interest also to note that from human pregnancy urine, but not from normal female human urine, have been isolated pentacosane and heptacosane, $C_{25}H_{52}$ and $C_{27}H_{56}$.

Products

Petroleum Benzin, N.F. (Petroleum Ether, Purified Petroleum Benzin), b.p. 35–80°, is a mixture of hydrocarbons, chiefly pentanes, hexanes, and heptanes, obtained as one of the fractions from the refining of petroleum. It is not used as a medicinal agent, but it is extensively employed as a solvent in the extraction of fats and fatty oils in defatting drugs, e.g., ergot and digitalis, and as an immiscible solvent for the isolation of constituents from drugs and the products of syntheses. The commercial benzin employed in dry cleaning is not generally suitable for chemical and pharmaceutical use.

Kerosene (Deodorized Kerosene) has been used in the manufacture of various pharmaceutical and cosmetic products for many years. The pharmaceutical use of ordinary kerosene was greatly limited by its strong characteristic odor which could not be concealed easily and by the presence of unsaturated hydrocarbons and other impurities which caused a burning sensation and often gave rise to acute dermatitis. There is now available refined kerosene, freed from impurities and possessing practically no odor, b.p. about 175–260°. Deodorized kerosene can be readily perfumed. The purity and volatility of deodorized kerosene make it an excellent solvent for nonvolatile mineral oil in hair oils and brilliantines. Its low surface tension and low absolute viscosity make it a good solvent for liniments, antiseptics, hair tonics, and other pharmaceutical and cosmetic products for external use. Ordinary kerosene is extensively used as the solvent for pyrethrum flowers and derris root in the manufacture of insecticide and insect-repellent preparations.

Liquid Petrolatum (Mineral Oil, White Mineral Oil, Liquid Paraffin, Paraffin Oil) is a mixture of hydrocarbons obtained as a product in the refinement of petroleum. It is sold under various trade names, e.g., Albolene, Nujol, and Stanolax. Two grades of liquid petrolatum are commonly used in pharmacy: one known as *Light Liquid Petrolatum*, N.F., and the other known as *Liquid Petrolatum*, U.S.P.; they must have a kinematic viscosity of not less than 38.1 centistokes at 37.8°. The kinematic viscosity is a partial measure of the lubricating value of the oils in the intestine. The higher-viscosity oils cause less leakage when they are used as laxatives. The liquid petrolatums used medicinally consist chiefly of aliphatic hydrocarbons containing from 14 to 18 carbon atoms. Certain oils, notably those obtained from California and Russian petroleum, contain cyclic polymethylene hydrocarbons having the saturation formula C_nH_{2n}. Mineral oils intended for medicinal use are purified to remove odoriferous sulfur compounds, acids, alkalies, and higher paraffins which solidify on chilling to 0°.

Liquid petrolatum administered internally is absorbed only to a limited extent and cannot act as a nutrient. Excreted unchanged, it serves to soften the feces and lubricate the intestinal tract, acting as a mild laxative. The oil is partially emulsified in the digestive tract, forming an emulsion with a capacity for holding water and making it resistant to absorption by the bowel. Since the emulsion seems to be of the oil-in-water type, the effect of petroleum oils can be due in part to lubrication and in part to softening of the feces.[5] The use of mineral oil as a laxative is to be discouraged; it interferes with the absorption of the oil-soluble vitamins; in the habitual user it may interfere with absorption from the small intestine; and it reacts unfavorably on the defecation reflex.[6]

Numerous products containing mineral oil with other laxatives are used medicinally, e.g., liquid petrolatum and agar, liquid petrolatum with agar and cascara, liquid petrolatum with agar and milk of magnesia, and liquid petrolatum with agar and phenolphthalein. These are usually emulsions, flavored and sweetened or unsweetened.

Liquid petrolatum is used also as a solvent vehicle in oil sprays containing compounds such as thymol, camphor, menthol, and eucalyptol; for materials used in dermatology, e.g., iodine, iodoform, thymol iodide; for mercurials; and in many cosmetic preparations such as baby oils, cold creams, cleansing creams, liquid brilliantines, sun-tan oils, brushless shaving creams, and hair tonics.

Petrolatum, U.S.P. (Amber Petrolatum, Petroleum Jelly, Yellow Vaseline), m.p. 38–60°, is a purified, semisolid, translucent mixture constituted almost exclusively of saturated hydrocarbons distilling above 300° obtained chiefly from paraffin-base (Pennsylvania) crudes. It is produced from petroleum fractions by successive treatment with sulfuric acid and sodium hydroxide to remove unsaturated and odoriferous compounds, by passing air or hot steam through the hot liquid to remove volatile hydrocarbons, and by decolorization while still hot with charcoal, fuller's earth, or other agents. The better grades are said to be made without the use of drastic reagents. A product of this type first was prepared by Chesebrough in 1871 and sold under the trade name Vaseline. Petrolatum is insoluble in water, almost insoluble in alcohol, and readily soluble in most organic solvents such as benzene, carbon disulfide, chloroform, ether, and petroleum benzin. Artificial petrolatums have been prepared by dissolving paraffin wax in liquid petrolatum.

Petrolatum is extensively used as an ointment base for such substances as boric acid and zinc oxide. It is also used in cosmetics, hair dressings, etc.

White Petrolatum, U.S.P. (White Petroleum Jelly, White Vaseline), is similar to petrolatum in composition and properties. It is simply a product from which the color has been adsorbed more completely.[7]

Paraffin, U.S.P. (Petroleum Wax), m.p. 47–65°, is a mixture of solid hydrocarbons obtained from petroleum purified by methods similar to those described under petrolatum. It is used to raise the melting point of ointments, to impregnate bandages, and as a protective in burns.

Prosthesis is carried out by using paraffin which has a melting point of about 40°, slightly above body temperature. It is melted and injected subcutaneously to correct

[5] Goodman and Gilman, *The Pharmacological Basis of Therapeutics*, 2nd ed., The Macmillan Co., New York, 1955.

[6] Morgan, *J. Am. Med. Assoc.*, **117**, 1335 (1941).

[7] For discussion, White Mineral Oil and Petrolatum in Pharmaceutical and Cosmetic Practice, see Meyer, *J. Am. Pharm. Assoc.*, **24**, 319 (1935).

deformities, e.g., as in face lifting. Since these compounds are very slowly absorbed, they will remain over long periods of time. The results are not permanent, and there is danger of embolism; the paraffin is gradually replaced by scar tissue.

UNSATURATED HYDROCARBONS

Olefins, Alkylenes, or Alkenes

It has been shown, in each case studied, that the unsaturated hydrocarbon is more active physiologically, i.e., as a hypnotic, than its saturated analog. Thus, trimethylethylene is more active than isopentane. The narcotic and toxic activities of the olefins increase with the molecular weight. They also increase in direct ratio to their solubility in oil and in inverse ratio to their solubility in water. Olefins with more than three carbon atoms in the chain are reported to affect circulation partly by stimulation of the vagus, and those with more than four carbon atoms cause increased reflex excitability. Experimentation has not revealed the fate of the simple olefins when absorbed into the animal system. There is reason to believe that they are metabolized in the same way as those unsaturated compounds that add on the elements of water at the double bond.

Olefinic hydrocarbons are found in many mineral oils, but, because of their great reactivity, they are present in very small amounts. Some Canadian oils, however, are reported to be quite rich in unsaturated hydrocarbons. The lower members of the alkene series are available in large quantities as by-products of petroleum cracking.

Ethylene, an important raw material in the chemical industry and used commercially as a ripening and coloring agent in the fruit and vegetable industry, is employed medicinally because, on being inhaled, it produces general surgical anesthesia. It undergoes practically no chemical change in the body and is almost quantitatively eliminated in the exhaled air. The patient's mind clears within two to three minutes after administration of the gas is stopped.

Favorable anesthetic action was observed as early as 1876, but the acutal introduction of ethylene into medicine came about in a curious manner. In 1908 Crocker and Knight observed that ethylene was toxic to carnations and other plants, putting them "to sleep." Naturally the question of the toxicity of ethylene toward animals arose and prompted Luckhardt and Carter (1923) as a matter of academic curiosity to investigate its effect on dogs; they were surprised at the deep anesthesia produced and the relatively low toxicity exhibited by the compound. The investigation carried to its logical conclusion resulted in the use of ethylene as a general anesthetic.

The ancient Chinese are known to have softened fruits from their orchards by placing them in a room in which incense had been burned. In modern times fruit growers used and still use oil stoves to get the same effects. The responsible agent was identified (1923) as ethylene. Ethylene aids the natural coloring processes of the fruit and hastens the hydrolysis of starch to sugars. The grower may pick the fruit while it is still green and firm, ship it long distances, and then ripen the fruit in transit or on arrival by means of ethylene.

Ethylene, U.S.P. (Ethene), $CH_2{=}CH_2$, is a colorless gas, b.p. $-103°$, of faint odor and slightly sweet taste. The commercial product is obtained by the dehydration of ethanol or from the cracking of petroleum hydrocarbons. After suitable purification, ethylene is compressed into metal cylinders, in which form it is available as a medicinal agent.

For use in anesthesia the gas is passed into an inhalation apparatus and administered alone or admixed with oxygen. One volume of ethylene is soluble in about 4 volumes of water at 0° and 7 volumes of water at 20°. It is also soluble in many organic solvents such as alcohol and ether. In the gaseous state and when mixed with air in proper proportions (3–34 per cent ethylene), it is explosive if brought in contact with an open flame or an electric spark.

Propylene (Propene), CH_3—CH=CH_2, a homolog of ethylene, is a colorless, inflammable gas, b.p. $-5°$. In its chemical and also its physiological properties it is remarkably like ethylene. It is reported to induce unconsciousness in 2 min., that the patient recovers consciousness promptly, and that neither mental excitement nor nausea follows its use. It is usually employed in 37 to 40 per cent concentration admixed with air and oxygen. Explosive mixtures with air are formed by 1.7 to 9 per cent by volume of propylene.

The anesthetic potency of propylene is reported to be 2.2 times that of ethylene, which is a greater increase than its acute toxicity; hence, its therapeutic index is greater. In the fruit and vegetable industry propylene gives favorable ripening results just as does ethylene; however, it is more costly.

Propylene is also used in the manufacture of isopropyl alcohol.

Butenes, of which there are three isomers, 1-butene, 2-butene, and 2-methylpropene, show all the properties of an unsaturated compound. Physiologically, all are more potent as anesthetics than either ethylene or propylene, but before producing complete anesthesia they first produce a state of excitement. The butenes also cause ripening in fruits.

Diolefins or Dienes

Compounds with two unsaturated bonds may be grouped into three general classes:

1. The allene type. These compounds contain the cumulated double bond system and have the general structure R—CH=C=CH—R'. Compounds having such structure are of theoretical interest, but they are rare.
2. Conjugate double bonds. These compounds have a system of alternate single and double bonds which chemically often behave as a unit.
3. Isolated double bonds. In these compounds, the double bonds are separated from each other by more than one single bond. Such compounds possess the properties conferred by a summation of the individual effects.

The presence of a second double bond as in isoprene increases the anesthetic activity.

Butadiene, CH_2=CH—CH=CH_2, b.p. 1°, is the simplest hydrocarbon with a conjugated system. This compound assumed great importance in the synthesis of rubberlike substances on a commercial scale. Because of its conjugate structure, it polymerizes readily not only with itself but also with other reactive, usually unsaturated, compounds. It is this reactivity which makes it possible to obtain from it the synthetic rubbers.

Isoprene (2-Methyl-1,3-butadiene, Hemiterpene), $CH_2{=}C(CH_3){-}CH{=}CH_2$, is an important diene or diolefin, not because of its availability, for in fact it is not readily available and its synthesis is difficult, but because of its apparent use in nature to build many of the natural products. This evidently involves a controlled polymerization, and often a simultaneous natural oxidation, reduction, or other chemical change. Compared to the simple saturated and ethylenic hydrocarbons, isoprene is more toxic, a dose of 80 mg. per 10 grams rat weight proving fatal after several hours.

Acyclic Polyisoprenoids

The hypothetical polymerization of the isoprene unit serves as the basis for terpene chemistry, and the isoprene rule has been invaluable in elucidating the structure of many natural products, as for example,

$$nC_5H_8 \longrightarrow (C_5H_8)_n$$

If $n = 2$, then the product is $C_{10}H_{16}$, a diisoprenoid or terpene; if $n = 3$, the product $C_{15}H_{24}$ is a triisoprenoid or a sesquiterpene; etc. The ultimate in such polymerization is natural rubber.

Although it is customary to speak of the isoprene unit, this does not mean that isoprene itself is the intermediate employed by nature. Experiments with guayule indicate that in this plant at least the starting point is the acetate ion, which passes through the following biosynthetic sequence: [8]

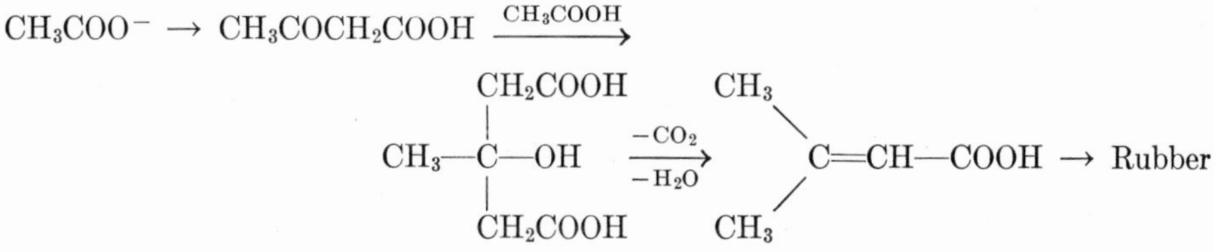

CH3COO− → CH3COCH2COOH
CH3COOH
CH2COOH
CH3—C—OH
CH2COOH
−CO2
−H2O
CH3
C=CH—COOH → Rubber
CH3

Ocimene, from the essential oil of *Ocimum basilicum*, and *myrcene*, found in oils of bay, verbena, and hops, are natural examples of open-chain diisoprenoids or terpenes. *α-Farnesene* is an example of the $(C_5H_8)_3$ open-chain compound, and

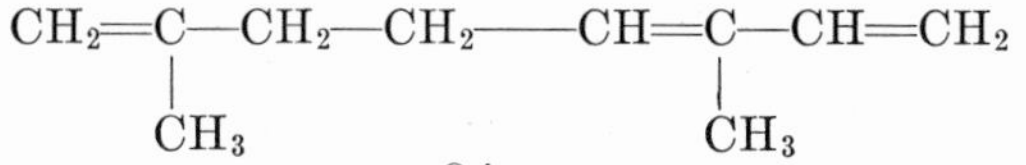

CH2=C—CH2—CH2—CH=C—CH=CH2
CH3
CH3

Ocimene

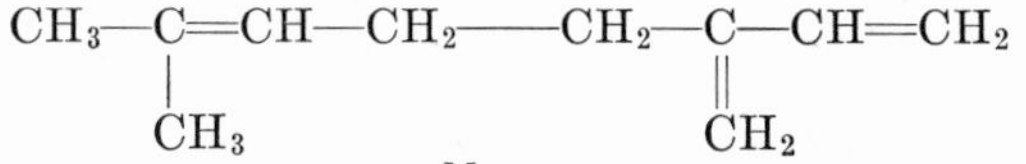

CH3—C=CH—CH2—CH2—C—CH=CH2
CH3
CH2

Myrcene

phytane, of the tetraisoprenoid type. Neither has been found in nature, but they are important as the parent hydrocarbons from which important products are

[8] Bonner, *J. Chem. Ed.*, **26**, 628 (1949).

structurally derived. It should be observed that in all these compounds the C_5

$$CH_3-C{=}CH-CH_2-CH_2-C{=}CH-CH_2-CH{=}C-CH{=}CH_2$$
$$\quad\quad\;\; | \quad\quad\quad\quad\quad\quad\quad\; | \quad\quad\quad\quad\quad | $$
$$\quad\quad CH_3 \quad\quad\quad\quad\quad\quad CH_3 \quad\quad\quad CH_3$$

α-Farnesene

$$CH_3CHCH_2CH_2-CH_2CHCH_2CH_2-CH_2CHCH_2CH_2-CH_2CHCH_2CH_3$$
$$\quad | \quad\quad\quad\quad\quad\quad | \quad\quad\quad\quad\quad\quad | \quad\quad\quad\quad\quad\quad | $$
$$\quad CH_3 \quad\quad\quad\quad CH_3 \quad\quad\quad\quad CH_3 \quad\quad\quad\quad CH_3$$

Phytane

units are joined head-to-tail.

Squalene (Spinacene), $C_{30}H_{50}$, is an example of an acyclic triterpene. Squalene is found abundantly in the liver oil of certain species of sharks and to a small extent in fresh olive oil and in yeast. It is normally present in sebum (average 8.4%), earwax (3.9%), and hair fat.[9] Because of its depilatory action it has been suspected in the etiology of male baldness.[10] Man is able to synthesize it from acetate,[11] and it has been shown to be a precursor in the biological synthesis of cholesterol.[12]

Karrer and Helfenstein [13] have synthesized squalene from farnesyl bromide as outlined. The synthesis of this hydrocarbon from geranylacetone and tetra-

$$2CH_3-CMe{=}CH-CH_2-CH_2-CMe{=}CHCH_2-CH_2-CMe{=}CH-CH_2Br + 2Na \rightarrow$$

$$CH_3-CMe{=}CH-CH_2-CH_2-CMe{=}CH-CH_2-CH_2-CMe{=}CH-CH_2$$
$$CH_3-CMe{=}CH-CH_2-CH_2-CMe{=}CH-CH_2-CH_2-CMe{=}CH-CH_2$$

2,6,10,15,19,23-Hexamethyl-2,6,10,14,18,22-tetracosahexaene
Squalene

methylene bromide was later reported by Schmitt.[14] The identity of synthetic squalene with the natural product has been questioned by Dauben [15] who has presented evidence that the two are double-bond isomers.

Lycopene, $C_{40}H_{56}$, the red pigment in the tomato and the watermelon, is an example of an acyclic tetraterpene. The total synthesis of lycopene from pseudoionone [16] has confirmed the structure assigned by degradative studies. This structure is shown on page 13 in relation to the carotenes.

Alkines or Alkynes

Alkines are characterized by the presence of the triple bond or acetylenic linkage, $-C{\equiv}C-$. Although the class is not a large one, it has grown rapidly with the advances in acetylene chemistry.

[9] Wheatley, *Biochem. J.*, **55**, 637 (1953); *C.A.*, **48**, 1462 (1954).

[10] Flesch and Goldstone, *J. Invest. Dermatol.*, **18**, 267 (1952); *C.A.*, **46**, 6747 (1952).

[11] Eidinoff *et al.*, *J. Clin. Invest.*, **33**, 333 (1954); *C.A.*, **48**, 6537 (1954).

[12] Woodward and Bloch, *J. Am. Chem. Soc.*, **75**, 2023 (1953).

[13] Karrer and Helfenstein, *Helv. Chim. Acta*, **14**, 78 (1931).

[14] Schmitt, *Ann.*, **547**, 115 (1941).

[15] Dauben and Bradlow, *J. Am. Chem. Soc.*, **74**, 5204 (1952); Dauben, *Helv. Chim. Acta*, **36**, 717 (1953).

[16] Karrer, Engster, and Tobler, *Helv. Chim. Acta*, **33**, 1349 (1950).

In general, the anesthetic or narcotic effect of alkines is greater than that of the corresponding alkanes or alkenes. Acetylene has a more pronounced anesthetic action than ethylene, but the toxic side effects are considerably more evident.

The chemical properties that characterize the triple bond are analogous to those of the double bond, i.e., they show all the properties of unsaturation. In addition, acetylene or a monosubstituted acetylene has a very reactive hydrogen atom. This hydrogen is readily replaceable by metals such as sodium and lithium, giving rise to valuable intermediates for the synthesis of important medicinals. Such methods have been particularly useful in the chemistry of the vitamins A and the carotenoids in general.

Acetylene, $HC{\equiv}CH$, is the simplest and most abundant member of this series. It is readily available in sufficient quantities to be useful as a raw material in many chemical industries. Although other methods of preparation are used, the classical reaction of calcium carbide with water to form acetylene serves as an excellent source.

Acetylene was first prepared by E. Davy in 1839 and in a pure state by Berthelot in 1849. It is a colorless, flammable gas with a garliclike odor. Although acetylene can be liquefied at 0° under a pressure of about 50 atmospheres, it is dangerously explosive when compressed alone. Usually it is dissolved in acetone under pressure; 300 volumes dissolve in 1 volume of acetone at 12 atmospheres pressure. Pine-oil flavor may be added to medicinal acetylene. The gas is usually admixed with oxygen for administration in about the ratio 40 per cent acetylene and 60 per cent oxygen.

Acetylene undergoes polymerization reactions, a property which is employed to advantage in the commerical preparation of products such as highly chlorinated rubber substitutes.

CYCLIC HYDROCARBONS

Cycloalkanes

In general the chemical and physiological properties of the cycloalkanes parallel those of the aliphatic hydrocarbons with the same number of carbon atoms. However, particular attention must be directed to the added stereochemical effects, owing to the inability of the members of the cycle to revolve freely as compared to the open-chain analogs.

In ring structures containing from 3 to 6 carbon atoms, the narcotic properties increase with increase in the number of atoms within the ring. When alkyl side chains are introduced into a ring system, the toxicity of the resulting compounds increases with the length of the side chain up to 6 to 10 carbon atoms and then decreases with increase in molecular weight. The substitution of an ethyl for a methyl radical in cyclohexane causes a marked increase in toxicity. The introduction of a double bond into the cycle causes an increase in narcotic and toxic activities. The cycloparaffins like the chain hydrocarbons may cause skin and mucous-membrane irritation. Little is known about the physiological activity of most of the cyclic hydrocarbons. Cyclohexane has been shown to produce narcosis in rabbits in doses of 0.8 g. per kg. body weight when given intraperitoneally.

Cyclopropane, U.S.P., is a colorless gas of characteristic odor and pungent taste, b.p. $-34°$ and m.p. $-127°$, soluble in water $1:27$ at $0°$. It was first proposed as a promising general anesthetic by Lucas and Henderson in 1929. Since that time, it has been used clinically with good results. It has a high oil:water partition coefficient of 65 at 35° compared to 13.2 for ethylene and 2–3 for acetylene, ether, and nitrous oxide. Only about 18 per cent of the gas is required. It is administered in a closed system with carbon dioxide and about 20 per cent oxygen. It is reported to be pleasant to take, to cause better muscular relaxation than nitrous oxide but not so much as ether, and to cause postanesthetic nausea more frequently than nitrous oxide. For convenient use, it is usually supplied in compressed form in metal cylinders. It is flammable and forms explosive mixtures with air and oxygen.

Cyclopropane is rapidly absorbed, and practically all is eliminated by way of the lungs; only a small amount diffuses through the skin.

It is prepared from 1,3-dichloropropane in refluxing acetone solution of sodium iodide by an adaptation of the Wurtz reaction.

$$
\begin{array}{ccc}
\text{CH}_2-\text{CH}_2\text{Cl} & & \text{CH}_2 \\
| & \xrightarrow[\text{Zn}]{\text{NaI}} & \diagdown \\
\text{CH}_2\text{Cl} & & \quad \text{CH}_2 \\
& & \diagup \\
& & \text{CH}_2
\end{array}
$$

Cyclopropane

Cyclobutane, b.p. 13°, may be prepared in poor yield by treating 1,4-dibromobutane with zinc or sodium, or by careful hydrogenation of cyclobutene. It has been examined pharmacologically and found to produce general anesthesia on inhalation.

Among the natural derivatives of cyclobutane are the truxillic acids, diphenylcyclobutanedicarboxylic acids, obtained by the hydrolysis of the truxillines, alkaloids accompanying cocaine in the coca leaves. See page 469.

Cyclopentane and **cyclohexane,** and their derivatives, are found extensively in Russian petroleum and, to a limited extent, in American petroleum. These mineral oils are a source for only limited amounts of the pure cyclic hydrocarbons because of the impracticability of isolation.

The six-membered cycles are important since many of the natural hydrocarbons from botanical sources and their derivatives belong to this series. This is particularly true for many compounds which are derived from the 1-methyl-4-isopropylcyclohexane or p-menthane skeleton, which may be considered as being structurally obtained from 2 isoprene units. p-Menthane itself does not occur naturally but may be obtained readily by the complete hydrogenation of any of its many naturally occurring unsaturated derivatives.

Cyclic Isoprenoids

The best-known cyclic hydrocarbons are the mono- and bi-cyclic diisoprenoids, most of them with some degree of unsaturation. In these compounds an ethylenic bond retains its characteristic properties. Many of the natural products are structurally derived from the *p*-menthane, 1-methyl-4-isopropylcyclohexane.

Dipentene, of which the optically active forms are known as (+)- and (−) limonene, occurs in oils from orange, dill, citron, fir cones, and other natural oils. α-Terpinene has been isolated from *Coriandrum sativum* and *Origanum marjoram.* γ-Terpinene is found in *Citrus medica* and *Coriandrum sativum.* Crithmene may be isolated from oil of samphire. α-Phellandrene composes 80 per cent of the oil from water fennel.

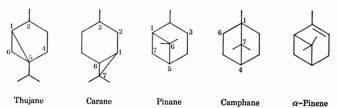

p–Menthane	Dipentene or Limonene $\Delta^{1,8(10)}$–Menthadiene	α–Terpinene $\Delta^{1,3}$–Menthadiene
γ–Terpinene $\Delta^{1,4}$–Menthadiene	Crithmene $\Delta^{1(7),4(8)}$–Menthadiene	α–Phellandrene $\Delta^{1,5}$–Menthadiene

The bicyclic diisoprenoids, or terpenes, are of importance, particularly to the chemist interested in natural products, as parent hydrocarbons of many naturally occurring derivatives. These structures are given.

Thujane	Carane	Pinane	Camphane	α–Pinene

α-Pinene is widely distributed in nature, being present in most of the oils obtained from the Coniferae. As the chief constituent of oil of turpentine it has been used from the earliest times, references to the oil being found as early as the thirteenth century. It is important for its solvent properties, being widely used in paints and for naval stores. It is also useful as a starting material for the synthetic preparation of camphor.

The cyclic triisoprenoids, also called sesquiterpenoids, may be further classified into those which are structurally derived from naphthalene and those derived from azulene.

Azulene, $C_{10}H_8$, m.p. 99°, forms blue platelets with a metallic luster. Its color, as also that of its derivatives, is ascribed to the system of five conjugated double bonds. The structure of the azulenes is established by ring expansion of indene derivatives; e.g., for azulene itself the synthesis is indicated.

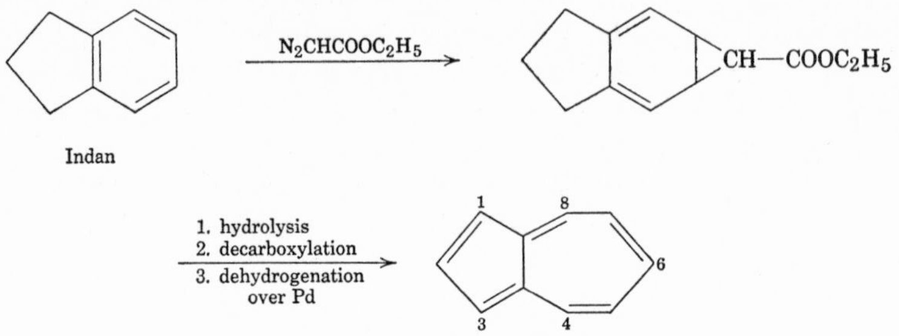

Indan

Azulene

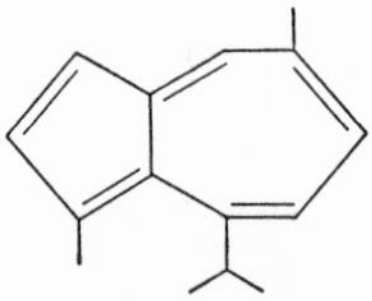

Chamazulene

The first of the natural azure-colored compounds to be encountered in nature was chamazulene in camomile oil.[17] It is the ingredient in the oil which possesses anti-inflammatory action,[18] and produces a beneficial effect in various skin afflictions.[19, 20]

None of the naphthalenic sesquiterpenoid hydrocarbons has found acceptance as a therapeutic agent.

Carotenes, Monocyclic and Bicyclic Octaisoprenoids

Because of their relationship to the vitamins A, the carotenes are the octaisoprenoids of greatest importance. The carotenes are widely distributed in nature and were first isolated in 1831. Six of these yellow to red pigments have been identified thus far and have been designated α, β, γ, δ, ϵ, and ζ. The carotenes, with such a high degree of unsaturation, are theoretically capable of existing in numerous *cis-trans* isomers. The natural compounds, however, are all *trans*, and this spatial arrangement is the most active biologically. The conversion of some of the double bonds into the *cis* structures decreases very appreciably the potencies of the products.[21]

[17] Ruzicka and Rudolph, *Helv. Chim. Acta*, **9**, 118 (1926).

[18] Heubner and Albach, *Arch. exptl. Path. Pharmakol.*, **192**, 383 (1939); *C.A.*, **34**, 2932 (1940).

[19] Hüter, *Z. deut. Parfüm.*, **28**, 153 (1942).

[20] Arnold *et al.*, *Pharmazie*, **4**, 220 (1949); *C.A.*, **43**, 8064 (1949).

[21] Deuel *et al.*, *Arch. Biochem.*, **7**, 247, 447 (1945).

The structures of only α-, β-, and γ-carotenes are known and these are presented in their relationship to lycopene. The preferred method of numbering of the carotenes is that suggested by Karrer.

C C
 \/
  C 7 8 9 10 11 12 13 14 15 15' 14' 13' 12' 11' 10' 9' 8' 7' 6' C 1' C
C2 6C-C=C-C=C-C=C-C=C-C=C-C=C-C=C-C=C-C=C-C C 2'
 | || | | | | ||
C3 5C-C   C   C   C   C   C5' 4' C3'
 \C/   C   C

Lycopene, 11 double bonds in conjugation, a total of 13 double bonds, no cycles.

C   C   C   C
 \ /   \   /
  C   C
 / \   / \
C   C-C=C-C=C-C=C-C=C-C=C-C=C-C=C-C=C-C=C-C-C=C-C   C
| || | | | | | | |
C   C-C   C   C   C   C   C-C   C
 \ /   \   /
  C   C

α-Carotene, 11 double bonds, of which 10 are in conjugation. By means of a biological process which is not understood, fission occurs at the center of the molecule and the left half may serve as a precursor of vitamin A.

C   C   C   C
 \ /   \   /
  C   C
 / \   / \
C   C-C=C-C=C-C=C-C=C-C=C-C=C-C=C-C=C-C=C-C=C-C   C
| || | | | | | | |
C   C-C   C   C   C   C   C-C   C
 \ /   \   /
  C   C

β-Carotene, 11 double bonds, all conjugated. On fission it is capable of forming two molecules of vitamin A.

C   C   C   C
 \ /   \   /
  C   C
 / \   // \
C   C-C=C-C=C-C=C-C=C-C=C-C=C-C=C-C=C-C=C-C=C-C   C
| || | | | | | || |
C   C-C   C   C   C   C   C-C   C
 \ /   \   /
  C   C

γ-Carotene, 12 double bonds, of which 11 are conjugated, one cycle. The left half of the molecule in capable of acting as vitamin A precursor.

In addition to his brilliant work on the proof of structure of the carotenes,[22] Karrer [23] has been able to effect a total synthesis of α-carotene from a mixture of α- and β-ionone and β-carotene from β-ionone.

[22] Karrer and associates, *Helv. Chim. Acta*, 1928–1930.
[23] Karrer and Eugster, *ibid.*, **33,** 1172, 1952 (1950).

Perhaps the greatest single aid in isolating and purifying these natural pigments was the chromatograph. The discovery of the principle of chromatography is due to Tswett, a Russian botanist, who allowed a solution of pigments in a solvent such as petroleum benzin, benzene, or carbon disulfide to trickle through a column of adsorbent, e.g., calcium carbonate. He observed the formation of definite bands in the column, the substance with the greatest adsorption affinity at the top, directly below a band of material with less affinity, etc. The column was removed, the various zones separated mechanically, and the adsorbate removed by an appropriate solvent. If necessary, the process could be repeated and further purification achieved.

This method of Tswett was practically a lost art for nearly a quarter of a century, until Willstätter employed it to show that its use makes possible a fine separation between related compounds. Thus, in the case of lycopene and the carotenes, lycopene, with 13 double bonds, shows the greatest adsorptive capacity and, hence, appears at the top of the column; γ-carotene, with 12 double bonds, appears below lycopene; next comes β-carotene since its 11 double bonds are in conjugation; last is α-carotene, for, although it has as high a degree of unsaturation as β-carotene, only 10 of its double bonds are in conjugation.

Chromatography has become one of the most important tools of the modern scientist.

Experiments with $C^{14}H_3COONa$ and $CH_3C^{14}OONa$ show that the side-chain methyl groups in the aliphatic chain of carotene are provided exclusively by the CH_3 portion of acetic acid and the carbon atoms to which they are attached come from the carboxyl.[24]

The relationship of the carotenes to the xanthophylls and the vitamins A is discussed in Chapter 3.

Carotene, N.N.R. (Pro-Vitamin A), $C_{40}H_{56}$, is a hydrocarbon pigment quite widely distributed in nature. Although it exists in several isomeric forms, the α, β, and γ isomers predominate and are the best known. Good sources are apricots, carrots, broccoli, sweet potato, squash, and many leafy vegetables. Dairy products in general are common sources of vitamin-A activity which may be regarded as derived from the carotenes.

Carotene products are assayed biologically in terms of vitamin-A potency. Pure β-carotene, the most important of the isomers, is used as an assay standard; one unit of vitamin-A activity (0.3 γ of vitamin A) is equivalent to 0.6 γ of β-carotene. Most of the carotene products on the market are prepared from vegetable sources.

The crystalline carotene, m.p. 172–178°, from natural sources is almost tasteless and has a slight aromatic odor. It is fat soluble and practically insoluble in water. The crystals are readily oxidized on exposure to air and sunlight and should be stored in dark, sealed containers.

Phytofluene, $C_{40}H_{64}$, is a colorless polyene hydrocarbon occurring widespread in the vegetable kingdom. Chemically it is similar to the carotenes and, indeed, is thought to be a precursor of the carotenoid pigments.[25]

[24] Grob and Butler, *Experientia*, **10**, 250 (1954); *C.A.*, **48**, 10796 (1954).
[25] Sheng and Sheng, *Genetics*, **37**, 264 (1952); *C.A.*, **46**, 7178 (1952).

AROMATIC HYDROCARBONS

The term *aromatic* as applied to organic chemistry has little if any relation to odor or aroma. A definition of aromatic hydrocarbons to distinguish them clearly from the aliphatic compounds is not readily achieved. The peculiar non-reactivity of the double bonds in an aromatic compound is their outstanding characteristic. Although benzene is unsaturated to the greatest degree possible, the low order of activity of benzene compared to that of an open-chain olefin is remarkable. This phenomenon is explained by the resonance principle, which is based on the theory that any double bond loses some of its reactivity characteristics when conjugated with another structural unit, thereby making possible more than one electronic configuration.

The most general source of aromatic hydrocarbons is the destructive distillation of coal and wood. The products probably do not exist as such in these materials but are formed during the pyrolytic reaction taking place in the distillation.

The synthesis of aromatic compounds from nonaromatic intermediates is primarily of theoretical interest because of the light it sheds on the structure and behavior of benzene and its homologs. Syntheses within the series of aromatic compounds are of particular importance in pharmaceutical chemistry and will be mentioned as occasion requires.

Benzene, benzol, b.p. 80°, does not occur naturally, but is widely distributed in the form of its derivatives which cover a vast group of medicinal chemicals. The physiological action of benzene, toluene, and xylene have been studied in considerable detail because of their use in industry and the danger to workers exposed to their vapors over long periods. Industrial poisoning caused by prolonged exposure in an atmosphere contaminated by such compounds may cause profound action on the central nervous system, and, in high concentrations, death may follow. Workmen unduly exposed to the vapors of these hydrocarbons show a decrease in both red and white corpuscles.

About 50 per cent of absorbed benzene is excreted through the lungs. However, the remainder is oxidized to phenol and polyhydroxy benzenes which are detoxified by conjugation with sulfuric and glucuronic acids.[26]

Benzene, toluene, and xylene, particularly the last two, are frequently employed as laboratory antiseptics and preservatives, and they are parasiticides for mites, lice, fleas, etc.

The introduction of an alkyl group into benzene increases the activity, and the activity increases with the length of the alkyl chain. Thus propyl and amylbenzene are progressively more active than benzene, toluene, or ethylbenzene. When two alkyl groups are introduced into the benzene ring as in xylene, the activity decreases, especially if the groups are adjacent; e.g., *o*-xylene is about one-fifth as active and *p*-xylene is about one-third as active as toluene.

Naphthalene, m.p. 80°, b.p. 218°, is found abundantly in coal tar. It is volatile and possesses a characteristic odor. It is used in moth balls and as an

[26] Porteous and Williams, *Biochem. J.*, **44,** 56 (1949).

industrial germicide and antiseptic. It is used extensively in the manufacture of phthalic acid and in the preparation of dye intermediates. Depending on conditions, naphthalene may be hydrogenated to the tetrahydro or the decahydro derivatives, known as tetralin and decalin, respectively. These hydrogenated compounds are used as solvents for extraction purposes.

Naphthalene   Tetrahydronaphthalene,   Decahydronaphthalene,
                                tetralin   decalin

If hydrogenated naphthalene compounds are heated with elemental sulfur, or better still with elemental selenium, the aromatic compound is again obtained. Such dehydrogenation is of great importance in establishing the structures of many naturally occuring polycyclic hydrocarbons, particularly of the sterol derivatives and the cyclic polyterpenes.

Anthracene, $C_{14}H_{10}$, m.p. 218° and b.p. 354°, is found in the higher-boiling fractions of coal tar. Its structure is that of 2,3-benznaphthalene. Its formula and the method of numbering are indicated. Anthracene is not used in medicine,

but some of its derivatives have some medicinal importance and others are widely used in the dyestuff industry.

Phenanthrene, m.p. 99.6° and b.p. 340°, is also found in coal tar and is undoubtedly formed during the destructive distillation. Its structure is that of 1,2-benznaphthalene. Although phenanthrene has value in dye chemistry and industry, the pharmaceutical chemist is interested in the medicinal products structurally derived from it. The phenanthrene ring system appears naturally in various stages of hydrogenation and substitution, e.g., in morphine and more particularly in the steroid compounds. The sterols and sterol-like substances are characterized by the carbon skeleton found in 1,2-cyclopentenophenanthrene. The accepted method of numbering the carbon atoms is indicated in the accompanying formulas. It will be noted that the convention adopted for the sterol skeleton does not follow that employed for phenanthrene. The sterol skeleton, present in natural products such as cholesterol, ergosterol, cardiac aglycones, sex hormones, etc., having a carbon chain substituted at position 17, when heated with elemental selenium or sulfur is converted into 3'-methyl-1,2-cyclopentenophenanthrene, frequently spoken of as Diels' hydrocarbon.

Hildebrandt studied the influence of hydrogenation upon the physiological action of phenanthrene derivatives. His results show that the toxicity diminishes almost logarithmically with the degree of hydrogenation.[27]

[27] *Arch. exptl. Path. Pharmakol.,* **59,** 140 (1908).

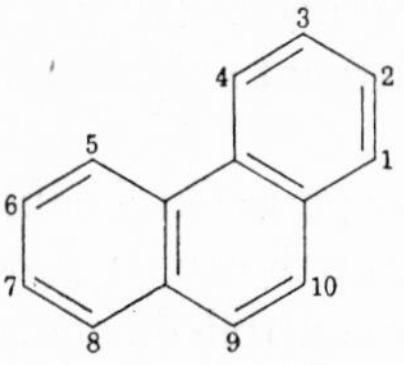

Phenanthrene

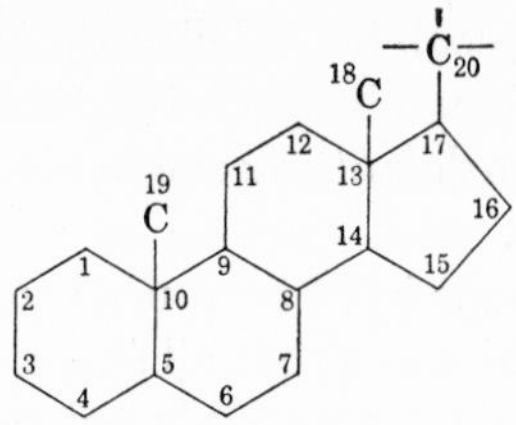

Sterol skeleton

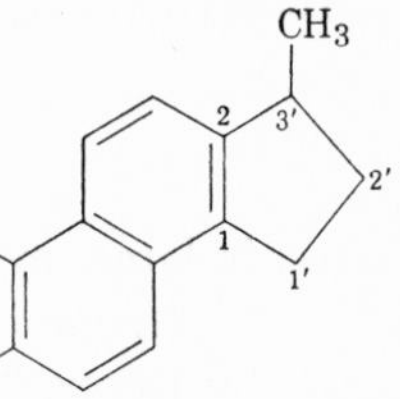

Se or S
dehydrogenation

3′-Methyl-1,2-cyclopentenophenanthrene
or Diels' hydrocarbon

Carcinogenic Hydrocarbons

There has been widespread interest in the cancer-producing activity of certain polynuclear aromatic hydrocarbons. This interest resulted from the observations: that repeated applications of certain coal-tar fractions to the ear skin of rabbits might cause cancer; that industrial workers who were frequently in contact with coal tar were especially susceptible to skin cancer; and that certain bile acids could be converted *in vitro* to the carcinogenic hydrocarbon, methylcholanthrene, I.

The careful fractionation of coal-tar concentrates followed by a study of the carcinogenic activity of the purified hydrocarbons reveals that all are derivatives of benz[a]anthracene, IV. Benzo[a]pyrene, II has been isolated and identified as

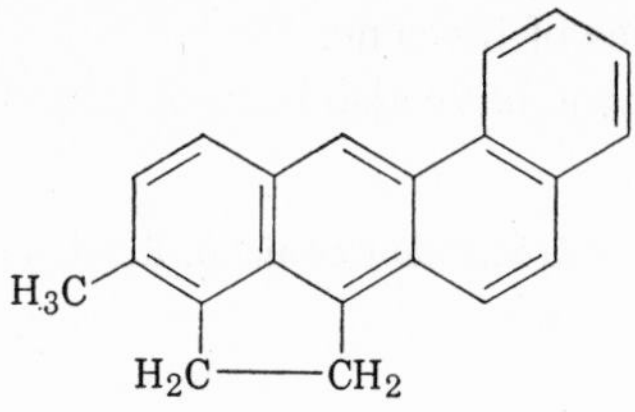

I

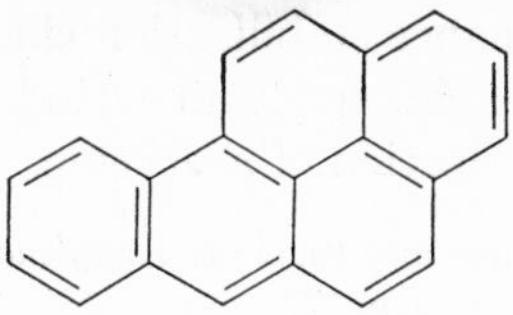

II

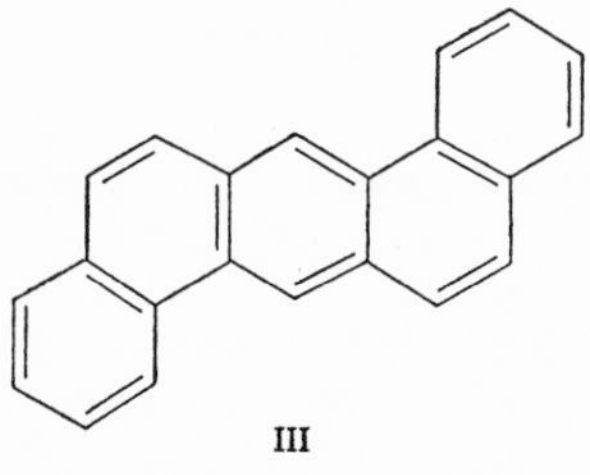

III

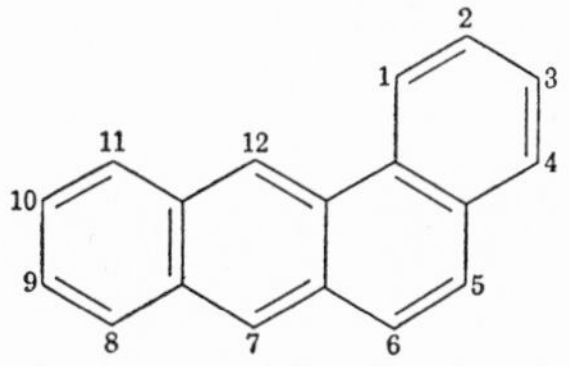

IV

an active carcinogen from coal tar. Dibenz[a,h]anthracene, III was the first cancer-producing hydrocarbon obtained by synthetic methods. It has been found that derivatives of benz[a]anthracene having a substituent at position 7, 8, or 12 are potent carcinogens.

The polycyclic hydrocarbons have been used to induce experimental cancer in mice under controlled conditions so that all stages of the growth can be observed and examined. When cancer is produced in animals under controlled conditions, possible curative agents can be tested advantageously.

Larger Cycles

Interest in larger cycles having a closed conjugated system led to the synthesis of cycloöctatetraene by Willstätter in 1913. Further progress in this direction was made by Reppe [28] and his co-workers who synthesized cycloöctatetraene by means of the polymerization of acetylene in the presence of nickel catalysts.

Many of the reactions of cycloöctatetraene result in rearrangement of the carbon skeleton, which led to the erroneous conclusion that it existed in several forms. The physical and chemical properties of cycloöctatetraene are consistent

Cycloöctatraene

with the 1,3,5,7 conjugated double-bond, eight-membered ring system. However, its chemical reactivity shows it to be olefinic in character and to have little of the resonance stabilization characteristics of benzene.

Cyclodecapentaene and cyclododecahexaene have also been obtained following the polymerization of acetylene.

[28] Copenhaver and Bigelow, *Acetylene and Carbon Monoxide Chemistry*, Reinhold Publishing Corp., N. Y., 1949, p. 177.

Compounds Composed of Carbon, Hydrogen, and Halogen

Replacement of one or more of the hydrogen atoms of the various hydrocarbons by one or more of the four halogens, fluorine, chlorine, bromine or iodine, gives rise to a host of new organic compounds. Nature produces very few compounds that contain halogen atoms as substituents. Fluoroacetic acid, chloramphenicol, and thyroxine are, therefore, representatives of types of substances rare in nature. As presently known all the rest of the halogenated compounds are available only from synthetic sources. As a group, they do not hold a prominent place in modern internal medicine, except for certain members that have found wide use as general anesthetics and anthelmintics. They find additional use because of their favorable solvent properties; for example, for the application of pesticides.

BIOLOGICAL ACTIVITY

Except for the few instances noted later under the individual compounds, the physiologically useful members of this group are those containing chlorine. From the medicinal standpoint they may be considered in three principal categories.

Hypnotic Activity

Hydrocarbons possess narcotic activity, but the halogenated hydrocarbons have this activity to an increased degree. The greater the extent of halogenation the greater is the hypnotic activity. As a rule, the chlorine-substituted products

19

are more active in this respect than the analogous bromine compounds, and these, in turn, are more effective than the iodine derivatives.

The toxicity of the chloro compounds seems to be related to the number of chlorine atoms and to the ratio of chlorine to carbon atoms in the molecules. When methane is converted successively into methyl chloride, methylene chloride, chloroform, and carbon tetrachloride, the toxicity and the anesthetic activity of the compounds increase to the maximum in carbon tetrachloride. The chloro derivatives of ethane also show increasing activity as anesthetics and become more toxic as the number of chorine atoms increases. Ethyl choride produces general anesthesia when given mixed with oxygen or air by inhalation. The dichloro derivatives are also anesthetic and better tolerated than chloroform; the ethylidene compound, CH_3—$CHCl_2$, is slightly less toxic than the symmetrical compound, CH_2Cl—CH_2Cl. Trichloroethane, CH_2Cl—$CHCl_2$, produces a deep anesthesia when administered under proper conditions. Hexachloroethane, a solid, when administered by injection in an oil emulsion or by inhalation of its vapor causes narcosis, showing that the activity continues after all the hydrogen atoms in the molecule have been replaced.

Narcotics have been used since antiquity to deaden pain, but safe anesthesia as we know it today was introduced about a century ago. Credit for its introduction must be divided among several men. In 1799 Sir Humphry Davy, announcing the anesthetic properties of laughing gas, suggested: "As nitrous oxide in its extensive operation appears capable of destroying pain, it may probably be used with advantage during surgical operations in which no great effusion of blood takes place." In 1842 Crawford W. Long, of Jefferson, Georgia, administered ether as a surgical anesthetic. However, his results were not sufficiently publicized to attract general notice. Horace Wells, a dentist in Hartford, Connecticut, witnessed a public demonstration of the effects of nitrous oxide in December 1844. Observing that it produced insensibility to pain, on the next day he had a tooth extracted while he was under the influence of the gas. The operation was a success, and he gave it wide publicity, which resulted in the introduction of the gas into dental practice in Hartford. In 1845 Wells tried ether but thought it inferior to nitrous oxide. In January 1845, Wells gave an unsuccessful demonstration of anesthesia in Boston. This apparently discredited nitrous oxide until its reintroduction by Colton in 1863, whose first demonstration had induced Wells to try the gas on himself.

A Boston chemist, Charles T. Jackson, during the winter of 1841–42 etherized himself into unconsciousness and conceived the idea of using ether as an anesthetic. He discussed his idea with Wm. G. T. Morton, a Boston dentist, who employed it successfully in September 1846. A month later a perfect demonstration of its value in surgery was given by J. C. Warren at the Massachusetts General Hospital.

"Chloroform parties," at which the guests would sit around a bowl of chloroform until they toppled unconscious to the floor, were becoming quite common in England. From this the use of chloroform in surgical anesthesia was a logical development. Simpson first used it on man in 1847.

One of Simpson's patients was Victoria, on whom he used chloroform during the delivery of the royal children. It is reported that the Queen was criticized on the basis of a passage in Genesis 3:16 (In sorrow thou shalt bring forth thy children); Simpson retorted that the first surgical operation of record, when "the Lord caused a deep sleep to fall upon Adam," was performed under surgical anesthesia.

The inhalation anesthetics, such as chloroform and ether, are physiologically active, not by virtue of any chemical reaction with the protoplasm, for they are excreted unchanged; rather they act by the physical and colloidal changes produced in the lipoids of the nerve tissue when they are dissolved in the fats. In compounds of this type the physiological activity is proportional to the solubility in oil to the solubility in water ratio. This is known as the Meyer-Overton theory; see page 520.

Anthelmintic Activity

An extensive series of experiments was carried out by Wright and Schaffer,[1,2] who attempted to correlate anthelmintic activity with the chemical constitution and physical properties of the compounds n-propyl chloride, n-butyl chloride, n-amyl chloride, n-hexyl chloride, 2-chlorobutane, 2-chloropentane, 3-chloropentane, tert-amyl chloride, ethylidene chloride, n-butylidene chloride, propylene chloride, trimethylene chloride, amylene dichlorides, 1,2,3-trichloro-propane, trichloroethane, s-tetrachloroethane, pentachloroethane, and trichloroethylene. They found that correlations between activity, structure, and properties were not always clear. Certain conclusions may be drawn from their work, namely: (1) Increase in the length of the carbon chain: (a) in n-monochloro compounds does not lead to a progressive increase or decrease in activity but n-hexyl chloride is more effective than n-amyl chloride; (b) in secondary monochloro compounds the activity increases, e.g., 2-chloropentane is almost five times as effective as 2-chlorobutane in removing hookworms from dogs; (c) in n-dichloro compounds with two chlorine atoms on the terminal carbon, the activity increases. (2) Content and distribution of chlorine atoms in the molecule: (a) addition of a chlorine atom to a carbon holding one or more chlorine atoms does not lead always to increased activity; (b) increase in the chlorine content of the molecule does not have a constant influence on activity; (c) isomeric compounds differ greatly in activity. (3) Water solubility: (a) optimum activity is given by compounds having a water solubility within the range between 1:5300 and 1:1250; (b) compounds more soluble than 1:1000 in water have little anthelmintic activity; (c) water solubility is the factor most definitely associated with the anthelmintic activity in the halogenated hydrocarbons. (4) There is no correlation between anthelmintic action on hookworms and ascarides.

Iodo and bromo compounds were found to be more irritant to the gastrointestinal tract than the corresponding chloro compounds. The effectiveness of the iodo and bromo compounds is influenced also by their water solubility, the optimum effect being obtained with those soluble 1:1700 to 1:1000.

Insecticidal Activity

The halogenated hydrocarbons have found perhaps their greatest importance in the broad field of insecticides. Since they are plentiful and relatively cheap, such compounds are widely accepted by public health agencies in their fight against the most common insect pests, flies and mosquitos.

Attempts to establish a theory of insecticidal action have been hampered by

[1] J. Parasitol., 16, 107 (1929); 18, 44 (1931).
[2] Am. J. Hyg., 16, 325 (1932).

many difficulties. Variations in the susceptibility of different species, methods of application of the insecticide, as well as the complex nature of insect physiology are some of these obstacles. However, some generalizations have been formulated in the class of *contact* insecticides. Sexton [3] has proposed that a contact insecticide must possess a certain degree of lipoid solubility contributed by the molecule as a whole but which may be attributable to a particular portion of the compound. This fat solubility enables the chemical to penetrate the cuticle of the insect. A second requirement for insecticidal activity is the presence of a toxic group, i.e., a grouping that causes combination with a vital cell constituent. An optimum degree of chemical reactivity is necessary for maximum biological potency. Finally, the correct balance between these two factors, physical and chemical, must be attained since one is useless without the other.

FLUORINE COMPOUNDS

Use has been made of the high toxicity of inorganic fluorine compounds as poisons against roaches, rodents, and other similar houshold pests. In low concentrations in drinking water, inorganic fluorides are thought to prevent dental caries in children. Organic fluorinated hydrocarbons are much less physiologically active than even the parent hydrocarbons. This is generally explained by the fact that the fluorine in an organic molecule is so firmly bound to carbon that little ionization occurs. Substitution of fluorine for chlorine in the methane series decreases toxicity, and the anesthetic activity is destroyed. Thus, flourinated hydrocarbons offer little promise as volatile anesthetics.[4]

On the other hand, the nontoxic properties of the fluorine hydrocarbons coupled with their useful physical properties have given rise to a series of compounds known as Freons. The most important of these is Freon 12, dichlorodifluoromethane, Cl_2CF_2, which because it is an easily liquefiable gas is used extensively in refrigeration. Freon 11 (fluorotrichloromethane) as well as Freon 12 are used as propellants in aerosols for spraying cosmetics and insecticides.[5]

CHLORINE COMPOUNDS

Chlorinated hydrocarbons are widely used as solvents, and they play an important role in many industrial processes from chemical manufacture to dry cleaning of clothing.

Methyl Chloride mixed with ethyl chloride and ethyl bromide has been used as a general anesthetic. When the gas is compressed it forms a colorless liquid having an ethereal odor and a sweet taste. Upon evaporation, it produces a temperature of about $-23°$, and when the evaporation is increased by a current of air a temperature of $-55°$ can be attained. It is used to a limited extent as a

[3] Sexton, *Soc. Exptl. Biol. Symposium No. III*, **1949**, 1; *Chem. Soc. Quart. Rev.*, **4**, 272 (1950).

[4] Lu, Ling, and Krantz, *Anesthesiology*, **14**, 466 (1953).

[5] Pantaleoni, *Am. Perfumer Essent. Oil Rev.*, **58**, 425 (1951).

local anesthetic applied on cotton or sprayed onto the skin, but, because it may cause blisters unless used with caution, it is mixed with ethyl chloride.

Methylene Chloride is an excellent solvent for fats and related compounds. It has been used to a limited extent as a general anesthetic by inhalation but it has a depressant action on the heart and respiratory function, increases the secretions from the tracheal and bronchial mucosa, and in general is considered to be less efficient than chloroform.

Chloroform, U.S.P. (Trichloromethane), $CHCl_3$, was first prepared simultaneously and independently in 1831 by Liebig in Germany, Souberian in France, and Guthrie in the United States. Its formula was established by Dumas in 1835. The chief methods for its preparation are: [6]

1. The haloform reaction on ethanol or on acetone:

$$CH_3—CHOH—R + NaOCl \rightarrow CH_3—CO—R + NaCl + H_2O$$

$$CH_3—CO—R + 3NaOCl \rightarrow CCl_3—CO—R + 3NaOH$$

$$CCl_3—CO—R + NaOH \rightarrow CHCl_3 + R—COONa$$

In the equations R may be H— or CH_3—. In practice the three reactions occur simultaneously.

2. The photochlorination of methane:

$$CH_4 \xrightarrow{3Cl_2} CHCl_3 + 3HCl$$

Chloroform, b.p. 61.2°, is a colorless liquid with a characteristic, ethereal odor and a burning, sweet taste. It dissolves slightly in water (1:210) but it is miscible with alcohol, ether, petroleum benzin, benzene, and fixed and volatile oils. Its vapors are nonflammable. It is used extensively as an industrial solvent for resins, rubber, fats, iodine, and many organic compounds.

With chloroform, an open flame or atmospheric oxgyen, in the presence of light and moisture as catalysts, can cause oxidation to trichloromethanol, and the subsequent elimination of HCl forms phosgene as indicated by the accompanying equations. Since phosgene is very toxic, chloroform for anesthesia must be free

$$2CHCl_3 + O_2 \rightarrow 2CCl_3OH$$

$$CCl_3OH \rightarrow \underset{\displaystyle Cl}{\overset{\displaystyle Cl}{C}}{=}O + HCl$$

of this substance. The formation of phosgene is prevented by preserving the liquid in small, well-filled, tightly stoppered cans or bottles. Small amounts of ethanol, 1 per cent or less, may be added to eliminate any phosgene formed as the innocuous ethyl carbonate.

[6] Stievater and Van Nostrand, *Encyclopedia of Chemical Technology*, Interscience Encyclopedia, Inc., New York, 1949, vol. 3, p. 843.

Chloroform has many disadvantages as a general anesthetic. It has a depressant action on the heart and respiratory center, causes renal irritation and depletion of the alkali reserve (bicarbonate) of the blood, etc. Consequently, it has been replaced to a considerable extent by other general anesthetics.

It is used in the form of a saturated aqueous solution and in spirit of chloroform as a hypnotic and flavor, in troches and lozenges as a cough sedative, and externally in liniments as a counterirritant.

Carbon Tetrachloride, N.F. (Tetrachloromethane), CCl_4, b.p. 76–78°, is manufactured by the action of chlorine upon carbon disulfide, a trace of iodine being used as catalyst,

$$CS_2 + 3Cl_2 \rightarrow CCl_4 + S_2Cl_2$$

$$CS_2 + 2S_2Cl_2 \rightarrow CCl_4 + 6S$$

Carbon tetrachloride is a colorless, mobile liquid having a characteristic odor quite similar to that of chloroform. It is practically insoluble (1:2000) in water, and miscible with alcohol, chloroform, ether, benzene, and practically all organic solvents. It is a good solvent for fixed and volatile oils. It is widely used as a solvent. It is nonflammable, and because of its heavy vapors it is finding wide use in fire extinguishers. However, its disadvantage as a fire extinguisher, especially in confined quarters and a large flame, is the fact that it forms poisonous phosgene, $COCl_2$. Carbon tetrachloride also possesses anesthetic properties just as does chloroform, but the narrow margin between the effective and toxic doses makes its use dangerous. This compound is a very effective and inexpensive agent for the treatment of hookworm; a single dose of 3–5 cc. followed by purging has proved highly effective. Although the anthelmintic dose is much less than the ordinary toxic dose following oral administration, some danger is connected with its use. If it is absorbed, it produces liver necrosis and kidney damage, especially if the patient suffers from calcium deficiency.

Ethyl Chloride, U.S.P. (Monochloroethane, Kelene), was first tried on animals in 1847 and in the following year was used surgically by Heyfelder; then it lay neglected until 1895. It is prepared commercially by the addition of hydrogen chloride to ethylene in the presence of aluminum chloride:

$$CH_2{=}CH_2 + HCl \xrightarrow{AlCl_3} CH_3CH_2Cl$$

Ethyl chloride is a colorless gas at ordinary temperatures, but it can be condensed to a colorless, mobile, very volatile liquid at low temperatures or under pressure, b.p. 12–13°. It is slightly soluble in water and is readily soluble in alcohol or ether.

Ethyl chloride is employed to some extent as an external local anesthetic. A stream of it is directed onto tissue surfaces rapidly enough to freeze the tissue, thus causing temporary insensitiveness to pain.

All the alkyl halides, especially all chloro and bromo derivatives, that boil between 25° and 50° act as narcotics. Ethyl chloride mixed with ethyl bromide has been used as an anesthetic under the names of Narcoform and Somnoform.

Other members of the halogenated hydrocarbon series, although possessing narcotic activity akin to that of chloroform, are not used medicinally because of their unfavorable side reactions. In fact, even chloroform is losing favor among anesthetists because of its deleterious action on the heart.

Ethylene Chloride (1,2-Dichloroethane), CH_2Cl—CH_2Cl, has anesthetic activity resembling that of chloroform, but it has been reported that, 10 to 12 hr. after narcosis, a corneal film appears which persists for several months. It is extensively used as a solvent for fats and as a spotting agent in dry cleaning.

Ethylidene Chloride (1,1-Dichloroethane), CH_3—$CHCl_2$, is reported to produce rapid induction and rapid recovery when used as an anesthetic but it produces also an unfavorable effect on the heart.

Methylchloroform, CH_3CCl_3, compares favorably with other anthelmintics for dogs. A dose of 0.1 ml. per pound is adequate for the removal of ascaris; a dose of 0.3 ml. is necessary for the removal of hookworms.[7]

Trichloroethylene, U.S.P. (1,1,2-Trichloroethene, Trilene), $CHCl{=}CCl_2$, made by passing tetrachloroethane over pumice at 400–500° ,with the removal of the elements of HCl, is a very stable compound, b.p. 88°. Its properties are similar to those of chloroform. It has been used to a limited extent as an anesthetic by inhalation. In the liquid state, it is very irritant to mucous surfaces. It is peculiar in that it seems to exercise a highly selective and strong anesthetic action on the trigeminal nerve. These properties have led to its use in trigeminal neuralgia.

In conjunction with nitrous oxide and oxygen, trichloroethylene has been found useful for prolonged dental procedures in children, the mixture producing a pronounced analgesic effect.[8]

In man, the dog, and calf it was observed that the major portion of administered trichloroethylene is eliminated in a manner not accounted for; small amounts appear in the urine as trichloroacetic acid and trichloroethanol, CCl_3-CH_2OH; no chloral was detected.[9]

Tetrachloroethylene, U.S.P. (Ethylene Tetrachloride, Perchloroethylene), $CCl_2{=}CCl_2$, with trichloroethylene is prepared from acetylene. Acetylene is allowed to react with chlorine to form tetrachloroethane. This chlorination reaction is preferably carried out in the presence of some carrier, e.g., antimony pentachloride, which overcomes the explosion hazard of working with acetylene. Treatment of tetrachloroethane with lime forms trichloroethylene. This may be converted into pentachloroethane, which, in turn, on treatment with lime, forms tetrachloroethylene.

It is a nonflammable, relatively unstable liquid, b.p. 120.8°, which like chloroform may give rise to phosgene on decomposition upon exposure to air, moisture, and light. It is insoluble in water and soluble in most organic solvents.

[7] Enzie, *Proc. Helminthol. Soc. Wash., D. C.*, **12**, 24 (1945).

[8] Yein, Teuscher, and Karp, *Quart. Bull. Northwestern Univ. Med. School*, **26**, 180 (1952); *C.A.*, **46**, 11455 (1952).

[9] Sero and Schulte, *Proc. Soc. Exptl. Biol. Med.*, **90**, 314 (1955); *C.A.*, **50**, 2853 (1956).

This compound was discovered by Hall and Shillinger [10] to be equally if not more effective against hookworms than carbon tetrachloride. It is considered less toxic than carbon tetrachloride. Tetrachloroethylene is usually administered in soft gelatin capsules.

Gamma Benzene Hexachloride, U.S.P. (Hexachlorocyclohexane, "666"), $C_6H_6Cl_6$, is a mixture of stereoisomers formed by the addition of chlorine to benzene under the influence of actinic light. Seven of the eight expected isomers have been characterized.[11] Of these the γ-isomer, which represents about 12 per cent of the product, alone is a highly active insecticide. Also known as Gammexane or Lindane, this isomer is useful against scabies and valuable against cockroaches. Material containing 99 per cent of the γ-isomer has a less musty odor.

γ-Hexachlorocyclohexane is not isosteric with inositol; [12, 13] therefore, earlier attempts to explain its insecticidal activity as a possible antagonist to inositol appear unwarranted.

Toxaphene is a complex mixture of compounds resulting from the chlorination of camphene until the product contains 67 to 69 per cent chlorine.[14] It is an amber waxy solid having high insecticidal activity.

Chlordane (1,2,4,5,6,7,8,8-Octachloro-2,3,3a,4,7,7a-hexahydro-4,7-methanoindene) is one of a group of highly chlorinated hydrocarbons possessing excellent insecticidal properties. As indicated, this chemical is made by the Diels-Alder addition of hexachlorocyclopentadiene and cyclopentadiene to form a product that is in turn further chlorinated. The commercial material is a mixture of the stereoisomers.

Chlordane

Aldrin (5,6,7,8,9,9-Hexachloro-1,4,4a,5,8,8a-hexahydro-1,4,5,8-dimethanonaphthalene) is prepared by the Diels-Alder addition of hexachlorocyclopentadiene with bicyclo-(2,2,1)-hepta-2,6-diene. Epoxidation of Aldrin produces

[10] North Am. Veterinarian, **6**, 41 (1925).
[11] Kolka, Orloff, and Griffing, J. Am. Chem. Soc., **76**, 3840 (1954).
[12] van Vloten, Kruissink, Strijk, and Bijvoet, Nature, **162**, 771 (1948).
[13] Bastiensen, Ellefson, and Hassel, Research, **2**, 248 (1949).
[14] Fleck, Bull. Am. Soc. Hosp. Pharm., **9**, 175 (1952).

Dieldrin. Both of these products are considered highly effective pesticides. Dieldrin has been found particularly useful against a wide variety of lawn pests.

Aldrin   Dieldrin

BROMINE AND IODINE COMPOUNDS

The bromo and iodo derivatives of the hydrocarbons are not used extensively as medicinal agents.

Methyl Bromide, CH_3Br, was first used as a fumigant in France in 1932. It is a gas, at ordinary temperature, b.p. 4.5°, which readily penetrates to all surfaces being treated. It is not harmful to plants and may be used to fumigate clothing, vegetables, plants, dried fruits, seeds, grain, etc. It is toxic to many pests and has been used for their control, e.g., lice, root-knot nematodes, red spiders, the larvae of *Cydia molesta* and *Carpocapsa pomonella*, and certain species of scale insects.

Ethyl Bromide, CH_3CH_2Br, b.p. 38–40°, closely resembles ethyl chloride in its properties. It has been used as an anesthetic by inhalation but chiefly as a local anesthetic in the form of a spray for minor surgery and neuralgic pain.

Bromoform (Tribromomethane), $CHBr_3$, closely resembles chloroform in properties and activity but since it is much less volatile, b.p. 148–150°, it is not suited for use as a general anesthetic. In the past, it was used as a sedative in whooping cough, seasickness, and asthma, but more effective sedative agents have replaced it.

Methyl Iodide, CH_3I, has been used successfully in fumigating against various insects but it is too expensive to be practical for such purposes.

Iodoform, N.F. (Triiodomethane), CHI_3, was discovered by Serullas in 1822. Its constitution was established by Dumas, who, unlike his predecessors, did not overlook the small amount (0.25 per cent) of hydrogen present.

Iodoform is usually prepared in the laboratory by heating ethyl alcohol or acetone with a solution of sodium hypoiodite (iodine dissolved in sufficient alkali hydroxide or carbonate to decolorize the iodine).

$$CH_3CH_2OH + 8I + 6NaOH \rightarrow CHI_3 + HCOONa + 5NaI + H_2O$$

This reaction is so delicate that yellow crystals having the characteristic iodoform odor are obtainable (on standing 12 hr.) from alcohol, acetone, isopropyl alcohol, acetaldehyde, and most compounds containing the CH_3—CO— group in dilutions of about 1 to 20,000 when concentrations of reagents are controlled. Methyl alcohol does not give this reaction, and so this test provides a method of distinguishing between methyl and ethyl alcohol.

Industrially, iodoform is made by the electrolysis of a solution containing alcohol, alkali, iodides, and carbonates. Free iodine is formed at the anode and reacts with the carbonate and alcohol.

Pure iodoform crystallizes in small, glistening, hexagonal, yellow plates having a very characteristic persistent odor. It melts at about 115°, sublimes readily, and is volatile with steam. It is practically insoluble in cold water, slightly soluble in alcohol, and readily soluble in chloroform and ether.

Iodoform is used as an antiseptic in the form of a dusting powder for wounds, in suppositories, etc. Its antiseptic value is thought to be dependent upon the liberation of iodine by proteins and acids. Because of the disagreeable odor of iodoform, it has been largely replaced by other medicinal agents.

HALOGENATED AROMATIC HYDROCARBONS

Halogenated aromatic compounds exhibit no anesthetic or narcotic activity. Chlorobenzene is much more toxic than benzene. *p*-Chlorotoluene is much more toxic than toluene or *m*- or *o*-chlorotoluene. The introduction of a chlorine or bromine atom into the side chain as in toluene or xylene forms lachrymatory substances, e.g., benzyl bromide. An increase in the number of halogen atoms in the benzene ring decreases the activity and toxicity, probably because of decreased solubility. Thus 1,4-dichlorobenzene and 1,3,5-trichlorobenzene are relatively nontoxic. They are somewhat irritant and have some antiseptic activity.

Dichloricide (*p*-Dichlorobenzene), m.p. 53°, b.p. 174°, is a white, crystalline solid of characteristic odor. It is insoluble in water and readily soluble in organic solvents. It is used in veterinary medicine in the form of ointments to treat itch and in solution to spray on wounds as an antiseptic, and to kill lice and other vermin. It is extensively used to destroy moths and their larvae, to preserve furs and woolen goods from attack by insects, and to kill roaches, peach-tree borers, etc.

Chlorophenothane, U.S.P. (DDT, Dichlorodiphenyltrichloroethane, 1,1,1-Trichloro-2,2-(*bis*-*p*-chlorophenyl)ethane), m.p. 108–109°, was first prepared in 1874. Its remarkable insecticidal activity was not disclosed, however, until the appearance in 1942 of the proprietary products Gesarol and Neocid, both of which were powerful contact and stomach poisons owing to their DDT content.

Technical DDT, obtained by condensing chlorobenzene and chloral or chloral hydrate in fuming sulfuric acid, contains about 75 per cent pure DDT along with substantial amounts of the less active *o,o'*- and *o,p'*-isomers. It has a mild, pleasant odor and a setting point of approximately 90°. The technical powder in 2 to 10 per cent concentrations in petroleum solvents is used as a spray. It is further purified for use in aerosol bombs in which liquefied Freon serves as the solvent and propellant. DDT is also available in the form of dispersible powders.

DDT is practically insoluble in water, slightly soluble in the lower alcohols, moderately soluble in aliphatic hydrocarbons, but freely soluble in aromatic hydrocarbons, halogenated hydrocarbons, ketones, ethers, and esters. It is a stable compound, but in the presence of an alkali or an iron catalyst it readily loses a molecule of hydrogen chloride from the ethane residue to give 1,1-dichloro-2,2-di-(p-chlorophenyl)ethylene, a compound having little insecticidal activity.

The chemical stability of DDT gives it a high residual effect against insects, especially the members of the *Diptera* and *Hymenoptera* orders. Its immediate knockdown power, however, is less than that of the pyrethrins. Its lethal concentrations for insect larvae and fish are of the order of one part in ten million parts of water. DDT is comparatively inactive against Protozoa, worms, and most vegetation with the exceptions of melons and grapes. The lethal dose of DDT for warm-blooded animals varies from 150 to 300 mg. per kg. The principal metabolite in warm-blooded animals is di(p-chlorophenyl) acetic acid.

The high potency, wide applicability, and low cost of DDT affords a compound for which it is difficult to provide a competitive product. However, this success has stimulated investigation into the effects of structure variation and into its mode of action.

Most alterations in the DDT structure and attempts to prepare chemically related compounds have resulted in a lowering of the insecticidal activity. The activities of some derivatives of the type formula $(p)R—C_6H_5—Y—C_6H_5—R'(p')$ are indicated in Table I.

In a comparison of these and other DDT analogs, certain cautious generalizations have been reached as to their mechanism of action. The requirement of an optimum degree of chemical reactivity combined with optimum physical properties must be met. The ability of DDT to decompose with the liberation of HCl, certainly a demonstration of chemical reactivity, may partially explain its toxic effect. Fat solubility is a most important physical property to be considered. The molecular shape of such chemical compounds is thought to be of particular importance in that their action may depend on a close fit with a specific enzyme. Thus, it has been demonstrated [15] that DDT-resistant flies are also resistant to the sterically similar compound, p-CH_3O—C_6H_4—$CH(CCl_3)$—C_6H_4—OCH_3-p', but not to chlorinated hydrocarbons of different molecular shape. In addition, Sumerford and his co-workers [16] have shown that p,p'-dichlorobenzhydrol, which has little or no insecticidal activity but which is of similar molecular shape, potentiates the action of DDT against resistant flies.

DDD (Dichlorodiphenyldichloroethane) and **DFDT** (Difluorodiphenyltrichloroethane) are commercially available DDT analogs for which useful insecticidal activity is claimed.[17]

[15] Keiding and van Deurs, *Nature*, **163**, 964 (1949).
[16] Sumerford, Goette, Quarterman, and Schenck, *Science*, **114**, 6 (1951).
[17] Riemschneider, *Pharmazie*, (*1*), **9**, 649 (1950); *C.A.*, **46**, 11551 (1952).

TABLE I

ACTIVITIES OF SOME DDT ANALOGS
Symmetrical Disubstituted Derivatives

R	R'	Y	Activity
Cl	Cl	$CCl_3-\overset{\mid}{\underset{\mid}{CH}}$	+++++
F	F	"	+++++
Br	Br	"	+++
I	I	"	+++
H	H	"	+
CH_3-	CH_3-	"	++
CH_3-CH_2-	CH_3CH_2-	"	++
$CH_3CH_2CH_2-$	$CH_3CH_2CH_2-$	"	+
OH	OH	"	−
$-OCH_3$	$-OCH_3$	"	+++
$-OCH_2CH_3$	$-OCH_2CH_3$	"	+++
$-OCH_2CH_2CH_3$	$-OCH_2CH_2CH_3$	"	−
CH_3COO-	CH_3COO-	"	−

Unsymmetrical Substituted Derivatives

R	R'	Y	Activity
H	Cl	"	+
CH_3	Cl	"	++
H	$-CO-CH_3$	"	−

Derivatives with Alterations in Bridge

R	R'	Y	Activity
Cl	Cl	$CHCl_2-\overset{\mid}{\underset{\mid}{CH}}$	++
F	F	"	+++
Br	Br	"	+
CH_3-	CH_3-	"	+++
$-OCH_3$	$-OCH_3$	"	++
H	H	"	+
Cl	Cl	$CHCl_2-\overset{\mid}{\underset{\mid}{CCl}}$	+++
Cl	Cl	$CCl_3-\overset{\mid}{\underset{\mid}{C}}-Cl$	−
Cl	Cl	$CCl_2=\overset{\mid}{C}$	+++
Cl	Cl	$CF_3-\overset{\mid}{\underset{\mid}{CH}}$	−
Cl	Cl	$CBr_3\overset{\mid}{CH}$	++++
Cl	Cl	$CH_2=CH\overset{\mid}{\underset{\mid}{C}}-H$	+

The high activity and the favorable differential in the toxicity of the *p,p'*-difluoro derivative for mosquito larvae and fish, as compared to that of DDT, have aroused some interest in this analog as a spraying material for large bodies of water having valuable fish populations. The knockdown power of the lower alkoxy analogs of DDT is marked, a property which becomes highly significant in view of the possible shortage and costs of pyrethrum and rotenone-bearing roots. Some of the derivatives patterned after DDT involving the introduction of unsaturated linkages, nitro groups, and ether linkages in the bridge portion of the molecule are highly active insecticides but somewhat too specific in their action for general use.

Carbinol analogs of DDT of the structure indicated have been found to be

X = F, Cl, or Br

good synergists. For example, 1 part of the carbinol with 10 parts DDT enhances the activity markedly.[18]

[18] Tahori, Kaluszyner, and Reuter, *Nature*, **176**, 266 (1955).

Hydroxyl Derivatives
of Hydrocarbons

ALCOHOLS

General Properties

Early chemists looked upon alcohols as alkyl hydroxides, analogous to the metallic hydroxides. To a limited extent there is some parallelism, but the properties of alcohols and their names are better appreciated if they are considered hydroxyl substituted hydrocarbons. Primary alcohols, $R—CH_2OH$, are those having one alkyl group and two hydrogens attached to the carbon atom bearing the hydroxyl group; secondary alcohols, R_2CHOH, have two alkyl groups and one hydrogen on the hydroxyl-bearing carbon; and a tertiary alcohol, R_3COH, contains no hydrogen atom on the hydroxyl-bearing carbon.

Most of the alcohols are liquids at ordinary temperature; the higher members are waxy solids. However, in other respects, introduction of a hydroxyl group into a hydrocarbon brings about a considerable change in physical properties. The hydroxyl is a solubilizing group; hence, the lower members of the series are soluble in water. The propyl alcohols are completely soluble in water. Solubility of the molecule decreases as the length of the carbon chain increases. As a general rule, secondary alcohols are more soluble than the corresponding primary alcohols, and the tertiary are more soluble than secondary alcohols. Thus, 1-butanol is soluble less than 10 per cent, 2-butanol is soluble more than 25 per cent, and *tert*-butyl alcohol is completely soluble in water.

Alcohols are found abundantly in nature. They are constituents of volatile oils in the free state and are often found in the form of esters in volatile oils,

32

fats, and waxes. Hydrolysis of these esters constitutes an important commercial source of many alcohols. Alcohols also occur widely as products of fermentation; many of the lower-molecular-weight monohydroxy alcohols, including pentanols, are formed in fermentation procedures.

Physiological Activity

The physiological effects produced by the hydroxyl group may be summarized under the following headings:

1. Confers sweetness. This effect is not appreciably apparent in the monohydric alcohols, but, as the number of hydroxyl groups in a molecule increases, this property becomes more pronounced. Thus ethylene glycol is slightly sweet; glycerol is definitely so; mannitol (hexahydroxyhexane) is almost sugarlike; all the sugars are polyhydric compounds.

2. The physiological activity of the alcohols is much more diverse than that of the hydrocarbons from which they are derived. Comparison is difficult for the lower members since the hydrocarbons are gases and are administered by inhalation, whereas the alcohols are liquid and are administered by mouth. The alcohols are poisons to the nerve cells and it has been established that the simpler members influence practically all nerve processes.

The action of ethyl alcohol has been studied extensively, and its various actions are: (a) An antiseptic and a hardening action on the tissues. (b) Lowering of body temperature especially in alcohol poisoning. (c) Deposition of a thick mucous deposit upon the gastric mucosa in chronic alcoholism which impairs digestive functions. (d) Action on the central nervous system causing excitation followed by depression; the higher brain centers are affected first. In acute cases of alcohol poisoning, stupor may be followed by death. (e) Individuals vary greatly in their resistance to the narcotic effects of alcohol.

TABLE II

Alcohol	Dose, g.	Effect on Rabbits	Relative Toxicity in Equimolar Solution	Relative Toxicity	M.L.D.* g./kg., Dog
Methyl	6–12	None	1	1.0	9.0
Ethyl	7	Intoxication	3	1.2	7.4
Ethyl	12	Sleep	—	—	—
Propyl	12	Fatal, 5 hr.	18	2.6	3.5
Butyl	3	Intoxication	36	3.7	2.4
Butyl	7	Narcosis and death	—	—	—
Amyl	2	Half sleep	120	4.5	1.95

* M.L.D. — Minimum lethal dose.

Except for quantitative differences, the other alcohols appear to have the same type of activity as ethyl alcohol. It has been reported that the administration of homologous normal alcohols to rabbits and to dogs gives the results shown in Table II.

It may be concluded, on the basis of available data, that the toxicities and activities of the normal primary alcohols increase with increase in the length of the carbon chain to from 6 to 8 carbon atoms and then decrease until alcohols containing a chain of about 16 carbon atoms are inert.

Of 26 alcohols, from C_1 to C_{11}, examined for disinfectant activity, n-pentanol was found most effective.[1] When tested for bactericidal activity against *Staphylococcus aureus* there was an increase in the following order: ethanol, propylene glycol, pentanol, propanol, butanol.[2]

3. Primary alcohols with branched chains are more active than those with straight chains. Rice, Jenkins, and Harden [3] studied a series of 2,2,2-trialkylethanols and found that all of them were more active than ethanol and had definite anesthetic properties, but that they were less active than tribromoethanol.

4. The secondary alcohols have a stronger narcotic action than the straight-chain primary isomers, and the tertiary alcohols are more active than the secondary. Thus, isopropyl alcohol is about twice as active as n-propyl alcohol, and *tert*-butyl alcohol is about twice as active as *sec*-butyl alcohol. The activity of the secondary and tertiary alcohols increases as the molecular weight increases for the lower members, e.g., *sec*-amyl and tert-amyl alcohols are more active than *sec*-butyl and *tert*-butyl alcohol, respectively. For *tert*-amyl alcohol (amylene hydrate) the narcotic activity is sufficiently pronounced to permit its use as a hypnotic.

5. Unsaturation causes an increase in the narcotic properties of the alcohols. In the tertiary acetylenic alcohols, lowered toxicity is combined with a favorable increase in activity. Also, with certain alcohols unsaturation causes a marked increase in toxicity. Thus, allyl alcohol is an active narcotic but it is highly irritant and it is a lachrymator.

6. The introduction of more than one hydroxyl group to form polyhydroxy compounds results in a decrease in activity. Thus glycol CH_2OHCH_2OH, glycerol $CH_2OHCHOHCH_2OH$, and mannitol $CH_2OH(CHOH)_4CH_2OH$ are practically inactive as narcotics. If the alkyl groups predominate greatly, a dihydroxy compound may show some narcotic activity. This is well illustrated in the pinacols, where the tetraethyl is much more active than tetramethylpinacol.

7. As a general rule, the presence of a hydroxyl group in an otherwise physiologically active molecule tends to decrease the toxicity.

These generalizations must not be taken too literally, for until the correlation between structure and physiological activity is more reliably established, it is impossible to state rules which are broadly applicable. Additional properties are mentioned under the individual alcohols.

Products

Methanol (Methyl Alcohol, Carbinol, Wood Alcohol, Columbian Spirit, Wood Spirit, Methyl Hydroxide), CH_3OH, ordinarily is not found free in nature, but

[1] Tanner and Wilson, *Proc. Soc. Exptl. Biol. Med.*, **52**, 138 (1943); *C.A.*, **37**, 2769 (1943).
[2] Ornstein and Thorsson, *Acta Path. Microbiol. Scand.*, **21**, 914 (1944); *C.A.*, **40**, 2867 (1946).
[3] *J. Am. Pharm. Assoc.*, **27**, 303 (1938).

it is found in natural esters such as methyl salicylate, and methyl anthranilate. The chief source of methanol is:

(a) Destructive distillation of wood, hence the name wood alcohol.

(b) Catalytic hydrogenation of carbon monoxide. Carbon monoxide and hydrogen under a pressure of about 200 atmospheres and at 450° are passed over zinc oxide:

$$CO + 2H_2 \rightarrow CH_3OH$$

Methanol is used commercially as a solvent, as a denaturant for ethanol, for the preparation of formaldehyde, etc. The oxidation products of methanol are:

$$CH_3OH \rightarrow \underset{\text{Formaldehyde}}{H_2CO} \rightarrow \underset{\text{Formic acid}}{HCOOH} \rightarrow \underset{\text{Carbon dioxide}}{CO_2}$$
$$\underset{\text{Methanol}}{}$$

Methanol lowers the freezing point of water more than does an equal volume of denatured alcohol. Furthermore, methanol evaporates less readily than denatured alcohol from water solutions of the same freezing point. Antifreeze grades of methanol which are characteristically colored and rust inhibiting are used in automobile cooling systems.

The extensive use of methanol in industry and the arts may lead to unfortunate complications if proper precautions are not taken against its imbibition. The acute toxic symptoms resemble acute alcoholic intoxication, but with more serious local effects. Individual susceptibility varies greatly, but blindness may occur after taking 10 cc.

Animals may tolerate up to 8 or 9 milliliters of methanol per kg. of body weight. But in man 1 ml./kg. may produce blindness or even death. In man the symptoms of methanol intoxication are slow in developing; the alkali reserve in the blood decreases steadily, and the symptoms become serious when severe acidosis is present. It might be assumed that methanol is oxidized *in vivo* by way of formaldehyde; however, investigators have been unable to demonstrate the presence of formaldehyde in the tissues. In fatal cases the formic acid in the blood ranged from 9 to 68 mg. per cent. Hence, it is not the acid *per se* which is responsible for the symptoms, although it is the condition of acidosis resulting from methanol poisoning which must be corrected in order to avoid unnecessary loss of vision. No enzymic process for the oxidation of methanol has as yet been established, but it is probably the same as that which oxidizes ethanol; for ethanol, properly used, mitigates the results of methanol imbibition.[4] Severe changes in the ganglionic cells of the retina have been observed in victims of methanol poisoning.

In animals the toxic manifestations of methanol poisoning differ in that the symptoms of acidosis are absent.[5]

Alcohol, U.S.P. (Ethanol, Ethyl Alcohol, Grain Alcohol, Methylcarbinol, Cologne Spirit, Wine Spirit), CH_3CH_2OH, is the alcohol normally meant if the word alcohol is used without other modification. The chief commercial sources are:

1. Synthesis. Synthetic ethyl alcohol may be produced by a number of different methods. Two methods of interest are:

   (a) From acetylene, by hydration in the presence of mercuric salts and reduction of the resultant acetaldehyde; these steps may be summarized

   $$C_2H_2 + HOH \rightarrow (CH_2{=}CHOH) \rightarrow CH_3CHO \xrightarrow{H_2} CH_3{-}CH_2OH$$

   The hypothetical intermediate, vinyl alcohol, is unstable and spontaneously rearranges into the isomeric acetaldehyde. Although this method of synthesis ap-

[4] Röe, *Pharmacol. Revs.*, **7**, 399 (1955).
[5] Röe, *Nord. Med.*, **54**, 1549 (1955); *C.A.*, **50**, 2836 (1956).

parently is satisfactory and, with acetylene so readily available, is relatively economical, it still is not competitive on an economic basis with the fermentation industry.

(b) From ethylene, by formation of ethyl hydrogen sulfate, which is hydrolyzed by dilution. The cost of alcohol from this source compares favorably with that obtained by fermentation, and the ethylene is available at oil refineries as a by-product.

2. Fermentation of sugars and starches. The word ferment has its origin in the Latin, *fervere*, "to boil." The fermentation process is accompanied by an evolution of carbon dioxide, with an activity akin to boiling.

The use of starch in the form of grain as raw material for alcohol fermentation dates back to very ancient times. Starch is not directly fermentable by yeast and must, therefore, be converted to sugar. The procedure is to cook the starch (grain), cool, and then treat with barley malt, whose diastatic enzymes convert substantially all the starch to sugar. Yeast has a double action upon the sugar. This is brought about by the presence in the yeast of two enzymes, invertase and zymase. In the presence of invertase, sucrose undergoes conversion into sugars of the invert type:

$$C_{12}H_{22}O_{11} + H_2O \xrightarrow{\text{(invertase)}} 2C_6H_{12}O_6$$

Sucrose   Water   Invert sugar

The invert sugars are then converted by the zymase into ethyl alcohol and carbon dioxide:

$$C_6H_{12}O_6 \xrightarrow{\text{zymase}} 2C_2H_5OH + 2CO_2$$

Invert sugar   Ethyl alcohol   Carbon dioxide

From 1 mole of hexose, 180 g., it is possible theoretically to obtain a maximum of 2 moles of ethanol, 92 g.; 51.1 per cent of the sugar may, under ideal conditions, be converted into alcohol. The best yield reported was 48.5 per cent.

Among the by-products recovered from the fermentation process are carbon dioxide (compressed either to a liquid or a solid), potash for the manufacture of fertilizers, vitamin concentrates for feedstuffs, and binders for the foundry and coal-processing industries.

Ethyl alcohol in doses of 45–60 g. is definitely hypnotic. Larger doses produce narcotic effects or inebriation. The degree of inebriation is proportional to the concentration of alcohol in the blood; the following values have been suggested: At 0.1 per cent a third of the subjects are clinically inebriated; at 0.15 per cent half are diagnosed to be inebriated. A concentration of 0.15 per cent alcohol in the blood is taken as the critical concentration in the chemical diagnosis for drunkenness. A concentration of 0.15 per cent ethyl alcohol in the blood corresponds to a concentration of about 0.2 per cent alcohol in the urine.

Alcohol depresses the central nervous system. Its stimulant effect is really the result of lowering the normal restraining functions. It is rapidly absorbed from the small intestine. Nearly all the ethanol ingested is rapidly metabolized by means of oxidative enzymes in the liver to acetic acid or active acetyl. Further metabolic pathways include the conversion of acetyl into other body constituents such as cholesterol or its oxidation to carbon dioxide by way of normal carbohydrate metabolism.

The chronic use of alcohol and the dependence upon it for its physiologic effect is termed *alcoholism* and is recognized as a psychological disease. Treatment for the chronic alcoholic has been aided by the use of tetraethylthiuramdisulfide, Antabuse. (See page 278.)

Alcohol has long been recognized as a fairly effective germicide and for this use is recommended in concentrations of 50 to 70 per cent. However, it is felt by some [6] that too much emphasis in the past has been placed on diluting 95 per cent ethanol. When tested on the moist vegetative forms of bacteria, the latter concentration is also effective.

Ordinary ethyl alcohol is 95 per cent or 190 proof. It is impossible to purify alcohol further by ordinary fractional distillation, for it forms with water an azeotropic solution consisting of 95 per cent alcohol and 5 per cent water which distils at 78°, and pure or "absolute" alcohol boils at 78.3°. Ethyl alcohol is soluble in water in all proportions, usually with a contraction in volume; thus 52 volumes of alcohol and 48 volumes of water will produce but 96.3 volumes of dilute alcohol.

Absolute Alcohol may be prepared in various ways. In the laboratory, the water may be removed chemically by treatment with calcium oxide, calcium carbide, or aluminum ethoxide. Commercial absolute alcohol is prepared by adding benzene to ordinary alcohol and distilling the azeotropic mixture. After removal of a ternary and a binary fraction, the anhydrous alcohol can be distilled.

Propyl Alcohol (*n*-Propyl Alcohol, 1-Propanol, Ethylcarbinol), $CH_3CH_2CH_2OH$, is formed in small amount during the fermentation production of grain alcohol; propyl alcohol appears in the fusel oil fraction, from which it may be isolated by fractional distillation. This compound is used primarily for the preparation of propyl compounds, e.g., propyl halides, which are used in the synthesis of various derivatives.

Isopropyl Alcohol, N.F. (2-Propanol, Dimethylcarbinol), $CH_3CHOHCH_3$, does not occur naturally. It may be obtained by the reduction of acetone or the hydration of propylene.

$$CH_3COCH_3 \xrightarrow{H_2} CH_3CHOHCH_3$$

$$CH_3CH{=}CH_2 \xrightarrow{H_2SO_4} \underset{\underset{OSO_3H}{|}}{CH_3CHCH_3} \xrightarrow{H_2O} CH_3CHOHCH_3 + H_2SO_4$$

Because of its ready availability at economical costs it is used as a substitute for ethyl alcohol in many applications, being used in rubbing alcohols, shaving lotions, astringent solutions, etc. It is reported that a 40 per cent solution of isopropyl alcohol has antiseptic properties comparable to those of a 60 per cent solution of ethyl alcohol. It has been recommended as a substitute for ethanol in the cleansing of the skin and in the disinfection of clinical thermometers, surgical instruments, etc. *Isopropyl Alcohol Rubbing Compound, N.F.*, contains 68 to 72 per cent isopropyl alcohol.

[6] Morton, *Ann. N. Y. Acad. Sci.*, **53**, 191 (1950).

Pharmacologically isopropyl alcohol resembles ethyl alcohol. It is easily oxidized and disappears from the blood at about the same rate. It is more toxic than ethyl alcohol and is said to produce considerable temporary prostration. No instances of eye injury have been reported.

It is a good solvent for creosote and is used to remove this substance from the skin to prevent creosote burns.

The isomeric butyl alcohols, C_4H_9OH, important as solvents and useful as reagents and intermediates, find no direct use in medicine. n-Butyl alcohol and isobutyl alcohol are available from fermentation sources; tert-butyl alcohol is formed by the sulfation of isobutylene and hydrolysis of the resulting sulfate ester.

Of the isomeric pentyl alcohols, $C_5H_{11}OH$, the tertiary amyl alcohol is the only one to find medicinal use.

Amylene Hydrate, U.S.P. (Tertiary Amyl Alcohol, Dimethylethyl Carbinol), is prepared by treating amylene with a mixture of sulfuric acid and water maintained at 0°. The mixture is then neutralized with alkali and distilled.

$$CH_3-CH{=}\underset{\underset{CH_3}{|}}{C}-CH_3 + H_2O \xrightarrow{H_2SO_4} CH_3-CH_2-\underset{\underset{CH_3}{|}}{\overset{\overset{CH_3}{|}}{C}}-OH$$

Amylene hydrate, b.p. about 97–103°, is a clear, colorless, volatile liquid having a characteristic odor and a burning taste, soluble 1:8 in cold water, and miscible with alcohol, chloroform, ether, and benzene.

Amylene hydrate is used as a hypnotic and sedative. It is said to have no harmful effect on the heart and is used in insomnia, epilepsy, whooping cough, etc. It is administered orally in capsules, rectally by enema in suspension with acacia, and intramuscularly by injection.

Alcohols of higher molecular weight, that is, $C_6H_{13}OH$ and above, find no medicinal use. Beginning with lauryl alcohol, n-$C_{12}H_{25}OH$, however, pharmaceutical interest appears. Lauryl, myristyl, $C_{14}H_{29}OH$, cetyl, $C_{16}H_{33}OH$, and stearyl, $C_{18}H_{37}OH$, alcohols, all normal primary alcohols which become available by reduction of the corresponding fatty acids, when converted into their alkyl sodium sulfates of general formula R—O—SO$_3$Na are known as Gardinols or Avirols. They are excellent wetting agents, forming a group of detergents which find wide application. They are further discussed under sulfate esters, page 277.

Cetyl alcohol occurs as the ester of several fatty acids, notably as cetyl palmitate in beeswax. Stearyl alcohol is found in *Plexaura flexuosa*, an invertebrate marine animal. Ceryl alcohol, n-$C_{26}H_{53}OH$, occurs as its cerotic ester in Chinese wax. Melissic or myricyl alcohol, n-$C_{30}H_{61}OH$, is present as the palmitate in beeswax and carnauba wax.

Cetyl Alcohol, N.F., and **Stearyl Alcohol, U.S.P.,** are unctuous solids usually marketed as flakes or granules and consisting chiefly of $CH_3(CH_2)_{14}$-

CH_2OH and $CH_3(CH_2)_{16}CH_2OH$, respectively. They are used in ointment bases and creams to produce smoothness of texture and to make them hydrophilic, i.e., capable of absorbing water.

POLYHYDROXY ALCOHOLS

Theoretically the simplest dihydroxy derivative of a hydrocarbon is dihydroxymethane, which might also be considered the first member of a homologous series of alkyl- and dialkyl-dihydroxymethanes. Such compounds are known by their derivatives, chiefly their acetals, page 105, but as a rule they are unstable, losing a molecule of water to form carbonyl derivatives, aldehydes, or ketones. Hence the first member of the dihydroxyl substituted hydrocarbons is dihydroxyethane, CH_2OHCH_2OH, or ethylene glycol.

Many polyhydroxy alcohols have found an important place in pharmacy and medicine. Particular use is made of their physical properties as solvents for pharmaceutical products, as emollients and demulcents in cosmetics and toilet goods, and for a host of specific purposes in Galenicals.

Chemically, the polyhydroxy alcohols have been made the basis of a large group of more complex ethers and esters. The properties of the polyethylene glycols or Carbowaxes as ingredients of ointment bases and the polysorbates or Tweens as dispersion agents are widely accepted [7] (see page 81).

Certain of the polyhydroxy alcohols have been shown to possess anticonvulsant activity, 1,3-butanediol being the most active of those studied.[8] All but ethylene glycol are used as their nitrate esters as vasodilating agents.

The role of the hydroxyl group as reducing toxicity and conferring sweetness in the parent hydrocarbon is clearly seen in these compounds. Glycerol is not only nontoxic but also is quite sweet. These qualities are even more pronounced in the hexahydroxyhexanes, such as mannitol and sorbitol.

The dihydroxyhydrocarbons or glycols are synthesized from readily available unsaturated hydrocarbons formed during the cracking process of petroleum refining. The two most important procedures are represented by the equations:

$$R-C=CH_2 \xrightarrow{HOCl} R-CHOH-CH_2Cl \xrightarrow{NaHCO_3} R-CHOH-CH_2OH$$

$$R-CH \underset{O}{\overset{}{\diagdown\diagup}} CH_2 \xrightarrow[\substack{\text{or water under} \\ \text{pressure and} \\ \text{elevated} \\ \text{temperature}}]{\text{dil. } H_2SO_4} R-HCOH-CH_2OH$$

Ethylene Glycol (1,2-Ethanediol) is a colorless, practically odorless liquid, b.p. 197°, with properties intermediate between those of alcohol and glycerol. It is extremely hygroscopic, absorbing approximately twice its weight of water. It is completely miscible with water and when mixed in the ratio of 60 parts with 40 parts of water the freezing point of the mixture is depressed to $-49°$,

---

[7] Lesser, *Drug & Cosmetic Ind.*, **69**, 316 (1951).

[8] Bornmann, *Arch. exptl. Path. Pharmakol.*, **213**, 114 (1951); *C.A.*, **46**, 1657 (1952).

the maximum that can be attained in mixtures of the glycol and water. It is extensively used as an antifreeze and as a solvent.

Although it has had some use as a substitute for glycerin in external preparations, it is unsuitable for use in pharmaceutical products because of the ease with which it is oxidized to oxalic acid in the body and gives rise to the symptoms of oxalate poisoning. After a fatal dose of ethylene glycol, crystals, considered to be oxalate, were found in the uriniferous tubules.[9]

Propylene Glycol, U.S.P. (Methylethylene Glycol), b.p. 187.4°, closely resembles ethylene glycol. It is reported to be physiologically harmless. It is employed as an antifreeze in dairy and brewery cooling systems. It is also used as a solvent in flavoring extracts, perfumes, and pharmaceutical preparations. A fine spray of propylene glycol is an effective bactericidal agent, useful in the air sterilization of hospital and office buildings.

Ethohexadiol, U.S.P. (2-Ethyl-1,3-hexanediol), $CH_3CH_2CH_2CHOHCH$-$(C_2H_5)CH_2OH$, obtained by the reduction of the aldol formed when butyraldehyde dimerizes, is employed as one ingredient in many commercial insect repellents. 2-Butyl-2-ethyl-1,3-propanediol and similar glycols are finding use as insect repellents.[10]

Glycerin, U.S.P. (Glycerol, 1,2,3-Propanetriol), $CH_2OHCHOHCH_2OH$, is an important compound. It was first isolated by Scheele (1779). Its empirical formula was determined by Pelouze; its structure was established by Berthelot and Wurtz (1836). Its structure follows from the fact that it may be obtained from 1,2,3-trichloropropane by heating with water to 170°. It is found as a constituent of fats and lipids, from which it may be obtained by hydrolysis or saponification. It may also be prepared by fermentation processes. A commercial synthesis is indicated.

$$(1) \quad CH_2{=}CHCH_2OH \xrightarrow{Cl_2 + H_2O} \begin{Bmatrix} CH_2ClCHClCH_2OH \\ CH_2OHCHClCH_2OH \\ CHClCHOHCH_2OH \end{Bmatrix} \xrightarrow[\text{alkali}]{\text{buffered}}$$

$$CH_2OHCHOHCH_2OH$$

$$(2) \quad CH_2{=}CHCH_2Cl \xrightarrow{Cl_2 + H_2O} \begin{Bmatrix} CH_2OHCHClCH_2Cl \\ CH_2ClCHOHCH_2Cl \end{Bmatrix} \xrightarrow[\text{alkali}]{\text{buffered}}$$

$$CH_2OHCHOHCH_2OH$$

Glycerol acts both as an emollient and as a demulcent. It is used on chapped hands and rough skin; however, since the anhydrous glycerol has a great affinity for water, it should never be used for such purposes except in the form of a solution. Undiluted glycerol injected into the rectum causes evacuation in a few minutes, and usually without pain; use is made of this property in the glycerol suppository, which is glycerol containing sodium stearate to harden it. In pharmacy, glycerol finds wide use as a sweet vehicle and as a solvent miscible with water. It is used in tobacco as a moistening agent, but this use is not without objection since on combustion one of its pyrolysis products is acrolein. It

---

[9] Boemke, *Arch. path. Anat. u. Physiol. (Virchow's)*, **310**, 106 (1943).

[10] Smith, *Chem. Specialties Mfrs. Assoc.*, 80 (1950); *C.A.*, **45**, 5870 (1951).

is employed as a preservative for ferments and vaccines. In concentrations of 25 per cent or greater it is definitely antiseptic. No toxic symptoms, in man, have been observed; this is to be expected since it is a natural constituent of fats.

Glycerol has found value as a vehicle in combination with certain antibiotics, particularly for topical administration. In addition to its solvent action in antibiotic preparations, it is useful as a source of carbon in the culture media of various microorganisms from which the antibiotics are formed,[11] making possible improved production yields.

Erythritol (Tetrahydroxybutane, Erythrite), CH_2OH—$CHOH$—$CHOH$—CH_2OH, can exist in two optically active forms (just as does tartaric acid) and one mesoform or internally compensated form. The D- and L-erythritol are known only from synthetic sources. Mesoerythritol is found free in algae and as the ester of lecanoric acid in lichens.

L-Erythritol may also be obtained by the reduction of D-threose.

$$CH_2OHCHOHCHOHCHO \xrightarrow{H_2} CH_2OHCHOHCHOHCH_2OH$$

Erythritol is used as the tetranitrate for much the same purpose as glycerol trinitrate, and has like physiological action.

Pentaerythritol (2,2-Bis-hydroxymethyl-1,3-propanediol) in the form of its tetranitrate, has found use in medicine as a vasodilator.

$$\begin{array}{c} CH_2OH \\ | \\ HOCH_2-C-CH_2OH \\ | \\ CH_2OH \end{array}$$

Pentaerythritol

The pentahydroxypentanes, though of considerable interest to the student of carbohydrates, have no particular application in medicinal or pharmaceutical chemistry. The hexahydroxyhexanes, however, are of appreciable value. The isomerism in these compounds, as in erythritol, is caused by asymmetry within the molecule.

D-Mannitol, $CH_2OH(CHOH)_4CH_2OH$, occurs extensively in natural products, being the main constituent of manna, the dried juice of the various manna plants; it is also found in such widely different plants as celery, olives, and jasmin.

In addition to its use as the hexanitrate to produce vasodilatation, mannitol exhibits an unusual metabolic pattern. Carr and Krantz [12] have shown that, although small amounts are absorbed and converted to glycogen, most of the mannitol is excreted unchanged in the urine. This has suggested the use of mannitol as a sweetening agent in diabetic and low-caloric diets.

D-Sorbitol, the most widely used of the hexahydric alcohols, is found in fruits and berries and is prepared by the hydrogenation of glucose. Its physical properties are useful in pharmacy and industries as a vehicle or solvent for many

---

[11] Lesser, *Am. Profess. Pharmacist*, **17**, 135 (1951).

[12] Carr and Krantz, *Advances in Carbohydrate Chemistry*, Vol. I, Academic Press, New York, 1945, pp. 181–187.

compounds and as a humectant in cosmetics, tobacco, and glues. In addition to its use in the synthesis of ascorbic acid, it is used in combination with polyethylene glycols for the formation of the Tweens (see page 81).

Sorbitol has been recommended as a substitute for sugar in the diabetic diet, as not producing significant hyperglycemia.[13] Its sweetening and "bodying" effect have recommended it as an ingredient in ice cream for diabetics.[14]

Dulcitol, a mesoisomer of the hexahydrohexanes, is found almost pure in the manna from Madagascar. It may also be obtained by the reduction of galactose.

UNSATURATED ALCOHOLS

Compounds having in their structure a double bond and a hydroxyl group exhibit, as would be expected, properties of the two functional groups. The simplest unsaturated alcohol, structurally, is vinyl alcohol, CH_2=CHOH. This compound is unstable, however, and rearranges into acetaldehyde:

$$CH_2=CH-OH \rightarrow CH_3-CHO$$

Such rearrangement also is characteristic for the substituted vinyl alcohols. Hence, the stable unsaturated alcohols are those in which the hydroxyl group is not attached to an unsaturated carbon atom; the first member of such a series is allyl alcohol.

Allyl Alcohol, CH_2=CH—CH_2OH, b.p. 97°, is a mobile liquid with a suffocating odor. Like propyl alcohol, it is miscible with water in all proportions. Being unsaturated, it readily adds bromine, hypochlorous acid, chlorine, etc. Allyl alcohol, when applied to the skin, is very irritating. Its toxic dose is greater than the narcotic dose. The chief pharmaceutical interest in this unsaturated alcohol arises from its use as an intermediate for the synthesis of the allyl halides, which are employed in the preparation of medicinally useful compounds, e.g., the allyl-substituted barbituric acids.

Higher alkenols, especially the C_{10} open-chain, unsaturated alcohols are of particular interest, for they are natural alcohols, occurring in essential oils and belonging to the terpene group. As may be expected, these compounds are structural derivatives of the 2,6-dimethyloctane skeleton. **Citronellol,** found in oil of citronella and in oil of roses, is such an alcohol.

$$CH_3-\underset{\underset{CH_3}{|}}{C}=CH-CH_2-CH_2-\underset{\underset{CH_3}{|}}{CH}-CH_2-CH_2OH$$

Citronellol
3,7-Dimethyl-6-octen-1-ol

Geraniol, $C_{10}H_{18}O$, a colorless oil with pleasant odor, b.p. 114–115°/12 mm., is present in many essential oils, including geranium oils. It is stereoisomeric

[13] Carr and Krantz, *Advances in Carbohydrate Chemistry*, Vol. I, Academic Press, New York. 1945, pp. 175, 192.

Wick, Almen, and Joseph, *J. Am. Pharm. Assoc.*, **40**, 542 (1951).

[14] Tracy and Edman, *Ice Cream Trade J.*, **46**, No. 7, 50, 83 (1950); *C.A.*, **45**, 778 (1951).

with nerol, $C_{10}H_{18}O$, b.p. 125°/25 mm., which is found in oil of neroli, oil of bergamot, etc. Both geraniol and nerol on hydrogenation take up four atoms of hydrogen to form the identical primary alcohol $C_{10}H_{22}O$; this same saturated alcohol is obtained by the hydrogenation of citronellol. Hence, geraniol and nerol have two double bonds. Both give the same oxidative degradation products, the identification of which locates the position of the unsaturated bonds between carbon atoms 2 and 3, and between 6 and 7. The structure 3,7-dimethyl-2,6-octadiene-1-ol permits geometric isomerism involving the 2,3 double bond. Geraniol is predominantly the *trans*-isomer. Oil of neroli consists predominantly of the *cis*-isomer, to which the name *nerol* has been given. The distinction between the two isomers is indicated by the relative ease with which they undergo cyclization to dipentene. Allylic rearrangement of either affords *linalol*, a tertiary alcohol, $C_{10}H_{18}O$, which may be isolated in optically active form from Mexican oil of linaloe, rose oil, and bergamot oil.

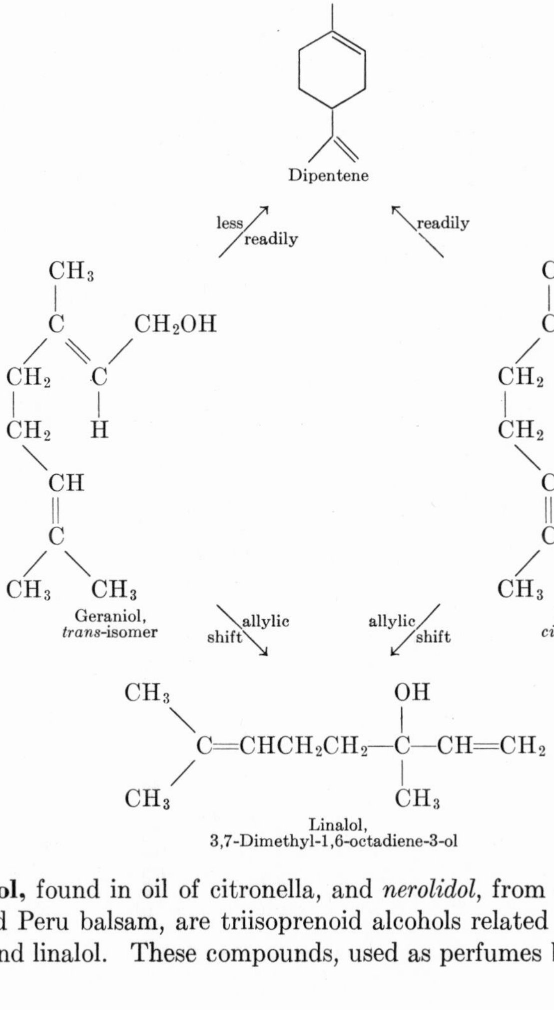

Dipentene

Geraniol,
trans-isomer

Nerol,
cis-isomer

Linalol,
3,7-Dimethyl-1,6-octadiene-3-ol

Farnesol, found in oil of citronella, and *nerolidol*, from oils of bitter orange, neroli, and Peru balsam, are triisoprenoid alcohols related to each other as are geraniol and linalol. These compounds, used as perfumes but otherwise medic-

$$(CH_3)_2C=CHCH_2CH_2C(CH_3)=CHCH_2CH_2C(CH_3)=CHCH_2OH$$

Farnesol
3,7,11-Trimethyl-2,6,10-dodecatriene-1-ol

$$(CH_3)_2C=CHCH_2CH_2C(CH_3)=CHCH_2CH_2-\overset{\displaystyle OH}{\underset{\displaystyle CH_3}{C}}-CH=CH_2$$

Nerolidol
3,7,11-Trimethyl-1,6,10-dodecatriene-3-ol

inally unimportant, are of interest as bridging the gap between the diisoprenoid and the tetraisoprenoid alcohols.

Oleyl Alcohol is a mixture of alcohols consisting chiefly of $CH_3-(CH_2)_7-CH=CH-(CH_2)_7-CH_2OH$. It is employed in ointments to increase their smoothness and capacity to absorb water.

Phytol is an example of a C_{20} natural alcohol built up of four isoprene nuclei. Phytol may be isolated from chlorophyll, of which natural pigment it is a constituent, although the exact relationship is unknown. Its empirical formula is $C_{20}H_{40}O$. It is a primary, unsaturated alcohol; its properties show it to be a substituted allyl alcohol. Fission of the double bond with ozone yields glycolic aldehyde and a methyl ketone, $C_{16}H_{33}CO-CH_3$. These products account for all carbon atoms in phytol. The ketone was synthesized from perhydrofarnesyl bromide and ethyl acetoacetate as indicated.

$$Me_2CHCH_2CH_2-CH_2CHMeCH_2CH_2-CH_2CHMeCH_2CH_2Br +$$

$$\underset{\displaystyle Na}{}-\overset{\displaystyle COCH_3}{\underset{\displaystyle }{CH}}-COOEt \rightarrow C_{15}H_{31}-\overset{\displaystyle CO-CH_3}{\underset{\displaystyle }{CH}}-COOEt \xrightarrow{HOH}$$

$$CH_3CHCH_2CH_2-CH_2CHCH_2CH_2-CH_2CHCH_2CH_2-CH_2CO$$
$$\quad\quad\;|\quad\quad\quad\quad\quad\quad\;|\quad\quad\quad\quad\quad\quad\;|\quad\quad\quad\quad\quad\quad|$$
$$\quad\;CH_3\quad\quad\quad\quad\quad\;CH_3\quad\quad\quad\quad\quad\;CH_3\quad\quad\quad\quad\quad CH_3$$

6,10,14-Trimethyl-2-pentadecanone

The synthesis of this ketone proves the presence in phytol of the isoprene carbon skeletons. Thus the structure of phytol becomes:

$$CH_3CHCH_2CH_2-CH_2CHCH_2CH_2-CH_2CHCH_2CH_2-CH_2C=CHCH_2OH$$
$$\quad\quad|\quad\quad\quad\quad\quad\quad\;|\quad\quad\quad\quad\quad\quad\;|\quad\quad\quad\quad\quad\quad|$$
$$\quad CH_3\quad\quad\quad\quad\quad\;CH_3\quad\quad\quad\quad\quad\;CH_3\quad\quad\quad\quad\quad CH_3$$

Phytol
3,7,11,15-Tetramethyl-2-hexadecene-1-ol

An optically active phytol has been isolated from nettles; and the (+)-, (−)-, and (±)-phytols have been studied by Karrer and co-workers.[15]

Acetylenic alcohols, compounds containing a triple bond as well as a hydroxyl group, have shown considerable value as sedatives and hypnotics. The most useful members of this series are tertiary acetylenic alcohols in which the effects

[15] Karrer, Simon, and Zbinden, *Helv. Chim. Acta*, **27**, 313 (1944).

of the tertiary hydroxyl group and the acetylenic linkage have been combined in a single compound having fair potency with low toxicity.[16] Such compounds are synthesized by the addition of sodium acetylide to a ketone in the presence of liquid ammonia.[17]

$$C_2H_5 - \overset{\overset{\displaystyle O}{\|}}{C} - CH_3 \xrightarrow{\text{NaC} \equiv \text{CH}} C_2H_5 - \underset{\underset{\displaystyle C \equiv CH}{|}}{\overset{\overset{\displaystyle OH}{|}}{C}} - CH_3$$

Methylparafynol

Methylparafynol, 3-methyl-1-pentyne-3-ol (Dormison, Oblivon), has been selected as the best compound of those studied for use as a mild sedative in insomnia.[18] It is safe in relatively high doses and exhibits few symptoms of "hangover." In dogs, metabolism occurs through the acetylenic group.[19] Despite optimistic reports regarding the hypnotic efficiency of methylparafynol, some question its value.[20] The half ester of phthalic acid with methylparafynol is reported [21] as an oral anthelmintic for canine whipworms.

CYCLIC ALCOHOLS

Cyclic alcohols are of considerable interest, and for the medicinal and pharmaceutical chemist the cyclohexanols are of considerable importance. Cyclohexanol is prepared by the hydrogenation of phenol. Its properties, both physical and chemical, very closely resemble those of n-hexanol, and in industry it has much the same use.

Inositol, N.F. (Hexahydroxycyclohexane), $C_6H_6(OH)_6$, is found in heart muscle and in other tissues; it is also found in unripe beans and peas, and it is commercially obtainable from the "steep water" after soaking corn in the manufacture of starch. In most of its properties it resembles the sugar alcohols, the hexahydroxyhexanes. It is a component fraction of "bios." The term bios antedates the word vitamin and it was used in Ide's laboratory (Louvain, 1901) to designate the then unknown factors necessary in the growth of the yeast plant. Bios is now known to be a mixture of the B vitamins. Inositol may be a primary and essential vitamin. Woolley [22] found that it was a curative factor for the alopecia produced in mice fed on a special diet. However, all evidence indicates that inositol is a supporting and not a specific dietary constituent.

Inositol in combination with choline has had some use as a lipotropic agent in preventing or alleviating arteriosclerosis. It is thought that such agents are

[16] Papa, Villani, and Ginsberg, *Arch. Biochem. and Biophys.*, **33**, 482 (1951); *J. Am. Chem. Soc.*, **76**, 4446 (1954).

[17] Saunders, *Organic Syntheses*, Vol. 29, John Wiley & Sons, New York, 1949, p. 47.

[18] Margolin, Perlman, Villani, and McGavack, *Science*, **114**, 384 (1951).

[19] Perlman and Johnson, *J. Am. Pharm. Assoc.*, **41**, 13 (1952).

[20] Lasagna, *J. Pharmacol. Exptl. Therap.*, **111**, 9 (1954).

[21] Burch, *Vet. Med.*, **49**, 291 (1954).

[22] Woolley, *J. Biol. Chem.*, **139**, 29 (1941).

involved in the conversion of neutral fats to phospholipids, thereby preventing the deposition of fat in the liver. The role of inositol is not clearly established.[23]

Menthol, U.S.P. (1-Methyl-4-isopropyl-3-cyclohexanol, 3-Menthanol, 3-Terpanol, Hexahydrothymol), $C_{10}H_{20}O$, is said to have been known in Japan for more than 2000 years. It occurs in peppermint oils, mostly free and to some extent as the acetate. It is usually obtained from the volatile oil of *Mentha arvensis* (Japanese peppermint oil). Many synthetic menthols have appeared on the market. Most of them consist of mixtures of various stereoisomers from which it is possible to separate the official menthol.

Menthol has three asymmetric centers (indicated in the formula by asterisks); hence, there are 2^3 or eight possible optical isomers. These are discussed in greater detail on page 472.

Its structure is indicated by its synthesis from thymol on hydrogenation, and by its conversion into thymol on dehydrogenation.

Menthol   Thymol

It is a crystalline compound, m.p. 41–43°, with a characteristic mintlike odor, soluble in most organic solvents and slightly soluble in water. When mixed with about equal amounts of such compounds as camphor, thymol, phenol, and chloral hydrate, it forms eutectic mixtures.

Rubbed on the skin menthol causes a refreshing sensation followed by a slight burning and pricking sensation. It is used as a counterirritant in neuralgia and headache, being applied by means of menthol pencils, and as a constituent of analgesic balms. It has very slight antiseptic value but seems to be a stimulant to inflamed mucous surfaces especially of the nose and throat. Nasal sprays consisting of menthol dissolved in liquid petrolatum and the vapor supplied from menthol inhalers have been used to give relief from colds, catarrh, chronic bronchitis, etc. It is also used in mentholated cigarettes and cough drops for its counterritant effect on mucous surfaces. It is used to some extent internally for the relief of gastric pains as in dyspepsia.

Isomeric with the menthols are the carvomenthols, 2-menthanol. They may be obtained by the hydrogenation of carvacrol, and these may, in turn, be dehydrogenated to carvacrol.

Terpin (1,8-Menthandiol) is a dihydroxy derivative of menthane. On dehydration with phosphoric acid it forms the terpineol of commerce which is a mixture of α-, β-, and γ-terpineol.

---

[23] Bessey, Lowe, and Salomon, *Ann. Rev. Biochem.*, **22**, 606 (1953).

| Terpin | α-Terpineol | β-Terpineol | γ-Terpineol |

α-Terpineol is a natural constituent of many oils, e.g., cardamom and cajeput.

Terpin Hydrate, N.F., is obtained when turpentine in alcohol is treated with dilute nitric acid. It was formerly given the open-chain structure but this structure is not consistent with its melting point and its loss of water over sulfuric acid at room temperature.

The hydrate is a crystalline solid, m.p. 102–105° with loss of water and formation of the *cis* form of 1,8-terpin (see Terpin). The *trans* form of terpin which does not give a hydrate is also known, m.p. 157°.

It is used chiefly in the form of an elixir, often with codeine, as an expectorant in bronchitis. It has some slight antiseptic, diuretic, and diaphoretic activity.

| Terpin hydrate | α-Santalol | β-Santalol |

Santalol, found in sandalwood oil, is a mixture of α and β isomers whose structures are believed to be as shown. Good grades of the East Indian sandalwood oil contain from 90 to 97 per cent of the total alcohols having urinary antiseptic activity.

Carotenols and Vitamins A

Hydroxyl derivatives of the hydrocarbons of the carotene family discussed in Chapter 1 are natural plant pigments called carotenols and occur as widely distributed in nature as the carotenes themselves. Although the exact location of the hydroxyl groups of some of these compounds remains unknown, tremendous strides have been made in the structure determination of many carotenols. For example, cryptoxanthin, $C_{40}H_{56}O$, is 3-hydroxy-β-carotene; zeaxanthin, $C_{40}H_{56}O_2$, is 3,3'-dihydroxy-β-carotene; xanthophyll, $C_{40}H_{56}O_2$, is 3,3'-dihydroxy-α-carotene; rubixanthin, $C_{40}H_{56}O$, is 3-hydroxy-γ-carotene.

Perhaps the most important phase of the chemistry of the carotenols from the medicinal standpoint is that concerned with vitamin A. A close connection between carotene and a growth factor was suspected for many years.

The determination of the complex structure of vitamin A and its relationship to the carotenes is one of the outstanding achievements of science. Moore showed that carotene is converted in the body to vitamin A. About the same time, Karrer and his co-workers [24, 25] determined the chemical constitution of plant carotene [25] and of vitamin A obtained from fish-liver oil.[26] Karrer and his associates demonstrated that carotene and vitamin A contained the β-ionone ring, two rings in carotene with an aliphatic, methylated, polyene chain made up of isoprene residues arranged in pairs and joined in reverse order at carbon atoms 15 and 15'. Heilbron and associates [26] substantiated Karrer's formula. Karrer et al.[27] completed the proof of the correlation between the structure of carotene and vitamin A by showing that the crystalline, natural vitamin A from fish oils when hydrogenated was identical with a synthetic perhydrovitamin A which was prepared starting with β-ionone.

Vitamin A, U.S.P. (Axerophthol), may be considered as derived from β-carotene in the following manner:

Vitamin A₁

β-Carotene is only one pigment of this group of compounds which may be considered a provitamin A. There are at least ten natural as well as a large group of synthetic provitamins A.[28] Their activities compared to crystalline vitamin A vary considerably, indicating the extent to which they are isomerized and metabolized to vitamin A itself. For example, on a weight basis, β-carotene has only 50 per cent of the activity of vitamin A, showing that only one of two possible molecules of the vitamin result from the metabolism of the plant pigment.

The function of vitamin A in the living organism is not understood completely. It is known that certain types of night blindness (nyctalopia) as well as other abnormalities of the eye result from a deficiency of this vitamin. The role of vitamin A in the chemistry of vision is discussed under retinines, page 51.

[24] Helv. Chim. Acta, **13,** 1084 (1930).
[25] Helv. Chim. Acta, **14,** 1431 (1931).
[26] Biochem. J., **26,** 1194 (1932).
[27] Helv. Chim. Acta, **16,** 557 (1933).
[28] Karrer, Endeavour, **7,** 8 (1948).

A second important function of vitamin A is concerned with growth, the normal structure and healthy condition of teeth, mucous membranes, conjunctiva, and particularly with the epithelial tissue in general. However, with normal uptake and in the absence of disease, there is no reason to believe that additional quantities of vitamin A are beneficial in the promotion of growth, resistance to infections, etc. Evidence [29] is mounting that massive doses of vitamin A exhibit toxic manifestations at least in infants.

Some of the disabilities associated with old age are attributed, despite seemingly normal diets, to a deficiency of vitamin A, and the vitamin is being used in geriatrics.[30]

A deficiency of vitamin A may be caused by: (1) inadequate intake; (2) inadequate absorption due to disease, e.g., obstructive jaundice which results in the absence of bile without which the fat-soluble vitamins are poorly absorbed; (3) inadequate utilization, e.g., disease of the liver; (4) increased requirements as in pregnancy, tuberculosis, and hypothyroidism.

The minimum daily requirements of vitamin A are 1500 units for infants, 3000 units for children, and 4000 units for adults. Therapeutic doses should be at least three times these requirements. Quantities in excess of those actually needed are stored in the liver and the vitamin is available for further use. **Vitamin A₁**, or crystalline vitamin A, consists of pale yellow needles, m.p. 63–64°. It is fat soluble and insoluble in water. It is unstable in air and light and in the presence of rancid fats, but stable to alkalies.

The structure for vitamin A has been confirmed by various syntheses, and the synthetic product is steadily replacing the natural material on a commer-

$$\text{β-Ionone} \quad \xrightarrow[\text{2. LiAlH}_4]{\text{1. BrCH}_2\text{COOC}_2\text{H}_5 + \text{Zn}} \quad C_{11}H_{17}-\underset{\underset{\text{CH}_3}{|}}{C}=CH-CH_2OH \xrightarrow{\text{MnO}_2}$$

$$C_{14}H_{21}-CHO \xrightarrow[\text{CH}_3\text{COCH}_3]{\text{Al(OCMe}_3)_3} C_{14}H_{21}-CH=CH-\underset{\underset{\text{CH}_3}{|}}{C}O \xrightarrow{\text{BrCH}_2\text{COOC}_2\text{H}_5 + \text{Zn}}$$

$$C_{14}H_{21}-CH=CH-\underset{\underset{\text{OH}}{|}}{\overset{\overset{\text{CH}_3}{|}}{C}}-CH_2-COOC_2H_5 \xrightarrow[\text{2. LiAlH}_4]{\text{1. } -\text{H}_2\text{O}}$$

Vitamin A₁

[29] Bair, *J. Am. Med. Assoc.*, **146**, 1573 (1951); Harrison and Mercer, *Cleveland Clinic Quart.*, **20**, 424 (1953).

[30] Lesser, *Drug & Cosmetic Ind.*, **72**, 762 (1953).

cial basis. β-Ionone has proved to be the most useful starting material for synthesis of the vitamin, and an improved method is indicated on page 49.[31]

Another synthesis, developed by Isler,[32] converts β-ionone into a C_{14} aldehyde, which is then condensed with an appropriate C_6 fragment.

Vitamin A_1 has a biological activity of 3,340,000 International (U.S.P.) units per gram.   The methyl ether, the corresponding acid, the epoxide, and certain ester analogs of synthetic vitamin A have substantial biological activity, but most of the other synthetic analogs and isomerides of vitamin A_1 which have been prepared are singularly lacking in potency.

Vitamin A, like the carotenols, exists in a number of *cis-trans* isomers.   Ordinary crystalline vitamin A, as well as most commercial synthetic vitamin A, is the all-*trans* isomer.   However, fish-liver oils are known to contain mixtures of isomers one of which is neo-vitamin A.

In addition to the synthetic material, the chief sources of vitamin A in nutrition, other than the carotenes, are the liver oils from cod, shark, halibut, burbot, percomorph, and other fishes, and concentrates prepared from the fish-liver oils.

Cod Liver Oil, U.S.P., is obtained by refining the oil of *Gaddus morrhua* by chilling it to about 0° to separate most of the stearins as solids which are filtered out.   The refined oil must contain not less than 850 U.S.P. units per gram.   One per cent of added flavoring substances is permitted.

Nondestearinated Cod Liver Oil, U.S.P., must meet the same requirements as the official cod liver oil for vitamin A.   It is the form in which much of the cod liver oil is imported and is not used directly to a great extent.

Vitamin A concentrates are prepared by molecular distillation of the fish-liver oils, whereby the natural esters of the vitamin may be obtained in high concentration.   These concentrates may then be incorporated into tablets, placed in capsules or dissolved in oil alone or admixed with other vitamins to provide a wide variety of suitable dosage forms.

Oleovitamin A, U.S.P., is a solution of natural vitamin A in oil.   It contains about 57,500 units of vitamin A and about 1000 units of vitamin D in each gram.   Oleovitamin A is usually administered in capsules.

Vitamin A_2 is a second vitamin of structure similar to vitamin A_1 and exists as a fraction of fish-liver oils.   This was clearly established by Shantz and his co-workers [33] with its purification, preparation of crystalline derivatives, and the determination of its biological activity.   Vitamin A_2 has an activity of 1,300,000 International Units per gram.

For some time the constitution of this second vitamin A was the subject of considerable controversy.   However, its total synthesis by Jones and associates [34]

[31] Wendler, Slater, Trenner, and Tishler, *J. Am. Chem. Soc.*, **73**, 719 (1951).

[32] Isler, *XIIth Intern. Congr. Pure Appl. Chem.*, Section 10, paper 98, Sept. 13, 1951.

[33] Shantz, *Science*, **108**, 417 (1948); Shantz and Brinkman, *J. Biol. Chem.*, **183**, 467 (1950).

[34] Farrar, Hamlet, Henbest, and Jones, *Chemistry & Industry*, **1951**, 49; *J. Chem. Soc.*, **1952**, 2657.

together with proof offered by others [35] gave confirmation to the 3-dehydrovitamin A_1 structure, that is, with a safranal type of cycle.

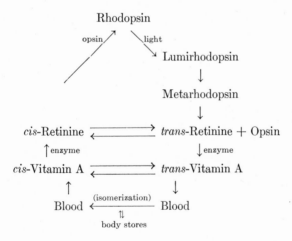

Vitamin A_2

It was early recognized that the chemistry of vision is intimately associated with vitamin A and its corresponding aldehyde, known as retinine. Though many details still await solution, it is clear that light-sensitive pigments are found in the retina of the eye. These have been identified as proteins bearing carotenoid prosthetic groups, and they are colored and sensitive to light. On exposure to light, the pigments bleach, and retinine, freed from the protein, is converted, during the visual process, into vitamin A. In the dark, this process reverses and vitamin A is oxidized to retinine to recombine with the light-sensitive pigment.

Four pigments are known, formed by combining two retinines with two visual proteins or opsins.[36] Retinine$_1$ combines with rod opsin to form rhodopsin and with cone opsin to make iodopsin. Retinine$_2$ combines with rod opsin to make porphyropsin and with cone opsin to make cyanopsin. The visual cycle has been summarized in the accompanying scheme for rhodopsin, also commonly known as visual purple.[37]

Rhodopsin

opsin / \ light

Lumirhodopsin

↓

Metarhodopsin

↓

cis-Retinine ⇄ trans-Retinine + Opsin

↑ enzyme   ↓ enzyme

cis-Vitamin A ⇄ trans-Vitamin A

↑   (isomerization)   ↓

Blood ←——— Blood

⇅

body stores

STEROLS

The sterols comprise a large group of naturally occurring substances which are derived from the hydrocarbon, cyclopentanoperhydrophenanthrene. The term steroid has been widely adopted for a large number of derivatives which include: (1) the sterols, (2) the bile acids, (3) the cardiac aglycones, (4) the sapogenins of digitalis and sarsaparilla, (5) vitamin D, (6) hormones of the

[35] Fieser, *J. Org. Chem.*, **15**, 930 (1950); Karrer and Schneider, *Helv. Chim. Acta*, **33**, 38 (1950).

[36] Wald, Brown, and Smith, *Science*, **118**, 505 (1953); Wald, *Am. Scientist*, **42**, 73 (1954).

[37] Wald, *Ann. Rev. Biochem.*, **22**, 497 (1953); Baumann, *ibid.*, **22**, 527 (1953).

adrenal glands, (7) the genins of the toad poisons, and (8) many carcinogenic hydrocarbons.

Sterols occur in every cell of plant or animal origin, though they appear to be absent from the cells of bacteria. It can be said that they are present in every cell with a developed nucleus. The sterols of animal origin are known as zoösterols, those of plant origin as phytosterols, and those from fungi as mycosterols. The close relationship between these sterols is shown by a comparison of their formulas. Their chemistry is quite well understood. They undoubtedly play a very important part in all life processes. The more important products derived from the sterols are considered under appropriate headings, such as the cardiac glycosides, bile acids, etc.

Cholesterol is the principal animal sterol. Stigmasterol is widely distributed in plants. Ergosterol, found also in ergot, is the principal yeast sterol.

Cholesterol, U.S.P. (Cholesterin), occurs in all cells of man either free or as an ester of fatty acids. The total quantity of cholesterol in the body is about 0.3 per cent of the wet weight, the largest amounts being present in the skin and nervous tissue. Cholesterol is a likely precursor of many steroid hormones and plays a key role in the transport of neutral fat.

Cholesterol is water insoluble but soluble in most organic solvents. It is used along with its esters in ointment bases to render them hydrophilic. Its place in pharmacy is becoming increasingly important.[38]

Although the structure of cholesterol has been known since 1932, its total synthesis was described for the first time by Woodward in 1951.[39]

The formula for cholesterol indicates the method of numbering and the relative configuration. The degradation of ring A to D(+)malic acid [40] enables the scientist to speak with considerable accuracy on this point.

Cholesterol

In this molecule the two methyl groups, C_{18} and C_{19}, are *cis*. The hydroxyl group at position 3 is *cis*, and the configuration at this position is designated as β-; the hydrogen atoms at C_9 and C_{17} are *trans* and are designated as α-.

In the reduction of the double bond the hydrogen atom adding to C_5 may take a position α or *trans* to the angular methyl group at C_{10}, giving rise to a compound in which rings A and B are *trans;* this compound is known as cholestanol. Or the hydrogen atom

[38] Lesser, *Drug & Cosmetic Ind.*, **73**, 52, 758 (1953); **74**, 200, 357 (1954).

[39] Woodward, Sondheimer, and Taub, *J. Am. Chem. Soc.*, **73**, 3548 (1951).

[40] Prelog *et al.*, *Helv. Chim. Acta*, **36**, 325 (1953).

may take the β-position, that is, *cis* to the methyl group, and rings A and B become *cis;* this isomer is known as coprostan-3β-ol.

Cholesterol, along with lipid material, is a prominent component of the lesions occurring in atherosclerosis in humans. The controversial role of cholesterol in this type of pathology has been stressed by Gofman and his associates,[41] and some workers have thought that dietary cholesterol may be responsible. On the other hand, it has been found that acetate is converted *in vivo* via squalene into cholesterol as indicated.[42, 43] It will be noted that in the conversion of squalene into cholesterol, there is a loss of three carbon atoms.

Hexaisoprenoid arrangement of
carbon atoms in squalene

Sitosterol

In dihydrositosterol the double bond is hydrogenated.

Sitosterol, N.N.R. (Cytellin), is a mixture of 80–90 per cent β-sitosterol and β-dihydrositosterol. It appears to facilitate fecal elimination of cholesterol and thus is proposed for treatment of hypercholesterolemia.

Vitamins D

Vitamin D consists of several distinct but closely related chemical substances each having the ability to prevent and to cure rickets, a disease in humans characterized by the defective calcification of the bones. McCollum and his associates named the antirachitic substance in cod liver oil, "Vitamin D," and the term has been retained and applied by custom to include *all* antirachitic steroid substances.

Discovery of the fact that certain sterols, from the unsaponifiable matter of animal fats, became antirachitic upon exposure to ultraviolet irradiation led to the treatment of ergosterol, from ergot and yeast, by this procedure. The chemical changes produced in ergosterol by ultraviolet irradiation may be represented as follows:

Ergosterol $\rightarrow$ Lumosterol $\rightarrow$ Tachysterol $\rightarrow$

Calciferol $\rightarrow$ Toxisterol $\rightarrow$ Suprasterols

[41] Gofman, Lindgren, Elliot, Mantz, Strisower, and Herring, *Science*, **111**, 166 (1950); *Am. J. Med.*, **11**, 358 (1951).

[42] Dauben and Takemura, *J. Am. Chem. Soc.*, **75**, 6302 (1953).

[43] Schwenk, Todd, and Fish, *Arch. Biochem. Biophys.*, **49**, 187 (1954).

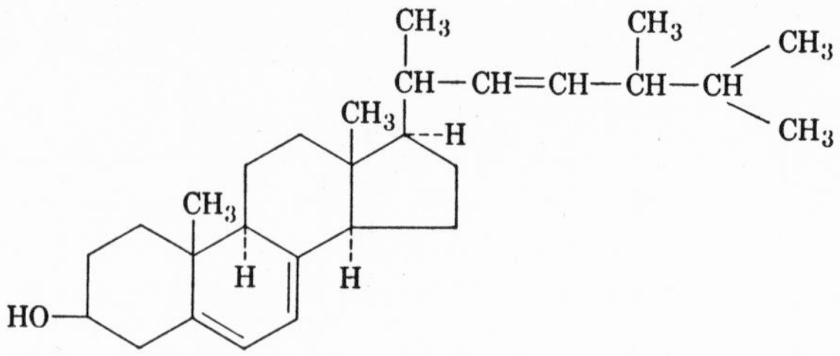

Ergosterol
(Provitamin D$_2$)

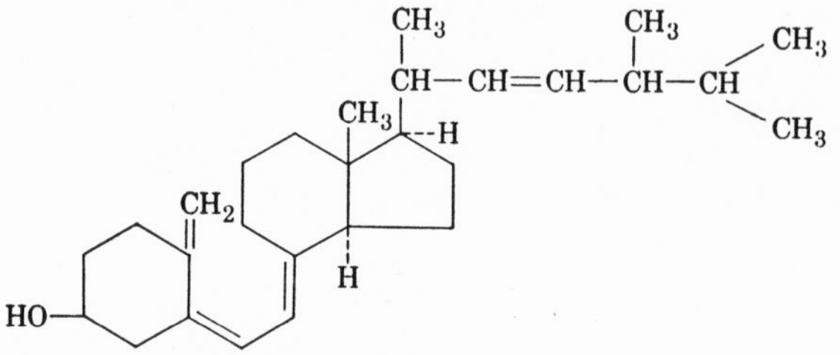

Calciferol
(Vitamin D$_2$)

Of these substances, only calciferol is strongly antirachitic.

Toxisterol and the suprasterols result from excessive irradiation of calciferol and, as impurities, are probably responsible for the toxic effects of vitamin D reported in humans.

Vitamin D and preparations containing this vitamin are used in the treatment and prophylaxis of rickets and tetany. There is good evidence that vitamin D along with the parathyroid hormone regulates calcium and phosphorus metabolism and that it is an essential factor in the mechanism controlling growth and mineralization of the teeth and bones. Consequently, it is used in a number of conditions believed to be caused by faulty calcium and phosphorus metabolism, such as dental caries and arthritis. Some cases of psoriasis have been reported to be improved by massive doses of vitamin D.

Deficiency of vitamin D is caused chiefly by inadequate intake. This may be caused by poverty which prevents the poor from purchasing those relatively expensive foods listed as rich in vitamin D. Individuals living in crowded cities where the streets are narrow and where smoke and dust prevent the penetration of the ultraviolet rays of the sun do not secure the vitamin D formed in the skin by the sun's rays. Inadequate absorption due to disease and abnormal requirements in disease and during pregnancy and lactation are other factors that predispose to deficiency.

The average daily requirement of vitamin D is from 400 to 800 U.S.P. or International Units. Since 1949, the International Unit (I.U.) of vitamin D has been defined as the vitamin D activity of 0.025 γ of pure vitamin D$_3$ or activated 7-dehydrocholesterol.

Calciferol, U.S.P., Vitamin D_2, is obtained in crystalline form, m.p. 115–118°, and is marketed as irradiated ergosterol in oil (Viosterol). The crystals have a potency of 40 units of vitamin D (U.S.P.) per microgram.

Vitamin D_3 (Activated 7-Dehydrocholesterol) is the natural vitamin D occurring in various fish liver oils along with vitamin A. It consists of white crystals, m.p. 82–84°, levorotatory, soluble in alcohol, acetone and ether, but insoluble in water. Crystalline vitamin D_3 in humans is of equal potency to vitamin D_2.

Vitamin D_4 (Activated 22-Dihydroergosterol) is nearly as active as calciferol. Other sterols that have been irradiated and examined for their vitamin D activities are 7-dehydrositosterol, 7-dehydrostigmasterol, and 7-dehydrocampesterol. Dihydrotachysterol, from the reduction of tachysterol (an isomer of calciferol), in combination with calciferol is particularly useful in raising the level of serum calcium.

The relationship between some of these compounds is illustrated by their formulas on the following page.

From what has been said and from the formulas given, it is evident that 7-dehydrocholesterol is the natural precursor of vitamin D, and it is from this substance that the vitamin D activity is derived on exposure of the skin to sunlight or ultraviolet light. 7-Dehydrocholesterol may be obtained by boiling acetylcholesterol in acetic acid with quinone under the influence of mercury light.[44] Another synthesis prepares 7-bromocholesteryl acetate, which on heating with diethylaniline loses hydrogen bromide; the resulting 7-dehydrocholesteryl acetate is then hydrolyzed.[45]

The total synthesis of cholesterol having been realized, the total synthesis of vitamin D_3[46] may now be considered as solved.

Synthetic Oleovitamin D, U.S.P., is a solution of activated ergosterol (vitamin D_2) or activated 7-dehydrocholesterol (vitamin D_3) in an edible vegetable oil. It must contain at least 10,000 units of vitamin D in each gram.

Concentrated Oleovitamin A and D may be a fish-liver oil, or a solution of a fish-liver oil or concentrates of vitamins A and D in an edible vegetable oil. It contains about 57,500 units of vitamin A and about 11,500 units of vitamin D in each gram. It is usually administered in the form of capsules, which are official.

Oleovitamin A and D, N.F., may be a fish-liver oil, a mixture of a fish-liver and an edible vegetable oil, or a solution of concentrates of vitamins A and D in an edible vegetable oil or in fish-liver oil. It contains about 1000 units of vitamin A and about 100 units of vitamin D in each gram.

[44] Mazza and Migliardi, *Quad. nutriz.*, **8**, 85 (1941); *C.A.*, **37**, 3762 (1943).
[45] Henbest, Jones, Bide, Peevers, and Wilkenson, *Nature*, **158**, 169 (1946).
[46] Woodward, Sondheimer, and Taub, *J. Am. Chem. Soc.*, **73**, 3548 (1951).

7-Dehydrocholesterol
(Provitamin D₃)

Activated 7-Dehydrocholesterol
(Vitamin D₃)

22-Dihydroergosterol
(Provitamin D₄)

7-Dehydrositosterol

AROMATIC ALCOHOLS

Aromatic alcohols structurally are aliphatic alcohols in which a hydrogen attached to a carbon has been replaced by an aromatic hydrocarbon radical. They may be regarded as aryl derivatives of carbinol and often are so named. They have the chemical properties of the aliphatic alcohols. The chief marked difference is that the H and OH when alpha to the aromatic ring are unusually active.

Benzyl Alcohol, N.F. (Phenylmethanol, Phenylcarbinol), $C_6H_5CH_2OH$, b.p. 200–206°, occurs as the esters of benzoic and cinnamic acids in balsams of Peru and tolu, in many volatile oils, storax resin, etc. It is soluble about 1 to 25 in water and is soluble in fixed oils and miscible with alcohol, ether, and chloroform. It is synthesized by heating benzyl chloride with a base,

$$2C_6H_5CH_2Cl + Ca(OH)_2 \rightarrow 2C_6H_5CH_2OH + CaCl_2$$

It is markedly antiseptic and has a local anesthetic action on mucous surfaces and when injected. In low concentrations, it is nontoxic and relatively non-irritant, but the concentrations necessary for strong local anesthesia on injection are irritant. It is used in ointments, usually about 10 per cent, to relieve the itching of dermatitis and pruritis. It is also used in solutions for injection in concentrations of 1 to 4 per cent as an antiseptic stabilizing agent and to relieve pain on injection.

β-Phenylethyl Alcohol (Phenylethanol, Benzylcarbinol, Phenethyl Alcohol), $C_6H_5CH_2CH_2OH$, is found in rose oil and oil of neroli; because of its excellent and pleasant odor it is very useful as a perfume. It has been reported to be more anesthetic than benzyl alcohol and of about the same toxicity.[47]

PHENOLS

Phenols are compounds in which the hydroxyl group is substituted directly into the aromatic nucleus. As a general rule, the chemical properties of the phenolic hydroxyl group are similar to those of the alcoholic hydroxyl. There is one decided difference. It has been pointed out that sodium reacts with alcohols to liberate hydrogen and form sodium alkoxides; these are unstable in water. The phenolic hydroxyl is sufficiently acid so that it will react with aqueous solutions of alkali to form sodium salts of the phenols, for example, $NaOC_6H_5$. Other phenols form analogous salts. These alkali phenoxides are soluble in water, but they are salts of what may be called very weak acids, and, on the addition of carbon dioxide to their solutions, the phenol is liberated. The ionization constant for phenol is 1.3×10^{-10} as compared to about 1×10^{-18} for ethanol. It is this slightly acidic property that is responsible for the fact that phenol is sometimes known as carbolic acid, and for the designation as "tar acids" of the fraction obtained from coal tar which contains the lower phenols.

[47] Hjort and Eagan, *J. Pharmacol.*, **14**, 211 (1919).

Prolonged exposure to low concentrations of phenol may lead to injury to the kidney and to nutritional disturbances. Contact of phenol with the skin, except in diluted solutions, causes irritation, and, if the contact is prolonged, necrosis may result.

Phenol has come to be an important industrial material, for example, the phenolic-aldehyde resins are widely used and extensively applied. However, it is because of their antibacterial properties that phenols are of particular interest to pharmaceutical chemists.

The more common phenols, with names and properties, are listed in Table III.

TABLE III

PHENOLS

Common Name	Other Names	Melting Point ° C.	Boiling Point ° C.	Specific Gravity
Phenol	Hydroxybenzene, phenyl hydroxide	41	182	1.071_{25}
o-Cresol	o-Hydroxytoluene, 2-methylphenol, 1-hydroxy-2-methylbenzene	30.1	190.8	1.051
m-Cresol	m-Hydroxytoluene, 3-methylphenol, 1-hydroxy-3-methylbenzene	10	202.8	1.035
p-Cresol	p-Hydroxytoluene, 4-methylphenol, 1-hydroxy-4-methylbenzene	34.8	201.1	$1.039_{15.5}$
Catechol	1,2-Dihydroxybenzene	105	245	1.344
Resorcinol	1,3-Dihydroxybenzene	110	276.5	1.285_{15}
Quinol	1,4-Dihydroxybenzene, hydroquinone	170.5	286.2	1.332_{15}
Guaiacol	1-Hydroxy-2-methoxybenzene, catecholmonomethylether, 2-methoxyphenol	28	205.1	1.143_{15}
α-Naphthol	1-Hydroxynaphthalene	96	280	$1.099_{99.3}$
β-Naphthol	2-Hydroxynaphthalene	122	286	1.217
Pyrogallol	1,2,3-Trihydroxybenzene	134	309	1.453
Thymol	2-Isopropyl-5-methylphenol	51.5	231.8	0.969
Carvacrol	5-Isopropyl-2-methylphenol	0.5	237.9	0.976

Thymol and carvacrol (both containing the p-menthane carbon skeleton) occur naturally. Thymol is found in oil of thyme, and carvacrol is the chief constituent of oil of origanum. Chavicol, p-allylphenol, is present in bay oil and in oil of betel leaves. Catechol is found as a constituent of the catechu resins and in certain tannins. Resorcinol occurs as a constituent of many resins and tannins. Phloroglucinol occurs in some natural resins and in the glucoside, phloridzin. Pyrogallol is found in some tannins. Numerous compounds that may be regarded as derivatives of the phenols occur in natural products, e.g., phenolic ethers, aldehydes, ketones, and acids. Other phenols are not found as such in nature; they, as well as all the other phenolic bodies, are obtained by direct synthesis or by degradation of other compounds. Thus phenol and the three cresols are obtained by the distillation of coal, and they are the chief components of the so-called tar acids; guaiacol is a constituent of wood tar; pyrogallol is obtained by the pyrolytic decarboxylation of gallic acid, 3,4,5-trihydroxybenzoic acid.

Antiseptic Activity

Modern antisepsis began with Lord Lister (1865), who learned from Pasteur about bacterial infection and was the first to use phenol in combating infection in surgery. The next natural development was to use the cresols, thymol, and carvacrol. The next great advance was made about half a century later, when Johnson and Lane [48] reported that in a series of homologous alkylresorcinols the antiseptic potency increased with increase in the size of the alkyl. This discovery led, quite naturally, to the synthesis and examination of all manner of alkylated phenols, and the journals abound with original data regarding syntheses and bactericidal properties, and numerous patents have been issued covering nearly every conceivable phenolic derivative. These compounds have been evaluated for their antiseptic properties in terms of a standard known as a "phenol coefficient."

The term phenol coefficient is a ratio of bactericidal activity of the modified phenol as compared to phenol itself. Since the conditions of the test, the nature of the culture medium, the type and viability of the organisms, temperature, etc., influence the results so greatly, the official procedure is rather strictly prescribed. Even with the observance of these strict injunctions, it is often impossible for reputable workers in different laboratories to check each other's results within desirable limits. Nevertheless, the phenol coefficient of an antiseptic permits convenient comparison of the relative activities of phenolic compounds; however, it does not allow much conclusion as to the choice of any particular antiseptic for a specific condition.

The official method of assaying phenolic antiseptics for their potencies is described in *Circular* 198, United States Department of Agriculture, entitled "United States Food and Drug Administration Methods of Testing Antiseptics and Disinfectants, December 1931." It is estimated that in the official test for antiseptics, approximately 3×10^{12} molecules of phenol are required to kill one organism.

Table IV is compiled from various sources and from various data. Since all the results were obtained under conditions which do not justify strict comparison, the table is given only to show relative effects and to justify general conclusions as to the effect of chemical structure on bactericidal activity in the phenolic compounds.

On the basis of available data, several generalizations may be permitted:

1. Practically every phenolic compound possesses antibacterial properties.

2. As a rule the introduction into the phenolic molecule of groups or substituents such as alkyl, alkoxyl, alkylthiol, and halogen increases the bactericidal activity; the larger the alkyl group, the greater the antiseptic activity.

[48] *J. Am. Chem. Soc.*, **43**, **348** (1921).

TABLE IV

ANTISEPTIC ACTIVITIES OF PHENOLS

Phenol	Boiling Point ° C.		Melting Point ° C.		Phenol Coefficient		
					B. typhosus	S. aureus	
Phenol	182		41		1	1	
p-Cresol	202.8		34.8		2 – 2.5	2 – 2.5	(1,2,3,)
p-Ethylphenol	219		46		6.3– 7.5	6.3– 7.8	(1,2,3)
p-n-Propylphenol	233		22		18.3– 21.6	16.3– 24	(1,2,3)
p-n-Butylphenol	246	–250	—		46.7– 70	44 – 52	(1,2,3,4)
p-n-Amylphenol	262		<0		53. –197	125 – 139	(2,3,5)
p-n-Hexylphenol	155_{15}		—		33 –500	313 – 375	(2,3,5)
p-n-Heptylphenol	165_{15}		—		17 –20	625	(2,3)
o-n-Butylphenol	234	–237	—		75	52	(2,4)
m-n-Butylphenol	247	–249	—		—	52.3	(4)
p-sec-Butylphenol	241		61 – 62		—	27.5	(4)
p-tert-Butylphenol	236	–238	99		—	19 – 22	(4)
Resorcinol	277	–281	110		—	0.3– 0.37	(5)
4-Ethylresorcinol	131_{15}		97 – 98		—	1.5– 1.6	(5,6,7)
4-n-Propylresorcinol	172	-174_{15}	79.2– 79.4		4.8	4.3– 5	(5,6,7)
4-n-Butylresorcinol	196	-200_{24}	51.4– 51.7		15	8 – 22	(5,6,7)
4-n-Amylresorcinol	168	-170_6	72 – 73		47	30.3– 33	(5,7)
4-n-Hexylresorcinol	178	-180_7	62 – 62.5		147	46 – 98	(5,7,8)
4-n-Heptylresorcinol	—		70.4– 70.8		350	24 – 295	(5,7,8,9)
4-n-Octylresorcinol	—		70.2– 70.4		400	0 – 690	(5,8)
4-n-Nonylresorcinol	—		72.5– 73		—	0 –1000	(5,8)
4-Benzylresorcinol	—		76 – 77		18.3	11.3	(10)
4-Isohexylresorcinol	182	-183_6	69.5– 70		105	27	(5,8)
4-Cyclohexylresorcinol	—		124 –125		—	24 – 27	(9)
4-n-Hexylcatechol	—		164 –169		—	129	(11)
4-n-Hexylpyrogallol	—		104 –105		—	26	(12)
n-Hexylphloroglucinol	—		—		—	8	(13)
4-n-Hexyloxyphenol	48		—		18	67 – 100	(4,14)
3-n-Hexyloxyphenol	145_5		—		46	125	(15)
2-n-Hexyloxyphenol	114	$-116_{3.5}$	—		17	28	(16)
4-Chloro-2-n-hexylphenol	132_3		—		23	1250	(17)
2-Chloro-4-n-hexylphenol	273	–275	—		23.3	444 – 500	(3,18)
2-Methoxy-4-n-hexylphenol	165	-167_{15}	—		9		(2)
4-Fluoro-2-n-hexylphenol	—		—		62		(21)
4-n-Hexylthiophenol	—		58		40	200 – 230	(19,20)
5-n-Hexylresorcinol	—		—		22	49	

Notes on following page

1. Tilley and Schaffer, *J. Bac.*, **12**, 303 (1926).
2. Coulthard, Marshall, and Pyman, *Pharm. J.*, **123**, 509 (1929); *J. Chem. Soc.*, 1930, 280.
3. Klarmann, Shternov, Gates, and Bloomfield, *J. Lab. Clin. Med.*, **20**, 40 (1934).
4. Read and Miller, *J. Am. Chem. Soc.*, **54**, 1195 (1932).
5. Schaffer and Tilley, *J. Bact.*, **14**, 259 (1927).
6. Johnson and Lane, *J. Am. Chem. Soc.*, **43**, 348 (1921).
7. Leonard, *J. Am. Med. Assoc.*, **83**, 2005 (1924).
8. Dohme, Cox, and Miller, *J. Am. Chem. Soc.*, **48**, 1688 (1926).
9. Bartlett and Garland, *J. Am. Chem. Soc.*, **49**, 2098 (1927).
10. Klarmann and von Wowern, *J. Am. Chem. Soc.*, **51**, 605 (1929).
11. Miller, Hartung, Rock, and Crossley, *J. Am. Chem. Soc.*, **60**, 7 (1938).
12. Hart and Woodruff, *J. Am. Chem. Soc.*, **58**, 1957 (1936).
13. Klarmann, *J. Am. Chem. Soc.*, **48**, 2358 (1926).
14. Klarmann, Gatyas, and Shternov, *J. Am. Chem. Soc.*, **54**, 298 (1932).
15. Klarmann, Gatyas, and Shternov, *J. Am. Chem. Soc.*, **53**, 3397 (1931).
16. Klarmann, Gates, and Shternov, *J. Am. Chem. Soc.*, **54**, 1204 (1932).
17. Klarmann, Shternov, and Gates, *J. Am. Chem. Soc.*, **55**, 2576 (1933); *J. Lab. Clin. Med.*, **19**, 835 (1934).
18. Blicke and Stockhaus, *J. Am. Pharm. Assoc.*, **22**, 1090 (1933).
19. Suter and Hansen, *J. Am. Chem. Soc.*, **54**, 4100 (1932).
20. Miller and Read, *J. Am. Chem. Soc.*, **55**, 1224 (1933).
21. Suter, Lawson, and Smith, *J. Am. Chem. Soc.*, **61**, 161 (1939).

3. For a given alkyl group the greatest activity is found with the normal primary alkyl group; the isoalkyl groups are less active; activity decreases when the alkyl group is secondary; least activity is found in the tertiary alkyl groups.

4. A second phenolic hydroxyl group decreases the activity to approximately one-third. Thus resorcinol is about a third as active as phenol; *n*-hexylresorcinol with a phenol coefficient of approximately 70 is about a third as active as *n*-hexylphenol with a coefficient of about 200. The alkylpyrogallols and alkylphloroglucinols are still less active.

5. There is some indication of specificity, that is, preferential activity, against certain types of organisms. But the evidence is not sufficiently clear cut to justify definite conclusions.

6. The introduction of a hydroxyl group into the benzene ring decreases the narcotic and increases the convulsant activity. The relative toxicity of phenols is decreased by hydrogenation, etherification of the hydroxyl group, and alkylation of the ring.

A most interesting investigation in the field of phenols has been in the vermicidal and vermifugal properties. This work shows that many of the alkylated phenols are ascaricides and that they are effective in treating hookworm infestations. The best of all the compounds is hexylresorcinol, which is usually effective in one dose, and practically always effective if a second dose is administered.

The antifungal action of phenols and cresols has been reviewed by Stedman.[49] In clinical trials against dermatophytoses, 2,4-dinitro-*o*-cyclohexylphenol was superior to undecylenic acid but was more irritating. Although cresol derivatives have not been investigated as extensively as phenol compounds, *m*-cresyl acetate was found to be very effective against otomycosis.

[49] Stedman, *Bull. Natl. Formulary Comm.*, **18**, 153 (1950).

Monohydroxy Phenols

Phenol, U.S.P. (Carbolic Acid), C_6H_5OH, is a crystalline solid, m.p. 41–42°, with a characteristic odor. It often turns pink or red, owing to partial oxidation. It sublimes slowly and is readily distilled with steam.

Phenol is prepared according to the equations:

(a)
$$C_6H_5Cl \xrightarrow{\text{fused alkali}} C_6H_5OH$$
Chlorobenzene \qquad Phenol

(b)
$$C_6H_5SO_3H \xrightarrow{\text{fused alkali}} C_6H_5OH$$
Benzenesulfonic acid

(c)
$$C_6H_5N_2 \cdot HX \xrightarrow{H_2O} C_6H_5OH$$
Diazonium salt

Reactions (a) and (b) are used commercially, (a) finding greater acceptance. The last reaction is not practical for phenol but is representative of special cases for converting aromatic amines into their corresponding phenols.

Phenol is used as an antiseptic in solutions of ½ to 3 per cent strength to check bacterial growth as in gargles and lotions, e.g., *Phenolated Calamine Lotion, U.S.P.*; *Phenolated Water, Antiseptic Solution, N.F.*; *Alkaline Antiseptic Solution*; and *Dobell's Solution*. The mild local anesthetic action of phenol is utilized in the form of lotion and ointment, e.g., *Phenolated Oil* and *Phenol Ointment* in the treatment of itch. For the relief of earache, a 3 to 5 per cent solution in glycerol or olive oil is used. In high concentrations, phenol is caustic and it acts as a general protoplasmic poison. Internally, it is rapidly absorbed and so has little value as an intestinal antiseptic. The advent of more efficient antiseptics and analgesics has caused the use of phenol to decline.

Liquefied Phenol, U.S.P. (Liquefied Carbolic Acid), is a solution of water, 10 per cent, in phenol. It is a convenient solution in the preparation of more dilute phenol solutions, etc.

α-**Naphthol** (*α*-Hydroxynaphthalene) has a phenol coefficient slightly greater than phenol. A preparation known as Benetol consisting of a solution of this phenol in glycerol and soft soap is used as a disinfectant and deodorant in the forms: solution, capsules, tablets, ointment, vaginal suppositories, etc.

α-Naphthol \qquad β-Naphthol

β-**Naphthol** (*β*-Hydroxynaphthalene), with its *α*-isomer, occurs as a constituent of coal tar. It is reported to be much more effective as an antiseptic than phenol. It is irritant to the skin and mucous surfaces when applied in solution. Toxic results such as kidney irritation, eye damage, and reduction in the red blood cells have been reported from its absorption. It is used externally in the form of dermatological pastes and ointments 1 to 10 per cent for the treatment of acne, psoriasis, and other skin diseases. Internally, it is used as an anthelmintic in the treatment of hookworm infections, but it is inferior to thymol.

Polyhydroxy Phenols

The dihydric phenols resemble the monohydric in most of their chemical properties. The presence of a second hydroxyl group increases the solubility in water, and, when the hydroxyls are in the *ortho* or *para* position, the compounds are very easily oxidized; the *ortho* and *para* compounds are valuable reducing agents which serve as developers in photography. The three isomers are important constituents of drugs,

Catechol,	Resorcinol,	Quinol,
o-hydroxyphenol	m-hydroxyphenol	p-hydroxyphenol

The activities of the dihydric phenols are more intense than that of phenol, and the same orientation influences mentioned for the cresols seem to hold; e.g., in the frog and in the guinea pig the M.L.D. of catechol and quinol are equal and about half that of resorcinol.

Catechol (Pyrocatechin, *o*-Dihydroxybenzene) occurs in a number of resins, especially catechu. It is the most toxic of the three dihydric phenols. It is not used as such in medicine but it is used in the form of its monomethyl ether, guaiacol.

Quinol (Hydroquinone, *p*-Dihydroxybenzene) is also toxic, but less so than catechol and more so than phenol or resorcinol. It is used medicinally only in the form of derivatives such as the glycoside arbutin from *Uva ursi*.

The reducing action of hydroquinone makes it a valuable agent as an antioxidant or inhibitor for the stabilization of foods and chemicals.

Resorcinol, U.S.P. (Resorcin, *m*-Dihydroxybenzene), is less toxic and less irritant than the other two isomers. It is used as such and in the form of derivatives. It consists of white crystals that turn pink on exposure to air and light, m.p. 109–111°, soluble in water 1:0.9.

It has been used internally as an intestinal antiseptic. It is used chiefly by external application in the form of pastes, e.g., *Mild and Strong Resorcinol Paste*, and in the form of ointments, e.g., *Compound Resorcinol Ointment, N.F.*, in the treatment of skin diseases such as eczema, psoriasis, and acne, and in hair tonics to treat alopecia and seborrhea.

Resorcinol Monoacetate, N.F. (*m*-Hydroxyphenyl Acetate "Euresol"), $1,3\text{-}C_6H_4OH \cdot OOCCH_3$, is a lemon-colored oily liquid, slightly soluble in water but soluble in alcohol, acetone, and most organic solvents. It is used in the form of ointments, solutions, and lotions for the same purposes as resorcinol but is reported to be less irritant and to give a more prolonged effect because the resorcinol is gradually liberated by the hydrolysis of the ester.

The three isomeric trihydric phenols are not used extensively as medicinal agents,

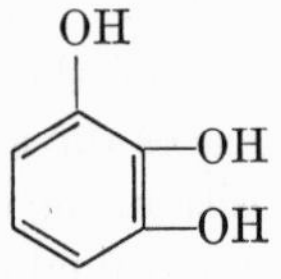

| Pyrogallol, 1,2,3-trihydroxybenzene | Hydroxyquinol, 1,2,4-trihydroxybenzene | Phloroglucinol, 1,3,5-trihydroxybenzene |

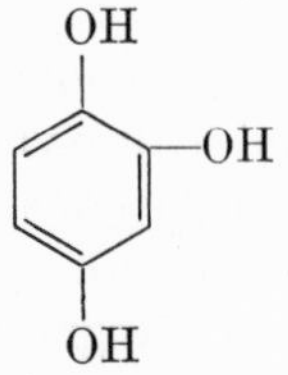

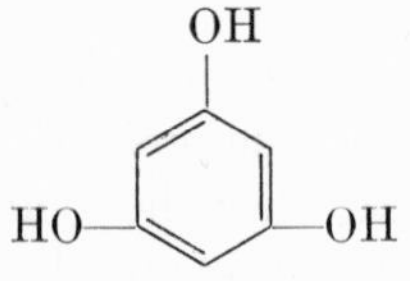

The introduction of a third hydroxyl group as in phloroglucinol decreases the toxicity; phloroglucinol is the least toxic of the di- and trihydric phenols. Whether the substituted group is hydroxyl or not, it seems that substitution in the *meta* position yields the least toxic compound. In phloroglucinol the maximum number of *meta* arrangements gives a relatively nontoxic product in terms of minimum lethal dose. However, as the number of hydroxyl groups attached to the benzene ring increases, the hemolytic acitivity of the compounds increases.

Pyrogallol, N.F. (Pyrogallic Acid), is made by heating gallic acid to decarboxylate it:

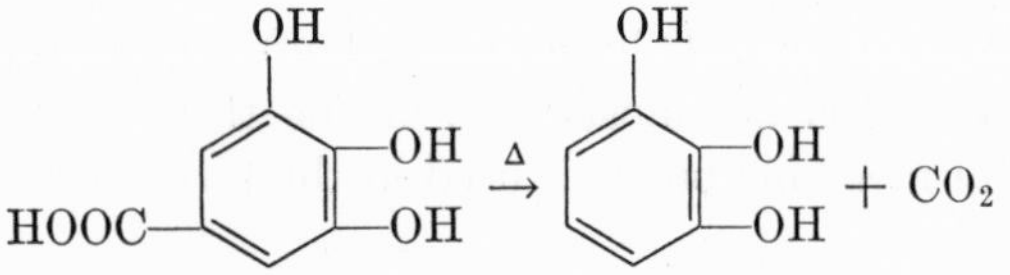

It is a white powder turning slightly gray on exposure to air and light, m.p. 130–133°, b.p. 309°, readily soluble in water 1:1.7 and in alcohol and ether. It is a powerful reducing agent; this property is utilized in gas analysis for the absorption of oxygen. It is an irritant, antiseptic, and caustic, producing a black stain when applied. It is used in the form of solutions, lotions, and ointments in the treatment of psoriasis, ringworm, and parasitic diseases of the skin and to a considerable extent in hair dyes. It is readily absorbed and may produce toxic symptoms unless used with caution and in moderate amounts.

Phloroglucinol (*sym*-Trihydroxybenzene) is not used medicinally. It occurs as a constituent of many resins and as the aglucon in the glucoside, phloridzin.

Anthralin, N.F. (Cignolin, 1,8,9-Anthratriol), m.p. 175–181°, is an odorless and tasteless yellow, crystalline powder, insoluble in water, slightly soluble in alcohol and ether, and soluble in chloroform and acetone. It forms yellowish-orange-colored fluorescent solutions in sodium hydroxide which oxidize readily in air. Anthralin is used by local application 0.1 to 1 per cent strength in cream and ointment form to treat psoriasis and dermatosis. It has less tendency to discolor the skin and cause dermatitis than chrysarobin.

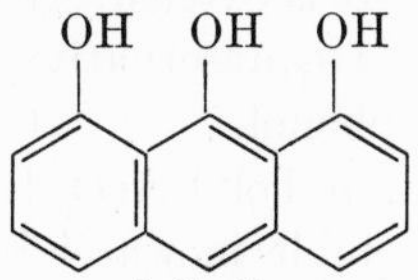

OH OH OH

Anthralin

Alkylated Phenols

The alkylated phenols and products derived from them are used extensively as antiseptics and bactericides. The simplest of these, the isomeric cresols, have

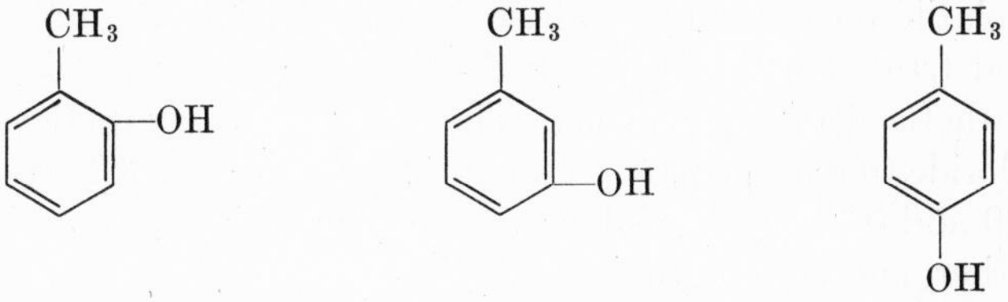

CH₃

—OH

CH₃

—OH

CH₃

OH

o-Cresol   m-Cresol   p-Cresol

been prepared synthetically but they are not used singly as antiseptics since they are more expensive than the mixture obtained from coal tar.

The alkylation of phenols alters the toxicity and antiseptic activity. Of the cresols, the *meta* compound is least toxic whereas the *ortho* and *para* isomers have different activities in different animals; e.g., the M.L.D. of o-cresol in the rat is greater than that of the *para* compound whereas in the dog the M.L.D. is greater for the *para* compound. The germicidal activity of the alkylated phenols is inhibited by soaps prepared from unsaturated fatty acids; there is no such inactivation in the presence of saturated fatty acid soaps.[50]

When two alkyl groups are present as in the xylenols, the activity is decreased. Likewise, in compounds such as thymol and carvacrol, the activity is decreased so that the compounds are less toxic than the xylenols.

Products

Cresol, U.S.P., is a mixture of o- m-, and p-hydroxytoluene obtained from coal tar. It is obtained from the middle layer or carbolic oil layer from which the fraction distilling between 195° and 205° is separated.

Cresol resembles phenol in properties, but, since it is less soluble in water (about 1:50), soap solutions are usually employed, e.g., *Saponated Solution of Cresol, N.F.* Various proprietary products such as Lysol, Creolin Pearson, and Phenoco are mixtures of cresols or homologs of cresol in soap solution.

Cresol is a stronger antiseptic than phenol and more economical. In the form of soap solutions and emulsions, it is used as an antiseptic for minor cuts and

[50] Hartung, U. S. pat. 2,251,934 (1941).

wounds, for the disinfection of hands, instruments, and discharges, as a deodorizer in toilets, etc. It is also used in dilute solution, usually 0.5 to 1 per cent, for irrigations and as a douche. It is extensively used as an antiseptic in veterinary medicine. It is also used as a preservative, e.g., in serums (about 0.4 per cent). Cresol is less toxic than phenol.

m-Cresyl Acetate (Cresatin, m-Tolyl Acetate), $CH_3C_6H_4O$—$COCH_3$, is an oily liquid, slightly volatile, insoluble in water but soluble in organic solvents. It is used as a spray in combination with menthol, camphor, and methyl salicylate in oil solution. It is mildly antiseptic and anesthetic in action.

Thymol, N.F. (Thyme Camphor), colorless crystals, m.p. 48–51°, has an aromatic odor and a very pungent taste. It is obtained from the volatile oils of thyme (*Thymus vulgaris* and other species), ajowan fruit (*Carum copticum*), and horsemint (*Monarda punctata*) and occurs to some extent in many other volatile oils. The volatile oil is treated with sodium hydroxide; the aqueous liquid is separated and treated with acid when the thymol is precipitated. It can also be made synthetically from cymene. Thymol may be synthesized by causing isopropyl chloride to react with m-cresol in the presence of $AlCl_3$ at temperatures between −20 and 0°.[51] It is soluble in water about 1:1000 and readily soluble in alcohol, ether, and chloroform.

Thymol   Carvacrol

It is an antiseptic and an anthelmintic. In dilute solution it has a pleasant taste and leaves a sensation of cleanliness. Consequently, it is a common constituent of most antiseptic and deodorant mouth washes and many preparations used as gargles. It is active against many yeasts and molds and is used as a preservative. It has a phenol coefficient of about 28 but is reported to be relatively ineffective in the presence of large amounts of organic matter. It has been used internally to a limited extent as an antipyretic and antiseptic. The chief internal use is in the treatment of hookworm infestations, when it is usually administered as a fine powder and followed by a saline cathartic. It is reported to be about one-fourth as toxic as phenol; possibly this is because it is less soluble and more slowly absorbed. Part of the absorbed thymol is destroyed, and the remainder is excreted as the ester of glycuronic acid or of sulfuric acid.

Carvacrol, $1:2:4-C_6H_3CH_3 \cdot OH \cdot C_3H_7$, is an isomer of thymol. It occurs in several volatile oils but is not used extensively in therapy. Its properties and activity closely resemble those of thymol.

[51] Carpenter, U. S. pat. 2,286,953; *C.A.*, **36**, 7242 (1942).

p-tert-Butylphenol (Butylphen) at a dose level of 0.2 gram per pound is effective in removing ascarids, hookworms, and whipworms from dogs.[52]

Octyl Cresol is a mixture of the octyl derivatives of the three isomeric cresols obtained from coal tar. It is a viscous transparent liquid having germicidal activity against Gram positive organisms. It has been used in triethylene glycol solution as a fog for the sterilization of hospital rooms.

Hexylresorcinol, U.S.P. (Caprokol), is an oily, pale yellow liquid which solidifies on standing, b.p. 178° at 8 mm., m.p. about 58°, soluble in alcohol, ether, chloroform, fixed oils, and in water about 1:2000. It has a pungent odor and an astringent taste. The preparation [53] of hexylresorcinol is carried out by the following reaction sequence:

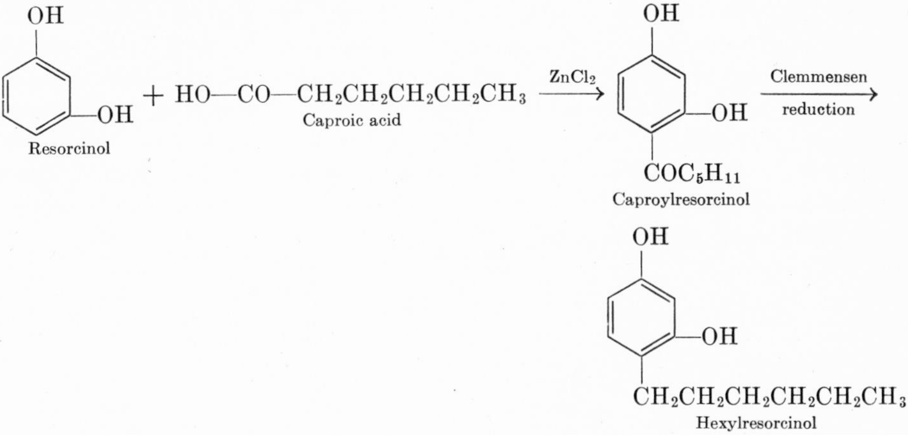

Resorcinol $+ HO-CO-CH_2CH_2CH_2CH_2CH_3 \xrightarrow{ZnCl_2}$ Caproic acid

$\xrightarrow{\text{Clemmensen reduction}}$

Caproylresorcinol

Hexylresorcinol

It is used as a general antiseptic and germicide in the form of solutions. It is also used as a urinary antiseptic, usually administered in solution in olive oil in capsules. It is an effective anthelmintic against ascaris and hookworms, administered as *Hexylresorcinol Pills, U.S.P.*, the crystals, or a solution in olive oil in gelatin capsules.

Urushiol is considered the chief constituent of poison ivy that is responsible for the effects of this plant. Hill, Mattacotti, and Graham showed that it could be reduced to tetrahydrourushiol. Tetrahydrourushiol has been synthesized and shown to have the structure of 3-*n*-pentadecylcatechol.[54] Chemical evi-

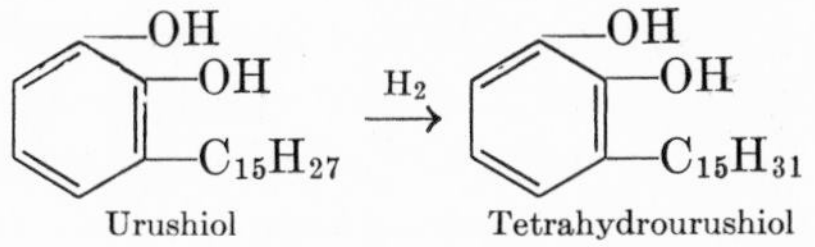

Urushiol   Tetrahydrourushiol

dence [55, 56] indicates that four components of common structural skeleton, but

[52] Enzie, *Proc. Helminthol. Soc., Wash., D. C.*, **11**, 55 (1944); *C.A.*, **39**, 351 (1945).

[53] Miller, Hartung, Rock, and Crossley, *J. Am. Chem. Soc.*, **60**, 7 (1938).

[54] Dawson, Wasserman, and Keil, *J. Am. Chem. Soc.*, **68**, 534 (1946).

[55] Symes and Dawson, *J. Am. Chem. Soc.*, **76**, 2959 (1954).

[56] Dawson, *Record Chem. Progr.*, **15**, 39 (1954).

differing in degree of unsaturation, constitute the poison ivy principle of urushiol. One of the components has a completely reduced side chain. The structures proposed for the olefinic components on the basis of degradation experiments are 3-(8-pentadecenyl)-pyrocatechol, 3-(8,11-pentadecadienyl)-pyrocatechol, and 3-(8,11,14-pentadecatrienyl)-pyrocatechol.

Cannabinol is one of a group of interesting phenols isolated from wild hemp (*Cannabis sativa*). Investigation of the chemistry of these phenols stimulated a series of researches by Adams *et al.*[57] which resulted in the proof of structure of these natural products as well as the synthesis of a host of homologs and analogs.

Cannabinol   Cannabidiol *   Tetrahydrocannabinol *

* The position of the ring double bond is not certain.

Although cannabinol and cannabidiol are physiologically inactive, tetrahydro-cannabinol and its homologs possess the euphoric stimulatory action of mari-huana, or Cannabis. One of these compounds, Parahexyl, 1-hydroxy-3-*n*-hexyl-6,6,9-trimethyl-7,8,9,10-tetrahydrodibenzopyran, has been given limited trial in the treatment of manic depressants and drug addicts.[58]

SYNTHETIC ESTROGENS

In an effort to obtain synthetic compounds having the biological activity of the female sex hormone, estrogen, Dodds and his co-workers [59] prepared a large group of stilbene derivatives. It was shown that the more complicated phenanthrene nucleus is unnecessary for estrogenic activity and that the more readily synthesized stilbenediols and their derivatives have a high order of activity. As a result, many compounds have been synthesized of considerable variation, the most important of which is diethylstilbestrol. However, Nicol and Helmy [60] have indicated that the synthetic are more toxic than the natural estrogens. Indeed, diethylstilbestrol was the most toxic of the synthetics tested; oral toxic-

[57] *J. Am. Chem. Soc.*, **71**, 1624 (1949), and previous papers.
[58] Thompson and Proctor, *N. Carolina Med. J.*, **14**, 520 (1953).
[59] Dobbs, Goldberg, Lawson, and Robinson, *Nature*, **137**, 996 (1936); *ibid.*, **142**, 34 (1938).
[60] Nicol and Helmy, *Nature*, **167**, 321 (1951).

ity was greater than intramuscular. Interestingly, combinations of two synthetic estrogens gave a lower toxicity than either one by itself.

Diethylstilbestrol, U.S.P. (α,α'-Diethyl-4,4'-stilbenediol, Stilbestrol), m.p. 169–172°, is an interesting phenolic compound possessing the characteristic physiological activity of the estrogenic hormones. It was introduced in Europe in 1939 under the name Stilbestrol. It is reported to be equally as active as estradiol (see page 130) and to be effective when administered orally or parenterally. Stilbestrol is used to treat symptoms of the menopause, senile vaginitis, gonorrheal vaginitis, suppression of lactation, etc. Forms of administration include tablets, suppositories, and sterile solutions.

Stilbestrol has been synthesized [61] from readily available initial materials. Oil-

$$CH_3O\langle C_6H_4\rangle—CH{=}CHCH_3 \xrightarrow[-80°]{+HBr} CH_3OC_6H_4—CHBr—CH_2CH_3 \xrightarrow[\text{2. KOH at 225°}]{\text{1. NaNH}_2}$$

$$\begin{array}{c} C_2H_5 \\ | \\ HOC_6H_4—C{=}C—C_6H_4OH \\ | \\ C_2H_5 \end{array}$$

Diethylstilbestrol

soluble esters such as the propionate, butyrate, benzoate, and caproate have been prepared and found to be less potent than stilbestrol, but the disuccinate in aqueous solution was as active as stilbestrol.[62] The oral estrogenic activity decreases in the homologous series of dimethyl to dipropyl ethers of stilbestrol.[63] The position isomers A and B although not inactive were relatively inactive as compared to hexestrol.[64]

$$HO\langle C_6H_4\rangle—\underset{\underset{CH(C_2H_5)_2}{|}}{CH}—\langle C_6H_4\rangle—OH$$
A

$$HO\langle C_6H_4\rangle—\underset{\underset{CH_2—C_2H_5}{|}}{\overset{\overset{C_2H_5}{|}}{C}}—\langle C_6H_4\rangle—OH$$
B

Nuclear methyl groups at position 3,3' in B increased its estrogenic activity four to five times; and a carbon-chain length of six to seven atoms gave optimum activity in a homologous series of 4,4'-dihydroxydiphenylmethane derivatives. A change in the positions of the phenolic hydroxyl groups yielded much less active compounds.

Diethylstilbestrol Dipalmitate (Stilpalmitate) is the dipalmitic acid ester of stilbestrol. It is administered in oil solution and has the same qualitative activity as stilbestrol, but, since it is absorbed more slowly, the effect is more prolonged and the unpleasant side actions are reduced.

[61] Kharasch and Kleinman, *J. Am. Chem. Soc.*, **65**, 11 (1943).
[62] Foreman and Miller, *ibid.*, 63, 2240 (1941).
[63] Sondern, Sealey, and Kartsonis, *Endocrinology*, **28**, 849 (1941).
[64] Campbell, *Proc. Roy. Soc.*, B (London), **129**, 528 (1940).

Diethylstilbestrol Dipropionate, N.N.R., is prepared by esterifying diethylstilbestrol with propionyl chloride. It is used in oil solution by intramuscular injection. It is slowly absorbed from the oil solution, causing lower concentration in the blood with more prolonged activity and fewer reactions, such as nausea.

Several compounds related to diethylstilbestrol are reported to cause fewer side reactions. They are less potent than diethylstilbestrol and must be used in greater dosage to cause the same effects.

Although diethylstilbestrol and related compounds appear to bear little structural similarity to the naturally occurring estrogens, it is believed that they are converted to them in the body and have the same actions. The low cost of their production and their effectiveness when administered orally give them a marked advantage over the naturally occurring estrogens.

Hexestrol, N.F. [3,4-*bis*-(*p*-Hydroxyphenyl)-*n*-hexane], is reported to produce

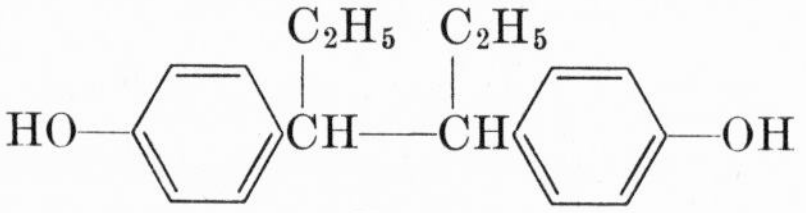

Hexestrol

the same clinical response as stilbestrol and the natural estrogens, and it is less likely to cause nausea than stilbestrol. It is administered orally in the form of tablets and, dissolved in oil, by intramuscular injection.

Mestibol, N.N.R. (Monomestrol, 3-*p*-Hydroxyphenyl-4-*p*-methoxyphenyl-3-hexene), m.p. 116–117.5° when recrystallized from a benzene petroleum ether mixture and 112–114° when recrystallized from alcohol, is a white, crystalline

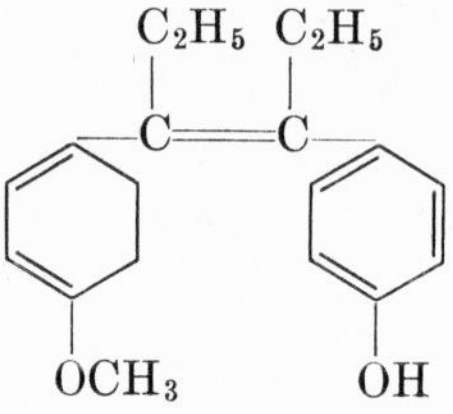

Mestibol

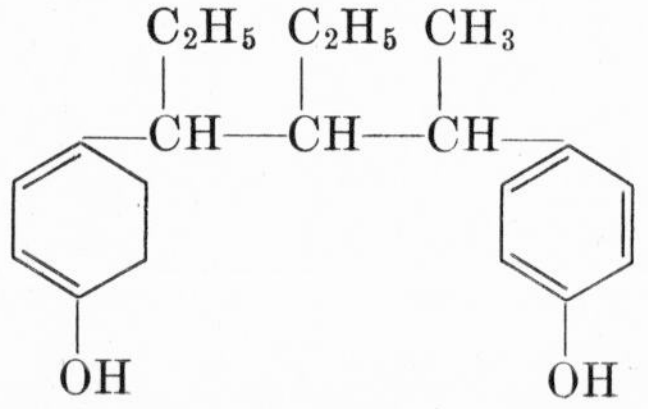

Benzestrol

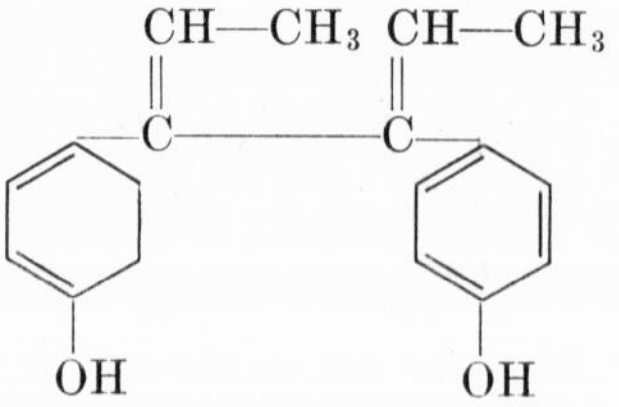

Dienestrol

powder insoluble in water and soluble in alcohol, acetone, ether, and fixed oils. It is used to treat the same conditions for which other estrogenic substances are employed. It is administered orally in tablets or by injection in oil solution.

Benzestrol, N.N.R. [Octofollin, 2,4-*bis*-(*p*-Hydroxyphenyl)-3-ethyl-hexane], m.p. 162–166°, is a white, crystalline powder, soluble in alcohol, fixed oils, and dilute sodium hydroxide, practically insoluble in water and dilute mineral acids. It is used in tablets and in oil solution for the same purposes as diethylstilbestrol and is claimed to be less toxic.

Dienestrol [3,4-*bis*-(*p*-Hydroxyphenyl)-2,4-hexadiene] is a white, crystalline powder, practically insoluble in water and soluble in alcohol. It is administered orally as tablets and is claimed to cause less nausea than diethylstilbestrol.

$$CH_3CH_2CO—O \qquad\qquad O—CO—CH_2CH_3$$

$$CH_3—\qquad\qquad\qquad —CH_3$$

$$CH_3CH_2—CH———————CH—CH_2CH_3$$

Meprane

Meprane [3-4-*bis*-(*m*-Methyl-*p*-propionoxyphenyl) hexane] is a colorless, crystalline powder, insoluble in water, slightly soluble in alcohol, and readily soluble in ether, acetone, or ethyl acetate. It is used for the same purposes as and is said to cause less nausea than diethylstilbestrol. It is usually administered in tablet form.

Chlorotrianisene, N.N.R. [TACE, Chlorotris-(*p*-methoxyphenyl)ethylene], is a white odorless crystalline powder administered in oil in capsule form. Its structural relationship to other synthetic estrogens becomes evident from a study of its structural formula. Its action is similar to that of other estrogens but is

$$OCH_3$$

$$CH_3O \qquad —C=C— \qquad OCH_3$$

$$Cl$$

Chlorotrianisene

more prolonged. It is stored in the body fat, and during metabolism its estrogenic activity is somehow enhanced; the amount of estrogenic activity recovered from the stool exceeds the amount originally administered in the form of chlorotrianisene.

HALOGENATED HYDROXYL COMPOUNDS

Alcohols

Halogenated alcohols, possessing both the halogen substituent and the alcoholic hydroxyl group, show the chemical properties expected of them. The halogenated alcohols that are of direct medicinal interest are relatively few and will be discussed individually.

Tribromoethanol, U.S.P. (Avertin), CBr_3—CH_2OH, was first prepared by Willstätter and Duisberg,[65] who employed beer hops to reduce bromal to the corresponding alcohol:

$$CBr_3—CHO \xrightarrow{\text{hops}} CBr_3CH_2OH$$

The Meerwein reduction of bromal is more convenient and affords good yields of the alcohol.

$$CBr_3—CHO \xrightarrow{Al[OCH(CH_3)_2]_3} CBr_3CH_2OH$$

Tribromoethanol is a crystalline material which is administered rectally in an oil solution for use as a general anesthetic.

On its appearance, tribromoethanol was hailed as an ideal anesthetic. However, experience shows that it is not without its elements of danger. For example, once too large a dose has been given, the excess cannot be removed or withdrawn. To overcome this handicap, the anesthetic may be administered in fractional doses. Occasionally a patient will develop an idiosyncrasy toward the compound. It is administered alone or with amylene hydrate, e.g., *Tribromoethanol Solution, U.S.P.*

Tribromoethanol is detoxified in the liver, combining with glycuronic acid, and is excreted rapidly and completely in the urine through the kidneys. Thus this halogenated alcohol is contraindicated in cases with liver and kidney dysfunction.

Trichloroethanol, prepared by reducing chloral with an aluminum alkoxide, is probably as potent a narcotic as tribromoethanol when compared on a weight basis; however, when compared on a molar basis it is about half as potent.

Chlorbutanol, U.S.P. (Trichloro-*tert*-butyl Alcohol, Trichloromethyldimethylcarbinol, Chloretone, Acetonechloroform), is synthesized by causing chloroform to condense with acetone.

$$
\begin{array}{c}
CH_3 \\
\diagdown \\
\quad\quad C{=}O + HCCl_3 \xrightarrow{KOH} \\
\diagup \\
CH_3
\end{array}
\quad
\begin{array}{c}
CH_3 \\
| \\
CH_3C—OH \\
| \\
CCl_3
\end{array}
$$

It is a white, crystalline compound, m.p. about 76°, having a camphoraceous odor and taste. It is very volatile even at ordinary temperatures and must be dried with great care to avoid loss. It is soluble in water 1:125, in alcohol 1:1; and it is very soluble in ether, petroleum benzin, glacial acetic acid, chloroform, and acetone. It is readily soluble in fixed, volatile, and mineral oils and in glycerol.

Chlorobutanol is a hypnotic, antinauseant, and a mild antiseptic. It is used as a hypnotic especially in animal work prior to anesthesia, and in insomnia, as a sedative in seasickness, persistent hiccough, etc., and as a preservative and antiseptic in nasal sprays, e.g., nasal sprays of epinephrine, and in solutions for injection.

[65] *Ber.*, **56**, 2283 (1923).

$$CH_3$$
$$|$$

Tribromo-*tert*-butyl Alcohol (Brometone), CH_3—C—OH, m.p. 167°, may

$$|$$
$$CBr_3$$

be prepared from bromoform and acetone in a reaction analogous to that employed in the synthesis of chloretone. It has a camphoraceous odor and taste. It is a sedative and hypnotic. It is claimed to have a sedative action similar to that of the bromides without producing bromidism. It is used in mild conditions of excitation and insomnia, headache, neuralgia, epilepsy, mania, in so-called narcotic abstinence, in hysteria, and in nervous affections generally.

Ethchlorovynol, N.N.R. (Placidyl), Ethyl β-chlorovinyl ethinyl carbinol, is a tertiary acetylenic alcohol incorporating a chlorine atom. It is reported [66] to be an effective hypnotic and anticonvulsant drug and is being marketed as a nonhabit-forming sedative, free from "hangover" effects.

$$C_2H_5$$
$$|$$
$$ClCH{=}CH{-}C{-}OH$$
$$|$$
$$C{\equiv}CH$$

Ethchlorovynol

Halogenated Phenols

The introduction of a halogen into the aromatic ring of the phenols usually increases the antiseptic activity. Although the irritant action and the toxicity are also increased, careful evaluation of the effects of halogenation have given rise to a wide variety of useful therapeutic compounds. Many of the data have been reviewed by Suter [67] as well as by van Oettingen.[68] In general, bactericidal action is greater if the halogen is *para* to the phenolic hydroxyl rather than *ortho*. Shirk and his co-workers report [69] a three- to tenfold increase in fungistatic effectiveness as a result of *p*-chlorination of phenols. Some halogenated phenols have also found use as anthelmintics.

Tetrachlorophenol, in a concentration of 25 per cent, is used with *p*-hydroxychlorodiphenyl and an emulsifier in a preparation that the Russians call "8502" as an insect repellent.[70] A solution of the sodium salt is a fungicide and a wood preservative.

Pentachlorophenol, used as its sodium salt (santobrite) or in hydrocarbon solvent (Penta), is an excellent wood preservative.

[66] P'an, Kodet, Gardocki, McLamore, and Bavley, *J. Pharmacol. Exptl. Therap.*, **114**, 326 (1955).

[67] Suter, *Chem. Revs.*, **28**, 269 (1941).

[68] van Oettingen, *Natl. Inst. Health Bull.* No. 190, U. S. Gov't. Printing Office, Washington, D. C., pp. 193–220.

[69] Shirk, Corey, and Poelma, *Arch. Biochem. and Biophys.*, **32**, 392 (1951).

[70] Hastings and Shimkin, *Science*, **103**, 639 (1936).

Chloro-*m*-cresol is found in many commercial antiseptics and has excellent bactericidal activity.

Chlorohexol (2-Chloro-4-hexylphenol), $1:2:4\text{-}C_6H_3 \cdot OH \cdot Cl \cdot C_6H_{13}$, is a clear liquid, insoluble in water and soluble in most organic solvents. It is reported to be an efficient antiseptic for use, when suitably diluted, in infections of the eyes, ears, nose, and throat.

Chlorothymol, N.F. (Monochlorothymol), $1:3:4:6\text{-}C_6H_2 \cdot CH_3 \cdot OH \cdot C_3H_7 \cdot Cl$, is a white, crystalline compound, m.p. 59–61°, of very pungent taste. It is almost insoluble in water but is soluble in alcohol, ether, and chloroform. It is an effective germicide used in the form of *Antiseptic Solution, N.F.* A proprietary preparation sold as Clymocol is a 6 per cent colloidal suspension which is miscible with water. It is used in 2 per cent solution for topical application as in wet dressings, in 0.5 per cent solution for bladder irrigations, and in 2 to 5 per cent solution for the disinfection of surgical instruments, etc.

Thymol Iodide, N.F. (Aristol), is a mixture of iodine derivatives of thymol, chiefly dithymol diiodide, $(C_6H_2CH_3C_3H_7OI)_2$, prepared by the action of iodine on thymol. It is a reddish amorphous powder, insoluble in water, which decomposes when heated with the evolution of the vapors of iodine. It is used as an antiseptic dusting powder in the treatment of wounds, abscess cavities, etc., as a substitute for iodoform. The antiseptic activity is believed to be caused by slow decomposition with the liberation of iodine and thymol.

Chloroxylenol (4-Chloro-3,5-dimethylphenol) and **Dichloroxylenol** (2,4-Dichloro-3,5-dimethylphenol) are good bactericides, fungicides, and preservatives. They have the unique advantage of being effective in the presence of soaps and detergents.

Hexachlorophene, N.N.R. (2,2'-Dihydroxy-3,5,6,3',5',6'-hexachlorodiphenylmethane), is the most successful compound resulting from the investigation of a series of hydroxydiphenylmethanes. It apparently is a highly effective skin antibacterial agent,[71] is useful in antiseptic soaps, and is recommended as a surgical scrub; its antibacterial effect is not lost when incorporated into soaps and detergents.

Hexachlorophene

Gump, U. S. pat. 2,250,480 (1941)

[71] *Drug & Cosmetic Ind.*, **72**, 622 (1953).

4

Ethers and Ether Peroxides

Ethers are organic oxides characterized by the general formula R—O—R'. They may be regarded as derived from alcohols, R—O—H, in which the hydrogen of the hydroxyl group is replaced by the hydrocarbon radical R'. Ethers are generally insoluble in water. They are solvents for such substances as fats, oils, alkaloids, and many other products; they are excellent solvents for extraction of natural products from crude drugs.

Chemically, ethers are quite inert, especially as compared to alcohols. They may, however, be split by appropriate reaction with acids. In general ethers behave somewhat like hydrocarbons and their physical, chemical, and, perhaps, even physiological properties may be favorably compared to hydrocarbons in which a —CH_2— group is replaced by an oxygen atom. Ethers slowly undergo peroxidation on prolonged contact with air; in a molecule in which there is also a double bond, a primary, or a secondary alcohol group, oxidation takes place with greater difficulty. Ethers may be chlorinated at room temperature. With strong mineral acids, ethers combine to form oxonium salts, $[R_2OH]^+ \cdot X^-$. The solubility of ethers in sulfuric acid is attributed to the formation of oxonium sulfates. The solubility of some inorganic salts in ethers is explained by the formation of similar salts.

PHYSIOLOGICAL ACTIVITY

Alkylation of the hydroxyl group in the alcohols causes a considerable increase in the narcotic activity of many compounds. The resulting ethers, especially the lower members of the series, are very volatile and rapidly absorbed.

75

Since they are usually given by inhalation, they produce their effect very rapidly. Dimethyl ether, CH_3—O—CH_3, the simplest dialkyl ether, is a prompt-acting anesthetic that produces a deep but transient narcosis. A concentration of 60 to 80 per cent by volume in the inhaled air is required for anesthesia in animals. Ethyl methyl ether has not been studied for its anesthetic potency.

Diethyl ether produces a more lasting narcosis, but continued administration is necessary for prolonged surgical anesthesia. The ethers in high concentration are toxic, causing death by cardiac failure. This occurs with ethyl ether when the concentration in the blood exceeds about 0.4 per cent. Ethyl ether is rapidly excreted so that a skilled anesthetist has little difficulty in maintaining anesthesia without danger of obtaining a toxic concentration in the blood. Diethyl ether is widely used as a general anesthetic.

Ethyl propyl ether is a good general anesthetic and may be used safely in man; it is more potent than diethyl ether.

As the series is ascended, i.e., the alkyl groups become larger and the molecular weight increases, the narcotic and toxic activities also become greater, owing to slower excretion. Such ethers are also less convenient to administer, and, since the margin between effective and toxic doses becomes narrower, they are not generally used. Ethers derived from di- and trihydric alcohols are more active than the alcohols themselves, but they lack the volatility of simple ethers and thus find no use as anesthetics.

Low-molecular-weight unsaturated aliphatic ethers all possess narcotic powers but except for ethyl vinyl and divinyl ethers are too toxic for medicinal use. Methyl allyl ether exhibits anesthetic properties in dogs, rats, and mice, but its toxicity and irritating quality render the compound unsuitable for use. Preliminary studies indicate that allyl ethyl, amyl allyl, diallyl, and ethyl isopropenyl ethers possess narcotic activity, but they are more irritating than diethyl ether; allyl ethyl and diallyl ether cause delayed death in a high percentage of mice. Divinyl ether, CH_2=CH—O—CH=CH_2, is the least toxic and the most useful of the low-molecular-weight unsaturated ethers. Its anesthetic action is prompt in onset, and recovery is less rapid than with diethyl ether. Ethyl vinyl ether, CH_3CH_2—O—CH=CH_2, Vinamar, is recommended for light planes of anesthesia [1] and for induction of anesthesia in children.[2] Isopropyl vinyl ether, $(CH_3)_2CHOCH$=CH_2, has an anesthetic index twice that of diethyl ether.[3] Induction is smooth, recovery is rapid and no respiratory irritation is evident. The onset of anesthesia by most unsaturated ethers is much slower than by diethyl ether and the recovery is more prolonged. The potency of most unsaturated ethers is greater than that of the saturated ethers.

The union of cyclopropane through an ether linkage with alkyl and alkenyl radicals results in the formation of compounds that exhibit anesthetic properties. Some of the compounds that have received considerable study are cyclopropyl methyl ether, cyclopropyl ethyl ether, and cyclopropyl vinyl ether. Cyclopropyl

[1] Slater, reported to Ohio Chemical and Surgical Equipment Co.

[2] Sadove and Wyant, *Current Researches in Anesthesia & Analgesia*, **34**, 235 (1955).

[3] Krantz, Carr, and Fassel, *J. Pharmacol. Exptl. Therap.*, **105**, 1 (1952).

methyl ether exhibits an anesthetic potency greater than ethyl ether but not as potent as chloroform.[4] No liver damage is evident in the monkey, and cardiac toxicity in the rat is possibly slightly more than with diethyl ether. Cyclopropyl ethyl ether has an anesthetic index twice that of diethyl ether. It produces no functional liver damage in monkeys, and no effect is evident on the

$$
\begin{array}{ccc}
\underset{\displaystyle CH_2 \overset{}{\diagup}\!\!\!\diagdown}{} & & \\
CH_2 \text{——} CH \text{—} O \text{—} CH_3 & CH_2 \text{——} CH \text{—} O \text{—} C_2H_5 & CH_2 \text{——} CH \text{—} O \text{—} CH{=}CH_2
\end{array}
$$

CH$_2$ triangle	CH$_2$ triangle	CH$_2$ triangle
CH$_2$——CH—O—CH$_3$	CH$_2$——CH—O—C$_2$H$_5$	CH$_2$——CH—O—CH=CH$_2$
Cyclopropyl methyl ether	Cyclopropyl ethyl ether	Cyclopropyl vinyl ether

frog's heart perfused with anesthetic concentrations. Cyclopropyl vinyl ether has a potency which approximates that of chloroform and an anesthetic index more than twice that of diethyl ether; no functional liver damage nor significant histopathological changes in the important viscera are observed in monkeys.[4]

Ethyl Oxide, U.S.P. (Solvent Ether, Sulfuric Ether), C_2H_5—O—C_2H_5, is the compound meant when the word ether alone is used. It was discovered about 1544 by Valerius Cordus, and its composition was established by Saussure (1807) and Gay-Lussac (1815). Its constitution was determined by Laurent and Gerhardt and confirmed by Williamson's synthesis in 1851.

$$C_2H_5I + NaOC_2H_5 \rightarrow C_2H_5OC_2H_5 + NaI$$

Diethyl ether is prepared commercially primarily by the dehydration of ethyl alcohol with concentrated sulfuric acid. Some ether is obtained for commercial use as a by-product in the hydration of ethylene to ethyl alcohol and from ethyl alcohol as a by-product in the manufacture of butadiene. Ether may also be prepared by passing vaporized alcohol over a catalyst at elevated temperature. For example, it may be prepared in about 75 per cent yield by passing alcohol vapors over alum at 200–230°. Other catalysts and conditions are reported in the literature.

$$2C_2H_5\text{—}OH \xrightarrow[\text{alum}]{200\text{–}300°} C_2H_5\text{—}O\text{—}C_2H_5 + H_2O$$

The preparation of diethyl ether by the dehydration of ethyl alcohol with sulfuric acid entails heating about 3 parts of concentrated sulfuric acid with 1 part of alcohol at approximately 127° to give 94–95 per cent of product. Distillation of the reaction mixture gives

$$CH_3CH_2\text{—}OH + H_2SO_4 \rightarrow CH_3CH_2\text{—}SO_4H + H_2O$$

$$CH_3CH_2\text{—}SO_4H + CH_3CH_2\text{—}OH \rightarrow CH_3CH_2\text{—}O\text{—}CH_2CH_3 + H_2SO_4$$

a fraction composed of ether, alcohol, water, and entrained sulfuric acid. This distillate is washed with dilute sodium hydroxide solution to remove acidic substances, and the ether-alcohol-water mixture is fractionated to give technical-grade ether containing very small amounts of alcohol, water, aldehydes, peroxides, and other impurities. Refined grades of ether are obtained from the technical grade by redistillation and dehydration, followed by alkali or charcoal treatment.[5]

[4] Krantz, Carr, and Evans, *Anesthesiology*, **5**, 291 (1944).

[5] For discussion of commercial production of ether, see W. L. Faith, D. B. Keyes, and R. L. Clark, *Industrial Chemicals*, John Wiley & Sons, New York, 1950, p. 287.

Diethyl ether is a colorless, very volatile, highly flammable solvent. It possesses a pleasant aromatic odor and sweetish burning taste. The boiling point of ether is 34.6°. The flash point is −45° (−49° F.), ignition temperature is 180° (356° F.), and explosive range (per cent by volume in air) is between 1.85 and 36.5 per cent. Ether is soluble in alcohol, chloroform, benzene, and petroleum ether. Ether at 20° dissolves in water to the extent of 7.5 grams per 100 grams of water.

Although ether may be purified readily, it must be protected against atmospheric oxygen, with which all ethers form ether peroxides, which are explosive. The initial product of the atmospheric oxidation is a hydroperoxide, and the formation of hydroxyethyl peroxide has been reported. Neither of these is as explosive as the peroxide residue from ether, for only the dialkylidene peroxides are explosive and dangerous. For ethyl ether the formation of diethylidene peroxide is explained as arising from the hydroperoxide. The presence of perox-

$$CH_3—CHOH—O—O—CHOH—CH_3$$
Hydroxyethyl peroxide

$$CH_3—CH—O—CH_2—CH_3 \rightarrow CH_3—CH \overset{O—O}{\underset{O—O}{\diagdown\diagup}} CH—CH_3$$
$$\underset{|}{O—OH}$$
Ether hydroperoxide   Peroxide

ides in the solvent ethers may be determined by the addition of sodium or potassium iodide solution. The liberation of iodine indicates that peroxides are present. The peroxides may be destroyed by the agitation of the ether with an aqueous solution of some reducing agent such as ferrous sulfate, sodium sulfite, for sodium hydrosulfite.

Practically, this peroxide formation is guarded against by placing the ether in filled vessels which are then sealed. Included in the sealed vessel may be some reducing agent such as copper wire or tannic acid. It has been reported that iron and copper are uncertain as inhibitors. Diphenylamine in concentrations even as low as 1×10^{-4} gives good results in preventing the formation of peroxides.[6]

Absolute Ether is ordinary ether freed of small amounts of water and alcohol in several ways, e.g., drying over calcium chloride and sodium; over sulfuric acid; over solid sodium hydroxide; or over calcium hydride. Such ether is spoken of also as "Grignard" ether, since it is employed in the Grignard reaction. According to Malinckrodt, Rands, and Ruehle,[7] trace amounts of sodium diethylthiocarbamate, $(C_2H_5)_2N—CS—SNa$, 0.05 p.p.m., prevent the formation of impurities, e.g., peroxides, in anhydrous ether.

Ether, U.S.P., is prepared specially for anesthesia and must meet the official requirements of quality and purity. It must be free of peroxides. To prevent peroxide formation, it is stored in small, well-closed containers. Once having been exposed for 24 hr. the contents must not be used for anesthetic purposes.

[6] Reimers, *Quart. J. Pharm. Pharmacol.*, **19**, 172 (1946); *C.A.*, **40**, 6210 (1946).
[7] *Chem. Eng. News*, **33**, 3194 (1955).

Except for the degree of purity, ether for anesthesia has the same properties and is prepared in the same way as diethyl ether used as a solvent.

Ether was introduced as an anesthetic in surgery by Dr. Long and Dr. Morton contemporaneously. It came into general use as an anesthetic in about the year 1850. It has several advantages: (1) it is easy to administer; (2) it gives excellent muscular relaxation; (3) the respiration and circulation are not markedly changed. It has some disadvantages such as causing respiratory and kidney irritation which can be avoided largely by skillful administration. It is one of the most generally used anesthetics for prolonged surgical operations. It continues to be widely used as a general anesthetic. It is absorbed almost instantaneously from the pulmonary epithelium and is eliminated through the same tissues. For deep anesthesia the concentration must reach about 140 mg. per cent in the blood.

Methylpropyl Ether, CH_3—O—$CH_2CH_2CH_3$, an isomer of ordinary ether, is reported to be 25 per cent more potent than diethyl ether and clinically superior, being relatively nontoxic and producing relaxation.

Isopropyl Ether and **Di-n-butyl Ether,** now that the corresponding alcohols are plentiful, are becoming increasingly available; because of their higher boiling points they offer certain advantages as solvents over ordinary ether.

Vinyl Ether, U.S.P. (Divinyl Oxide, Vinethene), CH_2=CH—O—CH=CH_2, is a representative of the unsaturated ethers. It is prepared by the elimination of two molecules of hydrogen chloride from β,β'-dichlorodiethyl ether:[8]

$$Cl—CH_2—CH_2—O—CH_2—CH_2—Cl \xrightarrow{-2HCl} CH_2=CH—O—CH=CH_2$$

Divinyl ether is a colorless, flammable liquid boiling at 28.3°. It decomposes on exposure to light or acid fumes to form acetaldehyde and a solid polymer. The product is stabilized by the use of some basic antioxidant such as phenyl-α-naphthylamine. It is slightly soluble in water but miscible with alcohol, ether, oils, and other organic solvents.

Vinethene is a product containing about 96 per cent pure divinyl ether, about 4.0 per cent absolute alcohol, and 0.025 per cent of an antioxidant. The clear, colorless liquid has a characteristic odor and boils at 28–31°. The product should be kept in a tightly stoppered container and stored in a cool, dark place. Owing to its susceptibility to decomposition, caution is indicated in the use of the product by limiting the capacity of containers to 200 ml. and restricting its use to within 24 hr. after exposure.

Vinyl ether is an effective inhalation anesthetic used for short surgical and dental procedures. The onset of anesthesia is rapid, causing unconsciousness within 40 to 60 seconds after the first inhalation, and complete muscular relaxation results in about $2\frac{1}{2}$ minutes. Postoperative excitement and other complications are usually absent. Vinyl ether is more toxic than diethyl ether, resulting in certain toxic manifestations. Owing to liver damage which may occur over prolonged administration of this agent, its use is confined to procedures

[8] Ruigh and Major, *J. Am. Chem. Soc.*, **53**, 2662 (1931); Lott, Smith, and Christiansen, *J. Am. Pharm. Assoc.*, **26**, 206 (1937).

of short duration. It should be administered with caution to patients having cardiovascular diseases, renal insufficiency, degenerative conditions, and in old age. It should never be used in cases of multiple sclerosis or hepatic damage.

HYDROXY ETHERS

When ethylene oxide is treated with various reagents under suitable conditions of temperature and pressure and with catalysts, the three-membered ring opens and yields many important compounds, such as the following.

Ethylene Glycol Monoethyl Ether (Cellosolve), $C_2H_5OCH_2CH_2OH$, b.p. 135.1°, and **Ethylene Glycol Monobutyl Ether** (Butylcellosolve), $C_4H_9OCH_2$-CH_2OH, b.p. 171°, are miscible with water and are valuable intermediates and solvents in syntheses. They are not suitable as solvents in pharmaceutical preparations. Diethylene glycol, $HOCH_2CH_2OCH_2CH_2OH$, obtained from ethylene glycol and ethylene oxide is a valuable industrial solvent. It is toxic and so is not suitable for pharmaceutical preparations. Numerous deaths resulted in 1937 from the use of this compound as a solvent for sulfanilamide.

Ethylene Glycol Monophenyl Ether (Phenoxethol) shows high bacteriostatic and bactericidal properties against *Pseudomonas pyocyaneus*. It may be employed in conjunction with quaternary ammonium compounds.

Carbitols are a group of hydroxy ethers obtained by making the ethers of diethylene glycol. They are high-boiling solvents useful in industry, e.g., butyl carbitol (the monobutyl ether of diethylene glycol), b.p. 222°, has the formula $C_4H_9OCH_2CH_2OCH_2CH_2OH$.

Polyethylene Glycols are polymers of lower glycols with approximate molecular weights of 200, 300, 400, and 600. The number associated with the trade name refers to the average molecular weight of the product. These glycols are somewhat viscous, water-white, hygroscopic liquids, completely soluble in water and in many organic solvents. These products are of special interest to manufacturers of cosmetics, ointments, and other preparations where blandness, water solubility, and lubricity are desirable.

Carbowaxes also are polymers of lower glycols but with approximate molecular weights of 950 to 7500. These various products are white, waxy, bland substances with consistencies from that of low-melting petrolatum to paraffin. They are water soluble and are used as bases or vehicles for a number of pharmaceutical and cosmetic preparations.

Methoxy Polyethylene Glycol and **Polypropylene Glycols** are other commercial preparations that find pharmaceutical application similar to the polyethylene glycols and Carbowaxes.

Polyethylene Glycols are prepared by condensing ethylene oxide with water

$$(n + 1)CH_2\!\!-\!\!CH_2 + H_2O \rightarrow HOCH_2(CH_2OCH_2)_nCH_2OH$$
$$\diagdown O \diagup$$

to form products whose physical properties are determined by their molecular weight, i.e., by the size of n in the given formula. They find wide application in pharmacy.

Polyethylene Glycol 300, N.F., m.w. 285 to 315, n varies from 5 to 6, and *Polyethylene Glycol 400, U.S.P.,* m.w. 380 to 420, n varies from 8 to 10, are viscous, clear, hygroscopic liquids, soluble in water, alcohol, acetone, and other glycols, but insoluble in aliphatic hydrocarbons and ether; they are heat stable and chemically quite inert. Used alone or in combination with other substances, they form elegant pharmaceutical vehicles for many purposes.

Polyethylene Glycol 1540, N.F., m.w. 1300 to 1600, n varies from 28 to 36, and *Polyethylene Glycol 4000, U.S.P.,* n varies from 70 to 85, are waxy solids, appreciably less soluble in water and, because of their favorable properties, lend themselves to compounding ointments of controlled consistency.

Polyoxyl 40 Stearate, U.S.P., $H(OCH_2CH_2)_nO$—$COC_{17}H_{35}$, n is approximately 40, is a waxy solid, light tan in color, congeals between 39° and 44°, is soluble in water, alcohol, acetone, and ether, but insoluble in mineral and vegetable oils. It is used as a hydrophilic ointment base.

Polysorbate 80, U.S.P. [Polyoxyethylene (20) Sorbitan Mono-oleate, Tween 80] is a complex mixture of polyoxyethylene ethers of mixed partial oleic ester of sorbitol anhydrides. It is an amber-colored liquid, soluble in water, alcohol,

$$HOCH_2(CH_2OCH_2)_6CH_2O - \quad CH_2OOCC_{17}H_{33}$$
$$OCH_2(CH_2OCH_2)_6CH_2OH$$
$$H \quad OCH_2(CH_2OCH_2)_6CH_2OH$$

Polysorbate 80

and vegetable oils. It is insoluble in mineral oil. It is used as an emulsifying aid and as a therapeutic agent for treating malnutrition due to faulty absorption of fats.

Methylcellulose, U.S.P. (Methocel), is a methyl ether of cellulose. Various grades are available, possessing different solubility and viscosity values which are attributed to the number of methoxyl groups. The glucose residue present in cellulose has three free hydroxyl groups which may be methylated. This makes several methyl celluloses possible. The type of greatest value contains 1 or 2 methoxyl groups per C_6 unit, a methoxy content of 29 per cent. Methylcellulose may be prepared by reacting methyl chloride or dimethyl sulfate with an alkaline solution of cellulose.

Methylcelluloses are white granules, soluble in cold but insoluble in hot water. A stable solution is best prepared by dispersing the granules in warm water and then chilling to +5°. Salts of mineral acids, phenols, and tannins coagulate methylcellulose in solution. Alcohol and glycol acetate prevent such coagulation.

Methylcellulose is a non-ionic emulsifying and thickening agent, and it is compatible with emulsifying agents, including gelatin. It is used to stabilize creams and ointments, for the preparation of adhesives, and as bulk laxatives.

The cellulose ethers dry to form firm, nonhygroscopic films; thus, methylcellulose offers promise as a substitute for gelatin in the manufacture of capsules.

Ethylcellulose (Ethocel) is an ethyl ether of cellulose. It is used in the manufacture of plastics and lacquers.

AROMATIC ETHERS

No simple diaryl ether is of physiological importance. Complex structures, such as the curare alkaloids, page 384, do contain the diaryl ether functions. Some alkyl aryl ethers are useful agents for the prevention, control, and treatment of diseases.

No single physiological effect is attributed to alkyl aryl ethers; rather their properties vary markedly for different members. Methyl phenyl ether, anisole, and ethyl phenyl ether are toxic and cause fatty degeneration of the liver and kidneys. Compounds containing an ether structure and a hydroxyl group have activities intermediate between the phenols and the aryl ethers. Thus, guaiacol and the monomethyl ethers of homocatechol are irritant to mucous membranes, have antiseptic activity, are mildly anesthetic on injection, and large doses cause paralysis and death in animals. Anethole is slightly antiseptic. In general, it may be said that the formation of an ether linkage on one or more of the hydroxyls in the polyhydric phenols increases the toxicity. Resorcinol dimethyl ether is more toxic than resorcinol. The presence of a free hydroxyl as in eugenol increases the antiseptic and narcotic activity, and the toxicity is reduced by about one-third. Methylene ethers, such as 4-allyl-methylenedioxy-benzene (safrole), are more strongly narcotic than eugenol, but the local irritant activity is less than that of anethole. Isosafrole has less narcotic activity than safrole; this may be caused by the greater stability of the alkyl group. The same relationship is found to exist in the apioles.

| Eucalyptol | Anethole | Safrole,
Methylene ether of
3,4–dihydroxy–
allylbenzene | Isosafrole,
Methylene ether of
3,4–dihydroxy–
propenylbenzene |

Some aryl glyceryl ethers produce curarelike effects in that they produce muscular relaxation. α-Glyceryl guaiacol ether is a potent anesthetic and also exhibits emetic properties. Ethers of polyhalogenated phenols, particularly the halogenated phenoxyethanols, show definite value as fungistatic compounds. Dibenzyl ethers emulsified and administered intrarectally to mice prove highly effective against pinworms. Diphenyl ethers with amino, hydroxy, halogen, and carboxy substituents have been examined for antitubercular activity. 4'-Amino-

2,4,5-trichlorodiphenyl ether and 4'-amino-2',2,4,5-tetrachlorodiphenyl ether completely inhibit growth of microorganisms in nutrient broth at a dilution of 1:1 million.

Eucalyptol, U.S.P. (Cineol), is the inner ether of terpin (1,8-terpanediol). It is the chief constituent of eucalyptus oil and also occurs in other volatile oils. It may be prepared synthetically by the dehydration of terpin hydrate. Eucalyptol is a colorless, optically inactive liquid possessing a camphoraceous odor with a spicy, cooling taste. It is insoluble in water but soluble in alcohol, oils, chloroform, ether, etc.

Eucalyptol is the chief constituent and the insecticidal component of *Eugenia haitiensis*. It is used to combat flies, mosquitoes, bedbugs, chiggers, etc.[9] It has antiseptic and expectorant activity and is used in many oily nose and throat sprays. It is used in veterinary practice as an inhalant for rhinitis, laryngitis, pharyngitis, and bronchitis. Excessive use may cause disturbance of the nervous system. Skin eruption is reported to occur in sensitive individuals.

Anethole, U.S.P. (*p*-Methoxypropenylbenzene), is the chief constituent of oil of anise and of oil of fennel. It is used as a carminative. The isomeric chavicol (*p*-allylanisole) is a constituent of oil of bay. Anethole may be prepared by the following sequence of reactions.

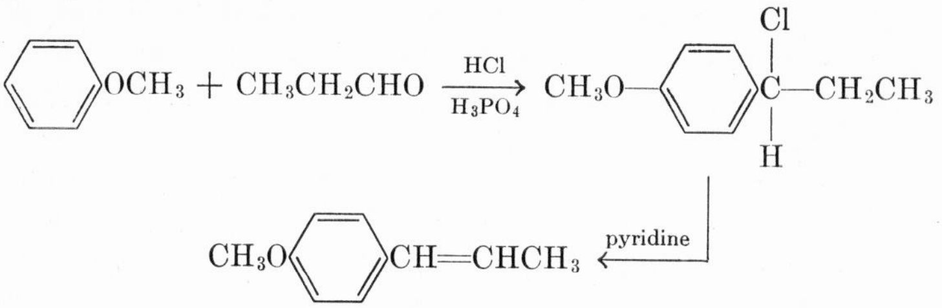

Anethole is a colorless or faintly yellow oil which crystallizes at 20–21°. It is insoluble in water but miscible in organic solvents. It is used as a carminative in place of oil of anise and in perfumery, particularly in the manufacture of soaps and dentrifices.

Safrole is the chief constituent of oil of sassafras. Isosafrole, which also occurs in the oil, yields piperonal, useful in perfumery, on oxidation. Other phenolic ethers of interest are myristicin from oil of nutmeg, apiole from celery fruit, dill apiole from oil of dill, and asarone from the roots of *Asarum europaeum* Linné.

Myristicin
methoxysafrole

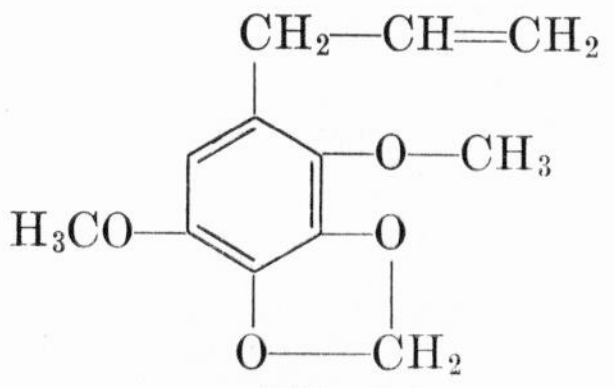

Apiole,
dimethoxysafrole

[9] Jacobson and Haller, *J. Am. Chem. Soc.*, **69**, 709 (1947).

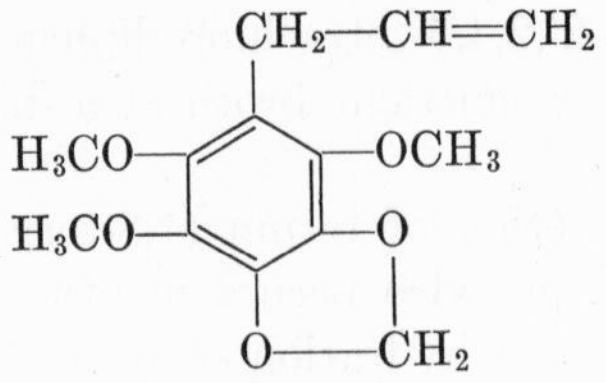

Dill apiole,
trimethoxysafrole

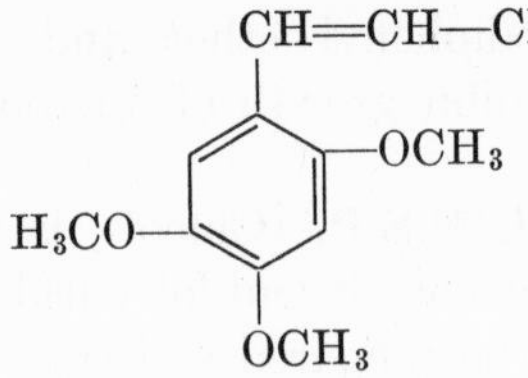

Asarone

Guaiacol, N.F. (*o*-Methoxyphenol, *o*-Hydroxyanisole), is the chief constituent of beechwood creosote. It also occurs in guaiac resin. It is prepared by fractionating beechwood creosote. It can be prepared by synthesis from catechol by methylation or from *o*-anisidine,

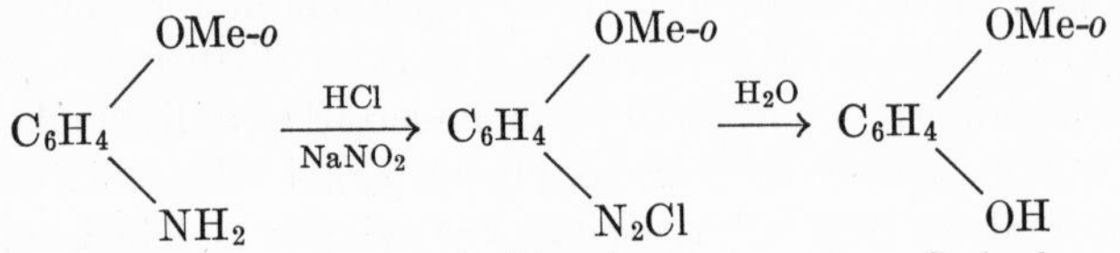

o-Anisidine   Diazonium   Guaiacol
salt

The guaiacol obtained from wood creosote is usually a liquid, b.p. 200–210°; that prepared synthetically is a crystalline solid, m.p. 28.5°, b.p. 203°. Guaiacol is slightly soluble in water (1:65) and is soluble in most organic solvents.

It was used extensively in the treatment of tuberculosis but the early hopes of its effectiveness have not been sustained. It has a mild local anesthetic activity, some antiseptic value, and derivatives have been used to treat intestinal fermentation. It also has some antipyretic activity but other products are superior to guaiacol for this purpose.

Guaiacol Carbonate (Duotal) is a white, odorless, almost tasteless, crystalline powder melting at 86–88°. It is prepared by passing phosgene into an aqueous sodium hydroxide solution of guaiacol. The product is insoluble in water, moderately soluble in alcohol, and slightly soluble in glycerol or in fatty oils. It is used as an expectorant as a substitute for guaiacol. This derivative of guaiacol is less irritating and less nauseating. It is slowly hydrolyzed internally to liberate guaiacol.

Eugenol, U.S.P. (4-Allyl-2-methoxyphenol), occurs in volatile oil of clove to the extent of about 80 per cent. The product is obtained from oil of clove and other natural sources by aqueous alkali extraction, acidulation of the alkaline solution, and subsequent purification by distillation of the oily layer. It is a

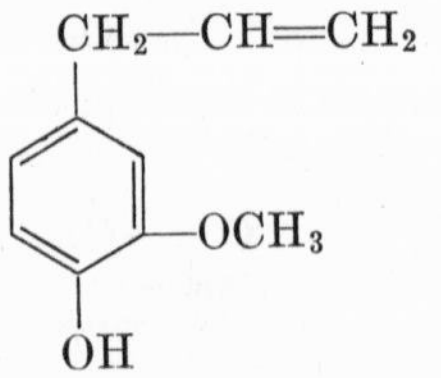

Eugenol

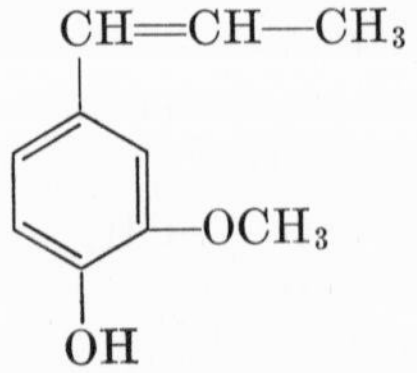

Isoeugenol

colorless or pale yellow liquid with a very pungent taste. The isomer, isoeugenol, also occurs in oil of clove.

On exposure to air it becomes darker and thicker. It is miscible with alcohol, volatile and fixed oils, but only slightly soluble in water. Isoeugenol reacts with ferric chloride to form the phenol-ferric complex.

Eugenol is a mild local anesthetic used on cotton or in solution to disinfect tooth cavities and allay pain in toothache. It is used in mouth washes for its antiseptic property and in perfumery as a substitute for oil of clove.

Creosote, N.F. (Wood Creosote), is a mixture of phenols, chiefly cresols and guaiacol, usually obtained from the tar resulting from the dry distillation of beechwood. It is an oily liquid, b.p. about 203–220°.

The use of creosote is similar to that of guaiacol. Once used extensively in the treatment of tuberculosis, it is now used chiefly in respiratory infections such as bronchitis.

Creosote Carbonate is a mixture of the carbonates of the constituents of creosote. The ester, prepared by treating an alkaline solution of wood creosote with phosgene, is a colorless to yellowish, clear, viscid, oily liquid, freely soluble in alcohol, soluble in fixed oils, and insoluble in water. It is used as an expectorant, and it is claimed to cause less gastrointestinal irritation and nausea than wood creosote.

Calcium Creosotate is a dark brown powder resulting from a loose chemical combination between approximately equal parts of creosote and lime. It is tolerated better than creosote when administered as a syrup or in tablets since it does not readily cause gastric distress and nausea.

Proposote (Creosote Phenylpropionate) is an amber-colored proprietary product, obtained by condensing creosote and phenylpropionic acid in the presence of phosphorus oxychloride and by subsequent purification. It is claimed that the resulting compound passes through the stomach with slight absorption and that the components are liberated in the intestines. Thus gastric irritation is reduced. Administered in capsules, it is used to treat bronchitis and coughs caused by bronchial infections.

Mephenesin, N.F. (3-o-Toloxy-1,2-propanediol, Tolserol, Myanesin), is a white powder, m.p. 70–71°, without odor and having a bitter taste. The product may be prepared in yields up to 67 per cent from o-cresol and glycerol α-monochlorohydrin in the presence of sodium ethoxide.[10]

It is freely soluble in alcohol, propylene glycol, and water, 1 in 85 at 20°. Urea and its derivatives, particularly urethane, increase its water solubility. Aqueous solutions are stable and can be sterilized by heating. The product

[10] Mørch, *Arch. Pharm. Chemi,* **54,** 327 (1947); *C.A.,* **42,** 2058 (1948).

may be dissolved in solutions of sodium chloride, glucose, barbiturates, and thiobarbiturates to give a clear preparation.

Mephenesin exhibits marked muscle-relaxing properties and possesses some analgesic activity; it is a spinal-cord and brain-stem depressant. It temporarily reduces. abnormal, exaggerated reflexes without interfering with voluntary or normal reflexes. It is recommended for use in producing relief in many types of neuromuscular spasms and in conditions of muscle spasm and rigidity, e.g., Parkinsonism, hemiplegia, diplegia, cerebral palsy, paraplegia, low back pain, bursitis, and arthritis.

α-**Glycerylguaiacol Ether,** $CH_2OHCHOHCH_2OC_6H_4OCH_3$-$o$, m.p. 78°, is used under the trade name of Resyl as an expectorant; it is a potent anesthetic but exhibits emetic properties.[11]

(3,4-Methylenedioxy-6-propylbenzyl)butyl Diethyleneglycol Ether,

exerts a synergistic effect on the pyrethrins, and like the pyrethrins it is quite nontoxic to warm-blooded animals. The synergistic effect is attributed to the methylenedioxyphenyl group.[12]

Anavenol (β-Hydroxyethyl β-Naphthyl Ether) is used with 5-allyl-5-(2-cyclo-hexenyl)-2-thiobarbituric acid in anesthesia for its synergistic effect.[13]

Anavenol

ETHER PEROXIDES

The formation of peroxides in ethers has already been mentioned. The only medicinally important organic peroxide is ascaridole. Ascaridole comprises about 60 per cent of the natural *Chenopodium Oil, N.F.* (American wormseed). Wallach [14] proposed the formula for ascaridole as an interpretation of the accompanying sequence of reactions.

Ascaridole   1,4–Terpin   1,4–Cineole

[11] Smith, *J. Pharmacol.*, **91**, 93 (1947).
[12] Wachs, *Science*, **105**, 530 (1947).
[13] Hobart, *Mfg. Chemist*, **24**, 14 (1953).
[14] Wallach, *Ann.*, **392**, 59 (1912).

Ascaridole has been synthesized by the photochemically sensitized addition of oxygen to α-terpinene,[15] and this is assumed to be the process for its synthesis in plants. It is an oily liquid which explodes when heated to 130° and reacts explosively with mineral acids.

Ascaridole is used as an anthelmintic against hookworm (*Ascaris lumbricoides*) and other nematodes and cestodes. It is usually administered on sugar. Oil of chenopodium is used for the same purpose, and its activity depends on its ascaridole content. The chemistry of ascaridole has been studied extensively by Nelson [16] and Thoms and Dobke.[17]

[15] Schenck and Ziegler, *Naturwissenschaften*, **32,** 157 (1945); *C.A.*, **40,** 2132 (1946).

[16] *J. Am. Chem Soc.*, **35,** 84, 1407 (1911).

[17] *Arch. Pharm.*, **268,** 128 (1930).

CHAPTER
5

Carbonyl Group

ALDEHYDES AND KETONES

The carbonyl group is characteristic for aldehydes, $\overset{R}{\underset{H}{>}}C:O$, and for ketones,

$\overset{R}{\underset{R'}{>}}C:O$, which are well-established organic compounds. As chemicals, both types of compounds are well known and important. As medicinal agents, however, few if any find use solely because of the carbonyl function, although many aldehydes and ketones have medicinal and pharmaceutical interest. Perhaps the most important medicinal derivatives are those which may be considered

as formed from the hydrol form of the carbonyl, e.g., from $\overset{R}{\underset{R'}{>}}C\overset{OH}{\underset{OH}{<}}$, in

which one or both of the hydrogen atoms of the hydroxyl groups are replaced by organic residues, that is, hemiacetals or acetals, of which the sugars and glycosides are examples.

It is to be expected that any functional group as active as the carbonyl is known to be might result in appreciable reaction with living tissue. Fortunately this seems not to be true except for formaldehyde, which is toxic in small doses. Acetaldehyde is also quite toxic, and it is the product to which nausea is attributed when the complete oxidation of ethyl alcohol is inhibited by Antabuse

(see page 278). Higher-molecular-weight aldehydes, beginning with heptalde-
hyde, n-C_6H_{13}—CHO, become more pleasant, and other members, particularly
the diisoprenoid aldehydes, such as citronellal and geranial, are components of
natural volatile plant oils.

The toxic protoplasmic reaction of formaldehyde may be comprehended from
its role in the formol titration of amino acids, where its purpose is to destroy the
zwitter-ion character and permit normal titration of the carboxylic group.

Dimethyl ketone, CH_3—CO—CH_3, propanone, commonly known as acetone,
b. p., 65.1°, is the first member of the ketone series. Higher members of the
series, more especially the cyclic diisoprenoids, such as carvone, thujone, verbe-
none, and camphor, have pleasant odors and are natural components of volatile
essential oils.

Physiological Activity

The effect of the carbonyl group *per se* on physiological activity has not been
studied extensively or systematically. In general it may be said that the carbonyl group tends to confer hypnotic properties on compounds. Thus, acetaldehyde and acetone have hypnotic activity. Increase in the size of the alkyl
group causes an increase in activity much as it does in the alcohols, but the toxicity also increases. Unsaturation of the aldehydes and ketones causes increased
activity and toxicity. Crotonaldehyde and allylaldehyde (acrolein) are markedly
irritant and lachrymatory. Mesityl oxide and phorone are strongly hypnotic but
also toxic. Aldehydes are, perhaps, more intense in their biological reactions.

$$\underset{\text{Mesityl oxide}}{\begin{array}{c} CH_3 \\ \diagdown \\ C=CH-\overset{\overset{\textstyle O}{\|}}{C}-CH_3 \\ \diagup \\ CH_3 \end{array}} \qquad \underset{\text{Phorone}}{\begin{array}{c} CH_3 CH_3 \\ \diagdown \diagup \\ C=CH-\overset{\overset{\textstyle O}{\|}}{C}-CH=C \\ \diagup \diagdown \\ CH_3 CH_3 \end{array}}$$

Ketones frequently show the properties of the corresponding secondary alcohols.

Aliphatic Aldehydes

Formaldehyde (Methanal), $\begin{array}{c} H \\ \diagdown \\ C=O \\ \diagup \\ H \end{array}$, is a colorless gas, b.p. $-19.2°$, m.p.

$-118°$, very pungent, and very irritating to the mucous membranes. The maximum permitted concentration of formaldehyde in industrial establishments is
not over 10 p.p.m., and even in that high dilution it is its own warning agent.
It was first prepared by Butlerov in 1859 by the hydrolysis of diacetoxymethane,
$CH_2(OCOCH_3)_2$, and by von Hofmann in 1868 by the direct oxidation of
methanol.

Formaldehyde is prepared by the atmospheric oxidation of methanol over
metal or metal oxide catalysts. The overall reaction is possibly represented by

two simultaneous equations

(1) $$2CH_3OH + O_2 \rightarrow 2HCHO + 2H_2O + 76 \text{ kg.-cal.}$$

(2) $$CH_3OH \rightarrow HCHO + H_2 - 20 \text{ kg.-cal.}$$

The hydrogen formed according to equation 2 is oxidized to water.

Formaldehyde reacts readily with proteins to denature them, and it is this property on which is based the use of this reagent as a bactericide, disinfectant, and deodorant.

Formaldehyde Solution, U.S.P. (Formalin), is a solution containing about 40 per cent by volume and 30 per cent by weight of formaldehyde. The solution gradually undergoes change due to the formation of a deposit of polymers of formaldehyde. The commercial product usually contains 12 to 15 per cent of methanol to prevent the formation of the polymers. It is used as a disinfectant and fungicide, e.g., against disease organisms in sick rooms and against plant smuts in grain. One pint of solution (formalin), when vaporized, will disinfect a room of 500 cu. ft. capacity.

Formaldehyde cannot be used on the body as an antiseptic because it is irritant, coagulating proteins in wounds, etc. Numerous derivatives have been made with the idea of securing a product that would gradually release formaldehyde and give a prolonged and mild antiseptic action. Compounds of formaldehyde with gelatin, casein, sugars, starches, etc., have been made. In general, they have proved too stable to release formaldehyde in antiseptic amounts or so unstable that they are highly irritant. Because of its hardening effect on tissues, formaldehyde is employed frequently and extensively to preserve anatomical and biological specimens.

Formaldehyde forms several polymers; of these only two will be mentioned here, α-trioxymethylene and paraformaldehyde. Trioxymethylene is the oxygen prototype of the polymers of the thioaldehydes and thioketones. Trioxymethylene is of theoretical importance. Paraformaldehyde is of commercial importance

$$\begin{array}{c} O—CH_2—O \\ |\qquad\qquad| \\ CH_2—O—CH_2 \end{array}$$
α-Trioxymethylene

$$\Big(HO—CH_2\,OH \quad H\,OCH_2OH\Big)_n$$
Paraformaldehyde

because on being heated it regenerates formaldehyde. It is prepared by evaporating solutions of formaldehyde; it is a linear polymer of the structure HO—CH_2—$(OCH_2)_n$—OCH_2—OH, in which n varies from 4 to 98. It may be considered as being formed from the aldehydrol structure of formaldehyde. It dissolves in hot water and shows all the properties of formaldehyde. Paraformaldehyde is marketed in cakes for use in fumigation.

Formaldehyde undergoes the Cannizzaro reaction, forming methanol and formic acid.

$$2HCHO \xrightarrow{\text{NaOH}} HCOOH + CH_3OH$$

Methenamine, U.S.P. (Hexamethylenetetramine, Hexamethylamine, Hexamine, Urotropine), is prepared by evaporating to dryness a solution of formaldehyde and strong ammonia water.

The formation of this compound may be represented to take place in the manner indicated. The compound consists of colorless, odorless crystals, m.p. about 263° with decomposition, soluble in water about 1:1.5, and readily soluble in alcohol and chloroform. When treated with acids, it liberates formaldehyde. Alkalies decompose it with the liberation of ammonia.

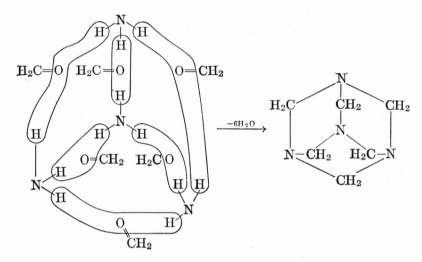

It is used as a urinary antiseptic. Its activity is considered to be caused entirely by the liberation of formaldehyde in acid urine. If the urine is not acid, methenamine is not effective. It is usually administered in the form of tablets followed by water or in solution in water. If the urine is not acid, some substance that will make it so is administered along with the methenamine, e.g., sodium dihydrogen phosphate. At one time it was thought that methenamine was valuable as a uric acid solvent since its aqueous solution readily dissolves uric acid in the test tube. This has not proved to be true in practice probably because the concentration that can be attained in the urine is insufficient to dissolve uric acid calculi.

Numerous derivatives of methenamine have been used medicinally. Some of these are:

Helmitol, the anhydromethylene citrate of methenamine.
Hexamine camphorate, derived from methenamine and camphoric acid.
Cystazol, methenamine sodium benzoate.
Hexalet, sulfosalicylic acid combined with methenamine.
Mandelamine, mandelic acid combined with methenamine.

Methenamine readily forms loose chemical combinations with a number of compounds. It is doubtful that these compounds have any advantage over a simple mixture of the components.

Methenamine Mandelate, U.S.P. (Hexamethyleneamine Mandelate, Hexa-methylenetetramine Mandelate, Hexamethaminium Mandelate), $C_6H_5CHOH-COO^- [(CH_2)_6N_4H]^+$, is a white, crystalline powder which melts at 127–130° and has a sour taste but practically no odor. It is very soluble in water and 1:10 in alcohol. It combines the urinary antiseptic action of both mandelic acid and methenamine, serving somewhat as its own acidifying agent to liberate formaldehyde from methenamine. However, for certain infections caused by urea-splitting bacteria the urine must be acidified 24 to 36 hr. prior to medication to provide a urinary pH necessary for the compound to exert its maximum effectiveness.

Sodium Formaldehydesulfoxylate (Rongolite, Formopone), $HO—CH_2—SO_2Na \cdot 2H_2O$, is a product resulting from the reduction of formaldehyde bisulfite with zinc dust and acetic acid. It was introduced in 1934 by Rosenthal as an antidote for mercury poisoning. Studies indicate that it has antidotal properties, but clinically it is not encouraging.

Acetaldehyde (Ethanal), $CH_3—CHO$, was first prepared by Fourcroy and Vauquelin (1800), and its composition was established by Liebig (1835). It appears in biological reactions, for example, in the deterioration of apples, when its characteristic odor may be recognized. It is an intermediate in the *in vivo* oxidation of ethyl alcohol, and, if the metabolism can be inhibited at that point, as may be done with Antabuse (page 278), the aldehyde may accumulate to dangerous concentrations. In the presence of sulfuric acid, acetaldehyde polymerizes to paraldehyde.

$$3CH_3CHO \underset{\text{dil. } H_2SO_4}{\overset{\text{conc. } H_2SO_4}{\rightleftarrows}}$$

$$\begin{array}{c} CH_3 \\ | \\ CH \\ \diagup \quad \diagdown \\ O \qquad O \\ | \qquad | \\ CH_3—CH \quad CH—CH_3 \\ \diagdown \quad \diagup \\ O \end{array}$$

Acetaldehyde   Paraldehyde

Paraldehyde, U.S.P., is a colorless liquid of characteristic odor and disagreeable taste, b.p. about 122°, solidifying at about 9°, soluble in water 1:8, and soluble in alcohol, ether, and chloroform. It is an efficient hypnotic, rapidly absorbed from the gastrointestinal tract or after intramuscular injection. Its fate in the body is unknown; about 80 per cent is destroyed, perhaps depolymerized in the liver to acetaldehyde and oxidized. Though its toxicity is low and the margin of safety large, it imparts a disagreeable taste and a persistent fusel oil odor to the breath.

Aromatic Aldehydes

Aromatic aldehydes are characterized in general by their odoriferous properties. Thus, these compounds are used primarily for their odor in perfumes and for their flavor in foods and pharmaceuticals.

Benzaldehyde, N.F. (Artificial Oil of Bitter Almond), is prepared commercially from toluene which is converted into benzalchloride and hydrolyzed with alkali or by direct oxidation of toluene by such agents as chromyl chloride or manganese dioxide.

$$C_6H_5CH_3 \xrightarrow{Cl_2} C_6H_5CHCl_2 \xrightarrow{alkali} C_6H_5CHO$$

$$C_6H_5CH_3 \xrightarrow{CrO_2Cl_2 \text{ or } MnO_2} C_6H_5CHO$$

Benzaldehyde is a colorless or yellowish liquid with a characteristic odor resembling bitter almonds and a burning taste. It must be stored in a well-stoppered bottle protected from light because benzaldehyde undergoes atmospheric oxidation to benzoic acid. Although benzaldehyde has some antispasmodic and a mild anesthetic activity, it is used chiefly as a flavor.

A number of phenolic aldehydes are constituents of volatile oils. Examples of some of these with name and formula are given. These are important prod-

| Salicylaldehyde | Anisaldehyde | Vanillin | Piperonal | Syringaldehyde |

ucts to the perfume industry but only vanillin is discussed here because of its pharmaceutical interest.

Vanillin, U.S.P. (3-Methoxy-4-hydroxybenzaldehyde), is a constituent of a number of volatile oils. One of the largest sources of vanillin is from the waste bisulfite liquors from the wood pulp and paper industry. It may be prepared synthetically from eugenol. It consists of white to yellow needles having a

vanillalike odor and taste. It is slightly soluble in water (1:100) and readily soluble in alcohol and other organic solvents. It volatilizes at 85°. Vanillin readily forms a bisulfite addition compound. By virtue of the phenolic hydroxyl group, vanillin reacts with alkali. It is prone to oxidation by air; thus, it should be stored in air-tight containers.

Unsaturated Aldehydes

Unsaturated aldehydes behave both as aldehydes and as compounds with a double bond. Unsaturated aldehydes constitute a class of compounds of which no particular member possesses any significant medicinal value. The lower members possess irritating properties by virtue of the unsaturated linkage, have a pungent odor, and are strongly lachrymatory. These properties are particularly pronounced for acrolein, propenal, $CH_2:CHCHO$. The higher members are pleasant-smelling liquids, and the best known are the diisoprenoid compounds isolated from various natural volatile oils.

Citronellal (3,7-Dimethyl-6-octenal), $(CH_3)_2C:CHCH_2CH_2CH(CH_3)CH_2-CHO$, is the naturally occurring aldehyde corresponding to citronellol.

Citral a and **Citral b** are geometric isomers of 3,7-dimethyl-2,6-octadienal with the formulas as indicated:

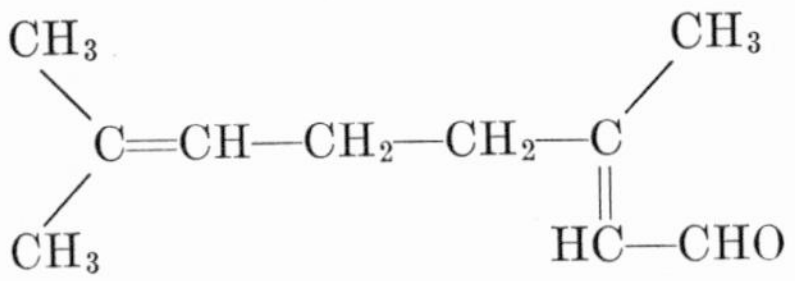

CH₃ structures

cis-3,7-Dimethyl-2,6-octadienal, citral *a* 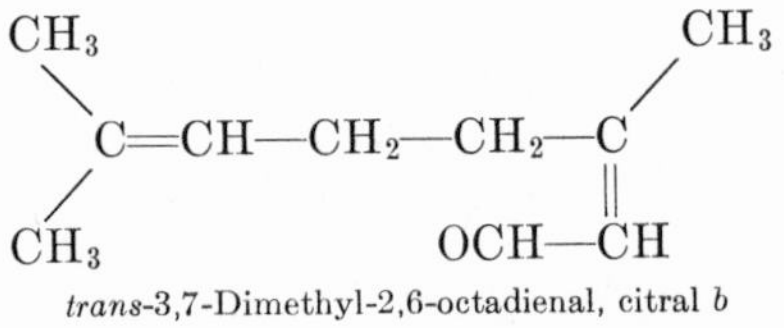   *trans*-3,7-Dimethyl-2,6-octadienal, citral *b*

Citral a is the aldehyde corresponding to geraniol, and citral b corresponds to nerol. Citral is found in various natural oils, especially in oil of lemon grass. Citral aids in epithelization in diseases of the cornea and in such cases exerts pronounced analgesic effects when instilled in small amounts.[1]

Cinnamaldehyde (Phenylacrolein), $C_6H_5CH:CHCHO$, is found in oil of cassia and is the chief constituent of oil of cinnamon.

KETONES

No physiologically useful compound is found among the simple aliphatic ketones, $R-\underset{\underset{O}{\|}}{C}-R'$. The lower members are useful as solvents and reagents.

Acetone (Dimethyl Ketone, 2-Propanone), $CH_3-CO-CH_3$, is the simplest and one of the most important ketones. It was prepared by Libavius in 1595 by heating lead acetate. Acetone is found in small amounts in human blood and normal urine; in ketonuria the amount of acetone is significantly higher; it is formed as a decarboxylation product from acetoacetic acid:

$$CH_3COCH_2COOH \rightarrow CH_3COCH_3 + CO_2$$

The synthetic production of the more than 3.3 million pounds of acetone used annually in the United States depends on the following methods:

[1] Balakhovskii and Budnitskaya, *Klin. Med.* (*U. S. S. R.*), **24**, No. 12, 23, (1946); *C.A.*, **41**, 6948 (1947).

1. The dry distillation of calcium acetate:

$$(CH_3COO)_2Ca \rightarrow CH_3COCH_3 + CaCO_3$$

This procedure is no longer able to compete economically with newer ones.

2. Fermentation by the Weizmann process. In this case the acetone is a by-product in the production of butyl alcohol.

3. Synthesis from propylene. For this purpose propylene, derived from petroleum, is first converted to isopropyl alcohol, which is then catalytically converted to acetone either by dehydrogenation or by oxidation:

$$CH_3CHOHCH_3 \rightarrow CH_3COCH_3 + H_2$$

$$2CH_3CHOHCH_3 + O_2 \rightarrow 2CH_3COCH_3 + 2H_2O$$

Acetone is relatively nontoxic.

Acetone, N.F., must be not less than 99 per cent pure. It is used as a pharmaceutical solvent.

Cyclic Ketones

The ketones derived from terpenes and other cyclic compounds seem to show no uniform type of physiological activity. In large doses, most of them cause excitement followed by depression through action on the central nervous system. Many of them have a hemolytic action on the blood. The hemolytic activity of the liquid keto-terpenes is closely related to their solubility in water. The hemolysis seems to result from a lowering of the surface tension by the dissolved keto-terpenes.

Naturally occurring ketones are present in a number of odoriferous oils of which several are of pharmaceutical importances.

Carvone   Menthone   Piperitone

Carvone [6,8(9)-p-Menthadiene-2-one], $C_{10}H_{14}O$, is a constituent of spearmint, oil of kuromoji, etc. On hydrogenation it forms hexahydrocarvacrol, and on dehydrogenation it forms carvacrol.

Menthone (3-Menthanone) is the ketone corresponding to menthol.

Piperitone (1-p-Menthen-3-one) occurs in a variety of eucalyptus oils. It possesses a pleasant camphoraceous odor.

Camphor is obtained in crude form from the wood of *Cinnamomum camphora* by steam distillation of pieces of trunk, limbs, and roots. The solid camphor so obtained is pressed into cakes to remove most of the water present. The product is purified by sublimation of a mixture of the crude camphor and lime. It may also be prepared synthetically as the accompanying reactions indicate.

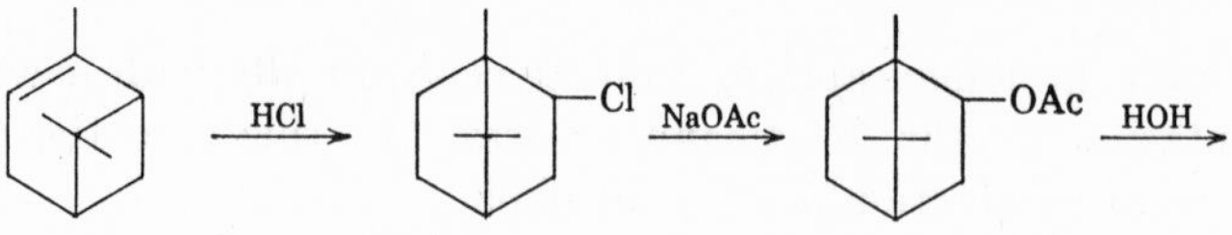

α-Pinene   Bornyl chloride   Bornyl acetate

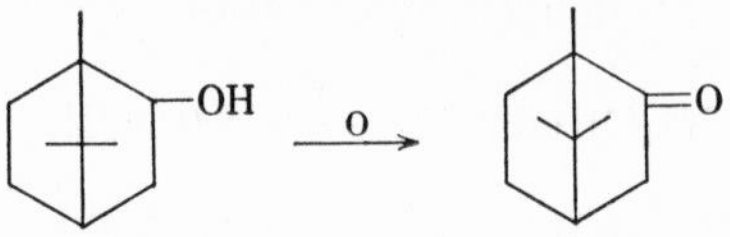

Borneol   Camphor

Camphor, U.S.P., is a white crystalline mass or translucent cake. It has a characteristic odor with a sharp taste. It is slightly soluble in water and soluble in alcohol. It forms a eutectic mixture with such substances as menthol, chloral hydrate, phenol, and resorcinol.

Natural camphor is dextrorotatory, and synthetic camphor is racemic. There is only a slight difference in physiological activity, the greater activity being attributed to the levo component.

Camphor is a mild irritant and antiseptic, often employed in the form of spirits or liniments. Applied externally it produces a mild analgesia and rubefaction with little sensory irritation. It is used clinically as a temporary cardiac stimulant. It is a household remedy in colds and bronchitis and is used as a diaphoretic and expectorant. In toxic doses it depresses and paralyzes the central nervous system; it produces nausea, vomiting, colic, etc.

Civetone is a ketone of large cycle. It is responsible for the characteristic odor of civet, the glandular secretion of the civet cat. The odor is disgustingly obnoxious, yet on extreme dilution it becomes very pleasant and is a valuable constituent of fine perfumes.

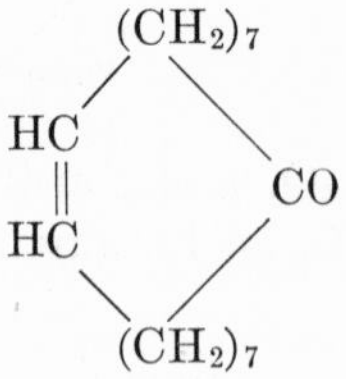

Civetone 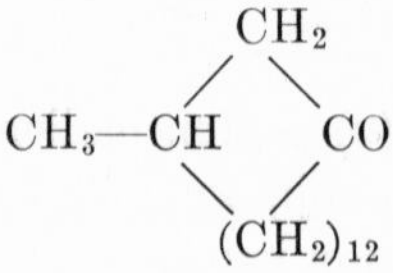   Muskone

Musk, the dried secretion of the preputial follicles of the musk deer, owes its value as a constituent of perfumes to muskone. Musk from the muskrat consists of normuscone (40 per cent) and dihydrocivetone (58 per cent). It also contains cyclotridecanone (1 per cent) and cyclononadecanone (0.7 per cent).

Ninhydrin (Triketohydrindene Hydrate), is a specific reagent for α-amino acids, which it oxidizes to liberate ammonia, carbon dioxide, and an aldehyde, as shown. The reduction product from the ninhydrin reacts with the liberated

$$RCH{\overset{COOH}{\underset{NH_2}{\Big\backslash}}} \quad \xrightarrow{\frac{1}{2}O_2} \quad RCHO + NH_3 + CO_2$$

ammonia and unchanged ninhydrin to give a blue substance according to the accompanying equation:

Ninhydrin   Reduced ninhydrin

(Blue color)

2,2,6-TRIMETHYLCYCLOHEXENYL DERIVATIVES

Citral readily reacts with active methylene groups to form citrylidene derivatives; these are easily cyclized to isomeric cyclocitrylidene derivatives as indicated, for example with the cyanoacetic acid compound. In a completely anal-

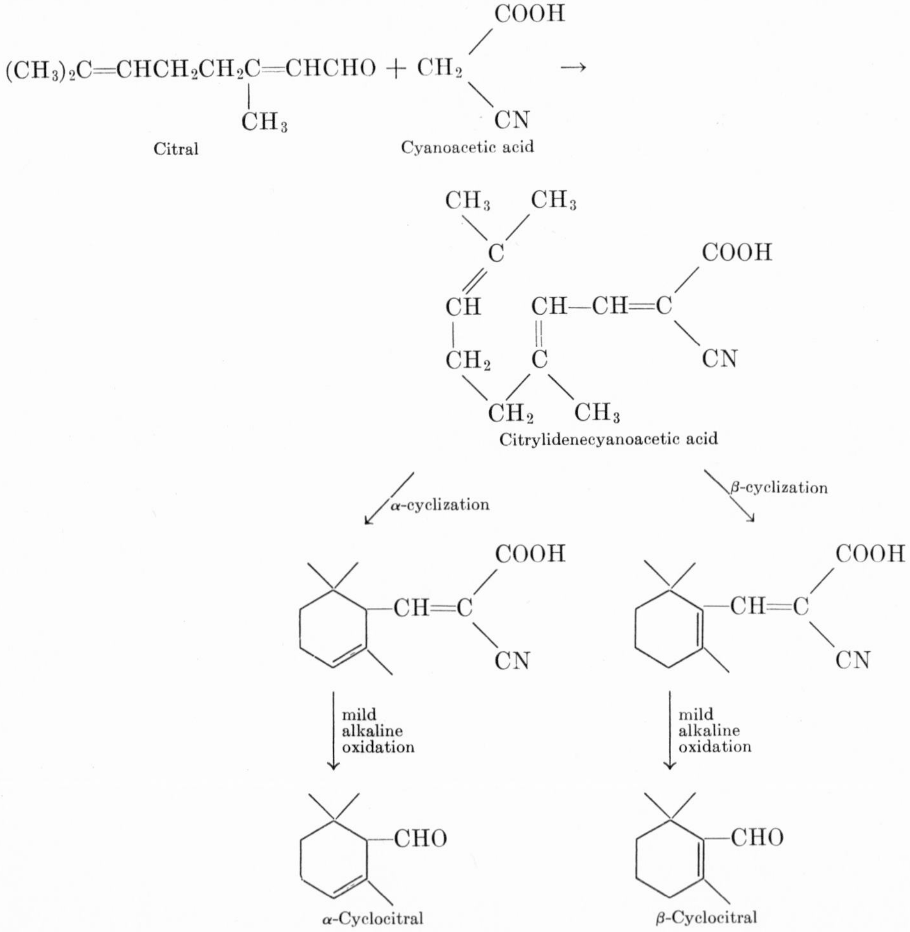

$$(CH_3)_2C=CHCH_2CH_2\underset{\underset{CH_3}{|}}{C}=CHCHO + CH_2\underset{CN}{\overset{COOH}{<}} \longrightarrow$$

Citral   Cyanoacetic acid

Citrylidenecyanoacetic acid

α-cyclization   β-cyclization

mild
alkaline
oxidation

mild
alkaline
oxidation

α-Cyclocitral   β-Cyclocitral

ogous manner, citral combines with acetone to form citrylideneacetone, more
commonly known as pseudo-ionone, which may be cyclized to the corresponding
α- and β-ionones, as indicated. The ionones, more particularly the α-isomer,
possess violetlike aromas and are used as perfumes. In other respects they are
physiologically quite inert. However, they merit the attention of the medicinal
chemist since they provide thirteen of the carbon atoms as found in vitamin A
(see page 49). It will be appreciated, therefore, that this type of cyclization,
by which citral is converted into cyclocitral compounds, has received considerable attention from the chemist.

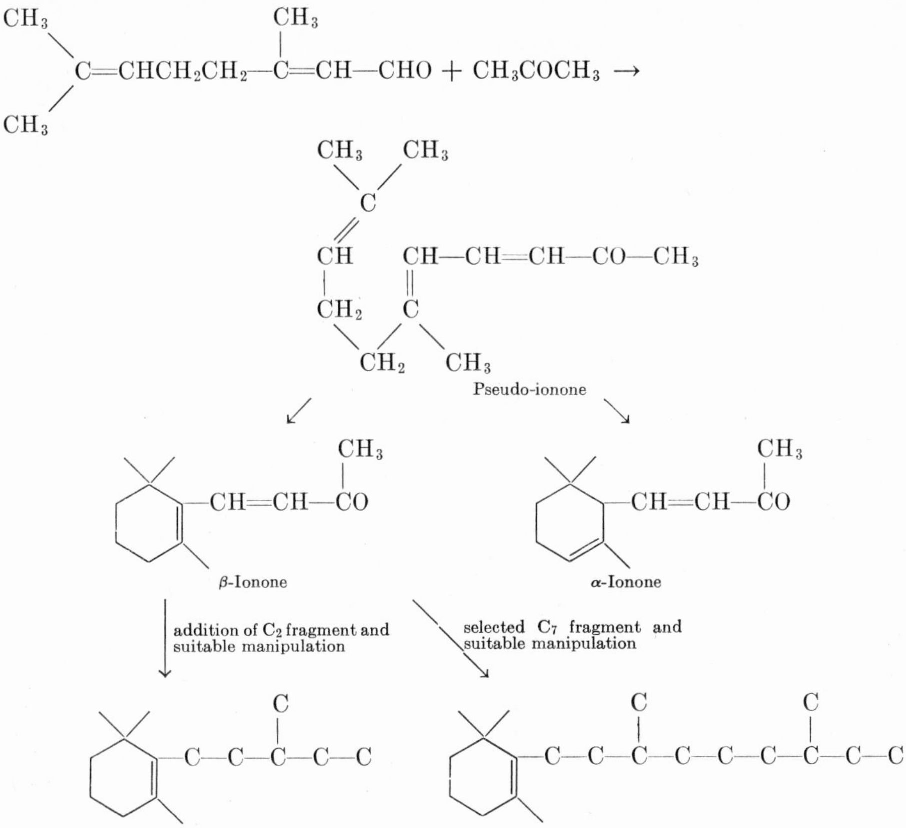

$$CH_3$$
$$\backslash$$
$$C{=}CHCH_2CH_2{-}\overset{\underset{\displaystyle CH_3}{|}}{C}{=}CH{-}CHO + CH_3COCH_3 \rightarrow$$
$$/$$
$$CH_3$$

$$\begin{array}{cc} CH_3 & CH_3 \\ \backslash & / \\ & C \\ & \| \\ CH & CH{-}CH{=}CH{-}CO{-}CH_3 \\ | & \| \\ CH_2 & C \\ \backslash & / \backslash \\ & CH_2 \quad CH_3 \end{array}$$

Pseudo-ionone

β-Ionone

α-Ionone

addition of C₂ fragment and suitable manipulation

selected C₇ fragment and suitable manipulation

Irone, a ketone found in orris root, possesses the characteristic odor of violets, an observation that suggested that it might be structurally related to ionone. The excellent work of Ruzicka and his co-workers [2] showed that in fact there is an extra methyl group in the 3-position of the cycle. However, the natural oil is not a pure principle but is composed of three isomers, for which the structures shown have been elucidated.

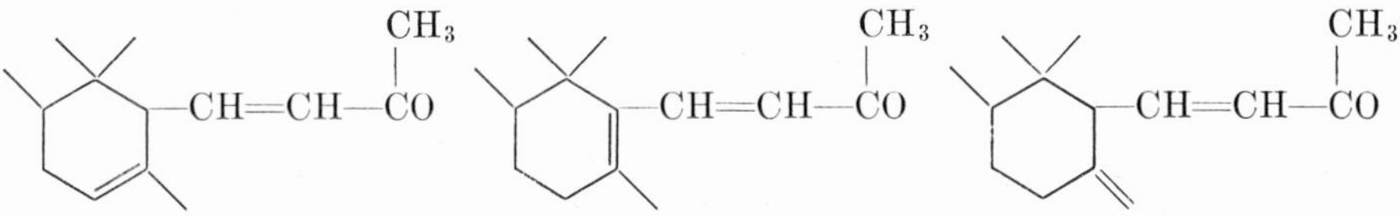

α-Irone

β-Irone

γ-Irone

QUINONES

Quinones are oxidation products of o- or p-dihydroxybenzenes or their derivatives. Catechol is easily oxidized to o-quinone; quinol (hydroquinone) readily forms p-quinone. Resorcinol and its derivatives do not form quinones.

[2] Ruzicka et al., Helv. Chim. Acta, **30**, 1807 (1947).

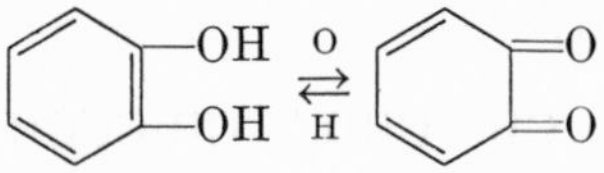

Catechol ⇄ o-Quinone

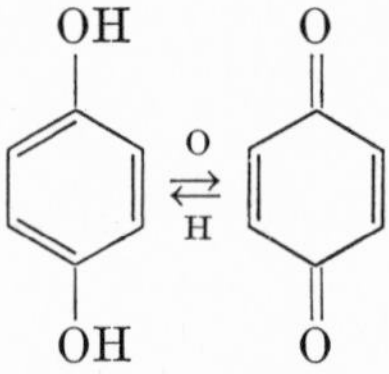

Quinol ⇄ p-Quinone

The quinones have been of interest for many years as synthetic chemicals and as naturally occurring constituents of plants. New interest in their medicinal possibilities was created through the discovery that vitamin K is a naphthoquinone derivative.

Phytonadione, U.S.P. (Vitamin K, Vitamin K_1, 2-Methyl-3-phytyl-1,4-naphthoquinone), is an antihemorrhagic factor. Its deficiency symptoms were first observed by Dam [3] in chicks; the tendency toward hemorrhage was overcome by adding spinach, alfalfa, kale, or fish meal to the diet. Dam called this then unknown factor the "Koagulationsvitamin," hence vitamin K. Dam and his associates, and also Doisy and his associates,[4] isolated the pure vitamin from alfalfa, calling it K_1 to distinguish it from a second active substance isolated by Doisy, McCorquodale, and their co-workers from putrefied sardine meal, which was called K_2. The structures of these two vitamins were shown to be as indicated. Almquist and Klose [5] showed that various simple naphtho-

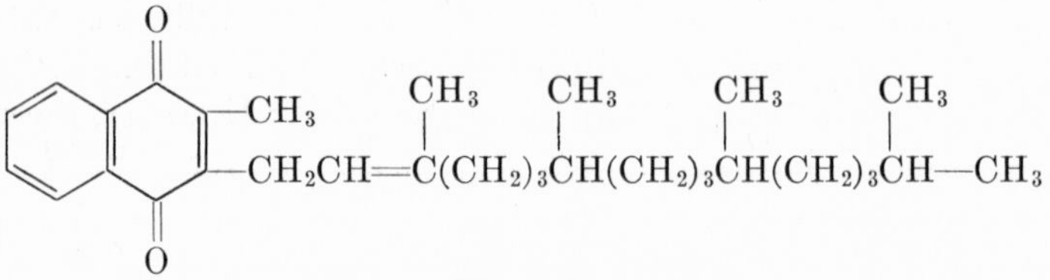

Vitamin K_1,
2-methyl-3-phytyl-1,4-naphthoquinone

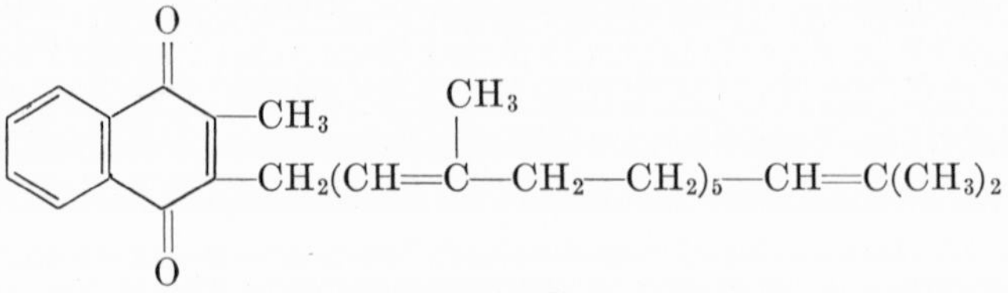

Vitamin K_2,
2-methyl-3-difarnesyl-1,4-naphthoquinone

[3] *Biochem. Z.*, **215**, 475 (1929).
[4] *J. Am. Chem. Soc.*, **61**, 1612 (1939).
[5] *J. Am. Chem. Soc.*, **61**, 1611 (1939).

quinones, such as phthiocol from the capsule of the tubercle bacillus, had vitamin K activity. A study of twenty-four 2-methyl-3-alkyl-1,4-naphthoquinones, assayed in the rabbit against various dicoumarol analogs showed that no activity is found in compounds in which the side chain is less than eight carbon atoms, that methyl branching and double bonds are favorable but not essential.[6] Nevertheless, the compound with optimum activity is 2-methyl-1,4-naphthoquinone.

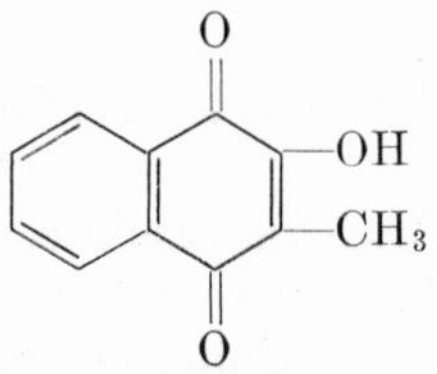

Phthiocol

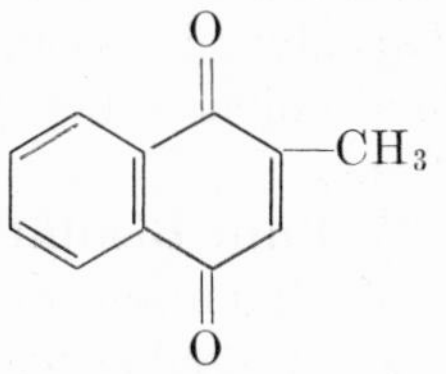

Menadione,
2-methyl-1,4-naphthoquinone

Vitamin K_1 was first synthesized in 1939 by condensing phytol with 2-methyl-1,4-dihydroxynaphthalene and oxidizing the product;[7] more efficient reactions have now been reported,[8, 9] one of which is shown.

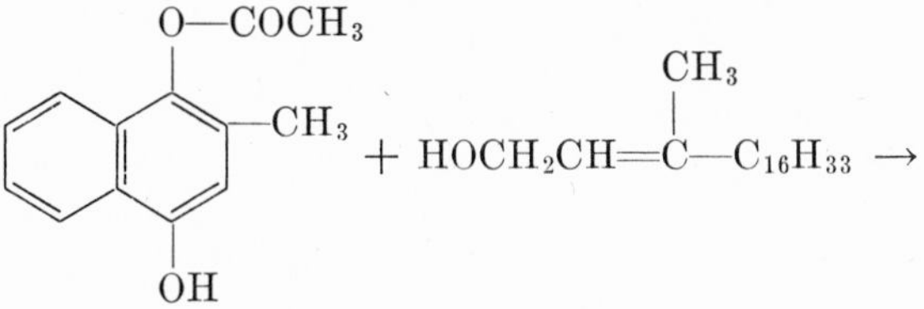

Using the acetyl derivative effectively prevents the formation of one undesirable by-product

Phytol

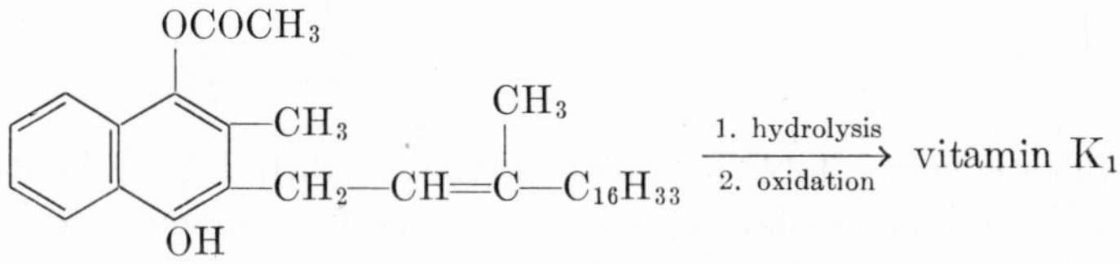

1. hydrolysis
2. oxidation → vitamin K_1

It is suggested that vitamin K acts by inhibiting the proteolytic enzymes which act on prothrombin. It apparently counteracts the effects of dicoumarol by lessening the rate of aerobic phosphorylation.[10]

Menadione, U.S.P. (Menaphthene, Menaphthone, 2-Methyl-1,4-naphthoquinone, vitamin K_3), is prepared commercially by the oxidation of 2-methylnaphthalene with potassium chromate in glacial acetic acid. It is a yellow, crystalline, practically odorless substance, m.p. 105–107°; it is practically insoluble in water and soluble in fats and in alcohol. Its solutions are neutral,

[6] Isler, Rüegg, Studer, and Jürgens, *Hoppe-Seyler's Z. physiol. Chem.*, **295,** 190 (1954).

[7] Fieser *et al.*, *J. Am. Chem. Soc.*, **61,** 2559 (1939).

[8] Isler and Doebel, *Helv. Chim. Acta*, **37,** 225 (1954).

[9] Hirschmann, Miller, and Wendler, *J. Am. Chem. Soc.*, **76,** 4592 (1954).

[10] Martius and Nitz-Litzow, *Biochim. et Biophys. Acta*, **12,** 139 (1953).

not affected by acids, but the compound is decomposed by alkalies. It is stable in the presence of moisture and air, when protected from light. Solutions may be sterilized by boiling, but they should always be protected from light. Menadione is used as an antihemorrhagic agent in infants and to reduce the tendency toward hemorrhage in a wide variety of conditions resulting from a reduction in the prothrombin level. It is reported to be of special value in the pre- and postoperative treatment of obstructive jaundice. Usually it is administered in tablet form or dissolved in vegetable oil.

The bulk of menadione is today added to poultry feed to prevent hemorrhagic disease in chickens.

Menadione Sodium Bisulfite, U.S.P. (Menadione Bisulfite, Hykinone), is the sodium bisulfite addition product of menadione, the bisulfite adding across the carbon-to-carbon double bond. It occurs as a white, crystalline product

2-Methylnaphthalene   Menadione

Menadione bisulfite

which is very soluble in water and only slightly soluble in alcohol.

Menadione bisulfite is a water-soluble form of menadione for intramuscular or intravenous use. Medicinally, it has the same activity as menadione.

Menadiol Sodium Diphosphate, U.S.P. (Synkayvite), is the tetrasodium salt of the diphosphoric ester of the reduced menadione, that is, of the hydroquinone analog. The diacetate of reduced menadione, also active and sometimes known as vitamin K_4, likewise is a prothrombogenic agent. Both esters presumably are effective after hydrolysis and *in vivo* oxidation of the free quinol to the quinone.

Menadiol sodium diphosphate, U.S.P.,
synkayvite

Menadiol diacetate,
vitamin K_4

4-Amino-2-methyl-1-naphthol,
vitamin K_5

It is worth noting that an amino analog of menadione, namely 4-amino-2-methyl-1-naphthol, listed by *Chemical Abstracts* as vitamin K_5, possesses powerful antimycotic activity [11] and is active against dermatophytes; [12] used as a food preservative, it was found to be low in toxicity and not to affect flavors.

Diphenadione, N.N.R. (Dipaxin, 2-Diphenylacetyl-1,3-indandione), is an anticoagulant, active when taken orally, and with actions similar to those of dicoumarol.

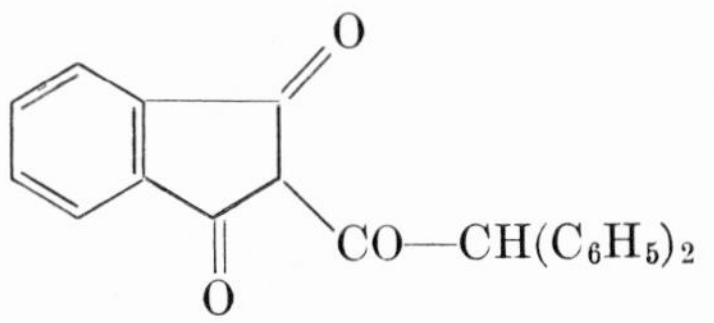

Diphenadione

Chrysarobin, U.S.P., is a microcrystalline powder varying in color from yellow to brown. It may be obtained by extracting Goa powder, a substance deposited in the wood of the tree, *Andira araroba*, with hot chloroform or benzene and by evaporating the extractive to dryness. It is a complex mixture of neutral principles, slightly soluble in water, soluble in alcohol about 1:400 and in chloroform about 1:15. It is irritant to mucous membranes and when applied to the skin. It is employed as an irritant, usually in about a 6 per cent ointment, to treat psoriasis, etc. Eder and Hauser [13] isolated a number of anthraquinone and anthranol derivatives from chrysarobin.

Constituents of Male Fern. Several complex quinone and ketone compounds are the effective constituents of *Aspidium filix mas* and related species of fern. The most active of these are filicinic acid and flavaspidic acid, both effective vermicides, useful against tapeworm.[14] Compounds in which a butyryl or isobutyryl group are introduced are actively vermicidal. Some of the formulas are given.

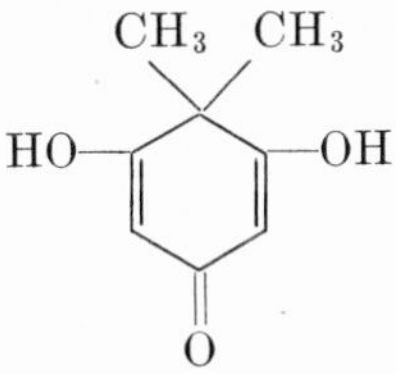

Filicinic acid 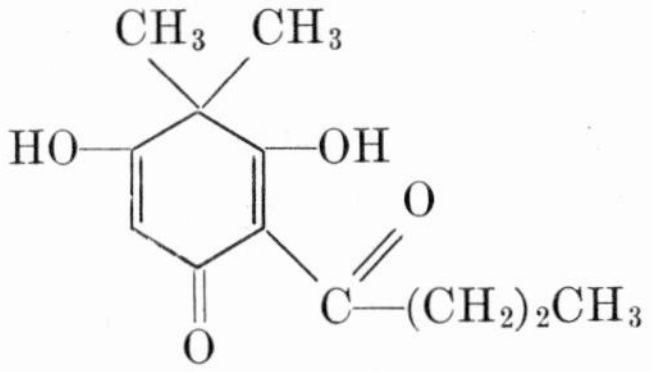   Butyrylfilicinic acid 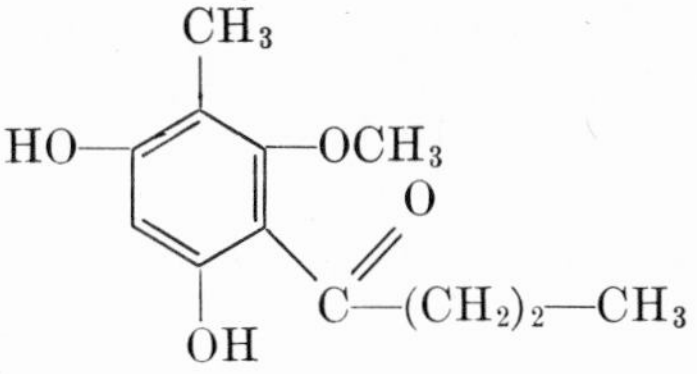   Aspidinol

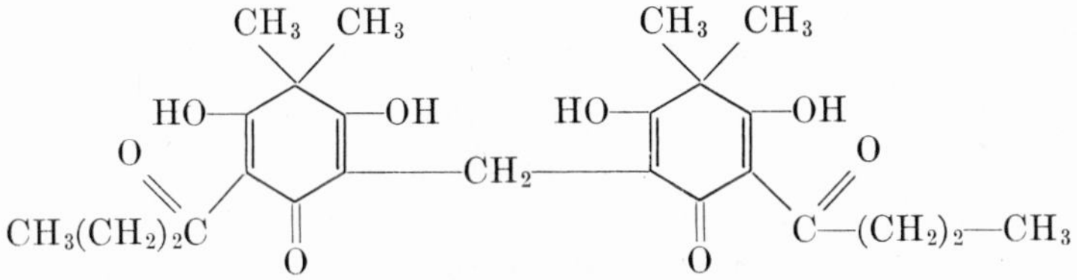

Flavaspidic acid

[11] Faggioli, *Igiene mod.*, **46**, 166 (1953); *C.A.*, **48**, 295 (1954).

[12] Arêafeão and Furtado, *Mycopathol. et Mycol. Appl.*, **5**, 121 (1950); *C.A.*, **48**, 11550 (1954).

[13] *Schweiz. Apoth. Ztg. Suppl.*, **1924**, 14.

[14] Huhtala, *Ann. Med. Exptl. et Biol. Fenniae*, **26**, Suppl. 5 (1948); *C.A.*, **44**, 8528 (1950).

Karrer and his co-workers [15] synthesized a large number of compounds of related structure. The most effective synthetic compound of those made was found to be phlorisocaprophenone.

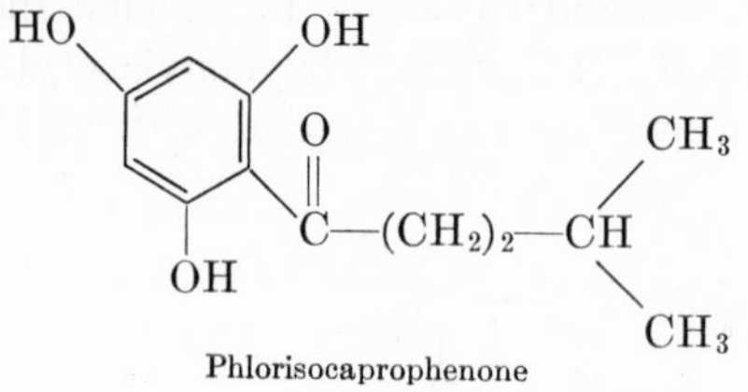

Phlorisocaprophenone

CARBOHYDRATES

The term carbohydrate, literally hydrated carbon, is applied to a class of compounds that are polyhydroxy aldehydes or polyhydroxy ketones. The name and the stereochemical configuration of carbohydrates are discussed elsewhere (page 453); therefore, the discussion here is limited mainly to the reactions involving the carbonyl group.

Monosaccharoses, monosaccharides, or simple sugars, contain predominantly five or six carbon atoms, and these may be further sub-classified as indicated according to the accompanying scheme. The specific name for the sugar de-

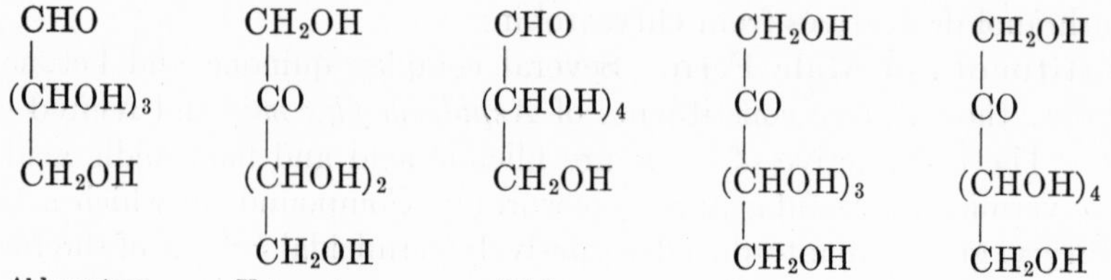

Aldopentose Ketopentose Aldohexose Ketohexose Ketoheptose

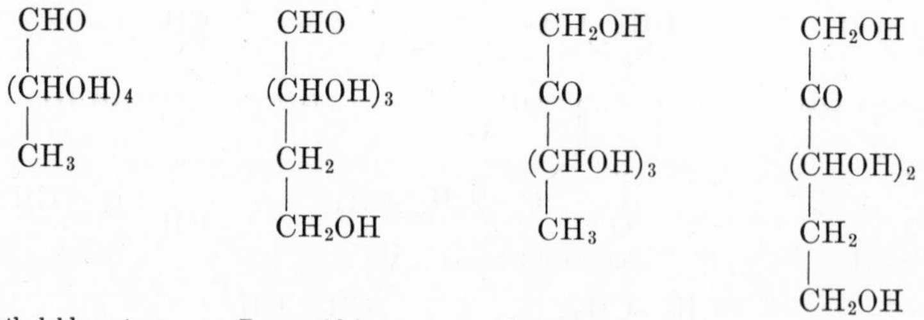

Methylaldopentose Desoxyaldohexose Methylketopentose Desoxyketohexose

pends on the configuration of the optically active carbon atoms. The biochemical and other properties of the individual compounds depend not only on the character of the carbonyl group but on their optical properties as well. For details along these lines reference should be made to suitable treatises.

An important and characteristic property of the simple sugars, particularly of the pentoses and hexoses, is the formation of internal hemiacetals, also some-

[15] Karrer *et al.*, *Helv. Chim. Acta*, **2**, 407, 466 (1921).

times spoken of as cyclic sugars. For example, an aldohexose forms two types
of such structures, as shown. Similar general structures may be written for

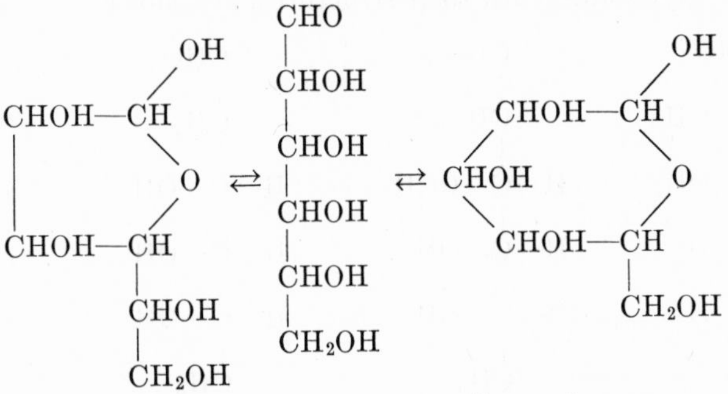

$$
\begin{array}{ccc}
\begin{array}{l}
\qquad\quad \text{OH}\\
\qquad\quad / \\
\text{CHOH}\!-\!\text{CH}\\
\ |\qquad\qquad \backslash\\
\ |\qquad\qquad\ \text{O}\\
\ |\qquad\qquad /\\
\text{CHOH}\!-\!\text{CH}\\
\ |\\
\quad\ \text{CHOH}\\
\ \ |\\
\quad\ \text{CH}_2\text{OH}
\end{array}
&
\rightleftarrows
\begin{array}{l}
\text{CHO}\\
|\\
\text{CHOH}\\
|\\
\text{CHOH}\\
|\\
\text{CHOH}\\
|\\
\text{CHOH}\\
|\\
\text{CH}_2\text{OH}
\end{array}
\rightleftarrows
&
\begin{array}{l}
\qquad\qquad \text{OH}\\
\qquad\qquad /\\
\text{CHOH}\!-\!\text{CH}\\
/\qquad\qquad\backslash\\
\text{CHOH}\qquad\quad \text{O}\\
\backslash\qquad\qquad /\\
\text{CHOH}\!-\!\text{CH}\\
\qquad\qquad |\\
\qquad\qquad \text{CH}_2\text{OH}
\end{array}
\end{array}
$$

Furan cycle, furanose   Pyran cycle, pyranose

ketoses and also for the pentoses. In the manner characteristic for hemiacetals,
they exhibit the chemical properties of a free carbonyl group.

Examination of these formulas reveals that in these cyclic compounds the
carbonyl carbon atom becomes asymmetric, thus giving rise to the α- and β-sug-
ars (see page 454), and is involved in the phenomenon known as mutarotation.

The carbohydrate carbonyl group also is known in the form of the mixed
acetal derivative for which the general chemical structures that come into consideration may be represented as shown. As acetals these compounds are quite

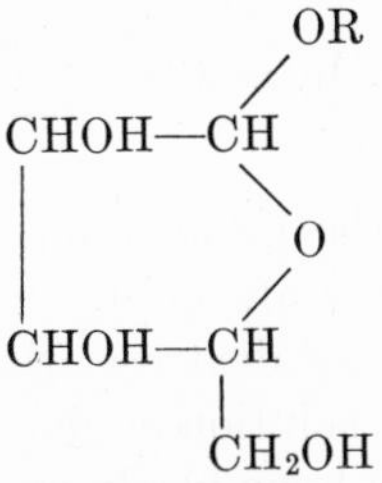

$$
\begin{array}{cc}
\begin{array}{l}
\qquad\quad \text{OR}\\
\qquad\quad /\\
\text{CHOH}\!-\!\text{CH}\\
|\qquad\qquad \backslash\\
|\qquad\qquad\ \text{O}\\
|\qquad\qquad /\\
\text{CHOH}\!-\!\text{CH}\\
\qquad\qquad |\\
\qquad\qquad \text{CH}_2\text{OH}
\end{array}
&
\begin{array}{l}
\qquad\qquad \text{OR}\\
\qquad\qquad /\\
\text{CHOH}\!-\!\text{CH}\\
/\qquad\qquad\backslash\\
\text{CHOH}\qquad\quad \text{O}\\
\backslash\qquad\qquad /\\
\text{CHOH}\!-\!\text{CH}\\
\qquad\qquad |\\
\qquad\qquad \text{CH}_2\text{OH}
\end{array}
\end{array}
$$

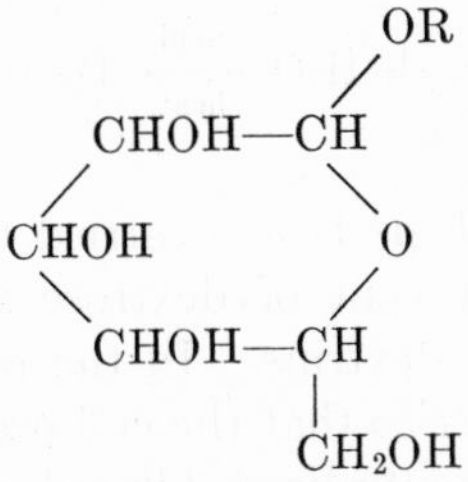

Acetal of furan cycle   Acetal of pyran cycle
(furanoside)   (pyranoside)

stable toward alkali but are quite readily hydrolyzed in the presence of acids.
This type of mixed acetal structure characterizes many natural products; hence
the nature of the R group is of tremendous importance. Broadly speaking these
acetals are conveniently divided into two classes: the first, in which R is another
sugar moiety, are called polysaccharides: the second, in which R is a nonsugar
residue, are called glycosides.

Monosaccharides

Pentoses do not occur as such, but many may be obtained by the hydrolysis
of polyoses known as pentosans, and from some glycosides. The most important
of these are:

L-Arabinose, found as a component in gum arabic, cherry gum, and mesquite
gum. D-Arabinose is found in certain glycosides. D-Xylose or wood sugar is ob-

tained from the xylans, such as wood, straw, corn cobs, peanut shells, and cotton-seed hulls. D-Ribose is a component of the ribonucleic acids. Sugars that occur in the cardiac glycosides, with their structures, are shown.

$$
\begin{array}{cccc}
\text{CHO} & \text{CHO} & \text{CHO} & \text{CHO} \\
| & | & | & | \\
\text{H—C—OH} & \text{CH}_2 & \text{CH}_2 & \text{HC—OH} \\
| & | & | & | \\
\text{H—C—OH} & \text{H—C—OCH}_3 & \text{H—C—OH} & \text{CH}_3\text{OCH} \\
| & | & | & | \\
\text{HO—C—H} & \text{H—C—OH} & \text{H—C—OH} & \text{HOCH} \\
| & | & | & | \\
\text{HO—C—H} & \text{H—C—OH} & \text{H—C—OH} & \text{H—C—OH} \\
| & | & | & | \\
\text{CH}_3 & \text{CH}_3 & \text{CH}_3 & \text{CH}_3 \\
\text{L-Rhamnose} & \text{D-Cymarose} & \text{D-Digitoxose} & \text{Digitalose}
\end{array}
$$

Dextrose, U.S.P. (D-Glucose, Grape Sugar). (For formula see page 453.) This aldohexose is the most common naturally occurring sugar. Ripe grapes contain 20 to 30 per cent of dextrose, hence the name grape sugar. It is the sole constituent of maltose, cellobiose, trehalose, starch, and cellulose. It also occurs combined with other monoses in sucrose, lactose, and with other substances in the natural heterosides.

Commercial glucose is obtained by the hydrolysis of polyoses, usually starch. In this country, it is usually prepared by heating cornstarch with acid:

$$(C_6H_{10}O_5)_x + H_2O \xrightarrow[\text{heat}]{\text{acid}} \text{Dextrins} \xrightarrow[\text{heat}]{\text{acid}} C_{12}H_{22}O_{11} + H_2O \xrightarrow[\text{heat}]{\text{acid}} 2C_6H_{12}O_6$$
$$\qquad \text{Starch} \qquad\qquad\qquad\qquad\qquad\qquad \text{Maltose} \qquad\qquad\qquad\qquad\qquad \text{Dextrose}$$

If the hydrolysis is not carried to completion, the product may contain from 20 to 40 per cent of dextrose and varying amounts of unconverted starch, maltose, and dextrins. In the preparation of pure dextrose, the hydrolysis is carried further so that the end product is a dilute solution of glucose. The solution is then neutralized, filtered, decolorized with bone black, and concentrated under vacuum to crystallize.

Pure dextrose crystallizes with one molecule of water. It is a colorless solid, soluble in water about 1:1.2, m.p. 86°; anhydrous dextrose crystallized from ethanol or acetic acid melts at 146°. It is about one-half as sweet as sucrose.

Glucose is the main source of energy in living organisms. In plants, it is stored largely as starch. The starch must be converted into glucose by enzymes before it can be transported in solution to regions of cellular activity and growth. When the carbohydrates are consumed by animals, they are broken down into monoses, chiefly glucose and fructose, before passing into the blood, and the fructose is converted into glucose in the liver under normal circumstances. The fact that carbohydrates form the major portion of the diet of many animals leads to the conclusion that glucose is the main source of ultimate energy in animal nutrition.

Glucose is stored in animals in the form of glycogen which is readily converted back into glucose by enzymes in the liver. The glycogen in the muscles is rapidly consumed during exertion, being replenished during rest, so that the concentrations may vary from 0.1 to 1.0 per cent. The amount of glycogen in the liver may also vary greatly according to the state of nutrition. In starving animals, it may be less than 1 per cent, and in well-fed animals it may be as high as 15 per cent by weight of fresh liver. When more glycogen is needed by the muscles, they obtain it from the blood sugar (glucose) and convert it into glycogen through the action of enzymes. At the same time, the liver supplies as much glucose to the blood as is taken from the blood by the muscles so that the total amount of glucose in the blood tends to remain unchanged. The minimum concentration, called the "fasting blood sugar" in a healthy individual is on the average about 0.1 per cent although the percentage may vary between 0.08 and 0.14 in adults and be as low as 0.06 in small children. The amount may increase to the maximum about 0.18 per cent in normal persons after carbohydrate consumption. The term "hypoglycemia" is applied to conditions characterized by less blood sugar than the normal fasting level. The term "hyperglycemia" is used to designate the condition where the blood-sugar level is higher than normal after ingestion of a large amount of carbohydrate. Hyperglycemia is common in diabetes and in certain other conditions. Hypoglycemia may be produced in normal animals by the injection of insulin.

The symptoms of hypoglycemia, i.e., nervousness, and perspiration, developing into tremors and convulsions, coma, and finally death, when the blood-sugar level falls below about 0.05 per cent, can be alleviated by the oral administration of glucose or sucrose or any other readily assimilated carbohydrate in the early stages, or by the intravenous administration of glucose in the later stages.

The body is unable either to oxidize glucose or to convert it into glycogen at the usual rate when the pancreas secretes insufficient insulin. Consequently, glucose accumulates in the blood. The resulting rise in the blood-sugar level depends on the carbohydrate consumption and also on the degree of impairment of the pancreas. In severe diabetes, the oral administration of 1 g. of glucose per kg. of body weight may cause the blood-sugar level to rise within an hour to as high as 0.4 to 0.5 per cent. In contrast to normal individuals, the blood-sugar level of diabetics may remain high for several hours and may exceed 0.2 per cent after fasting over night.

Reducing sugars appear in the urine when the concentration of blood sugar rises above the level called the "renal threshold," and a condition know as glycosuria results. The renal threshold may be defined as the minimum concentration of sugar in the blood at which sugar appears in the urine. The height of the renal threshold varies somewhat in normal persons between about 140 and 180 mg. of sugar per 100 cc. of blood or 0.14 to 0.18 per cent. In healthy persons, the consumption of carbohydrates does not cause the blood sugar to rise above the renal threshold and so reducing sugar is not found in the urine. In diabetes, the renal threshold is exceeded with the result that glucose is excreted in the urine. The resulting glycosuria may range from 0.3 to 10 per cent or more.

Pure dextrose is used in therapy as a source of energy. It is employed in a wide variety of conditions such as starvation from any cause, the pernicious vomiting of pregnancy, shock, and diabetic coma. Generally, it is administered intravenously in 5 to 50 per cent sterile aqueous solutions, or in a solution with salts, e.g., with physiological salt solution and with Ringer's solution, to render the products isotonic with the blood. Buffers are often added to such solutions to keep the products approximately neutral. Pure dextrose is the only form of glucose suitable for intravenous administration.

Liquid Glucose, U.S.P., is a thick syrup containing 79 per cent of solids. It is used in the manufacture of pharmaceuticals, e.g., the massing of pills and the preparation of pillular extracts. Since it contains dextrins, maltose, and some unhydrolyzed starch, it is never used intravenously, but it is a valuable form of carbohydrate used in many medicinal foods.

Invert Sugar Solution, N.N.R., is an equimolar mixture of levulose (D-fructose) and dextrose (D-glucose) obtained by the hydrolysis of sucrose by dilute acids or by enzymes.

Solutions containing 50 to 75 per cent of invert sugar in pure water are used in the injection treatment of varicose veins.

Levulose (D-Fructose or Fruit Sugar), a ketohexose, occurs in the juices of fresh fruits and in honey and combined with glucose in sucrose, and is the only sugar component of the polyose, inulin. It is obtained from inulin by acid hydrolysis. Levulose is levorotatory. Upon reduction, it yields the hexahydric alcohols, D-mannitol and D-sorbitol. It responds to the reactions of reducing sugars and forms oximes and osazones. With methyl phenylhydrazine, it gives both a hydrazone and an osazone and in this reaction differs from the aldoses which do not yield osazones with this reagent. It is sweeter than sucrose.

Disaccharides

Disaccharides comply with the general formula for sugar acetals, page 105, with R being a monose residue. It becomes apparent that there are two possibilities for the union of two monoses through acetal linkage. One of these is the one in which no hemiacetal is present, and the other is the one in which one

No hemiacetal in either moiety, hence, nonreducing sugar

of the monose components retains its hemiacetal group.

Hemiaceta lpresent, hence, reducing sugar

Sucrose, U.S.P., a nonreducing disaccharide, is widely distributed in plants. It is obtained chiefly from sugar cane (*Saccharum officinarum* Linné) and from the sugar beet (*Beta vulgaris* Linné). Sugar cane contains 15 to 20 per cent, and the sugar beet contains 10 to 15 per cent of sucrose.

Sucrose is used as a sweetening agent, diluent, and preservative in a number of pharmaceutical products, e.g., syrups, powdered extracts, troches, lozenges, and Lunosol, a colloidal silver preparation.

Sucrose is hydrolyzed in the stomach to form D-glucose and D-fructose. These sugars are absorbed, and the fructose is converted by the liver into glycogen from which glucose is regenerated as needed in metabolism.

Caramel, N.F., is formed when sucrose is heated at about 210°. It is a dark brown mass used to color medicinal products and beverages.

Lactose, U.S.P. (Milk Sugar), is present in the milk of mammals to the extent of about 3 to 5 per cent. It is made from the whey of milk after the fat and casein have been removed for butter and cheese making. Cow's milk from which lactose is usually prepared yields about 2.5 to 3 per cent of lactose. Lactose is a white, crystalline sugar, soluble to a lesser extent in water than D-glucose or sucrose. It has a slightly sweet taste. Since it contains the hemiacetal group, it can exist in both the α and β forms which undergo mutarotation to yield a product of $[\alpha]_D = +52.5°$. The common lactose is a mixture of the α and β forms, and it is a reducing sugar.

Lactose does not undergo direct alcoholic fermentation. After hydrolysis by the enzyme lactase, the hydrolytic products can be fermented to alcohol and carbon dioxide. It is extensively used as a diluent in powders, tablets, etc., in pharmaceutical technology.

Maltose or Malt Sugar is a product of the enzymic hydrolysis of starch by diastase. It is a white, crystalline compound, soluble in water and in alcohol, which usually crystallizes with one molecule of water. Maltose is dextrorotatory, and, having a hemiacetal group, it is a reducing sugar and exhibits the phenomenon of mutarotation. It is a fermentable sugar. It is converted by the enzyme maltase, present in yeast, to glucose, which is then fermented by zymase to alcohol and carbon dioxide.

Maltose is extensively used in specially prepared carbohydrate foods for the nutrition of infants and adult invalids. This usage is based on the assumption that maltose is more readily assimilable than other sugars and that it is a desirable supplement to the carbohydrate contained in cow's milk (lactose).

Malt Extract, N.F., contains maltose, dextrin, and amylolytic enzymes. The enzymes in the extract convert starches into water-soluble sugars. This extract is used in infant feeding chiefly because it has a distinct laxative effect as well as nutritive value.

Polysaccharides

Multiplication of the acetal linkages, that is, the addition of other monoses, in the manner indicated for the disaccharides, leads to tri-, tetra-, and so on to polysaccharides. They are important as food for living things, and the larger molecules help to form the cell walls in plants. On complete hydrolysis they form simple sugars containing, for the most part, five and six carbon atoms. It should be pointed out here that the acetal union may be of the α- or β-type (see page 454) and that the digestive enzymes are, with rare exceptions, stereo-specific and will hydrolyze only the α-configuration.

Starch, U.S.P. (Amylum, Corn Starch). Starch is widely distributed throughout the plant kingdom. It makes up about 75 per cent of corn, 20 per cent of potatoes, 65 per cent of wheat, and 75 per cent of rice. The starches from different vegetable sources, although they have α-type linkages, differ in their physical properties but all give glucose on complete hydrolysis.

Starch is used medicinally as a dusting powder; as an emollient in the form of the *Starch Glycerite, U.S.P.*; as a diluent in powders, tablets, and pills, etc.; and in poultices.

Glycogen (Liver Starch) is a glucosan which is widely distributed in the animal kingdom and occurs to some extent in the plant kingdom. It forms col-loidal solutions in water, produces a violet-red color with iodine, and is hydro-lyzed to glucose by dilute acids. It is stored in large amounts in the liver and muscles and is recognized as one of the most important animal foods.

Dextrins are composed of a mixture of similar glucosans. They are amor-phous polysaccharides intermediate between amylose and maltose. The dextrins are formed by heating starch to about 250° or by the action of dilute acids or diastase on starch. The products of starch hydrolysis that give a blue color with iodine are known as amylodextrins, those that give a red color are known as erythrodextrins, and those that give no color are known as achroödextrins. The dextrins are readily soluble in water.

The dextrins are used extensively in carbohydrate foods for infants and adult invalids on the assumption that they are more readily digested and assimilated than starch. They are often combined with maltose or other sugars in products such as "Dextri-Maltose," etc.

Inulin is a fructosan which occurs in many plants. It is obtained mostly from the tubers of the dahlia and the Jerusalem artichoke. It is soluble in hot water, is a nonreducing polyose, and is levorotatory. Hydrolysis by acids or inulase converts it entirely into D-fructose (levulose). It is not acted on by di-astase and does not yield a color reaction with iodine.

Cellulose is a glucosan which occurs widely distributed in nature as the chief structural material of plants. It may be regarded as long chains of glucose molecules linked together in β-glucosidic combination. It is resistant to hy-drolysis, but, on prolonged heating with acids, it is converted almost quanti-tatively into glucose. The enzyme cellulase converts it into cellobiose. It has been established that there are three free —OH groups for each glucose unit in cellulose, except the terminal units, which contain four.

Cellulose is insoluble in all ordinary solvents, but it dissolves in a solution of zinc chloride in hydrochloric acid and in a solution of ammoniacal cupric oxide. When treated with iodine, it gives a yellow color. The nitrates, xan-thogenates, and acetates of cellulose are of importance in industries as source materials for the preparation of explosives, lacquers, rayon, etc.

Cotton fiber contains 87 to 92 per cent of cellulose. When purified by washing with alcohol, ether, acids, and alkali, the product is practically pure cellulose. *Purified Cotton, U.S.P., Absorbent Gauze, U.S.P.*, and *Gauze Bandage, U.S.P.*, are used as surgical dressings.

For nitrocellulose, see pyroxylin, page 264.

Cellulose is not attacked by diastase or any of the other digestive enzymes in the human digestive tract. Consequently, cellulose in foodstuffs cannot be digested and functions merely to give bulk or roughage. Cellulose in the form of a flour is marketed for this purpose.

Oxidized Cellulose (Oxycel) is produced from cellulose by a special oxidizing process. It resembles surgical gauze. When applied to wounds or oozing surfaces it softens and forms a gelatinous clot, thus serving as a hemostatic agent. It is completely absorbable and need not be removed from wounds.

Pyrogens are toxic substances which produce fever and chills when they develop in preparations such as blood plasma, sera, and other fluid injection preparations.

The chemical nature of pyrogens is still an unsolved mystery.[16] They appear to include a heterogeneous group of substances, depending on their origin and development. Some have been characterized as of carbohydrate nature of high molecular weight,[17] e.g., as high as 62,000. Others contain in addition to the elements carbon, hydrogen, and oxygen, the elements phosphorus, nitrogen, and occasionally sulfur.[18] There is no definite chemical test for the presence of pyrogens.

Derived Carbohydrates

Hemicellulose preparations are often polysaccharide mixtures. It is possible to approach a structural characterization of these complex substances by an examination of their simpler hydrolytic fragments. Depending on the source, these may include pentosans, hexosans, and, at times, a uronic acid.[19] In general the hemicelluloses are insoluble in water, but they may be soluble in alkaline solution, from which they may be precipitated by the addition of acids or alcohol.

Gums. The gums are translucent, amorphous substances which either dissolve in water to form sticky solutions or swell to form a gel. They occur as exudates on the bark of trees or on fruits, particularly after wounding.

Plant gums always contain either D-galacturonic or D-glucuronic acid and at least two of the following sugars: D-galactose, L-arabinose, L-rhamnose, D-mannose, and D-xylose. In some gums, the hexuronic acid contains a methoxy group. The free acidic groups exist as their sodium, potassium, or magnesium salts.

Acacia, U.S.P. (Gum Arabic), has a complex molecule in which chains of L-arabinose, L-galactose, and L-rhamnose are interlinked with D-galacturonic acid units. An aldobionic acid from D-galactose and D-glucuronic acid is also present.

[16] Charonnat and Lechat, *Ann. pharm. franç.*, **9,** 17 (1951).

[17] Robinson and Flusser, *J. Biol. Chem.*, **153,** 529 (1944).

[18] Demers, *Can. Pharm. J.*, **83,** No. 8, 26 (1950).

[19] Jones, *Ann. Rev. Biochem.* **24,** 127 (1955).

It is used as a demulcent and is important in the preparation of emulsions, pills, and troches. Acacia is also used by intravenous administration to restore the normal colloidal osmotic pressure in the treatment of nephrotic edema. Its colloidal osmotic pressure is about the same as serum protein, and, since it does not permeate the capillary cell wall freely, it attracts fluid and increases the mobilization and excretion of the deposits from edema. It is usually administered as about a 6 per cent solution in physiological salt solution for this purpose. It is also used in the treatment of posthemorrhagic shock. For this purpose, ampuled solutions containing about 30 g. of acacia and 4.5 g. of sodium chloride in 100 cc. are diluted to about 400 cc. with sterile distilled water prior to injection. It has been reported that about 50 per cent of the injected acacia remains permanently stored in the liver, causing enlargement and impairment of that organ.[20, 21]

Tragacanth, U.S.P. (Gum Tragacanth), may be considered a mixture of a gum and bassorin. The gum portion (tragacanthin) is soluble in water and has been resolved into arabinose and geddic acid, an isomer of arabic acid. The bassorin portion only swells when treated with water, but dissolves in alkalies with the formation of methyl alcohol and a salt of bassoric acid which on hydrolysis yields large quantities of uronic acid. Tragacanth is used in pharmacy as a demulcent and for the preparation of suspensions of heavy powders, as an adhesive in troches, pills, etc., and as an emulsifying agent.

Sterculia Gum, N.F. (Karaya Gum, Indian Tragacanth), is the dried gummy exudate obtained from various species of *Sterculia* and *Cochlospermum*. It has been employed as a substitute for tragacanth in lotions, pastes, and emulsions. Its capacity to absorb water (1:25) and swell makes it of value for supplying bulk to the fecal mass in some cases of chronic constipation. When administered with water, it expands about six times and acts as a demulcent laxative. It often is combined with other laxative drugs, e.g., with cascara.

Mucilages. The mucilages, which resemble the gums, comprise a rather poorly defined group of carbohydrates. When added to water, they form a slimy liquid, and on hydrolysis they yield carbohydrate and noncarbohydrate products. The mucilages are commonly extracted from seeds or seed coverings. The common mucilages, chondrus and agar, when hydrolyzed yield carbohydrate, calcium sulfate, and sulfuric acid.

Mucilose consists largely of hemicelluloses derived from the seeds of *Plantago lieflingii*. It is used as a nonirritant laxative, supplying a mucilaginous bulk in the intestines as it expands by the absorption of water.

Chondrus, N.F. (Carragheen, Irish Moss), is the dried and bleached plant of *Chondrus crispus* or *Gigartina mamillosa*. It contains as much as 80 per cent mucilage. Chondrus has been used for many years to treat dysentery, chronic diarrhea, etc.

Agar, U.S.P. (Agar-Agar), has been a valuable culture medium in bacteriology for many years. Pharmaceutically it is used alone and with other sub-

---

[20] *J. Pharmacol. Exptl. Therap.*, **52**, 390–407 (1934).
[21] *Surg. Gynecol. Obstet.*, **64**, 772–84 (1937).

stances such as mineral oil and phenolphthalein in the treatment of chronic constipation. When taken into the intestinal tract, agar remains undigested and, by its absorption of water and swelling, adds bulk to the intestinal contents.

Pectin, N.F. The pectic substances form a chainlike network of intercellular material meshing in with the cellulose structure of plant cell walls. The water-insoluble precursor of pectin, protopectin, which makes up the bulk of the pectic substance of immature fruits is converted to the water-soluble pectin as ripening proceeds. Turgidity of the cellular structure of plants is due to the hydrophilic nature of pectin. Ripening processes, which continue through maturity and on to decay, hydrolyze pectins, de-esterifying and depolymerizing the molecules, producing pectinic acids and pectinates and finally pectic acid, pectates, and even the lower sugars.

The pectin molecule is composed of partially methyl-esterified α-D-galacturonide units in pyranose form, linked by 1,4-glycosidic bonds. There are usually 3 to 10 esterified carboxyls to every nonesterified carboxyl in the pectin molecule The average molecular weight is in the order of 150,000 to 300,000.

Portion of pectin molecule

Pectin of pharmaceutical quality is usually obtained commercially by mild acidic treatment of the white inner portion (albedo) of citrus fruit peel.

Powdered pectin is easily water soluble if precautions are taken to prevent clumping. The pectin may be wetted with alcohol, glycerol, or glucose syrup, before water is poured on it, or the dry pectin when mixed with sugar or other dry water-soluble materials may be stirred into water. Pectin is most stable in the pH range of 3.0–4.0 or 4.5. Pectin is precipitated from its aqueous sols by alcohols and ketones when these are present in amounts exceeding 40–45 per cent concentration. Pectin sols do not exhibit the sol-gel transformation under temperature changes like sols of gelatin and agar. True pectin gels form only in systems where the pH is not higher than 3.5, the sugar concentration exceeds 45–50 per cent, with pectin at 0.2–1.0 per cent concentration, depending upon its quality. Pectin when partially de-esterified produces heat-reversible gels with very low levels of alkaline earths, regardless of the sugar content.

The medical literature on pectin, although dating back to the writings of Braconnot in 1825, has become quite extensive only since 1925. Pectin sols, sterilized by autoclaving and properly clarified, have been used as a plasma substitute in the transfusion treatment of shock, and as a medium for the parenteral administration of certain therapeutic agents. Pectin, in the form of sols, tablets, capsules, or in powdered mixtures, is administered orally in treating diarrhea, bacillary dysenteries, colitis, and other intestinal disorders. De-esterification of the pectin by bacterial enzymes in the colon reduces the pH to an unfavorable environment for pathogens and also permits the pectin to form hydrophilic calcium pectinates which gel *in situ* to provide fecal bulk.

Finely divided solid pectin has been used with penicillin and streptomycin in oil for intramuscular injections in antibiotic therapy. Pectin is an oil-in-water emulsifier and serves in liquid multi-vitamin preparations and in many essential oil emulsions. Its acid-buffering ability makes it useful in antacid preparations for stomach disorders. The pectin pastes of the National Formulary are used for wound healing and treating bed sores and also as a base for vaginal jellies.

Nipectin, a proprietary product containing a small amount of nickel, which renders the pectin more soluble and increases the bactericidal action, has been introduced as a powder for addition to cereal, soup, milk, or other food in the treatment of diarrhea and dysentery in children.

Sodium Alginate (Algin, Kelgin) is a gelatinous substance obtained from various seaweeds. The complex molecule is made up of D-mannuronic acid units. It is soluble in cold water, forming a mucilage, and can be made into a gel by adding calcium citrate. It is used as a suspending agent in the manufacture of cosmetics and pharmaceuticals.

GLYCOSIDES OR HETEROSIDES

As previously mentioned, page 105, if a sugar is linked through acetal union with a nonsugar moiety the substance is known as a glycoside; hydrolysis affords a sugar, which may be a monose, a di- or tri-saccharide, and a nonsugar, which is spoken of as an aglycone. The natural glycosides yield a heterogeneous classification of aglycones.

The glycosides may be classified in various ways, some of which may be overlapping; for example:

1. Primary glycosides: those which occur in the plant and are not products formed by the hydrolysis of other glycosides, e.g., amygdalin.

Secondary glycosides: those which result from the hydrolysis of other glycosides, e.g., prunasin.

2. According to the nature of the aglycon, e.g., alcoholic, phenolic, cyanogenetic, steroidal, etc. That is, the aglycone belongs to the indicated general class of organic compounds.

3. According to the nature of the simple sugar component of the glycoside; thus, if the sugar is glucose the glycoside may be correctly called a glucoside (and the aglycone is called an aglucone; rhamnosides yield rhamnose, etc.).

4. According to the plant families from which the glycosides are obtained, e.g., coniferin comes from Coniferae, scillain comes from the Liliaceae, etc.

5. According to the physiological effect produced by the glycoside; thus, the digitalis glycosides are also known as cardiac glycosides.

Cyanogenetic Glycosides

The cyanogenetic glycosides, also known as cyanophoric glycosides, give hydrocyanic acid as one of their products of hydrolysis. The common cyanogenetic glycosides are derivatives of mandelonitrile (benzaldehyde cyanohydrin). They occur in many plants. Common sources are bitter almonds, wild cherry bark, cherry laurel leaves, and the pits of the kernel of the peach, plum, and cherry. The more common ones are listed in Table V.

TABLE V

Glycoside	Formula	Sugar		Aglycon
Amygdalin	$C_{20}H_{27}O_{11}N$	$\rightarrow$ Gentiobiose	$+$	D-mandelonitrile
Prunasin	$C_{14}H_{17}O_6N$	$\rightarrow$ Glucose	$+$	D-mandelonitrile
Prulaurasin	$C_{14}H_{17}O_6N$	$\rightarrow$ Glucose	$+$	DL-mandelonitrile
Sambunigrin	$C_{14}H_{17}O_6N$	$\rightarrow$ Glucose	$+$	L-mandelonitrile

The three simple stereoisomeric glucosides, prunasin, sambunigrin, and prulaurasin, are derived from 1 mole of glucose condensed with 1 mole of D-, L-, and DL-mandelonitrile, respectively.

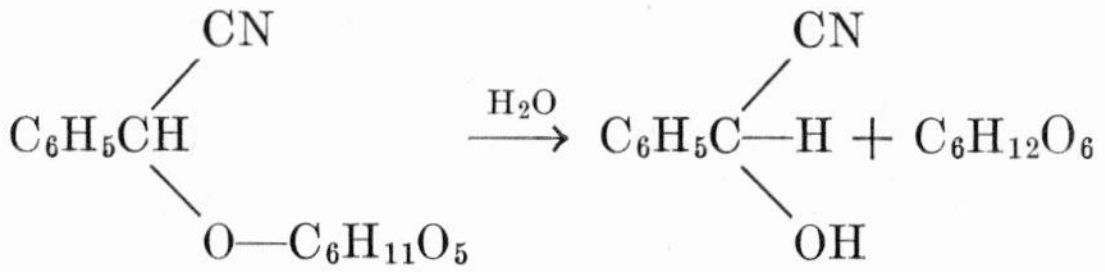

$$C_6H_5CH \begin{smallmatrix} CN \\ \\ O-C_6H_{11}O_5 \end{smallmatrix} \xrightarrow{H_2O} C_6H_5C \begin{smallmatrix} CN \\ -H \\ OH \end{smallmatrix} + C_6H_{12}O_6$$
Mandelonitrile

Amygdalin, a glycoside obtained from bitter almonds, is hydrolyzed by enzymes in two stages:

1. By amygdalase,

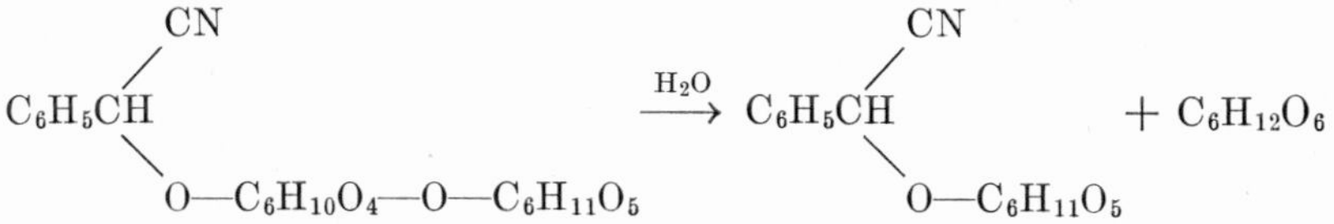

$$C_6H_5CH \begin{smallmatrix} CN \\ \\ O-C_6H_{10}O_4-O-C_6H_{11}O_5 \end{smallmatrix} \xrightarrow{H_2O} C_6H_5CH \begin{smallmatrix} CN \\ \\ O-C_6H_{11}O_5 \end{smallmatrix} + C_6H_{12}O_6$$
Amygdalin $\qquad$ Prunasin $\qquad$ Glucose

2. By prunase,

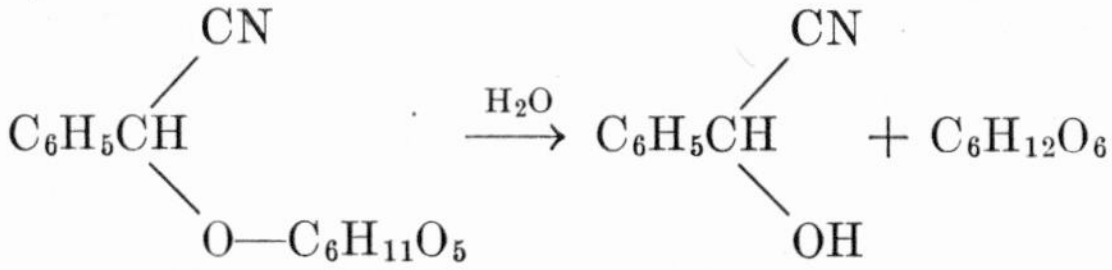

$$C_6H_5CH \begin{smallmatrix} CN \\ \\ O-C_6H_{11}O_5 \end{smallmatrix} \xrightarrow{H_2O} C_6H_5CH \begin{smallmatrix} CN \\ \\ OH \end{smallmatrix} + C_6H_{12}O_6$$
Prunasin $\qquad$ Mandelonitrile $\qquad$ Glucose

It was first obtained by Robiquet and Charlard in 1830. Haworth and Wylam [22] have shown that the two glucose molecules are linked in glycosidic

[22] *J. Chem. Soc.*, **123**, 3120 (1923).

union as 6-glucosyl-β-glucoside which is the same as the linkage in gentiobiose from gentian root. It was synthesized by Kuhn and Sobotka.[23] It is a colorless, crystalline, bitter substance, neutral in reaction, m.p. 200°.

Phenolic Glycosides

The phenolic glycosides are of some importance in modern medicine. The more important ones are listed in Table VI.

TABLE VI

PHENOLIC GLYCOSIDES

Glycoside	Formula		Sugar		Aglycon
Arbutin	$C_{12}H_{16}O_7$	→	Glucose	+	Quinol
Salicin	$C_{13}H_{18}O_7$	→	Glucose	+	Hydroxybenzyl alcohol
Coniferin	$C_{16}H_{22}O_8$	→	Glucose	+	Coniferyl alcohol
Gaultherin	$C_{19}H_{26}O_{12}$	→	Primeverose	+	Methyl salicylate
Phlorhizin	$C_{21}H_{24}O_{10}$	→	Glucose	+	Phloretin

Salicin occurs in varying amounts up to 7.5 per cent in many species of Salix and Populus. It forms colorless crystals, is soluble in water 1:25 and in alcohol 1:90, m.p. 201.5°. It has been used for many years as a remedy in the treatment of fever and rheumatism. Before the age of synthetic chemistry, it was the chief source of the salicylates. It is now used as an antipyretic, antiperiodic, and simple bitter. Upon oxidation, the saligenin yields salicylic acid which probably accounts for its value. It is better tolerated in the stomach than sodium salicylate which has largely displaced it in medical practice. Hydrolysis of salicin is indicated.

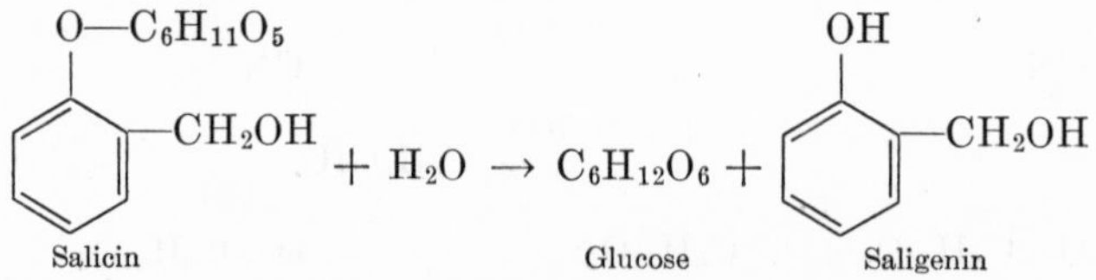

$$O-C_6H_{11}O_5 \qquad\qquad OH$$

Salicin $+ H_2O \rightarrow C_6H_{12}O_6 +$ Saligenin (with $-CH_2OH$ groups)

Glucose

Phlorhizin occurs in the bark and root bark of many rosaceous trees, is slightly soluble in water, soluble in alcohol 1:4, m.p. 170°. It is used to test the functional activity of the kidney. Injected hypodermically, it produces glycosuria (phlorhizin diabetes). Hydrolysis of phlorhizin is indicated.

[23] *Ber.*, **57B**, 1767 (1924).

Phlorhizin

$$C_6H_{12}O_6 +$$

Glucose   Phloretin

Arbutin occurs in *Aretostaphylos Uva-ursi* and in many genera of the Erica-ceae. It crystallizes in silky needles which are soluble in cold water 1:8, in hot water 1:1, in alcohol 1:16, and are insoluble in most organic solvents. It is used as a diuretic. It also has some bactericidal value because of the quinol formed on hydrolysis.

Coumarin Glycosides

The coumarin glycosides are widely distributed in plants. They are not of medicinal importance. A few of those found in drugs used medicinally with the products which they yield on hydrolysis are indicated in Table VII.

TABLE VII

COUMARIN GLYCOSIDES

Glycoside	Formula		Sugar		Aglycon
Skimmin	$C_{15}H_{16}O_8$	→	Glucose	+	7-Hydroxycoumarin
Aesculin	$C_{15}H_{16}O_9$	→	Glucose	+	6,7-Dihydroxycoumarin
Daphnin	$C_{15}H_{16}O_9$	→	Glucose	+	7,8-Dihydroxycoumarin
Fraxin	$C_{16}H_{18}O_{10}$	→	Glucose	+	6-Methoxy-7,8-dihydroxycoumarin

The structure of the lactone, coumarin, indicates the constitution of these glycosides. The lactone is formed from the *o*-coumarinic acid liberated on the hydrolysis of the glucoside, as indicated.

Coumarin glucoside   Coumarin

Hydroxyanthraquinone Glycosides and Aglycones

Hydroxy derivatives of anthraquinone occur widely distributed in plants both as glycosides and in the free state. They are red or yellow coloring matters used with mordants and formerly were of great importance in dyeing.

Many purgative drugs, such as rhubarb, senna, cascara, and aloes, contain derivatives which are present either in the free state or as glycosides. Since anthraquinone is the diketone produced by the oxidation of anthracene, all these anthraquinone substances may be regarded as products formed by oxidation, reduction, hydrolysis, and condensation from the hydrocarbon anthracene.

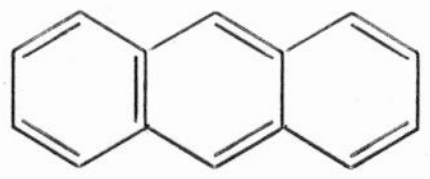

Anthracene 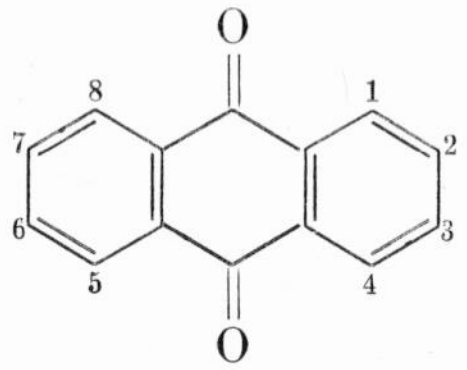   Anthraquinone

The more important glycosides belonging to this group are listed in Table VIII.

TABLE VIII

Glycoside	Sugar		Aglycon
Ruberythric acid	2 Glucose	+	1,2-Dihydroxyanthraquinone
Purpurin	1 Glucose	+	1,3-Dihydroxy-2-methylanthraquinone
Xanthopurpurin	1 Glucose	+	1,3-Dihydroxyanthraquinone
Frangulin	1 Rhamnose	+	1,6,8-Trihydroxy-2-methylanthraquinone
Polygonin	1 Glucose	+	Trihydroxyemodin
Barbaloin	Glucose	+	Aloe emodin

The relationship between some of the anthraquinone derivatives is shown by the accompanying formulas.

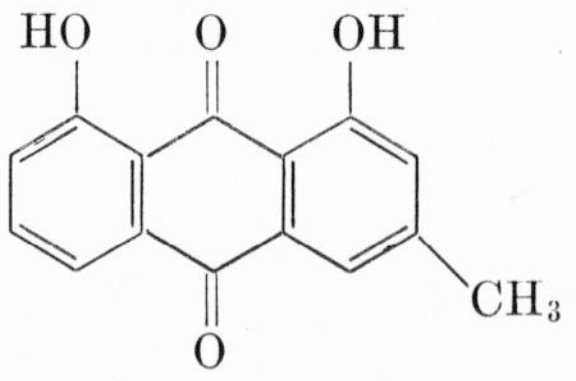

Chrysophanic acid

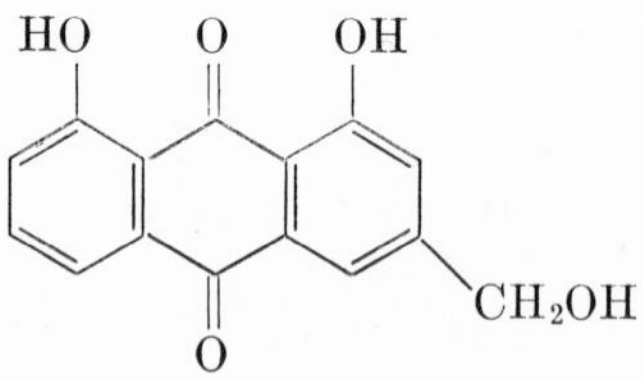

Aloe emodin

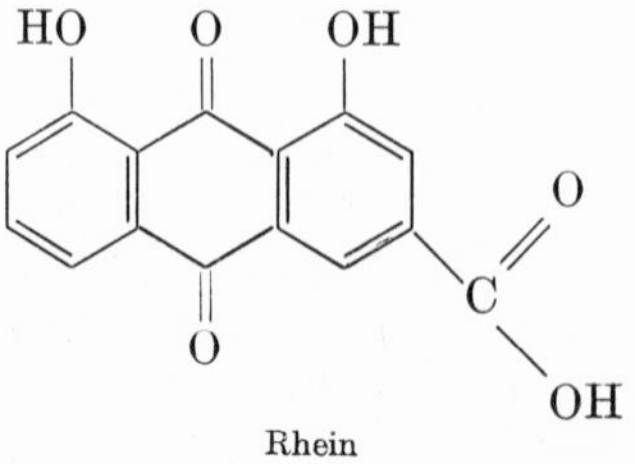

Rhein

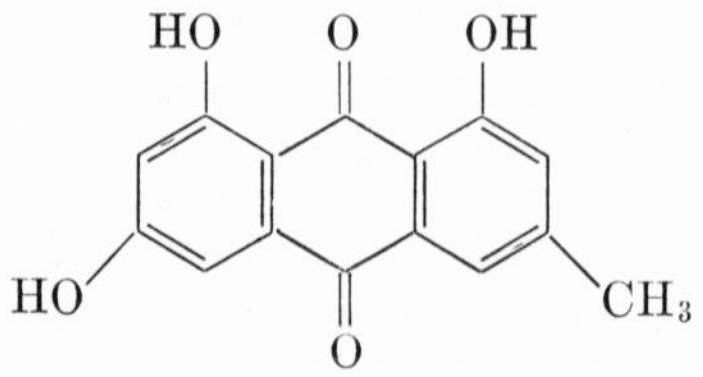

Frangula emodin

Partially reduced derivatives of anthraquinone, known as anthrones and anthranols, also occur in purgative drugs. In such drugs as rhubarb, senna, and cascara, the proportions of anthraquinone derivatives known to be present are frequently insufficient to account for the purgative action of the drug. In these the purgative action is supposedly due to small quantities of very active glycosidal derivatives or resin acids. A great number of other pigment glycosides having little or no medicinal use occur in drugs, e.g., anthoxanthin, flavone, flavanol, flavanone, xanthone, and anthoxanthin glycosides.[24]

Barbaloin yields the aglycon aloe-emodin-9-anthrone.[25]

Aloe-emodin-9-anthrone

Glycosides Containing Sulfur

A number of plants of the Cruciferae yield glycosides containing sulfur. When hydrolyzed by the enzyme, myrosin, these give rise to the mustard oils. The best-known representatives belonging to this class are sinigrin and sinalbin, found in the seeds of black and white mustards, respectively. When the black mustard seeds are crushed and moistened, the odor of allyl isothiocyanate is easily detected. The myrosin and sinigrin contained in separate cells do not interact until brought together by the destruction of the cell walls to form the oil of mustard as indicated.

$$CH_2{=}CH{-}CH_2{-}N{=}C{-}S{-}C_6H_{11}O_5 \xrightarrow[\text{myrosin}]{H_2O}$$
$$\underset{\underset{\text{Sinigrin}}{}}{O{-}SO_3K}$$

$$CH_2{=}CH{-}CH_2{-}N{=}C{=}S + KHSO_4 + C_6H_{12}O_6$$

Allyl isothiocyanate (oil of mustard)   Potassium   D-Glucose
                                            acid sulfate

Sinalbin upon enzymic hydrolysis yields D-glucose, p-hydroxybenzylisothiocyanate, choline, and sinapinic acid (3,5-dimethoxy-4-hydroxycinnamic acid).

Cardiac Glycosides and Aglycones

The most important glycosides used in therapy are a closely related group, which, because they increase the tone, excitability, and contractility of cardiac and arterial muscle, are called the cardiac glycosides. They occur in many

[24] For an extended consideration of many of these pigment glycosides see: Gilman, *Organic Chemistry*, Vol. 2, 1315–1340 (1943).

[25] Gardner and Joseph, *J. Am. Pharm. Assoc.*, **26**, 795 (1937).

poisonous plants which have been investigated more or less intensively, namely:

Scrophulariaceae: *Digitalis purpurea, Digitalis lanata,* and other species of digitalis.
Apocynaceae: *Strophanthus, Kombé, S. hispidus, S. sarmentosus, S. gratus,* and other species. *Thevetia neriifolia, Apocynum cannabinum, Nerium oleander,* and the *Ouabaio* tree.
Liliaceae: *Urginea maritima, Urginea indica* and *Convallaria majalis.*
Asclepidaceae: *Periploca graeca* and the *Uzara* tree

The composition of these glycosides is indicated in Table IX. The structures of the aglycons have been established, through numerous researches which began with Windaus in 1915, to have a steroidal character.

TABLE IX

Aglycon Structure of the Cardiac Glycosides

Glycoside	Aglycon	Position of OH Groups	R	Rings* A/B	C(3)OH/R*
Digitoxin	Digitoxigenin	3, 14	CH_3	*Cis*	*Trans*
Thevetin	Thevetigen	3, 14	CH_3	*Cis*	*Cis*
Uzarin	Uzarigenin	3, 14	CH_3	*Trans*	*Cis*
Digoxin	Digoxigenin	3, 12, 14	CH_3	*Cis*	*Trans*
Gitoxin	Gitoxigenin	3, 14, 16	CH_3	*Cis*	*Trans*
Periplocymarin	Periplogenin	3, 5, 14	CH_3	*Cis*	*Trans*
Sarmentocymarin	Sarmentogenin	3, 11, 14	CH_3	*Cis*	*Trans*
k-Strophanthidin	Strophanthidin	3, 5, 14	CHO	*Cis*	*Trans*
Cymarin	Strophanthidin	3, 5, 14	CHO	*Cis*	*Trans*
Convallatoxin	Convallatoxigenin†	3, 5, 8, 14	CH_3	—	—

* Probable structures.
† Probably contains a double bond between carbons 9 and 11.

The formulas of the following aglycons and glycosides illustrate how they may be derived from the steroidal ring system and from the data in Table IX. They also show how the structure of scillaren A, and k-strophanthin differ from the digitalis-type aglycons.

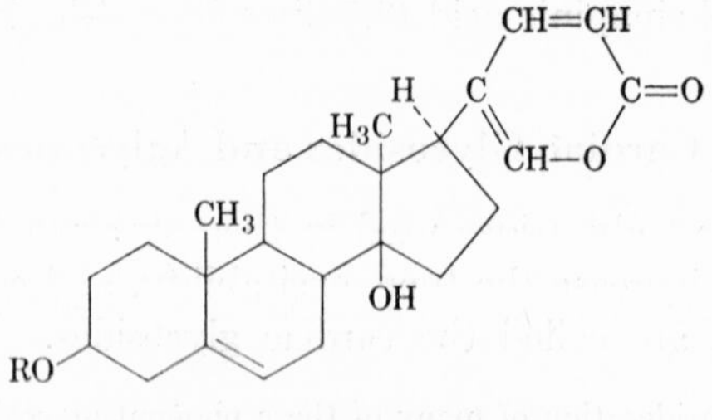

Scillaren A. R is a disaccharide residue
which forms rhamnose and glucose.

Digitoxigenin—sterically related to coprostanol, see page 52.
Urigenin is epimeric at position 5; it is sterically related to cholestanol.
Digoxigenin is 12β-hydroxydigitoxigenin.
Gitoxigenin is 16β-hydroxydigitoxigenin.
Sarmentogenin is 11α-hydroxydigitoxigenin.

Ouabagenin, R = H (also known as g-strophanthin.
Ouabain, R = rhamnose residue.
Strophanthidin C_{19} appears as —CHO.

In Table X are given the names of some important glycosides along with their hydrolytic products. The rings A and B may be either *cis* or *trans*. The hydroxyl on carbon 3 may be either *cis* or *trans* to C_{19} but it is generally *trans*. The principal aglycons have been shown to differ from each other chiefly in the number and positions of the hydroxyl groups and in the stereochemical nature of the ring system as shown in Table IX.

The drugs used today as cardiotonics were known to the ancients. Thus squill was known to Dioscorides, who described the preparation of a vinegar. Digitalis was described by Fuchs in 1542. Powders and salves of digitalis were described in the London Pharmacopoeia of 1722 but the drug seems not to have been used again until Dr. William Withering in his pamphlet "An Account of the Foxglove and Some of Its Medical Uses: with Practical Remarks on Dropsy and Other Diseases" acknowledged his indebtedness to a family recipe for the treatment of dropsy, which had been handed down as a secret remedy to an old Shropshire woman. This reawakened interest in the drug. Numerous efforts followed to isolate the pure active principles from squill and digitalis since these crude drugs and their preparations vary greatly in activity and often lose variable amounts of their activity on curing and on aging. Numerous mixtures of glycosides were isolated in these efforts. A successful conclusion was achieved by Stoll and his co-workers after they had developed a technic from ten years of intensive research. By careful extraction and avoidance of enzymic cleavage, to which the glycosides are particularly sensitive, Stoll *et al.* were able to isolate the pure crystalline glycosides of squill and digitalis. Similar methods resulted in the isolation of the pure glycosides from other related drugs and made possible a study of their structures.

The physiological activity of the drugs, preparations such as tinctures and fluidextracts, and the isolated glycosides and glycosidal mixtures of the so-called "cardiac glycoside" group are similar qualitatively but often differ quantita-

TABLE X

Some Cardiac Glycosides and Their Fission Products

Glycoside	Formula	Fission Products		
		Genin or Aglycon	+	Sugar
Digitoxin	$C_{41}H_{64}O_{13}$	→ Digitoxigenin	+	3 Digitoxose
Gitoxin	$C_{41}H_{64}O_{14}$	→ Gitoxigenin	+	3 Digitoxose
Digoxin	$C_{41}H_{64}O_{14}$	→ Digoxigenin	+	3 Digitoxose
Gitalin	$C_{35}H_{54}O_{11}$	→ Gitoxigenin	+	2 Digitoxose
Purpurea glycoside A	$C_{47}H_{74}O_{18}$	→ Digitoxigenin	+	3 Digitoxose + 1 glucose
Purpurea glycoside B	$C_{47}H_{74}O_{19}$	→ Gitoxigenin	+	3 Digitoxose + 1 glucose
Digilanide A	$C_{49}H_{76}O_{19}$	→ Digitoxigenin	+	2 Digitoxose + glucose + acetyldigitoxose
Digilanide B	$C_{49}H_{76}O_{20}$	→ Gitoxigenin	+	2 Digitoxose + glucose + acetyldigitoxose
Digilanide C	$C_{49}H_{76}O_{20}$	→ Digoxigenin	+	2 Digitoxose + glucose + acetyldigitoxose
Ouabain	$C_{29}H_{44}O_{12}$	→ Anhydro-ouabagenin	+	Rhamnose
Cymarin	$C_{30}H_{44}O_9$	→ Strophanthidin	+	Cymarose
Sarmentocymarin	$C_{30}H_{46}O_8$	→ Sarmentogenin	+	Sarmentose
Oleandrin	$C_{32}H_{48}O_9$	→ Gitoxigenin	+	Oleandrose + acetic acid
k-Strophanthin-β	$C_{36}H_{54}O_{14}$	→ Strophanthidin	+	Cymarose + glucose
Thevetin	$C_{42}H_{66}O_{18}$	→ Anhydrothevetigenin	+	2 Glucose + digitalose
Periplocymarin	$C_{30}H_{46}O_8$	→ Periplogenin	+	Cymarose
Uzarin	$C_{35}H_{54}O_{14}$	→ Anhydrouzarigenin	+	2 Glucose
Periplocin	$C_{36}H_{56}O_{13}$	→ Periplogenin	+	Cymarose + glucose
Scillaren A	$C_{36}H_{52}O_{13}$	→ Scillaridin A	+	Rhamnose + glucose
Proscillaridin A	$C_{30}H_{42}O_8$	→ Scillaridin A	+	Rhamnose
Convallatoxin	$C_{29}H_{42}O_{10}$	→ Convallatoxigenin	+	Rhamnose

tively; the quantitative differences are compensated for largely by biological standardization. The cardiac glycosides stimulate the vagus mechanism and increase the tone of the heart. They are used in cardiac insufficiency to secure compensation. They slow the rate of heartbeat, cause the heart to empty more completely, and they improve the cardiac output and thus have proved of value in auricular fibrillation. They also act as diuretics. Powders and galenical preparations of the crude drugs are used. Purified glycosides and glycosidal mixtures are used in the form of tablets, hypodermic tablets, solutions for injection, etc.

It has been shown that in the cardiac aglycons the double bond, the lactone ring in the side chain, and a favorable configuration of the ring system are necessary for specific heart action. These observations led to the careful examination [26] of 27 β,γ-unsaturated γ-lactones; it was found that β,γ-angelica lactone

β,γ-Angelica lactone   Ethyl coumalate

and methyl and ethyl coumalate caused systolic standstill in the ventricle of the frog but not of the cat.

One theory bases the activity of the cardiac glycosides on a relationship to the "hormone of heart contractility." [27]

Products

1. Purified mixtures of glycosides or single glycosides from digitalis are those obtained by various methods of extraction and purification and vary in potency: *Digalen, N.N.R., Digifolin, N.N.R., Digitan, N.N.R., Digilanid, N.N.R.* Other proprietary products that consist of the mixed glycosides of digitalis include Digifortis, Digiglusin, Diginutin, and Digipoten.

Single glycosides of digitalis include: *Digitoxin, U.S.P., Gitalin, N.N.R.*, and the proprietary *Digoxin, U.S.P. Lanatoside C, N.F.*, is obtained from *Digitalis lanata.* It is used like digitalis to increase cardiac efficiency.

2. Purified glycosides or glycosidal mixtures derived from strophanthus include: *Strophanthin, N.F.*, and *Ouabain, U.S.P.*

3. Purified glycosides from squill are: *Scillaren B, N.N.R., Scillaren, N.N.R.*, and *Urginin.*

4. A purified glycoside from *Thevetia neriifolia* is: *Thevetin*, $C_{29}H_{46}O_{13} \cdot 2H_2O$. It is soluble in water and is stable. It has an action on the heart similar to that of digitalis and is more rapidly effective. It is less cumulative and better tolerated than digitalis. Thevetin is usually administered intravenously.

Saponins

Rutin, see page 320.

The saponins are a widely distributed class of glycosides. They occur in many plants but are especially common in the Rosaceae, Caryophyllaceae, and Sapindaceae. They resemble the glycosides in many of their properties but differ chiefly as follows:

1. When shaken with water they form colloidal solutions with a stable soapy foam; hence their name. These solutions form emulsions with oils and resins.

2. They have a bitter and acrid taste, and the dust of saponin-containing drugs is usually very irritating to mucous membranes; on the nasal membranes they act as violent sternutatory irritants.

[26] Chen, Steldt, Fried, and Elderfield, *J. Pharmacol.*, **74**, 381 (1942).
[27] Kisch, *Exptl. Med. Surg.*, **4**, 4 (1946); *C.A.*, **41**, 218 (1947).

3. The saponins in low concentration destroy red blood corpuscles by hemolysis. For this reason, they are toxic when administered intravenously. The more toxic ones have have been called sapotoxins. Administered orally, they are not toxic; probably because they either are not absorbed or are hydrolyzed in the intestinal tract.

4. They are toxic to cold-blooded forms of animal life such as frogs, and extracts of plants containing saponin have been used as fish poisons. Some saponins have been reported to be toxic to fish in dilutions of 1 to 1,000,000. When acetylated, the saponins are converted into nontoxic derivatives.

5. They form molecular compounds with the higher alcohols and phenols which separate from alcoholic solution as solids. This property has been utilized to estimate sterols by precipitation with digitonin. The precipitates when extracted with ether yield the sterol and leave the saponin as an insoble residue.

6. Acid hydrolysis splits the saponins into sugars and an aglycon termed the sapogenin. The sapogenins generally yield readily crystallizable products on acetylization.

Jacobs and Simpson [28] showed the relationship of gitogenin and sarsapogenin to the sterols by dehydrogenating them with selenium to Diels' hydrocarbon. The work of others has established the constitution of the genins of a number of saponins. These studies have proved that sarsapogenin, smilagenin, tigogenin, gitogenin, and digitogenin all yield Diels' hydrocarbon on dehydrogenation with selenium. These have been called the digitalis saponins. Another group of saponins yield sapotalene (1,2,7-trimethylnaphthalene) when dehydrogenated with selenium. They are believed to be triterpenoid compounds.

The saponins of interest because of their relation to physiologically active substances are given in Table XI.

TABLE XI

IMPORTANT SAPONINS AND THEIR HYDROLYTIC PRODUCTS

Saponin	Source	Hydrolytic Products
Amolonin	*Chlorogalum pomeridianum*	Tigogenin + 3 glucose, 1 galactose and 2 rhamnose
Digitonin	*Digitalis purpurea* and *D. lanata*	Digitogenin + 4 galactose and 1 xylose
Gitonin	*Digitalis purpurea*	Gitogenin + 3 galactose and 1 pentose
Sarsaponin	*Radix sarsaparillae*	Sarsapogenin + 2 glucose and 1 rhamnose
Tigonin	*Digitalis purpurea* and *D. lanata*	Tigogenin + 2 glucose, 2 galactose and 1 rhamnose
Trillin	*Trillium erectum*	Diosgenin + 1 glucose

Numerous crude drugs such as quillaja, glycyrrhiza, senega, guaiac, and jalap also contain saponins. These are of slight interest since they are used chiefly as expectorants and diuretics. Others such as solanine from potato sprouts contain nitrogen and are of biochemical interest since they offer possibilities of a link between the glycosides and the alkaloids.

Marker and his co-workers [29, 30] have studied a number of sapogenins. Their

[28] *J. Biol. Chem.*, **105**, 501 (1935).

[29] *J. Am. Chem. Soc.*, **52-55** (1940–1943).

[30] *J. Am. Chem. Soc.*, **69**, 2373–2404 (1947).

work has led to the establishment of the structures of some of these complex compounds. The original series of articles should be read to understand properly the interesting relationship between these compounds and the sex hormones. The structures established as a result of their work show that these sapogenins are ketone acetals derived from the cyclopentanophenanthrene hydrocarbons.

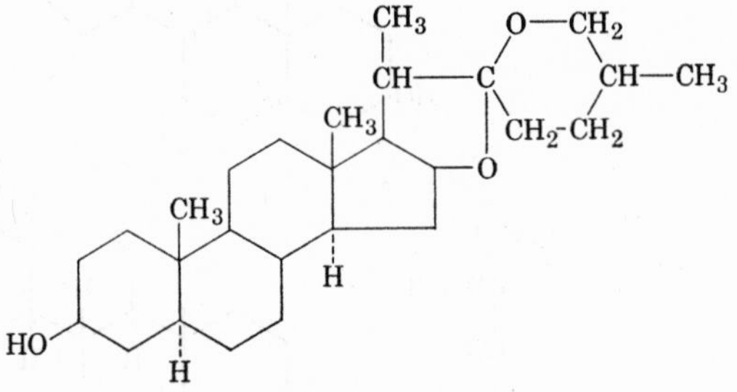

Sarsapogenin

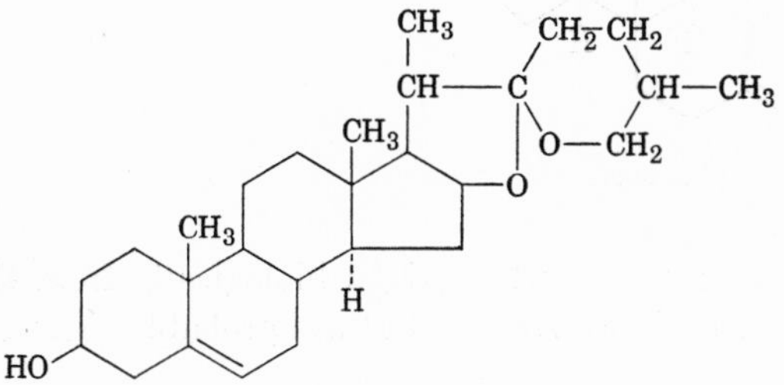

Diosgenin

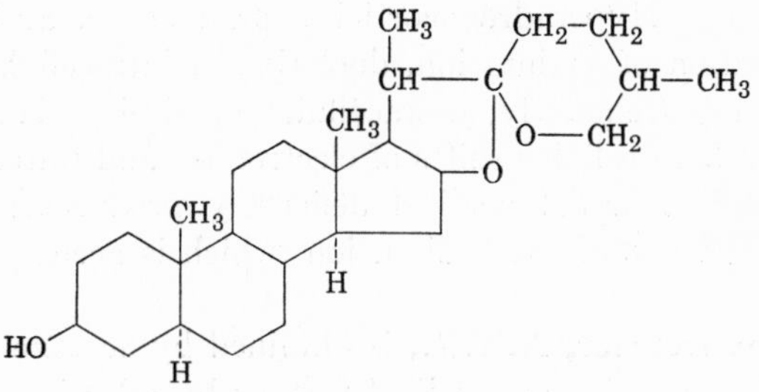

Tigogenin

HORMONES OF THE ADRENAL CORTEX

Responding to the stimulus of the adrenocorticotropic hormone, secreted by the anterior pituitary gland, the cortex of the adrenal gland elaborates a number of steroidal compounds. The total steroid output of the gland consists of 28 or 30 different compounds.[31] Forty to 60 per cent of the total amount ap-

[31] Roberts and Szego, *Ann. Rev. Biochem.*, **24**, 543–596 (1955).

pears as corticosterone and cortisol, which are probably derived *in vivo* from cholesterol according to the steps indicated.[32]

Corticosterone

The other steroids are probably derived biologically from these two and appear quantitatively as minor products but are probably more significant physiologically.

The two main functions of these hormones are (*a*) to regulate the body electrolyte balance and (*b*) to aid the liver and muscle in the metabolism of carbohydrate and protein. Hyperadrenocorticism produces expansion of extracellular fluid and retention of sodium ion, depletion of intracellular potassium and phosphate ions, and, frequently, extracellular alkalosis. The adreno steroids appear to play a role in cellular shifts of electrolytes and water and in the acid-base disturbances.[33] Adrenal cortical deficiency produces an abnormal and marked negative balance of the sodium ion, which is accompanied with shift of cellular fluids.

Adrenal Cortex Extract, N.N.R., is obtained by acetone extraction of the frozen adrenal glands and then purified further by selective precipitation and extraction technics. This process eliminates most of the epinephrine present in the original extract. The extract is useful in the treatment of Addison's disease and other types of adrenal cortical insufficiency.

The usual modes of administration are subcutaneous, intramuscular, or intravenous injection.

Cortisone Acetate, U.S.P. (Cortone Acetate, Cortogen Acetate, 11-Dehydro-17-hydroxycorticosterone-21-acetate), is prepared synthetically by a

[32] Pincus, *Ann. N. Y. Acad. Sci.*, **61**, 283 (1955).
[33] Roberts and Randall, *Ann. N. Y. Acad. Sci.*, **61**, 297 (1955).

lengthy process from desoxycholic acid. Total synthesis has also been achieved.[34]

Cortisone acetate is a white, colorless powder which melts with decomposition between 242 and 248°. It is practically insoluble in water, slightly soluble in alcohol but freely soluble in chloroform.

It is used for adrenal cortical insufficiency in ailments such as Addison's disease, rheumatoid arthritis and rheumatic fever, inflammatory and allergic diseases of the eyes, skin and mucosa, bronchial asthma, postoperative collapse, thermal burns, and other disorders.

It is contraindicated in hypertension or cardio-renal disorders where the possibility of increasing blood volume or pressure may be undesirable, in latent tuberculosis and mental derangement, and in active peptic ulcers.

It is usually administered intramuscularly in an oil suspension or subcutaneously in the form of pellets for more prolonged therapy.

Hydrocortisone Acetate, U.S.P. (Hydrocortone Acetate, 17-Hydroxycorticosterone-21-acetate), is a white, odorless, water-insoluble solid which melts between 218 and 223° with decomposition. It has the same qualitative metabolic and therapeutic properties of cortisone acetate. It has the advantage over the latter in that it causes less irritation and promotes a more prolonged and intense effect when administered into the intra-articular spaces affected with rheumatoid and osteoarthritis. Quantitatively hydrocortisone is more active.[35] It is the principal, probably natural, glycogenic steroid elaborated and secreted by the adrenal gland.[36]

Cortisone acetate

In hydrocortisone the carbonyl group in position-11 is reduced to carbinol.

Desoxycorticosterone acetate

Desoxycorticosterone Acetate, U.S.P. (Cortate), the acetic acid ester of desoxycorticosterone, occurs as a white or creamy white crystalline powder, which is odorless and stable in air. It is practically insoluble in water and only slightly soluble in vegetable oils.

Desoxycorticosterone acetate produces a beneficial result in Addison's disease, shock, and myasthenia gravis. It is reported to be effective for retention of sodium ion and to increase secretion of potassium ion. It is used for adrenal

[34] Woodward, Sondheimer, and Taub, *J. Am. Chem. Soc.*, **73**, 4057 (1951).
[35] Laidlaw *et al.*, *Ann. N. Y. Acad. Sci.*, **61**, 315 (1955).
[36] Boland, *Ann. N. Y. Acad. Sci.*, **61**, 349 (1955).

cortex replacement therapy. It is usually administered intramuscularly or by implantation.

Aldosterone (18-Oxocorticosterone, Electrocortin), isolated in 1953 from the amorphous fraction of adrenal extracts,[37] has been described as the principal life-maintaining hormone of the suprarenal gland and is presumably responsible for the potency of the amorphous extract.[38] Its activity in effecting sodium retention and potassium excretion is reported to be 30 or more times greater than that of 11-desoxycorticosterone acetate.[39] It has little or no antiinflammatory effect.

Aldosterone has been synthesized; the racemic synthetic product is about half as active as the natural (+)isomer.[40] The hormone probably exists as an equilibrium mixture with its cyclic hemiacetal.

Aldosterone

Modified Corticosteroids

The introduction of structural modifications into the hormones of the adrenal cortex opens the way to some very promising products. A halogen atom in the 9α-position of hydrocortisone affects very markedly the activity, the greatest increase appearing with the halogen atom of lowest atomic weight.[41]

9α-Fluorohydrocortisone is ten or more times more effective than hydrocortisone in controlling inflammation of arthritis;[42] it is an effective and more potent antirheumatic agent;[43] and its salt-retaining effects are increased,[44] which tends to cancel out its antiarthritic merit.

9α-Fluorohydrocortisone Acetate is eleven times more active than cortisone acetate.[45]

[37] Farrell and Richards, *Proc. Exptl. Biol. Med.*, **83**, 628 (1953).
[38] Roberts and Szego, *Ann. Rev. Biochem.*, **24**, 543 (1955).
[39] Simpson *et al.*, *Experientia*, **9**, 333 (1953); *Helv. Chim. Acta*, **37**, 1163 (1954).
[40] *Chem. Eng. News*, **33**, 3486 (1955).
[41] Fried, Herz, Sabo, Borman, Singer, and Numerof, *J. Am. Chem. Soc.*, **77**, 1068 (1955).
[42] Goldfien, Morse, Froesch, Ganong, and Thorn, *Ann. N. Y. Acad. Sci.*, **61**, 433 (1955).
[43] Boland, *ibid.*, 591.
[44] Renold, Haydar, Reddy, Goldfien, St. Marc, and Laidlaw, *ibid.*, 582.
[45] Fried, *ibid.*, 573.

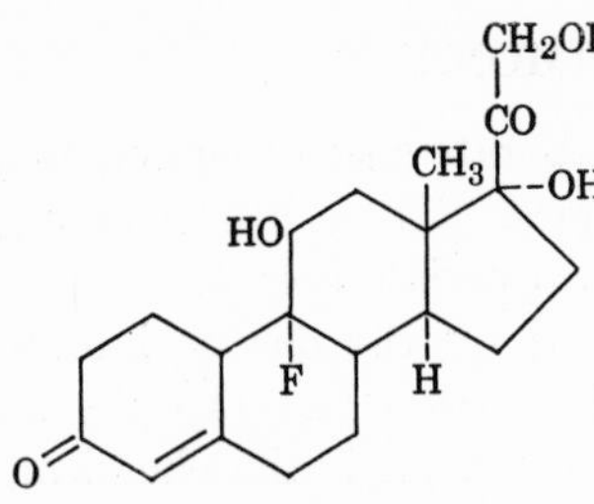

9α-Fluorohydrocortisone

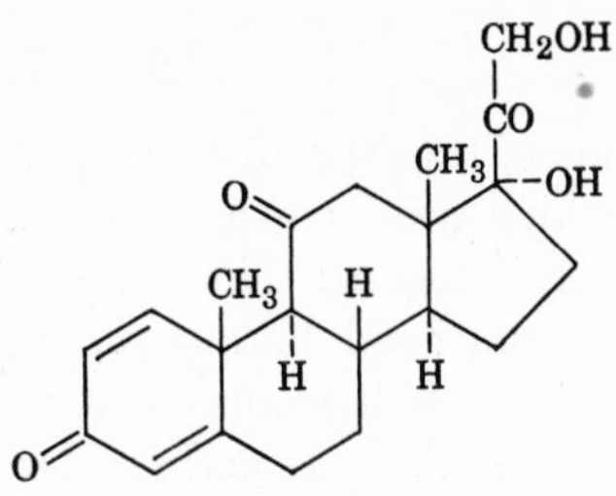

Prednisone

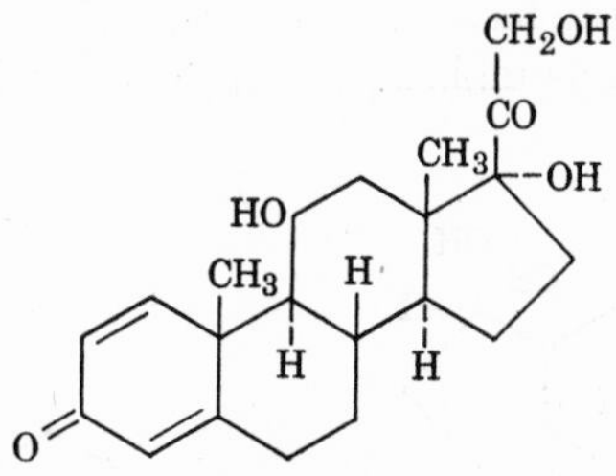

Prednisolone

The observation that by chemical means the physiological properties of the hormones may be significantly modified led to further studies resulting in the preparation of *Prednisone, N.N.R.* (metacortandricin) and *Prednisolone, N.N.R.* (metacortandralone).[46] These Δ^1-dehydroanalogs are reported to be four times more potent as antirheumatic agents than cortisone and hydrocortisone.[47]

The 9α-fluorodehydroanalogs have also been prepared. The acetate of 9α-fluoroprednisolone shows fifty times the potency of hydrocortisone with respect to glycogen deposition and a salt-retaining potency 4.6 times greater than desoxycorticosterone acetate.[48] 9α-Fluoroprednisolone acetate is about twenty-five times more active than hydrocortisone in the mouse liver assay and is, therefore, a potent glucocorticoid.[49]

The introduction of an alkyl group into the 2-position results in certain cases in marked enhancement in adrenal cortical activity. 2-Methyl-9α-fluorohydrocortisone is three times more potent than aldosterone in regulating electrolyte and fluid balance [50, 51] in experimental animals and also in man.[52] It is suggested that the presence of the methyl group in the 2-position alters the susceptibiltiy of the hormone to enzymic attack during metabolism.

[46] Hogg, Lincoln, Nathan, Hanze, Schneider, Beal, and Korman, *J. Am. Chem. Soc.*, **77**, 4438 (1955).

[47] Bunim, Black, Bollet, and Pechet, *Ann. N. Y. Acad. Sci.*, **61**, 358 (1955).

[48] Same as ref. 46.

[49] Hirschmann, Miller, Beyler, Sarett, and Tishler, *J. Am. Chem. Soc.*, **77**, 3166 (1955).

[50] Hogg, Lincoln, Jackson, and Schneider, *J. Am. Chem. Soc.*, **77**, 6401 (1955).

[51] *Chem. Eng. News*, **33**, 5576 (1955).

[52] Liddle and Richard, *Science*, **123**, 324 (1956).

THE SEX HORMONES

The glands of the reproductive system elaborate specific compounds of steroid character which are known as sex hormones. There are three types of sex hormones, or sexogens: The estrogenic or ovarian hormones responsible for estrus; the gestational hormones, elaborated by the corpus luteum; and the androgens, the male hormones elaborated by the testes. The physiological distinction between these is perhaps less definite than is the chemical difference. The production of these hormones is regulated by the gonadotropic hormones, which are protein in character and elaborated by the anterior pituitary gland. The sex hormones, in turn, have a reciprocal effect on the production of the gonadotropic hormones, thus maintaining a delicate biochemical balance.

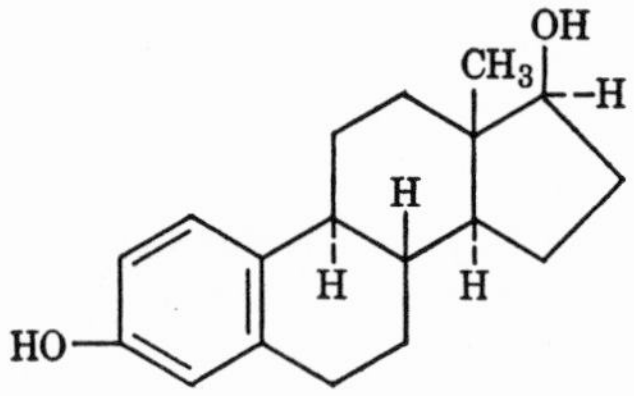

Estradiol-17β

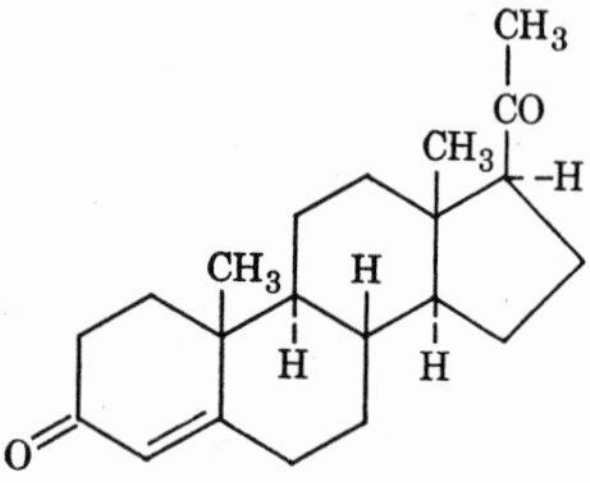

Progesterone

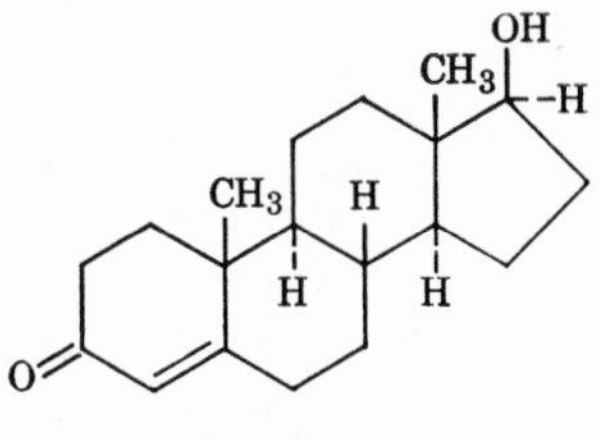

Testosterone

The three chief hormones are indicated. Other compounds of related structure appear to be metabolic transformation products.

For information on the mechanisms and operations of the delicate hormonal balance in the sex processes appropriate treatises should be consulted. The medicinal chemist will, nevertheless, be interested in those substances which are used therapeutically to maintain and correct this balance when necessary. For this purpose not only the natural hormones are employed, but in many instances a synthetic compound of related structure may be the drug of choice.

Estrogenic Hormones

The estrogenic hormones are responsible for the complete and normal development of the sexual organs, the secondary sex characteristics, and the maintenance of good health in the female. Chemically, all compounds are derivatives of 1,3,5(10)-estratriene.

1,3,5(10)-Estratriene

Estrone

Estradiol-17β

Estriol

The primary estrogenic hormone produced by the ovaries is estradiol (estradiol-17β). Other compounds of related physiological function of medicinal importance are estrone and estriol. These represent oxidation products of estradiol and excretion forms which qualitatively possess similar function but quantitatively are much weaker in activity. Examination of the formulas shows that the wide differences in estrogenic activity depend on comparatively small modifications in chemical structure.

Because of oxidation attributed to the microflora of the gastrointestinal tract, estradiol loses some of its activity after oral administration by being converted to the corresponding ketone. Following injection, estradiol is rapidly destroyed in the liver. Esterification affords greater resistance to this oxidation, which leads to the use of estradiol benzoate (the benzoyl on the hydroxyl at position 3) and estradiol dipropionate.

The production of estradiol in proper amounts by the ovarian follicles from childhood to the menopause constitutes an important and necessary function for the normal development of the female child and the proper maintenance of the reproduction process and good health in woman. Briefly, in the immature child the estrogenic hormones are responsible for (a) growth of secondary sex organs, (b) development of the breast, (c) development of genital tract, and (d) distribution of hair. In the sexually mature female these products (a) maintain the normal size, capacity, and functional activity of the accessory sex organs, (b) are responsible for bodily contours, distribution of fat, breast development, and growth and distribution of hair, (c) preserve the normal epithelium layer of the vulva and vagina, (d) influence normal contractility of the uterus by stimulating the muscle of the myometrium, (e) promote growth of duct tissue of the breast, (f) control the production of certain hormones of the anterior pituitary, including gonadotropic hormones, (g) aid in maintenance of normal conditions of nasal and oral mucous membranes, and (h) exert a powerful influence on psychic attitudes and the physical and mental health of the normal, hormonally balanced woman.

Estrogenic therapy is indicated in cases of estradiol insufficiency. Such replacement therapy may bring about a normal state of well being. Thus, it is used in sexual infantilism, senile vaginitis, menopausal syndrome for smoother transition, to control the activity of the anterior pituitary, juvenile vaginitis, and to produce an increase in muscle strength, bodily vigor, and mental faculties.

Although crystalline estradiol does not need to be assayed biologically because its effect can be determined on a weight basis, for purposes of comparison with other estrogens it is assayed biologically in terms of Rat Units (R.U.) or International Units (I.U.). The I.U. is equal to 0.0001 mg. (0.1 gamma) of crystalline estrone. One milligram of estrone is equivalent to 10,000 I.U. by definition or 1000 R.U. by actual bioassay. Therefore, 1 R.U. is equal to 10 I.U. The comparative activity of the estrogenic substances is:

1 mg. estradiol	120,000 I.U.
1 mg. estrone	10,000 I.U.
1 mg. estriol	1,500 I.U.

Epimerization at position 17, that is, conversion to estradiol-17α, reduces the activity to about a fortieth.

Estradiol, N.F. [Female Sex Hormone, Follicular Hormone, Progynon-DH, Estratriol-17β, 3,17β-Dihydroxy-1,3,5(10)-estratriene], is a white or creamy white crystalline powder or fine crystals, m.p. 173–179°. It is stable in air. It has a rotation in dioxane of not less than +76° and not more than +80° (100 mg. in 10 ml.). It is soluble in alcohol, sparingly soluble in vegetable oils, and almost insoluble in water.

This hormone has been isolated from human pregnancy urine, human placenta, and from horse testes. Stallion urine is rich in this hormone, but it is not a practical source.

It may be prepared synthetically by the hydrogenation of estrone by any of several methods, e.g., catalytically, with sodium and alcohol or with yeast.

Estradiol is administered orally in the form of tablets or topically for local treatment of the vagina in the form of suppositories.

Estradiol Benzoate, U.S.P. ("Dimenformon Benzoate," "Progynon-B"), is the benzoic acid ester of synthetic estradiol and is prepared by benzoylation of the 3-OH group of estradiol. It is a white or slightly colored crystalline compound which is stable in air. It is almost insoluble in water but sparingly soluble in vegetable oils.

The conversion of the natural hormone to the benzoate gives rise to a more desirable product because it is slowly absorbed and in turn the duration of activity is prolonged. It is usually administered in oil solution intramuscularly.

Estradiol Dipropionate, U.S.P. (Ovocylin Dipropionate), is prepared by acylation of 3,17-OH groups of estradiol. It is a white or slightly colored crystalline compound which is almost insoluble in water but sparingly soluble in vegetable oils.

Like estradiol benzoate, the dipropionate is absorbed more slowly and eliminated less rapidly than estradiol. Qualitatively it behaves like estradiol. It is about one-half as potent as estradiol benzoate but it possesses a more sustained action. It is administered intramuscularly in an oil solution.

Estriol, N.N.R. (3,16,17-Trihydroxy-1,3,5(10)-estratriene, "Theelol"), is a crystalline compound, m.p. 282°, practically insoluble in water, soluble in alcohol, dioxane, and oils, obtained mostly from pregnancy urine. It is usually administered in capsules. It is less active than estrone or estradiol.

Ethinyl Estradiol, U.S.P. [Estinyl, Lynoral, Oradiol, 17-Ethinyl-3,17-dihydroxy-1,3,5(10)-estratriene], is prepared by reacting estrone with potassium acetylide in liquid ammonia. Ethinyl estradiol is a fine, white crystalline powder which melts between 141 and 146°. It is practically insoluble in water but it is soluble in vegetable oils.

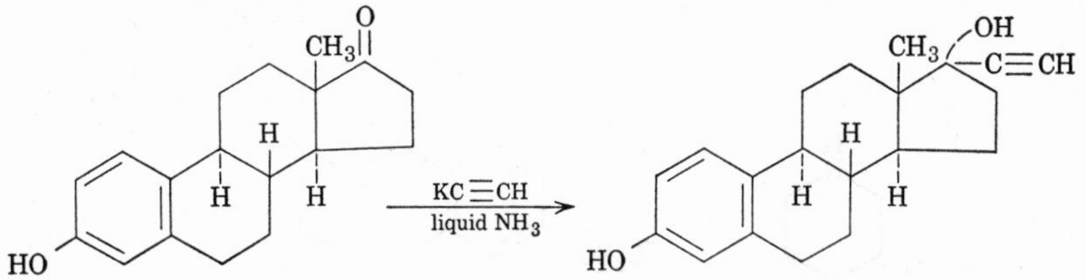

The ethinyl group retards the rate of deactivation of the estradiol molecule in the gastrointestinal tract and in the liver. In view of the increased stability caused by the ethinyl group, ethinyl estradiol can be given orally. It is one of the most potent estrogens.

Estrone, U.S.P. [3-Hydroxy-17-keto-1,3,5(10)-estratriene, "Theelin"], is a colorless, crystalline substance, m.p. 260°, practically insoluble in water, soluble in dioxane, in alcohol and in oils. It is usually administered in solution in a bland vegetable oil, or incorporated into suppositories. Maximum activity is obtained after intramuscular administration. It is active when given in larger doses by mouth, but it is oxidized by the intestinal flora. Mare's urine is a

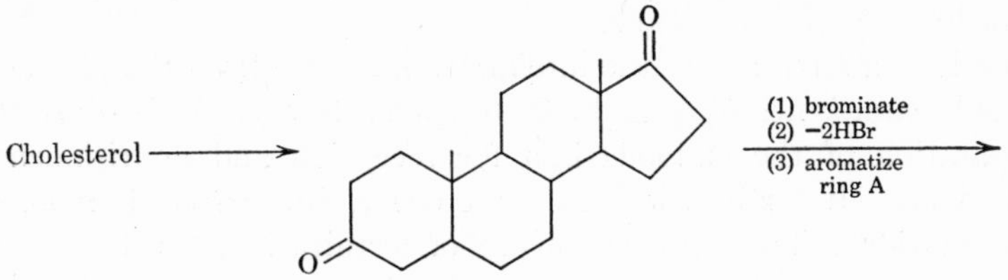

3,17-Androstanedione

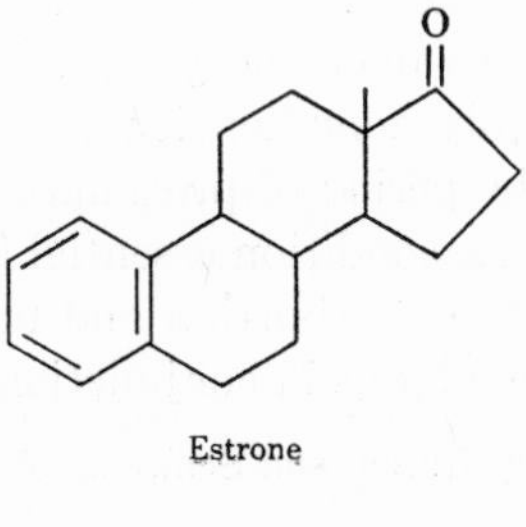

Estrone

source, or it may be synthesized from cholesterol via epiandrosterone, as indicated on page 133.[53]

Estrogenic Substances, Conjugated, N.N.R. (Premarin, Conestron, Hormestrol), is an amorphous preparation obtained from pregnant mare's urine. It consists primarily of natural estrogens conjugated with sulfuric acid to make them soluble in water. The chief constituent is sodium estrone sulfate along with varying small quantities of other equine estrogens and a large portion of nonestrogenic materials. It is administered orally for its estrogenic activity. The sulfate esters are more readily absorbed and circulated in the blood.

Piperazine Estrone Sulfate, N.N.R. (Sulextrex Piperazine), is represented by the accompanying formula. It is a fine, white or slightly colored crystalline powder which melts between 185 and 195°.

Piperazine estrone sulfate

The action and uses of piperazine estrone sulfate are similar to other naturally occurring conjugated estrogens.

Corpus Luteal or Gestational Hormones

The corpus luteal hormone, progesterone, is responsible for bringing about certain changes in the uterus for reception of the fertilized ovum and the retention of the growing fetus. It is also found in the placenta. It is derived from the parent hydrocarbon pregnane.

As a result of a stimulus by the luteinizing hormone from the pituitary gland the corpus luteum synthesizes and secretes progesterone. This causes the periodic preparation of the endometrium for reception and nourishment of the fertilized ovum. If fertilization does not occur, the corpus luteum regresses and menstruation follows. In the event of fertilization, the hormone regression does not occur and the continuous production of the hormone by the corpus luteum ensues; the corpus luteum becomes larger and the production of the hormone increases. Between the third and fourth month of pregnancy the placenta takes over the production of the hormone. This transition stage is critical and hormone deficiency during this period may result in abortion.

During the period of pregnancy progesterone suppresses ovulation, maintains the uterus in a condition essential for the growing embryo, inhibits uterine motility in threatening abortion and functional dysmenorrhea, induces development of mammary glands in conjunction with the estrogenics, and prevents menstrua-

[53] Hershberg, Rubin, and Schwenk, *J. Org. Chem.*, **15**, 292 (1950).

tion. The principal clinical indications are for (a) habitual abortion, (b) threatened abortion, (c) dysmenorrhea, (d) premenstrual tension, (e) functional uterine bleeding, and (f) toxemia of pregnancy.

Although progesterone is highly effective by injection, it is inactive orally. An orally effective progestin was discovered in ethisterone. Clinical investigations show that it duplicates the biological effects of progesterone. These two products constitute the medicinal agents used therapeutically for progestational activity.

Progesterone, U.S.P. (Progestin, Corpus Luteal Hormone, Δ^4-Pregnen-3,20-dione), is a crystalline hormone principle of the corpus luteum and placenta.

Progesterone is prepared synthetically by several methods. Stigmasterol, cholesterol, and the sapogenins serve as starting materials for these processes. A method for preparing progesterone from stigmasterol is shown.

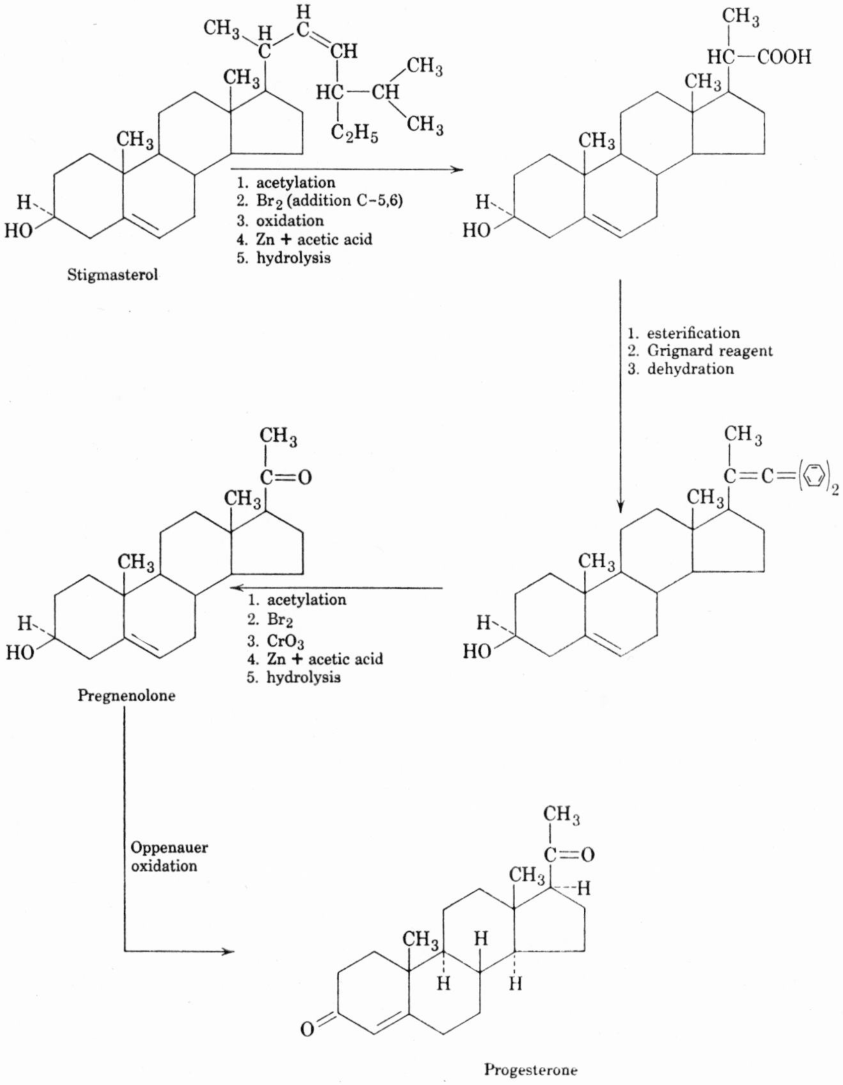

Stigmasterol

1. acetylation
2. Br$_2$ (addition C–5,6)
3. oxidation
4. Zn + acetic acid
5. hydrolysis

1. esterification
2. Grignard reagent
3. dehydration

1. acetylation
2. Br$_2$
3. CrO$_3$
4. Zn + acetic acid
5. hydrolysis

Pregnenolone

Oppenauer oxidation

Progesterone

Pregnenolone, one of the intermediates in the synthesis of progesterone, is also obtained as a by-product in the technical oxidation of cholesteryl acetate dibromide.

Progesterone occurs in two crystalline forms: progesterone, m.p. 128.5°, occurs in prisms; and progesterone, m.p. 121°, occurs as needles. These two forms have equal physiological activity. It is practically insoluble in water and is sparingly soluble in vegetable oils.

Progesterone is administered intramuscularly for maximum effect. It has a low order of activity orally.

Progesterone is sensitive to alkalies or light. It should be stored in tight, light-resistant containers.

Ethisterone, U.S.P. (Anhydrohydroxyprogesterone, Pranone, Δ^4-Pregnen-20-ine-17α-ol-3-one), is prepared from dehydroisoandrosterone as indicated. It occurs as white or slightly yellow crystals or as a crystalline powder. It is stable in air but affected by light. It is practically insoluble in water but slightly soluble in vegetable oils.

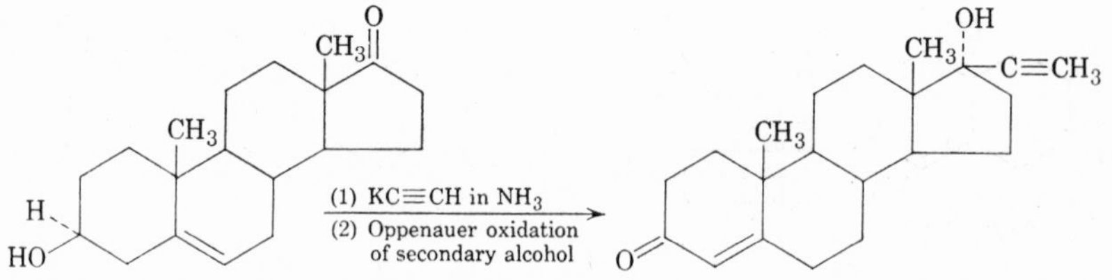

Ethisterone

Ethisterone possesses the same qualitative activity as progesterone. It has the advantage that it is active orally. The presence of the ethinyl group in the 17-position hinders deactivation of the compound by the microflora of the gastrointestinal tract and by the liver.

21-Hydroxypregnanedione, as the sodium salt of the acid succinate ester (P-55, Hydroxydione, Viadril), a solid steroid derivative, exhibits in experimental animals a pronounced effect as a depressant for the central nervous system. Administered intravenously or orally, it induces in the animal a state of surgical anesthesia; it shows promise of becoming a useful short-acting general anesthetic, with a therapeutic index more favorable than that of thiopental sodium. Thus far it has shown no sex, progestational, or cortical hormone effects.[54]

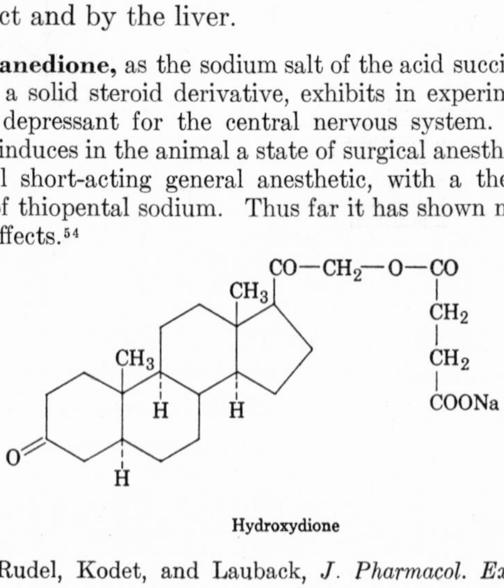

Hydroxydione

[54] P'an, Hutcheon, Rudel, Kodet, and Lauback, *J. Pharmacol. Exptl. Therap.*, **115**, 432 (1955).

Androgenic Hormones

The primary function of the androgenic hormones is to regulate the normal development of the male accessory sex organs and to maintain the secondary sex characteristics (depth of voice, distribution of facial and body hair and muscular and skeletal development). In addition they play a part in the normal health of the male in that they promote muscular strength and endurance, increase the resistance of the central nervous system to fatigue, and restore mental equilibrium and energy. A number of other activities are attributed to these hormones, such as influencing the blood supply and pigmentation of the human skin, relieve pain in certain forms of heart diseases such as angina pectoris, affect the blood so that it favors retention of sodium chloride and water and excretion of potassium. In the female, the androgenic hormones have an inhibitory effect on the pituitary gland and a neutralizing effect on excessive amounts of estrogenic substances.

In the male, the principal indications for androgenic therapy are (a) hypogonadism, (b) the male climacteric, (c) impotence, (d) benign prostatic hypertrophy, and (e) dwarfism. In the female, the principal indications are (a) functional uterine bleeding, (b) dysmenorrhea, (c) after-pains, (d) control of lactation, (e) breast engorgement, (f) chronic cystic mastitis, and (g) menopausal syndromes.

Chemically, the androgenic hormones are derivatives of Δ^4-androstene which is derived from the hypothetical hydrocarbon androstane.

Δ^4-Androstene   Androstane

Testosterone, R = H−
Testosterone propionate, R = CH_3CH_2CO-
Testosterone cyclopentylpropionate,

R = ⬡—CH_2CH_2CO-

The principal androgenic hormone, produced by the testis as a result of stimulation by the luteinizing hormone, is testosterone. The oxidation forms of testosterone are unimportant as medicinal agents because of their low order of potency. Testosterone is the most potent androgen known, but it has the disadvantage that orally it is inactive and parenterally its effects are rapid but of short duration. To prolong its action several esters have been introduced, namely, testosterone propionate and testosterone cyclopentylpropionate. These compounds are most effective when administered intramuscularly in a bland, vegetable oil. The esters show a more prolonged action than testosterone, the cyclopentylpropionic acid ester having the longer duration of the two esters used medicinally. The introduction of a methyl group in 17-position of testosterone gives rise to an orally active androgen, methyltestosterone.

Methyltestosterone

The dosage of the various crystalline androgenic substances is expressed in milligrams. For the determination of androgenic activity in extracts and body fluids, the capon comb method is used. For comparative purpose 1 mg. of testosterone is equivalent to 70 to 100 International Units.

Testosterone, U.S.P. (Oreton-F, Δ^4-Androstene-17-ol-3-one), occurs as white or slightly colored crystalline powder or crystals, which are tasteless and stable in the atmosphere. It melts at 152–156°. It is soluble in vegetable oils and insoluble in water.

Testosterone is prepared synthetically from cholesterol according to the sequence of reactions shown on the following page.

Testosterone is inactive orally. It is believed to be inactivated by the gastrointestinal microflora. It is administered intramuscularly. The absorption is quite rapid. It is also administered by implantation.

Testosterone

Testosterone Propionate, 'U.S.P. (Perandren, Neo-Hombreol, Oreton, Δ^4-Androstene-17β-propionyloxy-3-one), is prepared by esterifying the OH group in the 17-position. It occurs as white or creamy white crystals or crystalline powder. It is stable in air but sensitive to alkali. It is insoluble in water and soluble in vegetable oils. Testosterone propionate possesses a longer duration of action than testosterone. It is weakly active orally. It is usually administered intramuscularly.

Testosterone Cyclopentylpropionate, N.N.R. (Δ^4-Androstene-17β-cyclopentylpropionyloxy-3-one), is prepared by esterifying the OH group in the 17-position of testosterone. It occurs as a creamy, odorless, tasteless crystalline powder melting at 98–101°. It is freely soluble in alcohol, soluble in vegetable oils, and slightly soluble in water.

Qualitatively the action and uses of testosterone cyclopentylpropionate are the same as testosterone propionate. However, it possesses the advantage that it is more lasting in its androgenic effect. It is administered intramuscularly in cottonseed oil solution stabilized with chlorobutanol.

Methyltestosterone, U.S.P. (Oreton-M, Neo-Hombreol M, Metandren, 17-Methyl-Δ^4-androstene-17α-ol-3-one), is prepared from dehydroepiandrosterone by the accompanying scheme. It melts at 161–166°. It is a slightly yellow-

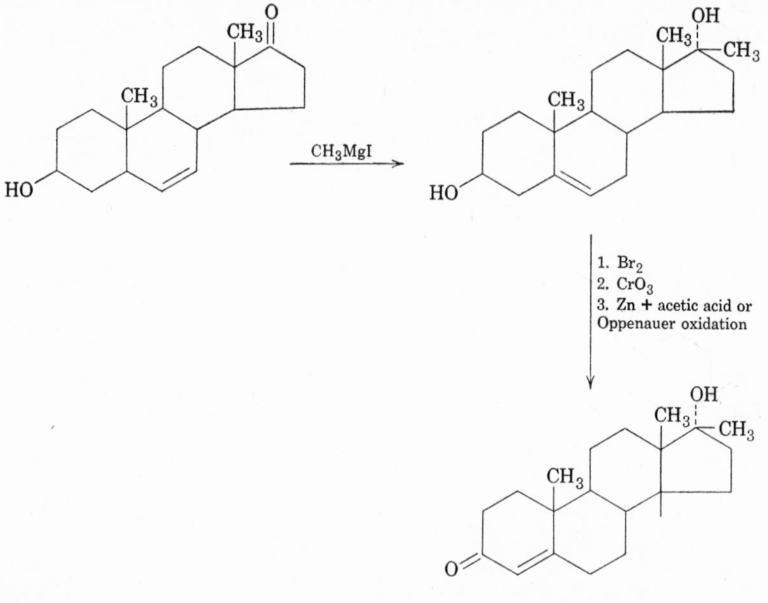

Methyltestosterone

ish, crystalline powder which is insoluble in water, soluble in alcohol and most organic solvents but slightly soluble in fixed oils.

Testosterone is poorly absorbed when administered by mouth, but its methyl derivative is active when given in tablet form sublingually or in ointment by inunction. Methyltestosterone is less active than testosterone by the capon test.

The favorable effect of a 9α-fluorine atom is seen in Halotestin (11β-17β-dihydroxy-9α-fluoro-17-methyl-4-androsten-3-one), reported to be ten times more potent than methyltestosterone as an androgenic agent and twenty times more active as an anabolic agent.[55]

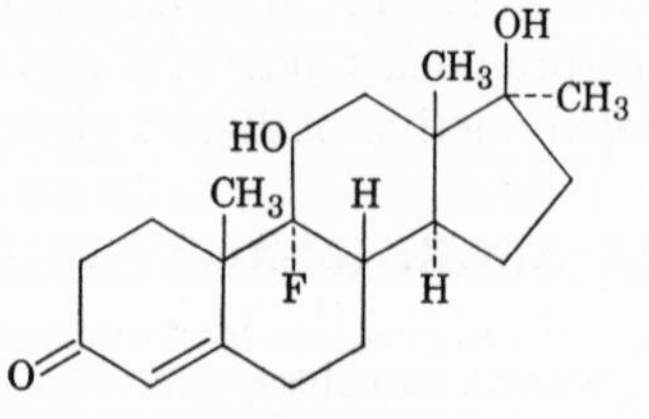

Halotestin 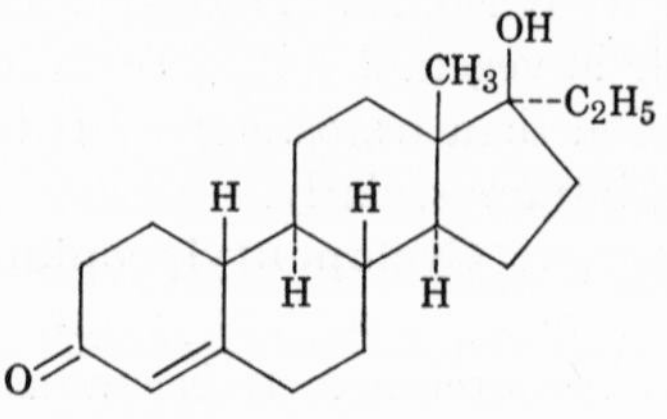   Nilevar

Nelivar (17α-Ethyl-17-hydroxynorandrostenone) is a sixteenth as potent as testosterone androgenically but equally as potent anabolically.[55]

[55] *Chem. Eng. News,* **34,** 2134 (1956).

CHAPTER
6

Carboxyl Group

MONOBASIC CARBOXYLIC ACIDS

The group —COOH is known as the carboxyl group. It is the functional group of the organic carboxylic acids, which ionize according to the scheme:

$$RCOOH \leftrightarrows RCOO^- + H^+$$

Organic acids are weakly acid since they ionize but slightly in polar solvents. The relationship of the carboxylic acids to primary alcohols and aldehydes is shown by the successive oxidation products of the alcohol:

$$R—CH_2OH \xrightarrow{\frac{1}{2}O_2} R—CHO \xrightarrow{\frac{1}{2}O_2} R—C=O$$
$$\underset{OH}{\mid}$$

Hence the carboxylic acids may be looked upon as the final oxidation product of primary alcohols or of aldehydes without rupture of the carbon skeleton. They also may be considered as hydrocarbons in which one hydrogen atom has been replaced by one carboxyl group. See Table XII.

Many aliphatic carboxylic acids are produced naturally; this is especially true for all the normal chain acids up to C_6, and above C_6 for the even-numbered carbon acids as high as C_{18}. The straight-chain, even-numbered C-acids from C_4 to C_{18} are found in fats; hence the name fatty acids. The higher acids are found as esters in many of the natural waxes.

Aliphatic saturated acids up to C_8 or C_9 are liquids, and the higher members are waxy solids. The lower members are water soluble. With increase in

TABLE XII

NORMAL ALIPHATIC ACIDS

Formula	Name	Melting Point ° C.	Boiling Point ° C.	Specific Gravity	Ionization Constant at 25°
H—COOH	Formic, methanoic	8.4	100.5	1.120	2.14×10^{-4}
CH_3—COOH	Acetic, ethanoic	16.6	118.1	1.099	1.86×10^{-5}
C_2H_5—COOH	Propionic, propanoic	−22	141.1	0.992	1.4×10^{-5}
C_3H_7—COOH	Butyric, butanoic	−7.9	163.5	0.959	1.48×10^{-5}
C_4H_9—COOH	Valeric, pentanoic	−59	187	0.942	1.6×10^{-5}
C_5H_{11}—COOH	Caproic, hexanoic	−4.5	202	0.929	—
C_6H_{13}—COOH	Oenanthic, heptanoic	−10	223.5	0.922	—
C_7H_{15}—COOH	Caprylic, octanoic	16	237.5	0.910	—
C_8H_{17}—COOH	Pelargonic, nonanoic	12	254	0.907	—
C_9H_{19}—COOH	Capric, decanoic	31	268.4	0.895^{30}	—
$C_{10}H_{21}$—COOH	Undecylic, undecanoic	29.3	228_{160}	—	—
$C_{11}H_{23}$—COOH	Lauric, dodecanoic	48	225_{100}	0.883	—
$C_{12}H_{25}$—COOH	Tridecanoic	51	236_{100}	—	—
$C_{13}H_{27}$—COOH	Myristic, tetradecanoic	58	250.5_{100}	0.858^{60}	—
$C_{14}H_{29}$—COOH	Pentadecanoic	54	257_{100}	—	—
$C_{15}H_{31}$—COOH	Palmitic, hexadecanoic	64	215_{15}	0.853^{62}	—
$C_{16}H_{33}$—COOH	Margaric, heptadecanoic	59.9	227_{15}	0.853^{60}	—
$C_{17}H_{35}$—COOH	Stearic, octadecanoic	69.3	383	$0.847^{69.3}$	—

molecular weight solubility decreases. All of them are soluble in most organic solvents. The lower members of the series have a characteristic odor, the higher members are odorless when pure. The salts of the lower-molecular-weight acids are soluble in water; for the higher members the alkaline earth and heavy metal salts are insoluble.

The presence of the carboxyl in a molecule increases the solubility in water. For example, butane is insoluble in water, butyric acid is very soluble; benzene is insoluble, benzoic acid is slightly soluble; phthalic acid is about twice as soluble as benzoic acid; hexane is insoluble, caproic acid is slightly soluble, and adipic acid is considerably more soluble than the monocarboxylic acid. Solubility is further increased if the free acid is converted into a salt, particularly the salt of an alkali or of an organic base.

Physiological Activity

The aliphatic carboxylic acids possess only to a very limited degree the physiological activity which characterizes the parent hydrocarbon. Only in large doses are they able to produce somnolence or hypnosis; the larger the proportion of the hydrocarbon residue in the molecule, the greater seems to be the effect.

The introduction of a carboxyl group into an active compound nearly always causes a decrease in activity. Consequently there are very few organic acids used directly as therapeutic agents. The simple aliphatic acids such as acetic and propionic are corrosive in the pure state, but when sufficiently diluted they are relatively nontoxic. In large doses the aliphatic acids are somewhat hypnotic, and this property increases with the length of the carbon chain to valeric acid which in the form of salts is used as a sedative, e.g., ammonium valerate. Most of the aliphatic acids are metabolized and serve as foods. The branched-chain acids are more active physiologically than those with a straight chain. The relatively low toxicity of the fatty acids may be assumed from their prevalence in nature and their presence in foodstuffs, particularly in the fats. Their role in plant and animal biochemistry is not completely understood.

Products

Carbon Dioxide, U.S.P. (Carbonic Acid Gas), CO_2, is added to oxygen in varying amounts, usually 5–7 per cent, in artificial respiration as a stimulant to the respiratory centers. The amount must be carefully regulated for it may act as a respiratory depressant or cause death by asphyxia, depending on relative, excessive amounts of carbon dioxide used.

The role of carbon dioxide as the raw material in photosynthesis early attracted the attention of scientists. The overall equation for the natural synthesis of sugars, i.e., hexoses, has long been represented by the equation

$$6CO_2 + 6H_2O = C_6H_{12}O_6 + 6O_2$$

Until quite recently it was believed that the first step was the reduction of carbon dioxide, in the presence of water, to formaldehyde, which, before reaching toxic concentrations in the plant tissues, was quickly hexamerized,

$$6HCHO \rightarrow C_6H_{12}O_6$$

In support of this hypothesis was the observation that formaldehyde, *in vitro* and in the presence of dilute alkali, polymerizes into a mixture of hexoses; [1] the enzymes in the plant were assumed to account for the stereospecificity of the reactions. Now, thanks to radioactive carbon and the brilliant discoveries of Calvin and his co-workers at the University of

[1] Vogel, *Helv. Chim. Acta*, **11**, 370 (1928).

California [2] and supporting contributions from others,[3] the mechanism of photosynthesis is better appreciated.

It is now known that the role of chlorophyll, the energy relationships, the rates and the sequence of compound formation are indeed complex and marvelous. Suffice it to say that from experiments with $C^{14}O_2$ supplied to algae, *Chlorella* or *Scenedesmus*, it has been possible to establish that carbon dioxide first unites with ribulose in the photosynthetic process to form a transient intermediate which then reacts with a two-carbon fragment to form phosphoglyceric acid, the latter becoming apparent within 10 seconds after initiating the photosynthetic process.[4] Within 15 seconds hexose labeled in all positions appears; soon tagged citric acid, sucrose, glutamic acid, alanine, and other compounds make their presence known by means of radioautographs.

One of the early products of the photosynthetic processes is radioactive "acetyl," which, via acetoacetic acid and further condensation, gives rise to the isoprenoid arrangement of carbon atoms. These reactions may be summarized schematically as indicated. The

$$CH_3COOH \rightarrow CH_3COCH_2COOH \xrightarrow[-CO_2]{+CH_3COOH}$$

$$\begin{matrix} CH_3 \\ \diagdown \\ \quad C(OH){-}CH_2COOH \rightarrow \\ \diagup \\ CH_3 \end{matrix} \left(\begin{matrix} C \\ \diagdown \\ \quad C{-}C{-}C \\ \diagup \\ C \end{matrix} \right)_n$$

Various isoprenoids

biosynthesis of squalene (page 8) in man and the conversion of this hexaisoprenoid into cholesterol [5] (page 53) give emphasis to the significance of the total photosynthetic processes.

Formic Acid, HCOOH, discovered in the seventeenth century by Sheffield, occurs free in the ant, especially the *Formica rufa*, in the processionary caterpillar, in the bristles of stinging nettles, the fruit of the soap tree, *Sapindus saponaria*, and in small amounts in the urine, perspiration, etc. It is manufactured commercially by passing carbon monoxide under a pressure of six to seven atmospheres at 150–170° into sodium hydroxide to form sodium formate, and the acid is obtained by treating the salt with sulfuric acid. It is a colorless, pungent, corrosive liquid, having an odor that resembles that of sulfur dioxide. It is soluble in water, alcohol, and glycerin.

Structurally, formic acid possesses the elements that characterize aldehydes and exhibits properties in agreement with such structure. For example, it is a strong reducing agent, producing free silver when warmed with ammoniacal silver nitrate.

[2] Calvin *et al.*, *J. Chem. Ed.*, **26**, 639 (1949); *ibid.*, **30**, 274 (1953); *Chem. Eng. News*, **31**, 1622, 1735 (1953); *J. Am. Chem. Soc.*, **73**, 2362 (1951); *ibid.*, **76**, 1760, 4348 (1954); *ibid.*, **77**, 2659 (1955).

[3] Granick, *Chem. Eng. News*, **31**, 748 (1953).

Bonner *et al.*, *J. Chem Ed.*, **26**, 268 (1949); *Science*, **120**, 549 (1954).

[4] Wilson and Calvin, *J. Am. Chem. Soc.*, **77**, 5948 (1955).

[5] Schwenk, Todd, and Fish, *Arch. Biochem. Biophys.*, **49**, 187 (1954).

Eidinoff *et al.*, *J. Clin. Invest.*, **33**, 333 (1954).

Dauben and Takemura, *J. Am. Chem. Soc.*, **75**, 6302 (1953).

Woodward and Bloch, *J. Am. Chem. Soc.*, **75**, 2023 (1953).

The official product is about a 25 per cent solution of formic acid in water. It is a colorless liquid with a pungent odor and a strongly acid taste. It is used in the form of the *Spirit* as an irritant (at one time the spirit was made by macerating ants with alcohol, and it had quite a reputation as a tonic on the supposition that it would confer on man something of the vigor and indefatigability of the insects). Internally, it has the same action as the acetates. (See methanol poisoning, page 35.) It is corrosive and irritating but relatively nontoxic when diluted. It possesses strong antiseptic properties and is used as a fungicide. Its value as a therapeutic agent is questionable.

Glacial Acetic Acid, U.S.P. (Ethanoic Acid), is a liquid containing about 99.4 per cent CH_3COOH. The concentrated acid was first prepared by Stahl in 1700. Berzelius in 1814 established its constitution. It is present in "pyroligneous" acid (obtained by the pyrogenic distillation of lignin or wood) to the extent of 4–6 per cent. Acetates are found in the perspiration, in fruits, and in plants.

Most of the world's supply of acetic acid is prepared by the oxidation of acetaldehyde. The acetaldehyde for this purpose may be obtained by the hydration of acetylene or by the oxidation of ethanol. Commercial glacial acetic

$$\left. \begin{array}{c} CH\equiv CH \xrightarrow[\substack{H_2SO_4 \\ air}]{HgSO_4 \ in} \\ CH_3CH_2OH \xrightarrow{} \end{array} \right\} CH_3CHO \xrightarrow[air]{(Mn^{+2} \ or \ Co^{+2})} CH_3COOH$$

acid is 99.6 per cent pure, or better.

It is nontoxic when diluted and possesses little therapeutic value. It is used as a solvent and for the preparation of dilutions for pharmaceutical application. The salts of acetic acid are employed extensively in connection with various ions.

Acetic Acid, U.S.P., is a solution containing between 36 and 37 per cent of acetic acid.

Diluted Acetic Acid, N.F., contains about 6 per cent CH_3COOH. It is used as an antidote for alkalies.

Sodium Acetate, N.F., and **Potassium Acetate, N.F.,** are used mainly as alkaline diuretics and to counteract acidosis. Sodium acetate, given intravenously, has a very low toxicity. In rats, the nutrition is not impaired by the consumption of concentrations up to $\frac{1}{4}$ per cent, but at levels of $\frac{1}{2}$ per cent nutrition is impaired. This explains the effects and risks in using vinegar for the treatment of obesity.

Propionic Acid (Propanoic Acid), CH_3CH_2COOH, has become of medicinal importance because of its useful fungicidal property. Although the free acid may be used to treat fungus infections, its salts, such as sodium, calcium, potassium, and copper, are preferred for they are more easily handled and are odorless.

Propionic acid may be prepared by (a) oxidation of propanol or (b) fermentation, using *Propionibacterium* on a number of substrates such as hexoses, pentoses, lactic acid, or glycerol. In the absence of carbon dioxide, glycerol is converted in good yields to propionic acid. It is a water-soluble, clear, corrosive liquid with a characteristic odor.

Sodium Propionate, N.F. (Mycoban), CH_3CH_2COONa, occurs as transparent, colorless crystals with a slight odor characteristic of the fatty acid. It is deliquescent in moist air. It is very soluble in water (1:1) and soluble in alcohol (1:24).

It is used as an effective agent in conjunction with the free acid in the treatment of fungus infections such as athlete's foot. The propionate-propionic acid mixture is reported to be only slightly better than the undecylenate-undecylenic acid mixture.

Stearic Acid, U.S.P., is a mixture consisting chiefly of palmitic acid, $CH_3(CH_2)_{14}COOH$, and stearic acid, $CH_3(CH_2)_{16}COOH$. It is obtained for commercial use by the hydrolysis of fats with superheated steam or the saponification of fats with alkalies.

$$
\begin{array}{l}
CH_2-O-\overset{\displaystyle O}{\overset{\|}{C}}-(CH_2)_xCH_3 \\[2ex]
CH-O-\overset{\displaystyle O}{\overset{\|}{C}}-(CH_2)_xCH_3 \; + \; 3NaOH \;\rightarrow\; CH-OH \; + \; 3CH_3(CH_2)_xCOONa \\[2ex]
CH_2-O-\overset{\displaystyle O}{\overset{\|}{C}}-(CH_2)_xCH_3
\end{array}
\qquad
\begin{array}{l}
CH_2-OH \\[2ex]
CH-OH \\[2ex]
CH_2-OH
\end{array}
$$

The free acid is obtained by acidifying a solution of the sodium salt. It is a solid, white, waxlike crystalline substance which is insoluble in water but soluble in organic solvents. It melts at about 55° and congeals not below 54°. Since fats are composed of glycerides containing such acids as oleic, linoleic, stearic, palmitic, and myristic, the official stearic acid is contaminated with these acids.

Stearic acid, U.S.P., is used in the preparation of suppositories, ointments, vanishing creams, and other cosmetics and stearates.

Sodium Stearate, U.S.P., is prepared by neutralizing stearic acid with sodium carbonate. It is a white powder with a soapy feel and tallowlike odor. It dissolves slowly in cold water or alcohol but is freely soluble in hot solvents. Aqueous solutions are strongly alkaline. It is used in the preparation of some ointments, suppositories, creams, and cosmetics.

Zinc Stearate, U.S.P., is prepared by reacting equivalent quantities of sodium stearate and zinc acetate in an aqueous solution. The precipitated zinc stearate is filtered off, washed, and dried. It is a white, fine, soft, bulky powder with a slight characteristic odor. It is neutral in reaction and melts at about 120°. It is insoluble in water.

It is used alone or mixed with other substances as a mild astringent and antiseptic in ointments and dusting powders. Inhalation causes pulmonary inflammation.

Soaps

The salts of the fatty acids C_{12} to C_{18} are called soaps; this is particularly true of the sodium, potassium, and amine salts. They are used for their surface-active and detergent properties. They may be prepared from the acid and appropriate base, but usually they are obtained by the alkaline hydrolysis of fats, as shown. The soap obtained in this manner is rarely the salt of a single acid.

$$
\begin{array}{ccccc}
CH_2O-COR & & CH_2OH & & \begin{cases} RCOONa \\ + \\ R'COONa \\ + \\ R''COONa \end{cases} \\
| & & | & & \\
CHO-COR' & + 3NaOH \rightarrow & CHOH & + & \\
| & & | & & \\
CH_2O-COR'' & & CH_2OH & & \\
\text{Fat} & & \text{Glycerol} & & \text{Soap}
\end{array}
$$

Nevertheless the character and quality of the soap is determined by the grade and quality of the fat. Thus Castile soap is made from olive oil; laundry soap is made from darker fats.

Hard Soap, N.F., is a sodium salt of acids having an acid value 185–205 and an iodine number 83–92. It is used in *Camphor and Soap Liniment, N.F.,* and in *Dentifrice, N.F.*

Medicinal Soft Soap, U.S.P., is a potassium soap obtained by the saponification of vegetable oils other than coconut and palm kernel oils, and without removal of the glycerol. It is used in *Medicinal Soft Soap Liniment, U.S.P.*

The zinc and sodium salts of stearic acid have already been mentioned. The salts of the alkaline earth and heavy metals are insoluble; yet some of them find pharmaceutical application as indicated in the accompanying summary:

Soap	Uses
Lead oleate	Ointments and plasters
Aluminum oleate	Oil thickener
Magnesium oleate	Dry cleaning of silk goods to prevent fires caused by static electricity when withdrawing goods from the bath
Copper oleate	Medicinally to treat ulcers, etc.
Zinc stearate	Dusting powders
Mercury oleate	Antiseptic dusting powder for wounds
Copper soaps	Insecticide and fungicide, paint for ship bottoms, etc.
Aluminum soaps	Lubricant, polishing mixtures, e.g., floor polish
Cadmium soaps	Waterproof paper, concrete, etc.
Zinc, nickel, cobalt, and chromium soaps	Waterproof paper, canvas, and leather

POLYBASIC ACIDS

Many of the dicarboxylic acids are found in nature; others are prepared synthetically by standard methods and are important in chemical industry. The lower members of the dibasic acid series with the carboxyl groups at the terminals of aliphatic chains are given in Table XIII.

TABLE XIII

DICARBOXYLIC ACIDS

Structure	Name	Melting Point ° C.	Boiling Point ° C.	Specific Gravity	Dissociation Constants	
					k_1	k_2
COOH | COOH	Oxalic, ethandioic	189	—	2.0	3.8×10^{-2}	—
CH$_2$ COOH COOH	Malonic, propandioic, methanedi-carboxylic	135.6	—	—	1.77×10^{-3}	4.37×10^{-6}
CH$_2$—COOH | CH$_2$—COOH	Succinic, butandioic, ethanedi-carboxylic	185	235	1.562	7.36×10^{-5}	4.50×10^{-6}
(CH$_2$)$_3$ COOH COOH	Glutaric, pentandioic	97.5	304	1.192^{106}	4.6×10^{-5}	5.34×10^{-6}
(CH$_2$)$_4$ COOH COOH	Adipic, hexandioic	151	265_{110}	—	3.9×10^{-5}	5.29×10^{-6}
(CH$_2$)$_5$ COOH COOH	Pimelic, heptandioic	103	272_{100}	—	3.33×10^{-5}	4.87×10^{-6}
(CH$_2$)$_6$ COOH COOH	Suberic, octandioic	140	279_{100}	—	3.07×10^{-5}	4.71×10^{-6}
(CH$_2$)$_7$ COOH COOH	Azelaic, nonandioic	106.5	360	1.029	2.82×10^{-5}	4.64×10^{-6}
(CH$_2$)$_8$ COOH COOH	Sebacic, decandioic	127	299.5_{100}	—	2.8×10^{-5}	—

The dicarboxylic acids, except for oxalic acid, are metabolized for the most part, and they have practically no physiological action.

Oxalic acid and most of its salts are local irritants and corrosives. Internally, it is readily absorbed and in sufficient doses produces oxalate poisoning by removal of the calcium from the blood and tissues as the insoluble calcium oxalate.

Cerium Oxalate is a mixture of several oxalates composed primarily of cerium and other closely related elements such as neodymium, praseodymium, and lanthanum. It has been employed against the vomiting of pregnancy. Since it is not absorbed, it is nontoxic even in large doses. It is of questionable value.

UNSATURATED ACIDS

Compounds containing both the carboxyl group and unsaturated bonds possess the properties characteristic of both functional groups; i.e., the one does not exert any particular modifying effect on the other.

The lower-molecular-weight unsaturated acids cause hemolysis of the red corpuscles.[6] Acrylic and oleic acids cause such hemolysis when injected into the blood stream. An analogous hemolytic effect is observed both *in vivo* and *in vitro* with dimethyloxythiolerucic acid, $C_{21}H_{38}(CH_2)_2OH \cdot COSH$, which has been isolated from pure cultures of staphylococci.

The unsaturated C_{18} acids, oleic acid, $C_{17}H_{33} \cdot COOH$, linoleic acid, $C_{17}H_{31} \cdot COOH$, and linolenic acid, $C_{17}H_{29} \cdot COOH$, are dietary essentials, possessing vitagenic properties that were once associated with vitamin F.

Undecylenic Acid, U.S.P., is a product composed mainly of undecylenic acid, $CH_2{=}CH(CH_2)_8COOH$, and small amounts of oleic and stearic acids. It is prepared by the vacuum distillation of castor oil, whereby the ricinoleic acid present in the glyceride undergoes fission to give *n*-heptaldehyde and undecylenic acid.

$$CH_3(CH_2)_5CHOHCH_2CH{=}CH(CH_2)_7COOH \rightarrow$$

$$CH_3(CH_2)_5CHO + CH_2{=}CH(CH_2)_8COOH$$

It is a soft, opaque mass or a yellow liquid with a characteristic odor. It is almost insoluble in water, but it is soluble in alcohol, chloroform, ether, benzene, and fixed oils. It congeals between 21 and 22°.

Undecylenic acid is one of the more potent of the fatty acids used as a fungistatic agent. It is applied topically as a solution or emulsion in concentration not to exceed 10 per cent. Local application occasionally produces irritation.

Zinc Undecylenate, U.S.P., is an amorphous white powder resembling zinc stearate. It is practically insoluble in water and in alcohol. Zinc undecylenate alone or with other fungistatic agents such as undecylenic acid or salicylanilide is used for certain fungus infections. Such proprietaries as *Zincundecate, N.N.R.,* and *Zincundesal, N.N.R.,* are examples of products that contain zinc undecylenate and are used because of their fungistatic activity.

Oleic Acid, U.S.P., $CH_3(CH_2)_7CH{=}CH(CH_2)_7{-}COOH$, is found as the glyceride in practically all vegetable and animal fats. Chicken fat contains much oleic acid. Human-fat, beef-tallow, and pork-liver lipids contain isomers of oleic acid, with the same iodine values but lower melting points.

It is obtained by saponification of fats or oils with sodium hydroxide and liberation of the free acid from the salt by acidifying with sulfuric acid. The impure acid is then treated with lead acetate to form the lead salt which, being ether soluble, is extracted with ether. After removal of the ether the residue is acidified to liberate the free acid. Barium oleate is then prepared, and the salt is purified by recrystallization from alcohol. The pure oleic acid is obtained by treating the salt with sulfuric acid.

[6] Okolov and Arutyunyan, *Voprosy Pitaniya,* **4,** No. 1, 109 (1935); *C.A.,* **32,** 6314 (1938).

The acid is a pale yellow to a brownish yellow liquid. On exposure to air it absorbs oxygen and darkens. When strongly heated in air it is decomposed with the production of acrid vapors. It is almost insoluble in water and is miscible with alcohol and fixed oils.

Oleic acid is used in pharmacy primarily for the preparation of oleates, see soaps, page 147.

Sodium Psylliate, the salt of the liquid fatty acids obtained by the hydrolysis of the oil from the seeds of *Plantago ovata*, commonly known as Indian Plantago seed, is used in *Sodium Psylliate Injection, N.F.*; the iodine number for the acids is not less than 130, and the acid value 130–160.

Sodium Morrhuate is prepared from cod liver oil. *Sodium Morrhuate Injection, U.S.P.*, is used as a sclerosing agent.

AROMATIC ACIDS

In aromatic acids the carboxyl group is attached directly to an aromatic nucleus.

Benzoic Acid, U.S.P., C_6H_5—COOH, was first discovered in gum benzoin in 1608 and isolated by Scheele from urine in 1785. Its constitution was established by Liebig and Wöhler, 1832, in their classical researches. It occurs naturally in gum benzoin, in a resin known in Peru as dragon's blood, in tolu balsams, in castoreum, and in cranberries; it is found in hippuric acid as the amide linked with glycine, $C_6H_5CONHCH_2COOH$. It may be prepared by the oxidation of toluene, of benzyl alcohol, or of benzaldehyde. It may be obtained also by the hydrolysis of benzonitrile, C_6H_5CN; and by the Friedel-Crafts reaction of phosgene on benzene. It is obtained commercially by the hydrolysis of benzotrichloride and by the decarboxylation of phthalic acid, as shown.

$$C_6H_5CH_3 \xrightarrow{Cl_2} C_6H_5CCl_3 \xrightarrow{H_2O} C_6H_5COOH$$

$$C_6H_4(COOH)_2 \xrightarrow[-CO_2]{\text{(Cr with other metals)}} C_6H_5COOH$$

Benzoic acid forms white crystals, usually as scales or needles, which sublime at moderate temperatures. It is usually odorless or may have a slight odor of benzoin or benzaldehyde. It is insoluble in cold water (1:275) and soluble in warm water (1:20). It is very soluble in alcohol and soluble in fixed oils.

Benzoic acid has about the same antiseptic activity as phenol, but in concentrations above 0.1 per cent it is likely to produce local irritation. Its irritant action and also its germicidal activity are reduced on its conversion into salts. It has a very low systemic activity and fatalities are unknown.

Healthy men receiving 0.3 g. daily for two months, then 0.6–1.0 g. daily for 1–2 weeks, and then 4–6 g. daily for shorter periods of time showed no deleterious effects.

Benzoic acid and all aromatic acids and their analogs, e.g., cinnamic acid, quinic acid, etc., are excreted in conjugation with glycine in the form of hippuric acid.

It can be demonstrated that the liver and kidneys, as well as many other organs, take part in the hippuric acid synthesis. Sodium benzoate injected intravenously can be used to test the function of the liver. In normal, human liver function benzoic acid is converted into hippuric acid; a determination of the amount and rate of excretion measures the functional activity and may be used to diagnose liver damage.

The hippuric acid excretion in the normal man averages about 0.7 g. per day and arises from the benzoic acid naturally present in foods or formed during metabolism.

Large doses of benzoic acid increase the elimination of uric acid. It has an antirheumatic action similar to but weaker than that of salicylic acid.

It is used externally as a mild antiseptic in ointments, lotions, and mouthwashes. Internally it is irritating to the stomach and therefore usually is administered in the form of its salts. It may be used as a food preservative but the sodium salt is preferred.

HALOGENATED ACIDS

Halogenated acids have the properties of the carboxyl group and also of characteristic halogenated compounds. Types of some of these compounds are illustrated in Table XIV.

TABLE XIV

HALOGENATED ACIDS

Formula	Name	Melting Point ° C.	Boiling Point ° C.	Specific Gravity	Ionization Constant
CH_3—COOH	Acetic	16.6	118.1	1.049	1.8×10^{-5}
$ClCH_2$—COOH	Chloroacetic	61.2	189.5	—	1.55×10^{-3}
Cl_2CH—COOH	Dichloroacetic	10	193.5	1.563	5×10^{-2}
Cl_3C—COOH	Trichloroacetic	57.5	195.3	1.617^{46}	2×10^{-1}
$BrCH_2COOH$	Bromoacetic	50	208	1.934	1.38×10^{-3}
ICH_2COOH	Iodoacetic	82	dec.	—	7.5×10^{-2}
$CNCH_2$—COOH	Cyanoacetic	66	108_{15}	—	3.7×10^{-1}
CH_3CH_2—COOH	Propionic	−22	141.1	0.992	1.34×10^{-5}
CH_3—CHCl—COOH	α-Chloropropionic		186	1.307	1.47×10^{-3}
$ClCH_2CH_2$—COOH	β-Chloropropionic	61	204	—	8.6×10^{-5}
$C_6H_4 \diagdown \genfrac{}{}{0pt}{}{Cl\text{-}o}{COOH}$	o-Chlorobenzoic	140.7			
$C_6H_4 \diagdown \genfrac{}{}{0pt}{}{Cl\text{-}m}{COOH}$	m-Chlorobenzoic	154.9			
$C_6H_4 \diagdown \genfrac{}{}{0pt}{}{Cl\text{-}p}{COOH}$	p-Chlorobenzoic	241.5			

Sometimes the introduction of a halogen atom into the carboxyl-bearing molecule increases the acidic properties; e.g., trichloroacetic acid ionizes to a degree comparable with that of the stronger inorganic acids. In the aliphatic acids, this modifying effect of the halogen on the carboxyl decreases as the halogen and the carboxyl become further removed from each other (compare α- and β-chloropropionic acids, Table XIV). The halogenated benzoic acids ionize to a greater degree than does the unsubstituted acid.

One other property is the increase in lability of a halogen in a position beta to a carboxyl group. The α-halogen acids are very stable; e.g., in α-chloropropionic acid, the chlorine atom is bound very firmly and not easily removed; but in the β-halogen acids, the halogen atom is removed with comparative ease as hydrohalogen acid; thus β-chloropropionic acid loses hydrogen chloride with comparative readiness to form acrylic acid.

Fluoroacetic Acid, FCH_2COOH, is one of the rare examples of a halogenated organic compound found in nature, appearing in "Gifblaar," *Dichapetalum (Chailletia) cymosum* (Hook) Engl., one of the most poisonous plants of South Africa.[7, 8] Its sodium salt, "1080" or "ten-eighty," is an excellent rodenticide.[9] This extreme toxicity stands in marked contrast to the safety of, say, dichlorodifluoromethane (page 22). The compound is so toxic because it is enzymatically converted into a fluorotricarboxylic acid which interferes with the vital tricarboxylic acid cycle at the citrate stage.[10]

Dichloroacetic Acid, $Cl_2CHCOOH$, is another of the rare halogenated organic compounds occurring naturally as an amide in chloromycetin, page 495.

Trichloroacetic Acid, U.S.P., CCl_3COOH, consists of colorless deliquescent crystals, very soluble in water 1:0.1 and readily soluble in alcohol. It is the most corrosive of the halogenated organic acids. It is used externally for the removal of warts, etc., either as such or in strong aqueous solution. The dichloroacetic acid is not so corrosive, and it is often used for the same purpose as the trichloroacetic acid.

The LD_{50} in mg. per kg. to white mice for many of the halogen-substituted acids, on oral administration in neutral solution, is: chloroacetic, 165; α-chloropropionic, 980; β-chloropropionic, above 2000; bromoacetic, 100; iodoacetic, 63; α-bromopropionic, 250; β-bromopropionic, above 2000; α-bromobutyric, 310; α-bromoisobutyric, over 2000; α-bromovaleric, 380; α-bromoisovaleric, over 2000. The β-halogenated and the α-halogenated branched-chain acids have lower toxicity.[11]

Iodine Derivatives of the Fatty Acids

A large number of iodine derivatives of the fatty acids have been introduced as medicinal agents. Some of them are relatively pure acid derivatives and

[7] Marais, *Onderstepoort J. Vet. Sci. Animal Ind.*, **20,** 67 (1944).

[8] Klingensmith *Science*, **102,** 622 (1945).

[9] Kalmbach, *Science*, **102,** 232 (1945).

[10] Peters, Wakelin, and Buffa, *Proc. Roy. Soc. (London)*, **B140,** 497 (1953); *C.A.*, **47,** 3979 (1953).

[11] Morrison, *J. Pharmacol.*, **86,** 336 (1946).

others are iodized fatty oils. In all the derivatives, the iodine is added to the double bond across unsaturated linkages of the fatty-acid portion of the molecule. Most of the iodine addition products of the fatty acids and oils are unstable in the presence of light and air, rapidly darkening in color and losing some of their iodine. They are rapidly decomposed by alkalies.

The iodized fatty acids and their salts and the iodized oils have an activity similar to that of the inorganic iodides. They pass through the stomach and are absorbed from the intestines like other fats and become deposited in the lipoid tissues. The fatty acid is gradually metabolized, liberating iodine in the form of iodides, so that a uniform concentration of iodides is maintained over a longer period of time than is obtained with the inorganic iodides. They are extensively used in prophylaxis against goiter.

The iodized acids, oils, and fats are used as contrast media in roentgenography. When injected in the form of emulsions or after thinning with some substance such as ethyl oleate, they permit diagnosis of tumors, lesions, etc.

Calcium Iodobehenate, N.F. (Calioben, Sajodin, Calcium Monoiodobehenate), $(C_{21}H_{42}ICOO)_2Ca$, is a white or yellow powder, insoluble in water and soluble in warm chloroform, containing about 23.5 per cent iodine. This product is prepared from erucic acid, an unsaturated acid obtained from rape oil, by adding hydriodic acid across the double bond and then forming the calcium salt. The sodium or potassium salts, typical soaps, are not used because of their irritating properties. The calcium salt is used as a substitute for the inorganic iodides and is usually administered as tablets or as the powder in capsules.

Iodostarine (Diiodotariric Acid), $C_{18}H_{32}I_2O_2$, is a white, crystalline powder, insoluble in water but soluble in most organic solvents, containing about 47.5 per cent iodine. It is administered in the form of tablets as a substitute for the inorganic iodides.

Oridine, N.N.R., is the calcium salt of the iodized fatty acids obtained from cottonseed oil. It contains about 24 per cent iodine and is administered in the form of tablets as a substitute for the inorganic iodides.

Stearodine (Calcium Iodostearate), $[CH_3(CH_2)_7CHI(CH_2)_8COO]_2Ca$, is the calcium salt of iodized stearic acid. The product is prepared by treating oleic acid with hydrogen iodide and then forming the calcium salt. It is used as a substitute for inorganic iodides and is administered in the form of tablets.

Iodized Oil, U.S.P. (Lipiodol), is an iodine addition product of vegetable oil or oils containing about 40 per cent iodine. It is a thick, viscous oil. It decomposes on exposure to air and sunlight and becomes dark brown in color. It is used as a substitute for the inorganic iodides and as a contrast medium in roentgenography and is administered in tablets or by injection.

Lipiodol Radiologique Ascendant, N.N.R., is an iodized poppy-seed oil containing about 10.5 per cent iodine. It is a yellow oily liquid, insoluble in water, which decomposes on exposure to light and air. It is administered by injection as a contrast medium in roentgenography.

Iodobrassid, N.N.R. (Lipoiodine, Lipodine, Ethyl Diiodobrassidate), $CH_3(CH_2)_7CHICHI(CH_2)_{11}COOC_2H_5$, is a white crystalline product without odor or taste which is prepared by treating the ethyl ester of brassidic acid with two atoms of iodine. Iodobrassid is used as a substitute for inorganic iodides and as a contrast medium for roentgenologic work.

Riodine, N.N.R., is a solution of an iodine addition product of castor oil in oil, containing about 17 per cent iodine. It is made by treating castor oil with HI. It is used in the form of pearls (small pills) as a substitute for the inorganic iodides.

HYDROXY ACIDS

Hydroxy acids have the properties of the hydroxyl and carboxyl groups. A hydroxyl group substituted in the α-position of a fatty acid increases the acidic properties to a slight extent. For example, the dissociation constant for propionic acid at 25° is 1.4×10^{-5}, and for lactic acid, $CH_3CHOHCOOH$, it is 1.38×10^{-4}. A hydroxyl group in the β-position has little influence on the carboxyl group, but the carboxyl group labilizes the β-hydroxyl to such an extent that it readily splits out water to form the α,β-unsaturated acid.

The γ- and δ-hydroxy acids readily lose one molecule of water to form inner esters which are five- and six-nembered heterocycles (see lactones), known as γ- and δ-lactones, respectively.

Lactic Acid, U.S.P. (α-Hydroxypropionic Acid), is a mixture of lactic acid, $CH_3CHOHCOOH$, and lactic anhydride. It was first identified by Scheele in sour milk. Lactic acid is found in many foodstuffs, e.g., buttermilk, wine, cheese, sauerkraut, etc.

Technically, it is obtained by the fermentation at 50° of molasses, whey, or corn sugar with either *Lactobacillus delbrückii* or *bulgaricus*. Since the acid formed is toxic in high concentrations to the organisms, lime or chalk is added to the mixture to neutralize the acid formed. Yields up to 60 per cent are obtainable.

Lactic acid is a colorless or usually yellowish, syrupy liquid. It absorbs water on exposure to moist air and decomposes when heated at normal pressure during distillation. Lactic acid is miscible with water, alcohol, and ether. Solutions are acid to litmus.

L-Lactic acid, known as sarcolactic or muscle lactic acid, increases in the muscle as a result of work; part of it is metabolized and a part is reconverted into glycogen. The acid plays a very important role in the process of muscle contraction.

Lactic acid-producing organisms and products containing them came into general use after Metchnikoff advanced the theory that autointoxication is brought about by intestinal putrefaction and that the products formed and absorbed bring about such conditions as arteriosclerosis and premature senility. The growth of the pathogenic organisms, according to Metchnikoff's theory, is altered or prevented by the presence of lactic acid-producing bacteria such as *Bacillus bulgaricus* in the intestinal tract.

The products used are: (1) milk soured by *Lactobacillus acidophilus* and (2) broth cultures of *L. acidophilus* converted into concentrates and used in the form of solutions or candied products. Usually, these products contain about 100 to 500 million living organisms per gram or cubic centimeter at the time of manufacture and about half this amount at the expiration date. The exact manner in which these preparations act is not known; they probably act by altering the intestinal flora so that the fermentative lactic-acid type predominates. The action seems to be due primarily to the organisms since the administration of purified lactic acid is without value.

Lactic acid is quite caustic in concentrated forms and thus needs to be diluted for use. It is added to infants' formulas to aid digestion and to decrease regurgitation. It is also used as a spermatocidal agent and in the preparation of lactates.

Mandelic Acid (Racemic Mandelic Acid) is prepared commercially by reacting benzaldehyde with sodium bisulfite, and the resultant product is reacted with sodium cyanide to give mandelonitrile. The nitrile is hydrolyzed with hydrochloric acid to give DL-mandelic acid, as shown. Mandelic acid occurs as

$$C_6H_5CHO \xrightarrow{NaHSO_3} C_6H_5CH \begin{subarray}{l} OH \\ \\ SO_3Na \end{subarray} \xrightarrow{NaCN} C_6H_5CH \begin{subarray}{l} OH \\ \\ CN \end{subarray} \rightarrow C_6H_5CHOHCOOH$$

Mandelonitrile   Mandelic acid

a white crystalline powder which gradually darkens and decomposes on exposure to light. It has a slight aromatic odor. Solutions are acid to litmus.

The use of mandelic acid in therapy originated after it had often been observed that patients with uncontrolled diabetes were quite free of infection of the upper urinary tract although susceptible to pyogenic infections in general. The added observation that urine containing large amounts of ketone bodies did not putrefy on standing in the laboratory led to the use of the ketogenic diet in the treatment of upper urinary tract infections. The factor responsible for the bacteriostatic effect was found by Fuller [12] to be β-hydroxybutyric acid. β-Hydroxybutyric acid cannot be administered by mouth to produce a similar effect because it is oxidized in the body. Rosenheim [13] studied a series of acids and discovered that mandelic acid possessed excellent bacteriostatic properties and was not oxidized in the body when administered by mouth but was excreted largely unchanged in the urine. Helmholtz and Osterberg [14] found that mandelic acid is most effective when the urine is markedly acid, a pH of 5.5 or less being necessary for best results. This led to the use of mandelic acid with ammonium chloride and sodium mandelate with ammonium chloride, the ammonium chloride being given to maintain acidity of the urine. The ammonium and sodium salts sometimes cause nausea. This has been overcome by the use of combinations such as *Calcium Mandelate, U.S.P.*, and methenamine mandelate, which seem to be effective without adding ammonium chloride to secure urine acidity. Various products, such as syrups, elixirs, and tablets of the mandelate salts, are administered orally, with careful control of the pH of the urine, for their bacteriostatic and bactericidal action against organisms causing infections (cystitis, pyelitis) of the upper urinary tract, e.g., *Bacillus coli*. Riebsomer *et al.*[15] have prepared a series of halogenated and alkylated derivatives of mandelic acid and have found that some of them are more active than mandelic acid *in vitro*.

[12] *Lancet*, **1**, 855 (1935).
[13] *Lancet*, **1**, 1032 (1935).
[14] *J. Am. Med. Assoc.*, **107**, 1794 (1936).
[15] *J. Am. Chem. Soc.*, **60**, 1015 (1938).

Calcium Mandelate, U.S.P. ($C_6H_5CHOHCOO)_2Ca$, is prepared by reacting a solution of a soluble calcium salt with sodium mandelate. Calcium mandelate occurs as a white, odorless crystalline compound which is slightly soluble in water and insoluble in alcohol.

Being quite insoluble in water, calcium mandelate produces less gastric irritation than the sodium or ammonium salts. It is hydrolyzed in the gastrointestinal tract to liberate the acid which is absorbed and excreted in the urine. It has the same systemic effect as does mandelic acid.

Tartaric Acid, N.F. (Dihydroxysuccinic Acid), HOCO—CHOH—CHOH—COOH, is present in many fruits, particularly in the grape. It is obtained from the wine lees or argol as a by-product of vinous fermentation as the crude potassium bitartrate. Tartaric acid occurs as colorless crystals or a fine crystalline powder which is stable in air and is odorless. It has an acid taste. It is very soluble in water and alcohol and forms insoluble salts with such ions as calcium and ferric.

Tartaric acid was the first compound on which Pasteur made his study of optical activity. He observed that at 27° there was a spontaneous separation of the enantiomorphous sodium antimony tartrates into the D- and the L-salts. He also discovered, with tartaric acid, the biochemical method of separation of optical isomers, the mold *Penicillium glaucum* destroying the D-component. Pasteur further discovered the method of resolution of D- and L-tartaric acids by conversion into the cinchonine salts and separation of the diastereoisomers.

The official tartaric acid is not used as a medicinal agent, but it is used in the manufacture of a number of salts of importance, e.g., salts of alkaloids and of effervescent salts, and for its flavor in beverages.

Potassium Bitartrate, N.F. (Hydrogen Potassium Tartrate, Cream of Tartar), KOCO—CHOH—CHOH—COOH, consists of crystals having a slightly acid taste, soluble in water about 1:162. Administered usually in solution, it acts as a saline cathartic.

Potassium Sodium Tartrate, N.F. (Rochelle Salt), KOCO—CHOH—CHOH—COONa, is a white powder or colorless crystals, soluble in water about 1:0.9, formed when potassium acid tartrate is neutralized with sodium hydroxide or carbonate. Administered in solution in water as such or in *Compound Effervescent Powder, N.F.*, it is used as a saline cathartic.

Citric Acid, U.S.P. (Hydroxytricarballylic Acid),

$$HO—\underset{\underset{CH_2COOH}{|}}{\overset{\overset{CH_2COOH}{|}}{C}}—COOH, \text{ is one}$$

of the most widely occurring natural acids, and biochemically it is indispensable, playing a vital role in the Krebs metabolic cycle as well as in the photosynthetic processes. It was first found in the juice of citrus fruits, and it is present in many other fruits. It is obtained commercially for the most part by the fermentation of sugar solutions with various molds, e.g., *Aspergillis niger* or *Citromyces pfefferianus*.

Citric acid occurs as colorless, translucent crystals or a white crystalline powder with a strongly acid taste. It is efflorescent in the air, very soluble in both alcohol and water. Aqueous solutions are unstable. As a β-hydroxy acid it readily loses water to form aconitic acid, an unsaturated tricarboxylic acid. The citrate ion is useful in preventing discoloration of solutions of tannin containing iron. It forms precipitates with strontium and calcium.

Citric acid is used as a flavor, e.g., as a practical substitute for lemon juice in *Syrup of Citric Acid, U.S.P.*

In therapy a salt rather than the acid is used.

Sodium Citrate, U.S.P., Potassium Citrate, N.F., and **Magnesium Citrate** are salts crystallizing with varying amounts of water, and, being readily soluble, are used in the form of aqueous solutions to secure the effects of the respective metal ions. All of them act as antacids, as diuretics, and as laxatives. Sodium citrate is also used in making *Anticoagulant Sodium Citrate Solution, U.S.P.*, and in the preparation of *Citrated Whole Human Blood, U.S.P.* Magnesium citrate is the chief ingredient in *Magnesium Citrate Solution, N.F.*, used as a pleasant tasting, effective, saline laxative.

Ricinoleic Acid (12-Hydroxy-9-octadecenoic Acid), $CH_3(CH_2)_5CHOHCH_2\text{-}CH\text{=}CH(CH_2)_7COOH$, an unsaturated, hydroxy, open-chain carboxylic acid, constitutes about 80 per cent of the fatty acid portion in the glycerides of castor oil. The acid has a strongly laxative action when taken into the alimentary tract.

Sodium Ricinoleate, N.N.R. (Soricin), is the sodium salt of the fatty acids from castor oil. The product is a white or slightly yellow, odorless or almost odorless powder. It is soluble in water and in alcohol. The aqueous solution is alkaline. Sodium ricinoleate is used as a sclerosing agent for the obliteration of varicose veins.

For levulinic acid, a keto acid, see calcium levulinate, page 516.

Cyclic Hydroxy Acids

Animal bile on hydrolysis affords an acidic fraction composed of a mixture of steroid acids collectively known as bile acids. These are derived from the parent cholanic acid, which in turn is structurally derived from coprostane. The four principal constituents are (1) lithochloic acid, 3α-hydroxycholanic acid, (2)

Coprostane   Cholanic acid

chenodesoxycholic acid, $3\alpha,7\alpha$-dihydroxycholanic acid, (3) desoxycholic acid, $3\alpha,12\alpha$-dihydroxycholic acid, and (4) cholic acid, $3\alpha,7\alpha,12\alpha$-trihydroxycholanic acid. The structures are as shown.

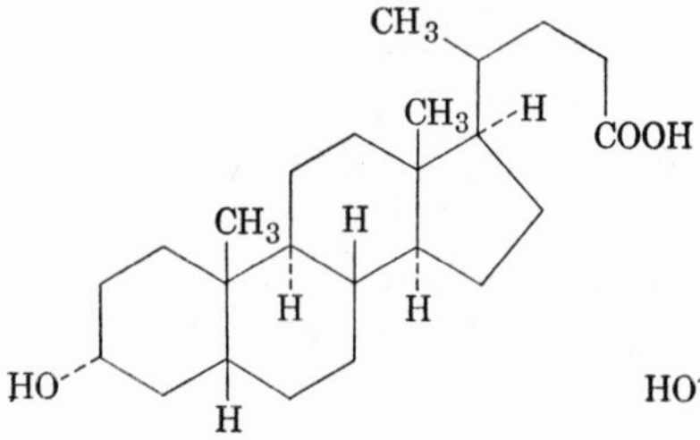

Lithocholic acid

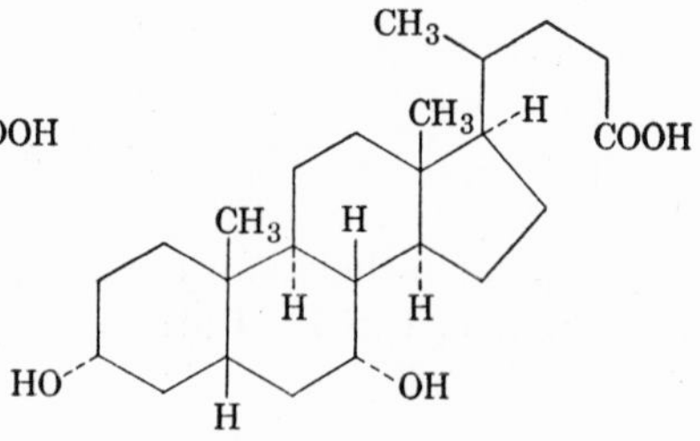

Chenodesoxycholic acid

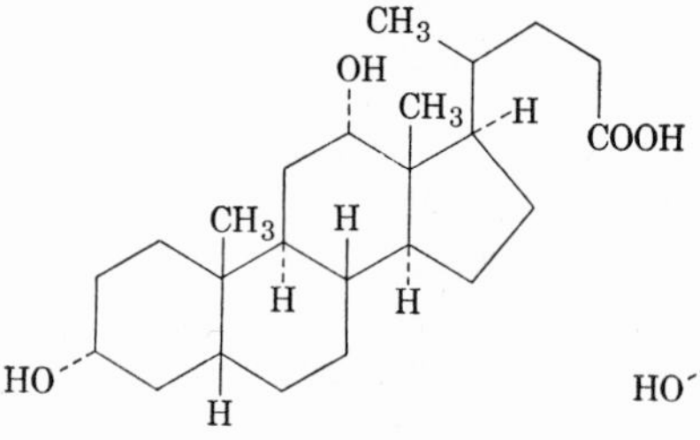

Desoxycholic acid

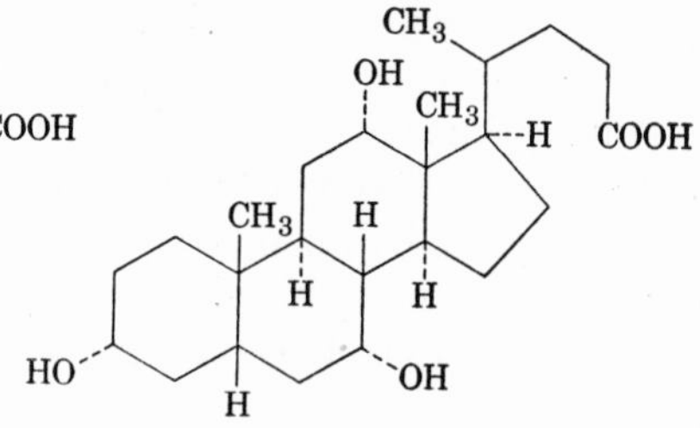

Cholic acid

These acids occur in the bile in peptidelike linkage with either glycine or taurine as water-soluble sodium salts and then are known as glycocholic or taurocholic acid, respectively.

$$C_{23}H_{36}(OH)_3CONHCH_2COOH \xrightarrow{HOH} C_{23}H_{36}(OH)_3COOH + NH_2CH_2COOH$$

Glycocholic acid   Cholic acid   Glycine

$$C_{23}H_{36}(OH)_3CONHCH_2CH_2SO_3H \xrightarrow{HOH}$$

Taurocholic acid

$$C_{23}H_{36}(OH)_3COOH + NH_2CH_2CH_2SO_3H$$

Cholic acid   Taurine

The bile acids are used in therapy in the form of their sodium salts. They are usually prepared from ox bile. The dried bile is extracted with absolute alcohol, and the dissolved bile salts are precipitated by the addition of ether. The resinlike precipitate becomes crystalline on standing. The glycocholate and the taurocholate can be separated by the addition of lead acetate to an aqueous solution of the sodium salts. Lead glycocholate is precipitated, and lead taurocholate can be obtained from the mother liquor by the addition of lead subacetate.

The bile salts are the chief active constituents of bile. They are used along with resinous cathartics to increase the efficiency. They are believed to aid in the emulsification of fat and aid in fat absorption. The bile salts also stimulate secretions by the liver. Bile salts which consist of mixtures of the sodium salts of the bile acids from ox blood are described in N.N.R. The salts are the main constituents of *Ox Bile Extract, N.F.* These products are usually administered in the form of tablets or capsules.

Dehydrocholic Acid (Decholin) is the 3,7,11-triketo derivative of cholanic acid. It is a white to weakly grayish yellow, fluffy powder which is very slightly soluble in water and slightly soluble in alcohol and glacial acetic acid. It is used as a choleretic, producing an increase in the output of bile with decreased viscosity and increased water content. It usually is administered as the sodium salt in tablet form or in solution by injection.

Aromatic Hydroxy Acids

Both *o*- and *p*-hydroxybenzoic acids may be synthesized by an adaptation of the Kolbe synthesis, in which a salt of phenol is heated under pressure with carbon dioxide, as indicated in the accompanying equations.

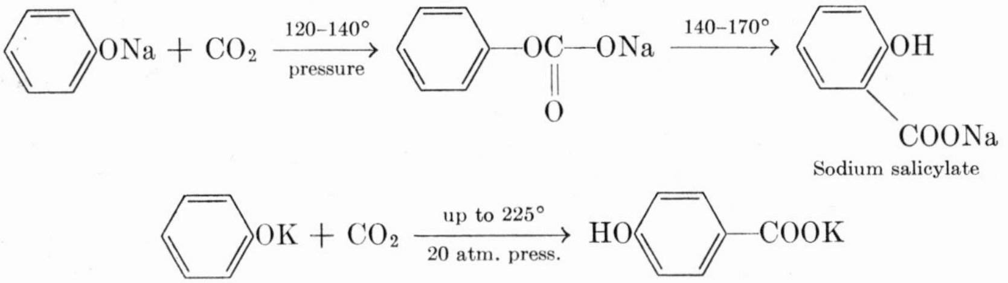

Sodium salicylate

Potassium
p-hydroxybenzoate
(for esters see page 175)

Salicylic acid and closely related compounds present a simple illustration of the obscure relationships that exist between chemical constitution and physiological activity. Phenol is practically inactive, and benzoic acid has been shown to be somewhat effective in the treatment of acute joint rheumatism, but less effective than salicylic acid, whereas phthalic and cinnamic acids are completely ineffective.

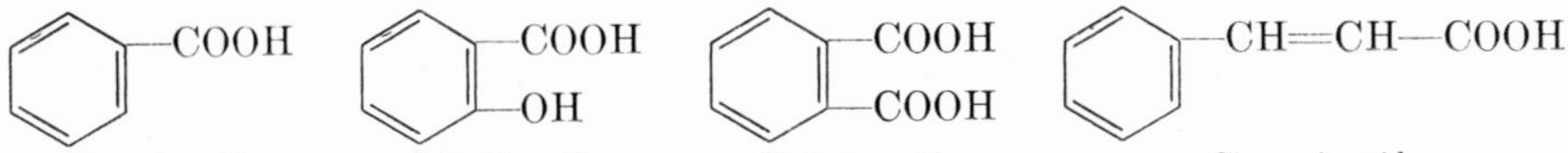

Benzoic acid   Salicylic acid   Phthalic acid   Cinnamic acid

The activity of salicylic acid as an antirheumatic is completely lacking in the *m*- and *p*-derivatives.

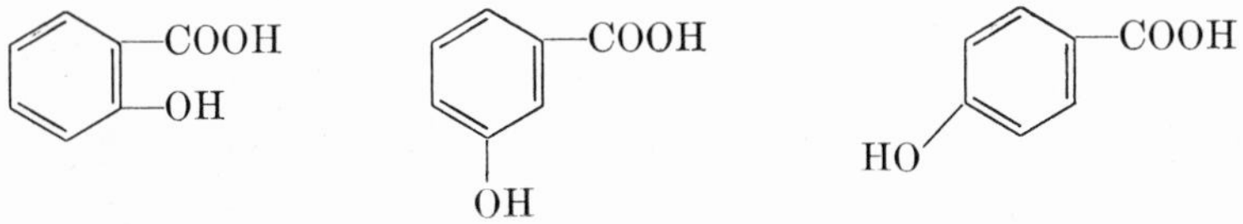

Salicylic acid,   *m*-Hydroxybenzoic acid   *p*-Hydroxybenzoic acid
o-Hydroxybenzoic acid

The higher homologs of salicylic acid are shown, of which the *p*-compound is the most effective, are somewhat less active than salicylic acid in the treatment

o-Cresotic acid   *m*-Cresotic acid   *p*-Cresotic acid

of acute joint rheumatism. It appears that the hydroxyl and carboxyl groups in ortho position are essential for maximum activity.

Salicylates

The value of numerous derivatives of salicylic acid, e.g., acetylsalicylic acid, methyl salicylate, and diplosal, which behave qualitatively like salicylic acid in acute joint rheumatism, depends partly on the salicylic acid liberated from them and partly on their lipoid solubilities and also on other unknown factors.

Salicylic acid and many compounds derived from it produce marked antipyretic and analgesic effects and give relief in rheumatic fever and rheumatic tonsilitis. The different compounds are qualitatively alike but quantitatively different in action. The gastric irritation and unpleasant taste of salicylic acid and its simple salts led to the introduction of less soluble compounds, e.g., esters. It was believed that these compounds would pass through the stomach unchanged, and thus avoid the nausea caused by salicylic acid. It was found that they do pass through the stomach largely unchanged, but the nausea, probably of central origin, remained. The alkyl esters, e.g., methyl salicylate, are absorbed better through the skin and have advantages for external use. The acyl esters, e.g., acetylsalicylic acid, are more strongly antipyretic and analgesic. The phenyl esters are antiseptic.

Replacement of the hydrogen of the hydroxyl group in salicylic acid by acyl radicals yields compounds that are less soluble in water, have a less objectionable taste, and a stronger antipyretic and analgesic action than the salicylate salts. Salicylic acid and other antiseptics act by displacing pantothenic acid from the protein molecule.[16]

Compounds formed by the replacement of the hydrogen in the carboxyl group of salicylic acid are more readily absorbed from the skin and are better for external use than salicylic acid.

Salicylic Acid, U.S.P. (*o*-Hydroxybenzoic Acid), is the most important of the three hydroxybenzoic acids. It was first discovered by Piria in 1839. It is found in the blossoms of *Spiraea ulmaria*, and its methyl ester is the chief constituent in oil of wintergreen.

Salicylates are readily absorbed from the upper intestinal tract, acetylsalicylic acid being absorbed somewhat more slowly; they spread rapidly through the tissues. Seventy to 80 per cent is excreted through the kidney as free acid or as a conjugate with glycine (*o*-hydroxyhippuric acid) or with glucuronic acid.[17]

[16] Ivanovics, *Naturwissenschaften*, **30**, 104 (1942); *C.A.*, **37**, 227 (1943).

[17] Alpen, Mandel, Rodwell, and Smith, *J. Pharmacol. Exptl. Therap.*, **102**, 150 (1951).

Salicylic acid occurs as white, needlelike crystals or as a fluffy, white crystalline powder which has a sweetish followed by an acrid taste. It is stable in air. Salicylic acid displays the characteristic properties of phenols, such as the formation of violet color with ferric ions and the formation of colored compounds, likely quinoids, by oxidizing agents or on standing in alkaline solution. Insoluble salts are formed with heavy metals such as silver, mercury, lead, etc., by virtue of the presence of the carboxyl group. It reacts with boric acid to form borosalicylic acid.

Salicylic acid and its compounds produce marked antipyretic and analgesic effects and give striking relief in the symptoms of acute articular rheumatism. The free acid is an antiseptic, an active irritant, and a slow corrosive; it is used in *Salicylic Acid Collodion, U.S.P.*, and *Salicylic Acid Plaster, U.S.P.*, as a corn remover.

Ammonium Salicylate, N.F., is a white, microcrystalline powder or colorless, lustrous prisms or plates, which is prepared by evaporating a slightly acid solution of salicylic acid and ammonium hydroxide. Its salts are stable in dry air but it is affected by light. It is very soluble in water and alcohol. It is used primarily for the internal administration of salicylic acid.

Sodium Salicylate, U.S.P., is a white, microcrystalline powder or it may have a pinkish tinge. The product is prepared by reacting equimolar quantities of salicylic acid and sodium bicarbonate. It has a faint characteristic odor with a sweet saline taste. It is soluble in water, alcohol, and glycerin. In solution it will darken on standing which may be lessened by the addition of sodium sulfite or bisulfite. Free salicylic acid is precipitated in an acid solution.

It is used for acute articular rheumatism and for its analgesic-antipyretic effect. It is usually given with sodium bicarbonate to lessen gastric distress or in enteric-coated tablets. The use of sodium bicarbonate is not recommended for it has been reported [18] that it decreases the salicylic acid plasma level and increases the amount excreted in the urine.

Strontium Salicylate occurs as a white, colorless crystalline powder, which is prepared by reacting 1 mole of strontium carbonate with 2 moles of salicylic acid. It has a somewhat sweet, salty taste. The salt is affected by light. It is very soluble in water. It is used, as other salicylic acid salts, for its salicylic acid content.

Acetylsalicylic Acid, U.S.P. (Aspirin), was synthesized by Gerhardt many years before it was introduced into therapy by Dreser in 1899. It is prepared by the acetylation of salicylic acid with acetyl chloride in the presence of pyridine or with acetic anhydride. Since the latter method is less expensive, it is the one generally employed industrially. In this process, salicylic acid is heated at 150–160° with an excess of acetic anhydride for 3 hr. and then the excess of acetic anhydride and the acetic acid formed in the reaction are distilled off *in vacuo*, and the residue is recrystallized from benzene or other solvent. The reaction can be carried out at lower temperatures if a promoter such as sulfuric acid is added.

[18] Smith, Gleason, Stoll, and Ogorzalek, *J. Pharmacol. Exptl. Therap.*, **87**, 237 (1946).

Salicylic acid   Acetic anhydride   Acetylsalicylic acid

It is a white, crystalline solid. The melting temperature of acetylsalicylic acid is influenced by the method of heating the melting-point bath. The official product should melt at 135° or above when the determination is made in a bath previously heated to 130°. It is soluble about 1:300 in water and 1:5 in alcohol.

Acetylsalicylic acid is stable in dry air, but, in the presence of moisture, it gradually hydrolyzes into salicylic and acetic acids. It is soluble with decomposition in alkali hydroxides and carbonates.

Acetylsalicylic acid, generally sold under the name *Aspirin*, is probably the the most extensively used analgesic and antipyretic at the present time. In 1946, for example, nearly 10 million pounds were prepared in the United States alone. It is used in tablets, as a powder usually enclosed in capsules, and in admixture with other substances in many pharmaceutical preparations for the treatment of colds, influenza, and other fevers, and of headache, neuralgia, and other pains. The sodium salt is used for the same purposes as the free acid.

The *in vivo* hydrolysis of acetylsalicylic acid has been studied in the rat after intravenous administration. More than 90 per cent was hydrolyzed in 30 to 40 minutes. After oral administration unhydrolyzed acetylsalicylic acid was found in the plasma within 30 minutes and persisted for about two hours.[19]

Soluble Aspirin is the calcium salt of acetylsalicylic acid, $(CH_3COOC_6H_4-COO)_2Ca$. It is a white, crystalline powder, soluble 1:5 in water.

Novaspirin (Salicitrin, Methylene-citrylsalicylic Acid) is the disalicylic acid ester of anhydromethylene citric acid. It is prepared by condensing the dichloride of anhydromethylene citric acid with salicylic acid.

It is a white, crystalline powder, m.p. 153–154°, practically insoluble in water

Novaspirin

[19] Routh, Knouse, and Paul, *Proc. Iowa Acad. Sci.*, **62**, 268 (1955); *C.A.*, **50**, 3629 (1956).

but soluble in alcohol.   Novaspirin is used as an analgesic and antipyretic and is similar to acetylsalicylic acid in action.

Diaspirin, made by condensing succinyl chloride with salicylic acid, and **Salisal** prepared by condensing two molecules of salicylic acid by means of an agent such as thionyl chloride, are of interest.

Diaspirin   Salisal

Methyl Salicylate, U.S.P. (Oil of Gaultheria, Oil of Wintergreen, Oil of Betula, Oil of Sweet Birch), $C_6H_4(OH)COOCH_3$, occurs in oil of wintergreen from *Gaultheria procumbens* and oil of sweet birch from *Betula lenta*.   It is also made synthetically by esterifying salicylic acid with methanol in the presence of sulfuric acid.

$$o\text{-HO}\text{---}C_6H_4COOH + CH_3OH \xrightarrow{(H_2SO_4)} o\text{-HO}\text{---}C_6H_4\text{---}COOCH_3$$

Methyl salicylate

It is a liquid, b.p. 219–224°, slightly soluble in water and readily soluble in alcohol.   The synthetic methyl salicylate and that from *Betula* are optically inactive, but that from *Gaultheria* is slightly levorotatory.

Methyl salicylate has been used internally for the treatment of rheumatism, gout, pleurisy, neuralgia, etc.   It is about two-thirds as toxic as sodium salicylate, and the effects are often delayed.   Possibly the slow action is caused by irregular absorption.   It is used externally for the most part as a counterirritant, usually in solution in fatty oils or in the form of a liniment.   It is also used as a flavor in many pharmaceutical preparations and as a perfume, e.g., in insecticides.

Ethyl Salicylate (Sal Ethyl), $C_6H_4(OH)COOC_2H_5$, the ethyl ester analogous to methyl salicylate, is a liquid, b.p. 230–232°, insoluble in water but soluble in alcohol.   It has the same uses as methyl salicylate but is reported to be less toxic and less irritant.

Spirosal (Monoglycol Salicylate, Glysal), $C_6H_4(OH)COOCH_2CH_2OH$, is the salicylic acid ester of glycol.   It is an oily liquid, distilling at 169–170° at 12 mm., slightly soluble in water, but readily soluble in fixed oils.   Spirosal is used for the same purposes as methyl salicylate but is said to cause less local irritation when applied with friction.

Mesotan (Salmester, Methoxymethyl Salicylate) is prepared by treating sodium salicylate with monochlorodimethyl ether and maintaining the temperature at 40°.

$$HOC_6H_4COONa + ClCH_2OCH_3 \rightarrow HOC_6H_4COOCH_2OCH_3 + NaCl$$

Sodium salicylate   Mesotan

It is an oily liquid, b.p. 153° at 15 mm., slightly soluble in water, but readily soluble in alcohol and fixed oils.

Mesotan is used externally like methyl salicylate as a counterirritant to relieve pain and swelling, especially in rheumatic conditions. It is not an efficient agent for the production of the systemic action of the salicylates.

Sal Ethyl Carbonate is the carbonic acid ester of ethyl salicylate, $[C_6H_4-(COOC_2H_5)O]_2CO$. It is a white, crystalline solid, m.p. 96–99°, insoluble in water and slightly soluble in alcohol.

It possesses the antipyretic and analgesic action of the salicylates. Being insoluble, it does not have the disagreeable taste and does not cause gastric irritation like the soluble salicylates. It is administered in tablets alone, or, when rapid analgesic or antipyretic effects are desired, in combination with amidopyrine.

Phenyl Salicylate, N.F. (Salol), is a white, crystalline powder with a slightly aromatic odor and a characteristic taste, m.p. 42°, practically insoluble in water (about 1:6700) and soluble in most organic solvents. It can be prepared in various ways:

1. By heating salicylic acid at 230°, when CO_2 is eliminated from one molecule of acid and the resulting phenol condenses with the remaining salicylic acid.

2. By heating equimolar quantities of salicylic acid and phenol with phosphorus oxychloride,

$$HOC_6H_4COOH + C_6H_5OH \xrightarrow[120°]{POCl_3} HOC_6H_4COOC_6H_5$$

Salicylic acid   Phenol   Phenyl salicylate

3. By condensing the sodium salt of salicylic acid and sodium phenoxide with carbonyl chloride and steam-distilling the reaction product,

$$HOC_6H_4COONa + C_6H_5ONa + COCl_2 \rightarrow HOC_6H_4COOC_6H_5$$

Sodium salicylate   Phenyl salicylate

Phenyl salicylate is excreted often unchanged in the feces. Its decomposition in the intestines is so slow and incomplete and the absorption of the phenol liberated is so rapid that effective germicidal concentrations are not established. It is used in diarrhea caused by intestinal fermentation, but its action is doubtful because of variability in its degree of hydrolysis. It has been used for enteric coating of pills. It is usually administered as the powder in capsules or cachets. Compressed tablets and pills of it do not disintegrate readily.

Gallic Acid (3,4,5-Trihydroxybenzoic Acid) is found in nutgalls, where it appears as a component of gallotannin. It is described as a reagent in U.S.P. XV. *Bismuth Subgallate, N.F.* (contains between 52 to 57 per cent Bi_2O_3), is used as an astringent, antacid, and protective in the treatment of gastric ulcers.

ACID ANHYDRIDES

Cantharadin is the active principle occurring in two species of insects, namely, Cantharides or Spanish flies from the dried beetles of *Cantharis vesicatoria* and Mylabris or Chinese cantharides from the dried beetles *Mylabris phalerata* or

M. cichorii. Cantharides contains from 0.4 to 1 per cent of cantharidin, and the Mylabris contains from 1 to 1.5 per cent. It consists of colorless crystals, m.p. 218°, which begin to sublime at about 85°. It is slightly soluble in water, alcohol, and most organic solvents.

Cantharidin

Hexahydro-3a,7a-dimethyl-4,7-epoxybenzofuran-1,3-dione

Cantharides is a powerful vesicant and irritant. It is used in the form of the *plaster* and the *cerate*, for counterirritation in rheumatic, neuralgic, and pleurisy pains, etc. It is sometimes used in the form of a tincture in the hope of stimulating hair growth in baldness. Taken internally it is toxic.

PHTHALEINS

Phthaleins are compounds obtained by the condensation of phenols with phthalic anhydride. A general equation illustrates their method of synthesis.

Phthalic anhydride   Phenol   Phenolphthalein

Phenolphthalein, X = H.
Phenoltetrachlorophthalein, X = Cl.
Tetrabromophenophthalein, X = Br.
Phenoltetraiodophthalein, X = I.

Phenolphthalein is used as a laxative. Other compounds of the phthalein type are used in medicine primarily as diagnostic agents.

Phenolphthalein, U.S.P., is prepared by heating a mixture of phenol and phthalic anhydride in the presence of zinc chloride at 115° to 120°. It is a white or slightly yellow, crystalline solid which dissolves in alcohol 1:15 and in solutions of alkalies but is practically insoluble in water.

Phenolphthalein may exist in two tautomeric forms, the one colored and the other colorless. The form predominating depends upon the pH of the solution. This tautomerism is structurally represented on page 166. The color change takes place at pH range 8.3 to 10, making this an indicator sensitive to low hydrogen-ion concentration, i.e., useful for titrating weak acids with alkali.

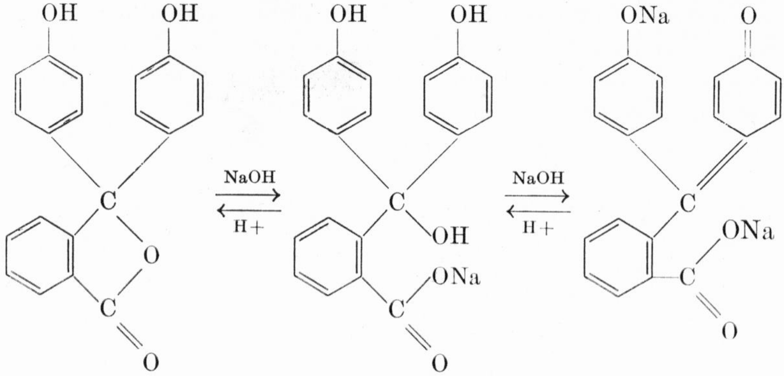

Phenolphthalein,
colorless

Phenolphthalein,
monosodium salt,
colorless

Phenolphthalein,
disodium salt, red

Phenolphthalein is a mild, tasteless purgative used extensively to treat constipation. It is dissolved in the small intestine by the aid of bile salts. Its action is attributed to motor stimulation of the intestines. Eighty-five per cent of the dose is excreted in the feces, and of the remaining 15 per cent some is excreted in the urine. It is used in tablet form or in combination with other laxatives, e.g., mineral oil. It is a common ingredient of many exploited preparations.

The yellow, impure form of phenolphthalein is about three times as active as the colorless product. At one time the greater laxative activity was attributed to the presence of hydroxyanthraquinones, but it has been shown that such contaminants are not present. The greater laxative property of the yellow form remains unexplained.[20]

The purgative action of phenolphthaleins is ascribed to the group (HO—$C_6H_4)_2$=C=. Confirmation of this hypothesis is found in the observation that, in general, compounds containing such a grouping, e.g., Isacen and Istizin, possess purgative activity.[21, 22] The glycosides of the hydroxyanthraquinones contain the same grouping.

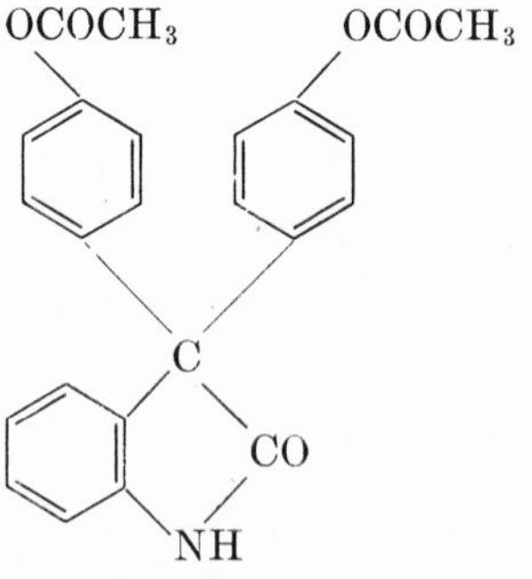

"Isacen"

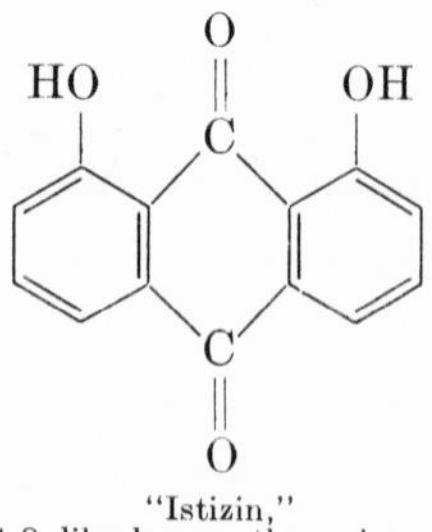

"Istizin,"
1,8-dihydroxyanthraquinone

[20] Hubacher and Doernberg, *J. Am. Pharm. Assoc.*, **37,** 261 (1948).

[21] Kaufman, *Z. angew. Chem.*, **40,** 831, 858 (1927).

[22] Easson *et al.*, *Quart. J. Pharm. and Pharmacol.*, **7,** 509 (1934).

Phenoltetrachlorophthalein was first studied pharmacologically by Abel and Rountree and was introduced by Rountree and his collaborators, Whipple and Marshall, in 1913, as an agent to test liver function. It is an odorless, stable, cream-white powder, practically insoluble in water, and readily soluble in acetone, alcohol, and ether, prepared by condensing tetrachlorophthalic acid with phenol.

Phenoltetrachlorophthalein is used to test the functional activity of the liver by a method perfected by Rosenthal (1922). For this purpose it is administered intravenously in the form of its disodium salt. The normal liver rapidly removes the dye from the blood, but when the liver function is impaired the dye is removed slowly, the rate depending on the degree of impairment.

Sulfobromophthalein Sodium, U.S.P. (Bromosulphalein Sodium, Disodium Phenoltetrabromophthalein Disulfonate), is a product developed by Rosenthal and White in 1924 as a substitute for phenoltetrachlorophthalein in the determination of hepatic function. It is prepared by sulfonation of tetra-

Tetrabromophenolphthalein   Sulfobromophthalein

bromophenolphthalein. It is a white, crystalline powder, readily soluble in water, alcohol, and acetone. The amount remaining in the blood after intravenous injection is determined colorimetrically and considered as a measure of hepatic function in the same manner as phenoltetrachlorophthalein. It has the advantage that only 0.002 g. per kg. of body weight is required for the test, whereas 0.005 g. per kg. of body weight of phenoltetrachlorophthalein is required.

Phentetiothalein Sodium (Tetraiodophenolphthalein Sodium, Disodium Phenoltetraiodophthalein, Iso-iodeikon) was introduced for roentgenologic examination of the gall bladder and to evaluate hepatic function simultaneously. It is prepared from tetraiodophthalic anhydride and phenol and occurs as bronze-purple, hygroscopic granules.

It is claimed to be better suited for intravenous injection than *Iodophthalein Sodium* because (a) smaller dosage may be used, (b) it is better tolerated, and (c) both gall bladder and liver function may be determined simultaneously on one injection.

Iodophthalein Sodium, U.S.P. (Tetraiodophenolphthalein Sodium, Tetraiodophthalein Sodium, Tetiothalein Sodium, Iodeikon), was introduced through the investigations of Graham, Cole, Gopher, and Moore in 1923, for the x-ray visualization of the gall bladder. It is prepared by iodinating phenolphthalein in alkaline solution. It is a violet, odorless, slightly hygroscopic, granular solid,

Phenolphthalein   + 4I$_2$ + 2NaOH →   Iodophthalein sodium

soluble in water and slightly soluble in alcohol.

Soluble iodophthalein is used for the roentgenologic examination of the gall bladder and for the test of liver function. After intravenous administration, it appears in the normal gall bladder in sufficient concentration to cast a shadow to the roentgen rays, and, when the liver function is impaired, it is retained in the blood. The determination of the amounts retained in the blood is used to measure the extent of liver impairment.

Fluorescein Sodium, U.S.P. (Soluble Fluorescein, Resorcinolphthalein Sodium), is a compound prepared by condensing resorcinol with phthalic anhydride in the presence of a dehydrating agent such as zinc chloride or sulfuric acid and converting the product to the sodium salt. The quinoid form in which fluorescein

Phthalic anhydride   Resorcinol   Fluorescein   NaOH →

Fluorescein sodium

exists as the disodium salt is an orange-red powder which dissolves readily in water to form fluorescent solutions. Upon treatment with acids, the quinoid tautomer is destroyed and the fluorescence disappears.

Soluble fluorescein is used as a diagnostic agent in ophthalmologic work. A dilute solution, usually 2 per cent, does not stain the normal cornea, but ulcers or parts deprived of epithelium and diseased areas of the endothelium are stained green and foreign bodies appear in a green ring. Loss of substance from the conjunctiva is indicated by a yellow coloration.

Phenolsulfonphthalein, U.S.P. (Phenol Red), is a phthalein which may be looked upon as phenolphthalein in which a C=O group has been replaced by an SO_2 group. It is prepared by heating saccharin with phenol in the presence of sulfuric acid. It is a red, crystalline powder which is relatively insoluble in

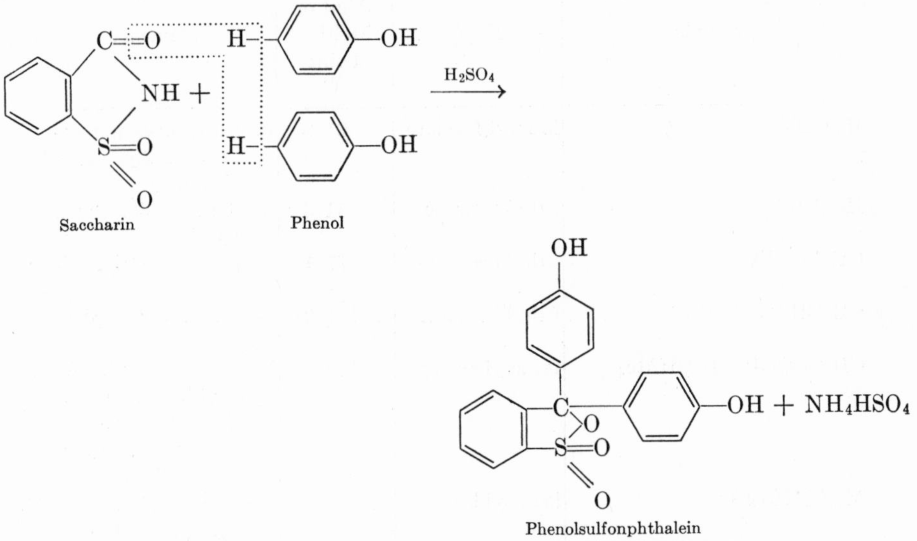

Saccharin   Phenol

Phenolsulfonphthalein

most solvents, but it dissolves in alkali solutions with the formation of a red color. The color change may be explained by a tautomeric shift as in phenolphthalein.

Phenolsulfonphthalein is employed as a diagnostic agent to determine the functional activity of the kidney. The test is based on the fact that the monosodium salt of phenolsulfonphthalein injected intramuscularly or intravenously is excreted by the urine in a shorter time interval when the kidney function is normal than it is when deficient functional activity exists. The quantitative determination of the amount of phenolsulfonphthalein excreted in the urine makes possible the estimation of the degree of functional deficiency.

ESTERS

Esters of Aliphatic Acids

The esters of the aliphatic acids comprise a very large group of compounds, which, with few exceptions, are unimportant as medicinal agents. Administered internally, they give some of the activity of the component parts of the respective esters but only to a slight degree since they are slowly hydrolyzed.

The esters of the organic acids are generally insoluble in water, soluble in ether, benzene, petroleum hydrocarbons, chloroform, etc. The lower, volatile members of the series have a pleasant odor and often are present in the natural fruit essences, as reference to Table XV will show.

TABLE XV

Some Esters

Formula	Name	Boiling Point or Melting Point °C.	Comments
HCOOMe	Methyl formate	31.8	Probably does not occur naturally. It is quite toxic.
HCOOEt	Ethyl formate	54.3	Used in artificial rum or arak.
CH_3COOEt	Ethyl acetate	77.1	Used as industrial solvent.
$CH_3CH_2CH_2COOEt$	Ethyl butyrate	121.3	Constituent in pineapples.
$CH_3COOCH_2CH_2CHMe_2$	Isoamyl acetate	142.5	Found in pear oil. As synthetic banana oil it is used as solvent for gun cotton and in bronzing liquid.
Me_2CHCH_2CO $\mid$ $OCH_2CH_2CHMe_2$	Isoamyl isovalerate	194	Found in apples.
$CH_3CH_2CH_2COO(CH_2)_4CH_3$	Amyl butyrate	184.8	Apricotlike odor.
$CH_3COO(CH_2)_7CH_3$	Octyl acetate	—	Found in oranges.
Me_2CHCH_2O $\mid$ $OC-C_6H_4-OH\text{-}o$	Isobutyl salicylate	—	Occurs in orchid perfume.
$Me_2CHCH_3CH_2O$ $\mid$ $OC-C_6H_4-OH$	Isoamyl salicylate	273	Occurs in orchid perfume.
$MeO-OC-C_6H_4-OH\text{-}o$	Methyl salicylate	223.3	Oil of wintergreen.
$MeOOC-C_6H_4-NH_2\text{-}o$	Methyl anthranilate	135_{15}	Occurs naturally in oil of neroli and in jasmine flowers. Used as grape odor.
$Me(CH_2)_{14}COO(CH_2)_{15}Me$	Cetyl palmitate	m.p.54	Chief constituent of spermaceti.
$Me(CH_2)_{14}COO(CH_2)_{29}Me$	Myricyl palmitate	m.p.72	Chief constituent of beeswax.
$Me(CH_2)_{24}COO(CH_2)_{29}Me$	Myricyl cerotate	—	Chief constituent of carnauba wax, Chinese waxes, etc.

Esterification of the carboxyl group in acids yields odoriferous compounds that are extensively used in perfumery and in the preparation of artificial flavors, e.g., ethyl formate (essence of rum), isoamyl acetate (pear oil), ethyl butyrate (pineapple oil), isoamyl isovalerate (apple oil), and a mixture of ethyl butyrate and amyl acetate (banana oil). Many other artificial essences are prepared by blending esters together and with other aromatic compounds such as aldehydes and ketones.

Acetic acid esters occur very extensively in nature. Plants apparently utilize this acid to detoxify many substances such as alcohols and phenols. Reference to the constituents of the volatile oils indicates in part the occurrence of acetic acid in such combinations.

The esters of the aliphatic acids with most of the hydroxyl compounds are considered under the respective hydroxyl compounds because they are closely related in physiological activities to the alcohols from which the esters are derived. In general, it may be said that an aliphatic acid combined with an active alcohol or phenol detoxifies the hydroxyl compound by decreasing the concentration of active component present at any one time through gradual hydrolysis of the ester. If the ester is sufficiently stable, the hydroxyl compound may be completely inactivated.

Many esters of the higher straight-chain normal alcohols with the longer straight-chain aliphatic acids occur in the natural waxes and are of commercial importance. These waxes, whose chief function in the plant seems to be to provide protection either against penetration of water (e.g., as in the leaves of the evergreen and in the skin of fruits such as the plum or grape) or against loss of water by evaporation in hot dry climates, and perhaps against fungal invasion, on hydrolysis form monohydric alcohols and monobasic carboxylic acids. The acids which are found in waxes include palmitic ($n\text{-}C_{15}H_{31}COOH$), cerotic ($n\text{-}C_{25}H_{51}COOH$), melissic ($n\text{-}C_{29}H_{59}COOH$); and among the alcohols are found cetyl ($n\text{-}C_{16}H_{33}OH$), ceryl ($n\text{-}C_{26}H_{53}OH$), and melissyl or myricyl ($n\text{-}C_{30}H_{61}OH$).

Many esters of polyhydric alcohols have been introduced commercially for use as hydrophilic ointment bases, emulsifying agents, dispersing agents, wetting agents, detergents, etc. They are employed extensively in pharmaceutical, cosmetic, insecticide, and other industries to alter the stability, miscibility, spreadability, consistency, penetration, etc., of products. Many of the commercial products are not pure compounds but consist of mixtures. Some typical compounds are: diethylene glycol monolaurate, propylene glycol stearate, glyceryl monostearate, and mannitol oleate.

White Wax and **Yellow Wax, U.S.P.** (Beeswax), consist mostly of a mixture of the esters of primary alcohols containing from 24 to 34 carbon atom chains esterified with fatty acids containing from 24 to 34 carbon atom chains together with paraffin hydrocarbons containing 25 to 33 carbon atom chains, some free acids, and alcohols. The natural wax is yellow, m.p. about 65°; when bleached, it yields white beeswax. It is used as a protective in the form of cerates, which may be medicated, and to raise the melting point of ointments and various cosmetic products.

Spermaceti, U.S.P., is obtained from the head of the sperm whale, m.p. about 42–50°, and it is almost pure cetyl palmitate. It is used to raise the melting point of pharmaceutical and cosmetic products such as ointments and creams.

Glyceryl Triacetate, N.F. (Triacetin), is prepared by heating a mixture of glacial acetic acid and glycerin. It is a colorless, oily liquid with a slight fatty

$$
\begin{array}{ll}
CH_2\!-\!OH & CH_2\!-\!OOC\!-\!CH_3 \\
| & | \\
CH\!-\!OH + 3CH_3\!-\!COOH \rightarrow & CH\!-\!OOC\!-\!CH_3 + 3H_2O \\
| & | \\
CH_2\!-\!OH & CH_2\!-\!OOC\!-\!CH_3
\end{array}
$$

odor and a bitter taste. It is soluble in water and in alcohol.

It is used in pharmacy primarily as a solvent for chlorazodin. It is being employed to prepare stable, nonirritating solutions of barbiturates which can be autoclaved.

Glyceryl Monostearate, N.F. (Monostearin), $CH_2OHCHOHCH_2OCOC_{17}$-H_{35}, is the monostearyl ester of glycerol. The official product contains traces of the di- and tri-ester. It occurs as a white, waxlike solid, beads, or flake. It dissolves in hot solvents such as alcohol and mineral or fixed oils but it is insoluble in water. It may be dispersed in hot water by the addition of a small amount of soap or a surface active agent.

It is used in pharmacy primarily as an emulsifying agent and a stabilizer for ointments.

Carbonic acid esters of the phenols have been extensively used. Whereas the phenols are irritant, toxic, and unpleasant-tasting compounds, the carbonic acid esters are insoluble and nonirritant. When administered, they are hydrolyzed and gradually liberate the phenol in the intestinal tract. Since the concentration of the phenolic substance is not great at any one time and is distributed throughout the intestine, the irritant and toxic effects are almost entirely eliminated.

The carbonic acid esters are insoluble in water but soluble in alcohol and ether. They are usually administered as the powder in capsules or tablets and have the same uses as the phenols from which they are derived.

Creosote Carbonate (Creosotate) is a mixture of carbonates derived from the various constituents of creosote. It is prepared by treating an alkaline solution of creosote with phosgene. It is a colorless or yellowish, viscid liquid which is immiscible in water but miscible in alcohol and fixed oils.

It is used as an intestinal antiseptic and as an expectorant. It produces less gastrointestinal irritation and nausea than creosote.

Chaulmoogric acid and hydnocarpic acid were shown by Power to be the chief constituents of the fatty oil obtained from the seeds of various trees of the Taraktogenos and Hydnocarpus genus. The oil from these seeds had been used since antiquity in India against leprosy. Prolonged treatment of patients with the impure oil, administered by mouth, could not be carried out because of its irritant action. Efforts to overcome this irritant action resulted in the preparation and general use of ethyl chaulmoograte and ethyl hydnocarpate prepared from the respective purified acids. The product most generally used is a mixture of the ethyl esters of the acids obtained from chaulmoogra oil.

Ethyl Chaulmoograte is a clear, pale yellow liquid, insoluble in water but soluble in alcohol, chloroform, and ether. It is composed of compounds such as those shown.

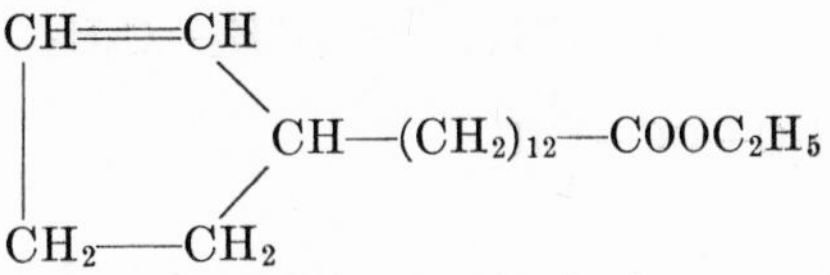

$$CH{=\!=}CH$$
$$\diagdown$$
$$CH{-}(CH_2)_{12}{-}COOC_2H_5$$
$$\diagup$$
$$CH_2{-\!-}CH_2$$

Ethyl chaulmoograte

$$CH{=\!=}CH$$
$$\diagdown$$
$$CH{-}(CH_2)_{10}{-}COOC_2H_5$$
$$\diagup$$
$$CH_2{-\!-}CH_2$$

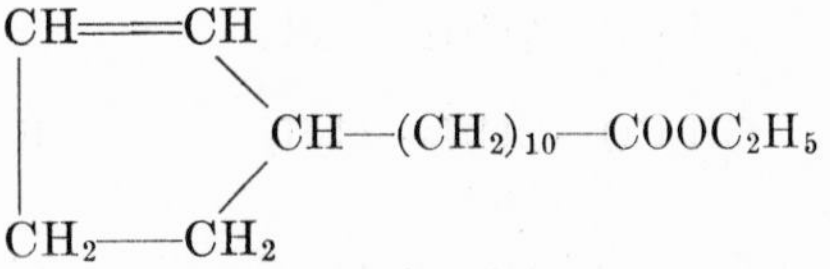

Ethyl hydnocarpate

The esters are usually administered alone or admixed with cod liver oil or other medicaments. They are often given by mouth and by intramuscular injection.

Numerous other compounds closely related to the unsaturated acids found in chaulmoogra oil have been studied. These have not proved superior to the natural fatty acids as agents for the treatment of leprosy.

Pyrethrins are constituents that occur in Dalmation insect flowers, *Chrysanthemum cinerariaefolium*. Staudinger and Ruzicka [23] isolated two active products to which they assigned the structures indicated. They are effective insecticides.

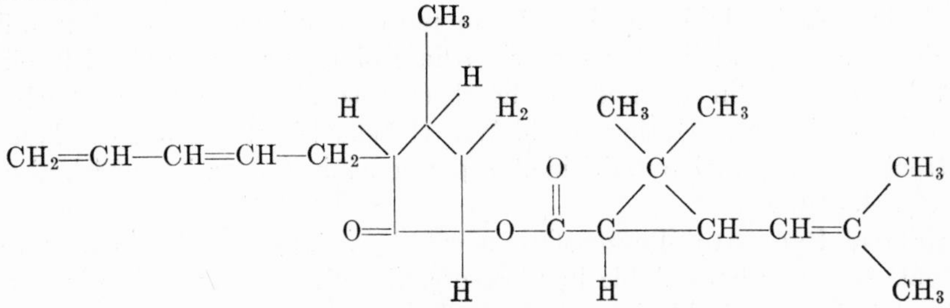

Pyrethrin I

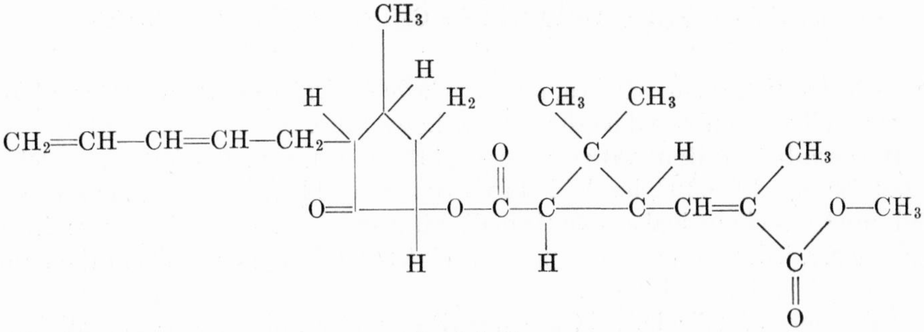

Pyrethrin II

Benzyl Succinate, the dibenzyl ester of succinic acid, is an almost tasteless, crystalline powder, stable in air, insoluble in water but soluble in alcohol, ether,

[23] *Helv. Chim. Acta*, **7**, 177, 210, 212, 236, 246, 377, 406, 448 (1924).

chloroform, and fixed oils. It is reported to be a nontoxic, nonhabit-forming antispasmodic. It lowers the tonus of smooth muscle. It is used to treat dysmenorrhea, intestinal colic, angina pectoris, renal and biliary colic, asthma, and other disturbances caused by spasm. It is usually administered in the form of tablets.

$$CH_2CO-OCH_2-C_6H_5$$
$$|$$
$$CH_2CO-OCH_2-C_6H_5$$
Benzyl succinate

$$CH-CO-OCH_2-C_6H_5$$
$$||$$
$$H_5C_6-CH_2O-OC-CH$$
Benzyl fumarate

Benzyl Fumarate, the dibenzyl ester of fumaric acid, is an almost tasteless solid. Its properties and uses are similar to those of benzyl succinate. It is usually administered in the form of tablets.

Esters of Aromatic Acids

Benzyl Benzoate, U.S.P., occurs naturally in Peru balsam and in some resins. It may be prepared synthetically from benzoyl chloride and benzyl alcohol. It is a colorless liquid with an aromatic odor and a burning taste, in-

$$C_6H_5COCl + HOCH_2C_6H_5 \rightarrow C_6H_5COOCH_2C_6H_5 + HCl$$
Benzyl benzoate

soluble in water, soluble in alcohol and most organic solvents. It is mildly anesthetic and is sometimes incorporated into ointments or dissolved in oil for the treatment of skin diseases. It has been used as an antispasmodic but is said to be inefficient. During World War II benzyl benzoate was employed in the tropics as an effective "miticide," a poison against the mites which abound in warm climates.

Guaiacol Benzoate (Benzosol) is a colorless, practically tasteless powder, insoluble in water but soluble in most organic solvents. It is prepared from guaiacol and benzoyl chloride. It is used as an antiseptic expectorant, as an

$$o\text{-}CH_3OC_6H_4OH + C_6H_5COCl \rightarrow C_6H_5COOC_6H_4OCH_3\text{-}o + HCl$$
Guaiacol benzoate

intestinal antiseptic in diarrhea, and to relieve cough in pulmonary tuberculosis. It is usually administered as the powder in capsules.

Betanaphthol Benzoate (Benzonaphthol) consists of colorless, tasteless crystals, m.p. 107–110°, insoluble in water but soluble in most organic solvents. It is used as an intestinal antiseptic in diarrhea and dysentery and as a vermifuge. Externally, it is used in 3 to 10 per cent ointments as a parasiticide in the treatment of alopecia, scabies, eczema, etc.

The esters of salicylic acid are described under salicylates. The aliphatic esters of p-hydroxybenzoic acid (the synthesis of the acid is indicated on page 159) are more commonly known as the *parabens*, compounds with useful bacteriostatic and mold-inhibiting properties.[24]

[24] Bandelin, *Drug & Cosmetic Ind.*, **64**, 430 (1949).

Methylparaben, U.S.P. (Methyl *p*-Hydroxybenzoate, Tegosept M, Methyl Parasept, Methylben), *p*-HOC$_6$H$_4$COOCH$_3$, is a slightly water-soluble, crystalline powder. It is employed as a preservative in pharmaceutical preparations. Concentrations of 0.05 and 0.5 per cent are used in *Hydrophilic Ointment, U.S.P.*

Propylparaben, U.S.P. (Propyl *p*-Hydroxybenzoate, Tegosept P, Propyl Parasept, Propylben), *p*-HOC$_6$H$_4$COOCH$_2$CH$_2$CH$_3$, a white powder or colorless crystals, slightly soluble in water, is reported to be about four to six times as effective as methylparaben. It is preferred to molds and, because of greater solubility in oil, is used in oil and fat preparations.

Tannins include ester types that on hydrolysis usually yield gallic acid as one component.

Chemically the term tannin includes all compounds possessing the property of transforming skins, of precipitating lime solutions, and of forming insoluble precipitates with alkaloids and lead salts. In addition to the ester group there is another which is related to anthocyanine and flavone.

The ester group of tannins includes depsides, which are esters of aromatic acids with oxyaromatic acids. A typical example of a didepside isolated from natural sources is lecanoric acid. Another is galloylgallic acid. Glucogallin and Hamemelitannin are examples of tannins that hydrolyze to gallic acid and a carbohydrate.

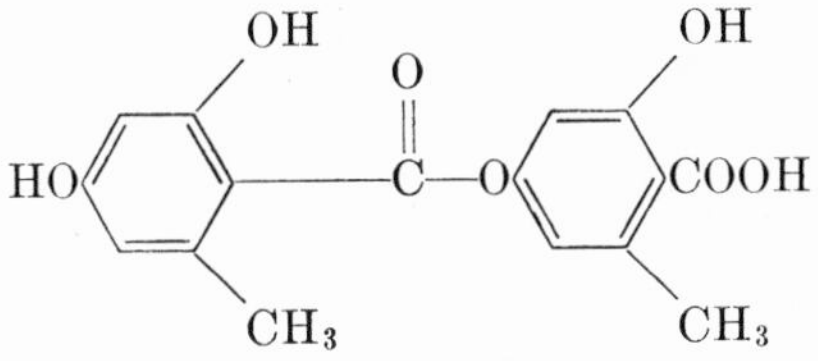

Lecanoric acid

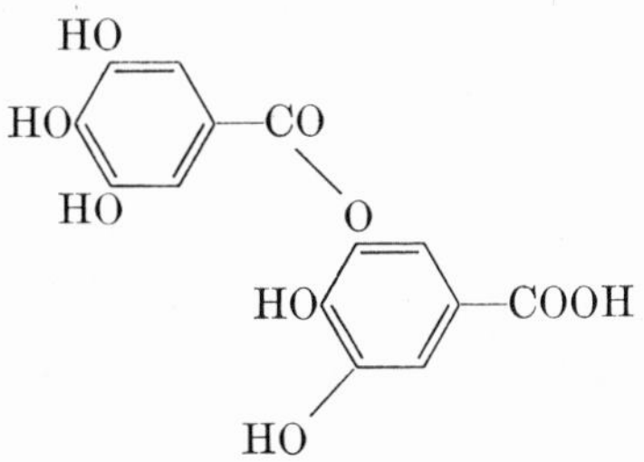

m-Galloylgallic acid

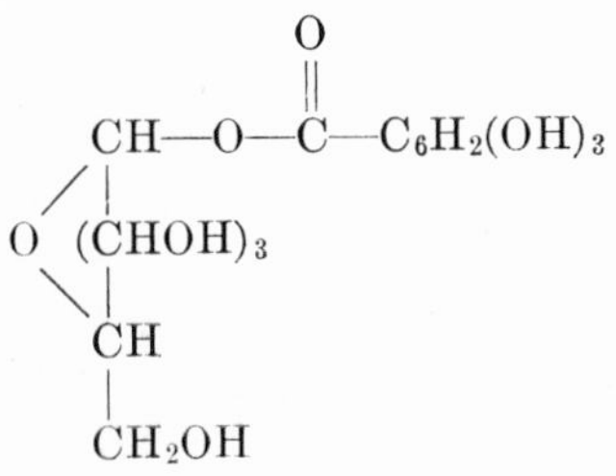

Glucogallin

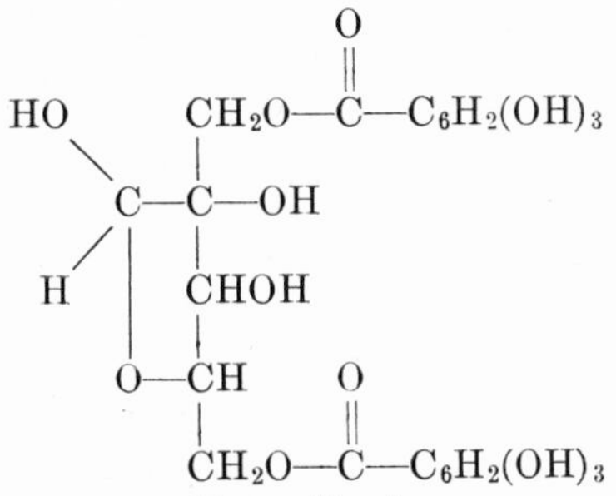

Hamemelitannin

Tannic Acid, N.F. (Gallotannic Acid, Tannin), is a mixture of compounds and is prepared from nutgalls by extraction with water saturated with ether. It is a light yellow, amorphous powder of strongly astringent taste, very soluble in water, alcohol, and glycerol and insoluble in ether, chloroform, and petroleum benzin. It is used as an astringent, hemostatic, and protein coagulant in various preparations such as: *Tannic Acid Glycerite, N.F.*, and *Styptic Collodion.*

Tannic acid in the form of a freshly prepared solution has been used extensively in the treatment of burns. The solution, applied as a wet dressing or sprayed on, precipitates the proteins in the burned surface to form a protective and mildly antiseptic coating beneath which the new tissue may be regenerated. It has been employed internally in the treatment of diarrhea. As such, it causes gastric irritation and nausea.

LACTONES

Intramolecular esters, compounds that have formed an ester with hydroxyl belonging to the same molecule, are known as lactones. In compounds where the hydroxyl group is in the γ- or the δ-position with respect to the carboxyl group, these two functional groups are in such position that they will readily react with each other to form an inner ester. The lactones, it will be observed,

$$
\begin{array}{c}
CH_2\!-\!CH_2 \\
|\qquad\; | \\
R\!-\!CH\quad C\!=\!O \\
|\qquad\; | \\
OH\quad OH
\end{array}
\xrightarrow{\;-HOH\;}
\begin{array}{c}
CH_2\!-\!CH_2 \\
|\qquad\; | \\
R\!-\!CH\quad C\!=\!O \\
\;\diagdown\;\diagup \\
O
\end{array}
$$
γ-Lactone

$$
\begin{array}{c}
\qquad\quad R \\
\qquad\quad | \\
CH_2\!-\!CH\!-\!OH \\
\diagup \\
CH_2 \\
\diagdown \\
CH_2\!-\!CO\!-\!OH
\end{array}
\xrightarrow{\;-HOH\;}
\begin{array}{c}
\qquad CH_2 \\
\diagup\quad\diagdown \\
CH_2\qquad CH_2 \\
|\qquad\qquad | \\
CO\qquad CHR \\
\diagdown\quad\diagup \\
O
\end{array}
$$
δ-Lactone

are stable five- or six-membered heterocycles. They show many of the properties of the esters.

γ-Lactones derived from the higher acids, including γ-hepta-, γ-nono-, and γ-undecalactones, have pleasant odors and are used in the perfume industry.

The lactone portion of the cardiac glycosides (page 119 *et seq.*) is the γ-lactone of the enol form of a γ-aldehyde-acid, as indicated. Hydrolysis of this lactone

$$
\begin{array}{c}
-C\!-\!-\!-\!CH_2 \\
\|\qquad\quad | \\
C\qquad C\!=\!O \\
\diagup\;\diagdown\;\diagup \\
H\qquad O
\end{array}
\xrightarrow{HOH}
\left[
\begin{array}{c}
-C\!-\!-\!-\!CH_2 \\
\|\qquad\qquad | \\
C\qquad\; C\!=\!O \\
\diagup\; |\qquad\; | \\
H\; OH\quad OH
\end{array}
\right]
\rightarrow
\begin{array}{c}
H \\
| \\
-C\!-\!-\!-\!CH_2 \\
|\qquad\qquad | \\
HC\qquad C\!=\!O \\
\|\qquad\qquad | \\
O\qquad OH
\end{array}
$$

Theoretical enol γ-Aldehyde acid

yields the theoretical enol, which readily shifts to the more stable γ-aldehyde-acid; reconversion of the acid into a lactone is possible, but it involves one of the hydroxyl groups in the polycyclic nucleus of the aglycon and does not regenerate the original lactone necessary for cardiac activity.

Ascorbic Acid, U.S.P. (Vitamin C), was isolated in crystalline form by Szent-Györgyi from various vegetable sources and from the adrenal glands.[25] Its constitution was established in 1933, and it was successfully synthesized later in the same year.[26] It widely is distributed in nature, and all animals seem to have the capacity to synthesize their requirements of this vitamin, except the primates and guinea pigs. Deprivation of vitamin C in humans results in deterioration of physiological functions, ending in scurvy.

The industrial synthesis of ascorbic acid is shown in summary.

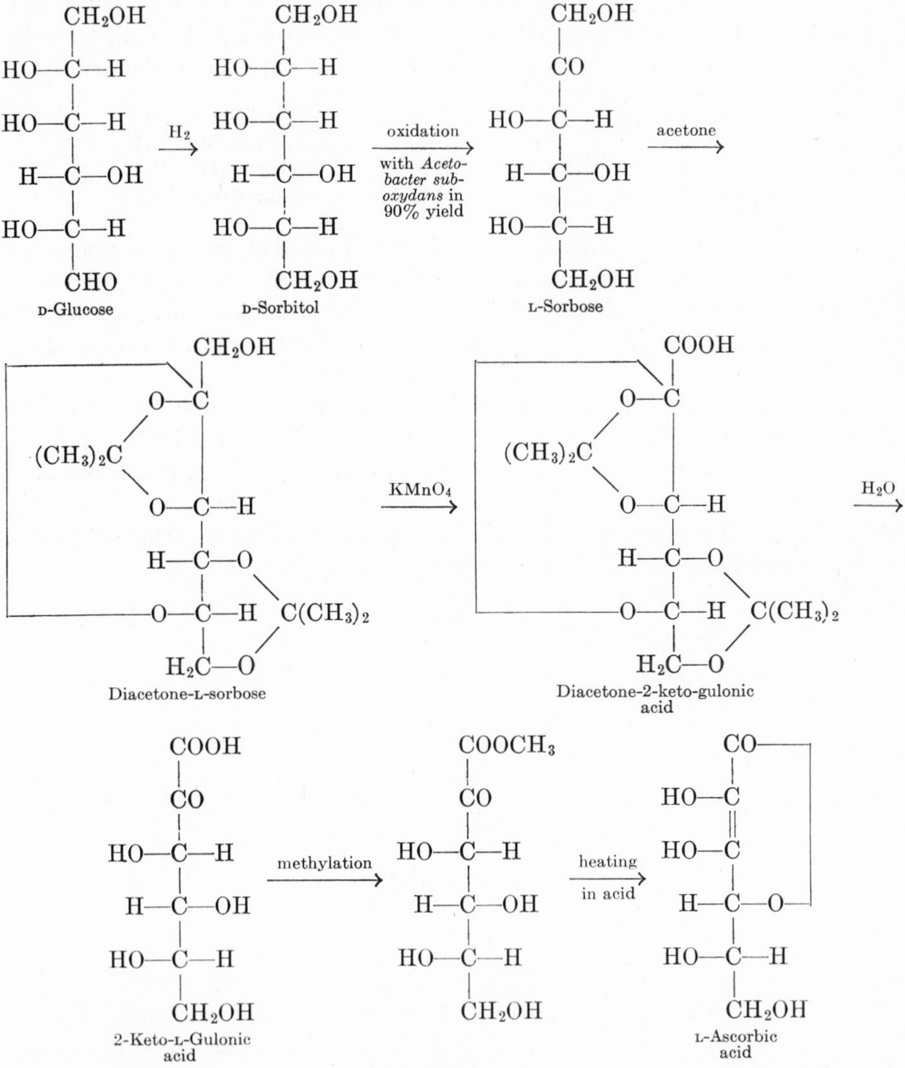

Reaction scheme:

D-Glucose $\xrightarrow{H_2}$ D-Sorbitol $\xrightarrow[\substack{\text{with Aceto-}\\ \text{bacter sub-}\\ \text{oxydans in}\\ 90\% \text{ yield}}]{\text{oxidation}}$ L-Sorbose $\xrightarrow{\text{acetone}}$

Diacetone-L-sorbose $\xrightarrow{KMnO_4}$ Diacetone-2-keto-gulonic acid $\xrightarrow{H_2O}$

2-Keto-L-Gulonic acid $\xrightarrow{\text{methylation}}$ (COOCH$_3$ compound) $\xrightarrow[\text{in acid}]{\text{heating}}$ L-Ascorbic acid

[25] Szent-Györgyi, *Biochem. J.*, **22**, 1387 (1928).
[26] Reichstein *et al.*, *Helv. Chim. Acta*, **16**, 1019 (1933); Haworth, *J. Chem. Soc.*, **1933**, 1419.

The official ascorbic acid is an odorless, white or slightly yellow, crystalline powder which slowly darkens on exposure to light, m.p. 189–192°. It is soluble in water about 1:3, in alcohol about 1:25, and in glycerol about 1:100; it is insoluble in benzene, chloroform, ether, and most fatty oils. It is relatively stable in air when dry but it deteriorates rapidly in aqueous solution at ordinary temperatures. It is a strong reducing agent that is reversibly oxidized to dehydroascorbic acid which is active, and it may be further oxidized to oxalic acid and trihydroxybutyric acid. The oxidation is hastened by alkalies and retarded by acids. Ascorbic acid is one of the least stable vitamins and may be largely destroyed in the canning of foods.

The unit of potency is defined as the antiscorbutic activity of 0.05 mg. of L-ascorbic acid. Thus 1 g. of the crystalline vitamin is equal to 20,000 units.

The daily requirements of ascorbic acid have been variously estimated as:

Infancy and childhood	25 to 75 mg. (500–1500 units)
Adolescence and maturity	75 to 150 mg. (1500–3000 units)
Pregnancy and lactation	150 to 300 mg. (3000–6000 units)
Acute deficiency	200 to 500 mg. (4000–10,000 units)

It is used in scurvy as a prophylactic and as a curative agent. It is reported to aid in the healing of peptic and duodenal ulcers, trench mouth, etc., and to be of value in some types of urticaria. It is usually administered in the form of tablets. No evidence of toxic effect from very large doses of ascorbic acid has been reported.

Ascorbic acid probably acts in regulating the oxidation-reduction processes in the living cell. Whether it takes part in enzyme formation is doubtful. Its biological activity is stereospecific. Various isomers have been synthesized and found to have little or no antiscorbutic activity; thus, L-glucoascorbic acid has about a fortieth the activity of vitamin C, and the D-glucoascorbic acid fed to mice and rats produced conditions resembling scurvy.[27]

```
O—CO
   |
   C—OH
   ||
   C—OH
   |
 —C—H
   |
H—C—OH
   |
H—C—OH
   |
  CH₂OH
```

D-Glucoascorbic acid

Santonin, N.F., was isolated from *Artemesia maritima* var. *anthelminticum* Linné, by Kehler and Alms in 1829, but the plant had been used since early

[27] *Encyclopedia of Chemical Technology*, Vol. 2, Interscience, New York, p. 159.

times as an anthelmintic. Caius and Mhaskar [28] showed that santonin is definitely effective in the treatment of infestations with ascaris, but a large proportion of the worms are only injured and not killed. Consequently, a large number of synthetic products have been made in an effort to improve the activity of compounds of this type. It is of interest to note that in all these compounds the lactone structure seems to be essential for activity.[29, 30] The formula generally accepted for santonin is a eudalene type of sesquiterpenoid.

Santonin

Santonin forms colorless crystals, m.p. 170–173°, insoluble in water but soluble in most organic solvents which become yellow on exposure to light. It is used as an anthelmintic against ascaris, usually being administered as the powder in capsules.

[28] *Indian J. Med. Research*, **11**, 377 (1923).
[29] Oettingen and Garcia, *J. Pharmacol.*, **36**, 355 (1929).
[30] Rosenmund and Schapiro, *Arch. Pharm.* (Berlin), **272**, 313 (1934).

CHAPTER

7

Amines and Amine Derivatives

AMINES

Amines are organic compounds in which one or more hydrogens of ammonia have been replaced by similar or different groups to form primary, secondary, or tertiary amines, respectively, depending upon the number of substituents. Amines of low molecular weight are gases at ordinary temperature and pressure, and those of higher molecular weight are liquids or solids which are soluble in ether. The nomenclature and some of the physical properties of some of the simpler amines are summarized in Table XVI.

Amines have certain properties in common with ammonia; they give an alkaline reaction in an aqueous solution because they behave as proton acceptors, thus affording an ammonium ion and giving rise to a high concentration of hydroxyl ions in solution. As may be noted from Table XVI, some of the simple amines are more basic than ammonia, for which the ionization constant is 1.8×10^{-5}. Amines react with acids to form salts; the unshared pair of electrons of nitrogen accepts the hydrogen ion with the formation of a covalent bond. The nitrogen-containing group thus acquires a positive charge and functions in an aqueous solution as a cation, which, like, for example, the cation of an alkali metal, unites with an anion to form a salt.

$$RNH_2 + H^+ \rightarrow RNH_3^+ \xrightarrow{X^-} RNH_3X$$

$$R_2NH + H^+ \rightarrow R_2NH_2^+ \xrightarrow{X^-} R_2NH_2X$$

$$R_3N + H^+ \rightarrow R_3NH^+ \xrightarrow{X^-} R_3NHX$$

180

TABLE XVI

AMINES

Molecular Formula	Structure	Name	B. P. °C.	M. P. °C.	Sp. Gr.	Dissociation Constant at 25° $k \times 10^{-4}$
CH_5N	CH_3NH_2	Methylamine	−6.5	−92.5	0.699_{-11}	5.0
C_2H_7N	$(CH_3)_2NH$	Dimethylamine	7.4	−96.0	0.680_0	7.4
	$C_2H_5NH_2$	Ethylamine	16.6	−80.6	0.689	5.6
C_3H_9N	C_2H_5—NH—CH_3	Methylethylamine	—	—	—	—
	$(CH_3)_3N$	Trimethylamine	3.5	−124	0.662_{-5}	0.74
	$CH_3CH_2CH_2NH_2$	n-Propylamine	48.7	−83	0.719	4.7
	$(CH_3)_2CHNH_2$	Isopropylamine	34	−101.2	0.694	5.3
$C_4H_{11}N$	$CH_3(CH_2)_3NH_2$	n-Butylamine	76	−50.5	0.740	—
	$C_2H_5CH(CH_3)NH_2$	sec-Butylamine	63	−104.5	0.718	4.4
	$(CH_3)_2CHCH_2NH_2$	Isobutylamine	68	−85.5	0.736	3.1
	$(CH_3)_3CNH_2$	tert-Butylamine	43.8	67.5	0.696	—
	$C_2H_5N(CH_3)_2$	Ethyldimethylamine	—	—	—	—
	$(C_2H_5)_2NH$	Diethylamine	56	−50	0.711	12.5
	$C_3H_7NHCH_3$	Propylmethylamine	—	—	—	—
$C_5H_{13}N$	$CH_3(CH_2)_4NH_2$	n-Amylamine	104	−55	0.766	—
	$Me_2CH(CH_2)_2NH_2$	Isoamylamine	95	−51	0.803	5.0
	$CH_3N(C_2H_5)_2$	Methyldiethylamine	63.5	—	—	2.7
$C_6H_{15}N$	$CH_3(CH_2)_5NH_2$	n-Hexylamine	128	−19	0.763	—
	$(C_3H_7)_2NH$	Di-n-propylamine	110.7	−39.6	0.738	10.2
	$(C_2H_5)_3N$	Triethylamine	89.5	−114.8	0.728	6.4
$C_7H_{17}N$	$CH_3(CH_2)_6NH_2$	n-Heptylamine	155.1	−23	0.777	—
$C_8H_{19}N$	$CH_3(CH_2)_7NH_2$	n-Octylamine	180	—	0.777	—
	$(C_4H_9)_2NH$	Di-n-butylamine	161	—	0.767	—
	$(C_4H_9)_2NH$	Di-isobutylamine	138.8	−70	0.745	4.8
$C_9H_{21}N$	$(C_3H_7)_3N$	Tripropylamine	156	−93.5	0.757	5.5
$C_{12}H_{27}N$	$(C_4H_9)_3N$	Triisobutylamine	191.5	−21.8	0.766	2.6
C_6H_7N	$C_6H_5NH_2$	Aniline	184.4	−6.2	1.022	4.6×10^{-10}
C_7H_9N	$o\text{-}MeC_6H_4NH_2$	o-Toluidine	200.7	−24.4	0.998	3.3×10^{-10}
	$m\text{-}MeC_6H_4NH_2$	m-Toluidine	203.3	−31.5	0.989	5.5×10^{-10}
	$p\text{-}MeC_6H_4NH_2$	p-Toluidine	200.5	43.7	1.046	2.2×10^{-9}
	$C_6H_5CH_2NH_2$	Benzylamine	184	—	0.920	—
	$C_6H_5NHCH_3$	Methylaniline	195.7	−57.0	0.986	—
$C_{10}H_9N$	$C_{10}H_7NH_2$	α-Naphthylamine	301	50	1.131	9.9×10^{-11}
	$C_{10}H_7NH_2$	β-Naphthylamine	306.1	110.2	1.061_{98}	2×10^{-10}
$C_5H_{11}N$	$CH_2\left\langle\begin{smallmatrix}CH_2CH_2\\ \\CH_2CH_2\end{smallmatrix}\right\rangle NH$	Piperidine	105.8	−9	0.860	1.6×10^{-3}
C_5H_5N	$CH\left\langle\begin{smallmatrix}CH=CH\\ \\CH-CH\end{smallmatrix}\right\rangle N$	Pyridine	115.3	−42	0.982	2.3×10^{-9}
NH_4OH	—	Ammonium hydroxide	—	—	—	1.8×10^{-5}

The complete replacement of all hydrogen atoms in the ammonium ion by means of organic residues, e.g., as in R_4N^+, gives rise to the quaternary ammonium ion. Such compounds may be prepared, for example, by complete alkylation of ammonia or an amine, as illustrated in the equations,

$$R_3N + R'X = R_3NR'X$$

$$H_3N + 4RX = R_4NX + R_3NHX + R_2NH_2X + RNH_3X$$

The substituted ammonium salts, including the quaternary, exhibit varied and numerous interesting chemical properties. It is recommended that these be reviewed by referring to appropriate textbooks.

Physiological Action

No single characteristic physiological action is attributed to simple aliphatic amines. Methylamine, dimethylamine, trimethylamine, and ethylamine have a depressing effect on the central nervous system. The simple methylated and ethylated ammonias may produce a slight transient hypotension.[1] Methyl, ethyl, propyl, and isobutylamine administered subcutaneously to experimental animals at greater than fifteenth molar concentration produce acute gastric erosion and ulcer.[2] Beginning with n-propylamine, sympathomimetic properties appear, which reach their optimum in compounds in which the aliphatic radical contains six or seven carbon atoms. The higher-molecular-weight aliphatic amines, such as hexadecylamine, n-$C_{16}H_{33}NH_2$, and octadecylamine, n-$C_{18}H_{35}$-NH_2, possess germicidal and anesthetic properties, neither of which is of adequate quality to justify the use of these amines in competition with better-established agents. Introduction of an additional amino group into n-amylamine at the omega carbon atom gives the structure of cadaverine, a depressor. With cyclohexylamine, as compared to n-hexylamine, the physiological response is slower in appearing but more prolonged in duration; otherwise its activity resembles that obtained with open-chain compounds. Simple secondary and tertiary amines show spasmolytic properties simulating those of papaverine.[3]

The simple quaternary ammonium salts produce block at the sympathetic ganglia, many of them competing with acetylcholine for the receptors in the ganglion. Frequently the quaternization of a physiologically active amine confers on it spasmolytic and curare-like properties.

High-molecular-weight quaternary ammonium compounds are useful as cationic detergents and antiseptics.

[1] Hauschild, *Arch. exptl. Path. Pharmakol.*, **201**, 569 (1943); *C.A.*, **38**, 1281 (1943).

[2] Kanatake, *J. Biochem. (Japan)*, **27**, 405 (1938); *C.A.*, **32**, 8550 (1938).

[3] Barlow, *Introduction to Chemical Pharmacology*, John Wiley & Sons, New York, 1955, pp. 164 ff.

Simple Amines

Tuaminoheptane (Tuamine, 2-Aminoheptane), may be prepared from 2-heptanone by reductive amination by either chemical or catalytic procedures, as indicated. It is a colorless or pale yellow liquid, slightly soluble in water and readily soluble in ether.

$$CH_3(CH_2)_4—CO—CH_3 + NH_3 \xrightarrow[\text{(catalyst)}]{H_2} CH_3(CH_2)_4—\underset{\underset{NH_2}{|}}{CH}—CH_3$$

$$CH_3(CH_2)_4—CO—CH_3 + HCONH_2 + HCOOH \xrightarrow{\text{(heat)}} CH_3(CH_2)_4—\underset{\underset{NH_2}{|}}{CH}—CH_3$$

The compound behaves as a vasoconstrictor and sympathomimetic amine. Its vapors are used effectively in acute rhinologic conditions. Cardiac patients should use the product with caution. It is used in an inhaler device in the form of the carbonate for effective treatment of nasal conditions and in the form of the sulfate, *Tuaminoheptane Sulfate, N.N.R.*, in 1 to 2 per cent isotonic solutions for application to mucous membranes.

Methylhexaneamine, N.N.R. (Forthane, 1,3-Dimethylpentylamine), $CH_3—CH_2—CH(CH_3)—CH_2—CH(CH_3)—NH_2$, is prepared by methods analogous to those employed for tuaminoheptane, using 4-methyl-2-hexanone as the ketone. It is a colorless or pale yellow liquid which is slightly soluble in water but soluble in alcohol and ether.

It is a volatile sympathomimetic amine whose salts possess the action and uses of other vasoconstrictors. Methylhexaneamine carbonate is used as an inhalant for its local vasoconstrictor action on the nasal mucosa, producing temporary relief in nasal congestion. It is used as an adjunct in the treatment of infectious rhinitis, sinusitis and allergy.

Oenethyl Hydrochloride (2-Methylaminoheptane Hydrochloride), $CH_3—(CH_2)_4CH(NHCH_3)CH_3 \cdot HCl$, is a water-soluble, vasopressor substance recommended for use against the hypotension associated with spinal anesthesia. It is usually administered in aqueous solution intravenously or intramuscularly while the blood pressure is being continuously checked.

Octin (6-Methylamino-2-methyl-2-heptene), $(CH_3)_2C{=}CH—CH_2—CH_2—CH(NHCH_3)—CH_3$, is a colorless, oily liquid which is used as an antispasmodic. It is available in solution as the hydrochloride, in tablets as the mucate, and as crystalline acid tartrate. These salts are white or almost white powders which are freely soluble in water and alcohol. The hydrochloride is hygroscopic.

The base and its salts act as prompt and prolonged relaxants of the smooth muscle musculature of the genitourinary, gastrointestinal, and biliary tracts.[4] These products are used in vesical and urethral spasm and urethral colic due to

---

[4] Gruber, *J. Pharmacol.*, **56**, 284 (1936); Brücke and Jesserer, *Arch. exptl. Path. Pharmakol.,* **190**, 515 (1938).

calculi or other causes; they aid materially in the passage of stones. It is used for irritable colon and in migraine and tension headaches.

Cyclopentamime and propylhexedrine (page 232) are cyclic analogs of these open-chain simple amines.

Quaternary Ammonium Compounds

Tetraethylammonium Chloride (Etamon, TEA), $(C_2H_5)_4NCl$, is a deliquescent crystalline product which is freely soluble in water and alcohol.

The cation, tetraethylammonium, is effective in blocking vasomotor impulses to the blood vessels, producing reduction of gastric acidity and gastrointestinal motility and partial or complete block of impulses to structures enervated by the autonomic nervous system such as the eye, sweat gland, and bladder.

Bis-quaternary Ammonium Salts. Chou and Elio [5] prepared a series of compounds of general structure $R_3\overset{+}{N}(CH_2)_n\overset{+}{N}R_3$, in which n varied from 2 to 13 and the R groups were either methyl or ethyl. These compounds exhibited, as a rule, greater ganglionic-blocking properties than did tetraethylammonium, and of the series *Hexamethonium* salt showed up most favorably.[6]

Hexamethonium Bromide [Vegolysen, C-6, Hexamethylene-1,6-bis(trimethylammonium) Dibromide], $[(CH_3)_3\overset{+}{N}-(CH_2)_6-\overset{+}{N}(CH_3)_3]Br_2^{-2}$, occurs as crystals which are soluble in water and alcohol. Aqueous solutions are stable and may be autoclaved. It is compatible with procaine hydrochloride and thiopental sodium.

It is used in the treatment of severe hypertension.

Decamethonium Bromide [Syncurine, C-10, Decamethylene-1,10-bis(trimethylammonium) Dibromide], $[(CH_3)_3\overset{+}{N}-(CH_2)_{10}-\overset{+}{N}(CH_3)_3]Br_2^{-2}$, is a crystalline product which is soluble in water and alcohol. Aqueous solutions are stable and may be sterilized. The product is compatible with procaine hydrochloride and thiopental sodium.

It is a potent muscle relaxant with properties similar to curare but free of histaminelike effects. It is used as an adjunct to surgical anesthesia for relaxation of the muscles, in electric shock therapy, and in endotracheal intubation.

Quaternary Ammonium Detergents and Antiseptics. A study [7] has been made of the relationship of chemical structure to germicidal activity in a series of quaternary ammonium salts of the type as shown, where A is alkyl, aryl,

[5] *Brit. J. Pharmacol.*, **2**, 268 (1947).
[6] Paton and Zaimis, *ibid.*, **4**, 381 (1949).
[7] Rawlins, Sweet, and Joslyn, *J. Am. Pharm. Assoc.*, **32**, 11 (1943).

aralkyl, or cycloalkyl; Z is halogen; R′ is hydrogen, methyl, or substituted methyl; X is chloride or other anion; and n is 2 or 3. This study revealed the following conditions for maximum germicidal activity: (1) the cation preferably should contain one long chain, one short aralkyl group, and two short alkyl groups; (2) the total length of the long chain should be 12 to 16 atoms; (3) closed-ring substituents on the aromatic nucleus are inferior to alkyl groups; (4) halogen substitution in the aryl groups does not increase and may decrease activity; (5) the anion may be derived from any simple mineral or organic acid.

Quaternary ammonium salts of the type shown, in which n varies from 2 to 16,

$$CH_3 \overset{(CH_2)_n—CH_3}{\underset{N(CH_3)_3SO_4CH_3}{\overset{|}{CH}}}$$

are reported active against hemolytic streptococci and pneumococci.[8]

Benzalkonium Chloride, U.S.P. (Zephiran Chloride), is a mixture of quaternary ammonium salts of the general formula $[C_6H_5CH_2\overset{+}{N}(CH_3)_2R]Cl^-$ in which R represents alkyl groups varying from $—C_8H_{17}$ to $—C_{18}H_{37}$. It is a white, amorphous powder which is very soluble in water and alcohol. Its aqueous solutions are very bitter, foam strongly when shaken, and are alkaline to litmus.

It is a cationic detergent with emulsifying properties and possesses keratolytic activity which aids the wetting and penetration of tissue surfaces. It is incompatible with anionic detergents such as ordinary soaps.

Benzalkonium chloride is a germicide and disinfectant used externally in alcoholic and aqueous solutions in concentrations of 1:40,000 to 1:1000. For the sterilization of surgical instruments, operating room equipment, and rubber products, concentrations of 1:5,000 to 1:1,000 are employed.

Benzethonium Chloride, U.S.P. [Phemerol Chloride, Benzyldimethyl-p-(2,4,4-trimethyl-2-pentyl)phenoxyethoxyethylammonium Chloride Monohydrate], is a colorless crystalline powder which is soluble in water. Solutions

$$(CH_3)_3CCH_2 \overset{CH_3}{\underset{CH_3}{\overset{|}{\underset{|}{C}}}} —OCH_2CH_2OCH_2CH_2—\overset{CH_3}{\underset{Cl^- \ CH_3}{\overset{|}{\underset{|}{+N}}}}—CH_2— \cdot H_2O$$

Phemerol Monohydrate

greater than 2 per cent are precipitated by mineral acids and many salts. It is a cationic detergent, and its action and uses are similar to those of benzalkonium chloride.

Cetyl Pyridinium Chloride, N.N.R. (see page 338).

[8] Grumbach, *Schweiz. med. Wochschr.*, **71**, 1520 (1941); *C.A.*, **38**, 218 (1944).

Methylbenzethonium Chloride, N.N.R. (Diaparene Chloride), is a cationic detergent closely related structurally to benzethonium chloride. It has

$$(CH_3)_3CCH_2-\underset{\underset{CH_3}{|}}{\overset{\overset{CH_3}{|}}{C}}-\langle\rangle-OCH_2CH_2OCH_2CH_2-{}_+\underset{\underset{CH_3}{Cl^-}}{\overset{\overset{CH_3}{|}}{N}}-CH_2-\langle\rangle\cdot H_2O$$

surface activity and disinfectant properties similar to those of other cationic agents.

Aromatic Amines and Derivatives

Aniline, phenylamine, $C_6H_5NH_2$, is used extensively in chemical industry for the manufacture of many products, such as dyes, resins, and explosives; it is also employed as a solvent. It is quite toxic, and workers unduly exposed to aniline vapors may show various symptoms, for example, skin eruptions, nervousness, dimness of vision, weakness, nausea, and cyanosis. It is detoxified by oxidation to p-aminophenol, which is then excreted in conjugated form. The substitution of alkyl or aryl groups at the nitrogen atom modifies somewhat the activity, but the products still behave qualitatively like unsubstituted aniline. Acylation yields compounds having a much less intense toxicity. The introduction of derivatives of aniline as antipyretics was based on the discovery (1886) by Cohn and Hepp that acetanilid has antipyretic and antineuralgic properties.

Acetanilid, N.F. (N-Phenylacetamide, Antifebrin), $C_6H_5NHCOCH_3$, is prepared by refluxing 1.4 parts of acetic anhydride and 1 part aniline until no more aniline remains, or, more economically, by heating aniline in an excess of acetic acid.

$$C_6H_5NH_2 + CH_3COOH \rightarrow C_6H_5NHCOCH_3 + H_2O$$

It occurs as crystals, m.p. 114–116°. It dissolves in water 1:190, is readily soluble in alcohol, ether, glycerol, and other organic solvents. It is employed as an antipyretic and analgesic, being used in many proprietary headache powders. In man, a minor portion is deacetylated to form a precursor of the substance that converts hemoglobin to methemoglobin.[9] The major portion is oxidized in the liver to p-hydroxyacetanilid, which is then excreted as the glucuronide or the sulfate ester. The analgesic as well as the toxic properties of acetanilid are attributed to this p-hydroxy derivative, which is formed *in vivo*.[10, 11]

Extensive efforts have been made to improve upon acetanilid by means of various structural modifications, of which the introduction of an ethoxyl group in the para position is the most successful This resulted from the observation by Schmiedeberg (1884) that the body converts aniline into p-aminophenol, which is excreted as the glucuronide or as the sulfuric acid ester. A subsequent study of homologous ethers of p-hydroxyacetanilid showed that the methyl

[9] Brodie and Axelrod, *J. Pharmacol. Exptl. Therap.*, **94**, 29 (1948).

[10] Flinn and Brodie, *J. Pharmacol. Exptl. Therap.*, **94**, 76 (1948).

[11] Smith and Williams, *Biochem. J.*, **44**, 239 (1949).

ether, $p\text{-}CH_3OC_6H_4NHCOCH_3$, methacetin, possessed maximum antipyretic and analgesic activity; however, the ethyl ether, though slightly less active, is preferred since it is less hemolytic.

Acetophenetidin, U.S.P. (Phenacetin), was first prepared by Hinsberg (1887), who was seeking a use for a quantity of p-nitrophenol which had accumulated as a by-product from the dye works. The synthesis is indicated by the equations.

OH $\xrightarrow{\text{NaOH}}$ ONa $\xrightarrow{\text{C}_2\text{H}_5\text{Cl}}$ OC$_2$H$_5$ $\xrightarrow{[\text{C}_6\text{H}_5\text{N}\equiv\text{N}]\text{Cl}}$

OC$_2$H$_5$ (N=N—C$_6$H$_5$) $\xrightarrow{\text{H}_2}$ OC$_2$H$_5$ (NH$_2$) *p*-Phenetidin $\xrightarrow{\text{AcOH}}$ OC$_2$H$_5$ (NHCOCH$_3$) Acetophenetidin

Acetophenetidin consists of odorless, white, crystalline scales, or a crystalline powder, having a slightly bitter taste, m.p. 134–136°. One gram is soluble in 1310 ml. of water, and it is readily soluble in most organic solvents.

In the body acetophenetidin is converted into p-hydroxyacetanilid, the active metabolite.[12]

Acetophenetidin and its congeners are extensively used as antipyretics for the reduction of temperature in fevers and as analgesics for the relief of pain. All of them should be used cautiously since they cause hemolysis of the red blood corpuscles and act as heart depressants.

A number of compounds similar to acetophenetidin have been prepared in which the acetyl is replaced by some other radical. All of them, like acetophenetidin, depend for their action on the liberation of p-aminophenol or acetylaminophenol.

Phenocoll (Aminophenacetin, Glycocoll-p-phenetidin) prepared by Schmidt and Majert in 1890, by the action of ammonia on bromoacetyl-p-phenetidin, has action similar to that of acetophenetidin.

$$p\text{-}C_2H_5O\text{—}C_6H_4\text{—}NH\text{—}COCH_2Br + NH_3 \rightarrow p\text{-}C_2H_5O\text{—}C_6H_4\text{—}NH\text{—}COCH_2NH_2$$

The hydrochloride of phenocoll is soluble in water. Consequently it is absorbed rapidly and produces a prompt response, but the effects disappear rapidly. Early claims that phenocoll possessed value as an antimalarial could not be confirmed. It and the corresponding phenocoll salicylate are reported to be strongly antipyretic and analgesic and to have value as substitutes for salicylates in rheumatic fever.

[12] Smith and Williams, *Biochem. J.*, **44**, 239 (1949).

Replacement of the hydrogen of the hydoxyl group in p-acetaminophenol by other than the simple alkyl groups mentioned has been accomplished. Thus p-acetaminophenyl benzoate, p-C_6H_5COO—C_6H_4—$NHCOCH_3$, p-acetethyl-aminophenyl acetate, p-CH_3COO—C_6H_4—NEt—$COCH_3$, p-acetaminophenoxy-acetamide, p-NH_2COCH_2O—C_6H_4—NH—$COCH_3$, and a number of related compounds have been prepared and found to have no practical value in therapy. Only one compound of this type has attained extensive use, namely, phenetsal.

Phenetsal (Salophen) is p-acetaminophenyl salicylate. It is a white, crystal-

line solid, m.p. 187–188°, insoluble in water and soluble in most organic solvents and in solutions of alkalies.

Phenetsal was introduced as a substitute for salol, the action of which it re-sembles. It is thought that it is hydrolyzed in the intestine to liberate salicylic acid and p-aminophenol.

Crotamiton, N.N.R. (N-Ethyl-o-crotonotoluide), possesses bacteriostatic and fungistatic properties, and it is reported to be useful for topical application in the treatment of scabies.

Crotamiton   Edrophonium

Edrophonium, N.N.R. (Tensilon, m-Hydroxyphenyl Dimethyl Ethylammo-nium Chloride), a derivative of m-aminophenol, exhibits the pharmacological activity qualitatively similar to that of acetylcholine. It is an effective antag-onist to curare. It is useful for the evaluation of therapy in myasthenia gravis.

Medicinal Dyes

The observation by Ehrlich that certain dyes used as stains in histological work specifically stain fixed tissue gave rise to the conception that compounds might be produced which would combine with and destroy the parastic causes of disease without injury to the cells of the body. In the period from about 1900 to 1912, Ehrlich and his co-workers studied numerous dyestuffs and their work stimulated investigations by others.

A considerable number of dyes are used as antiseptics, chemotherapeutic agents, and for specific effects upon tissue cells in modern therapy. The dyes now used medicinally are mostly synthetic products introduced in comparatively re-cent years. Considerable confusion concerning the composition of dyes exists because various manufacturers of commerical dyestuffs make similar dyes that are qualitatively and quantitatively different in composition. Diluents such as dextrose or salts are often added, the commercial dye being judged by its tinctorial value. Much of this confusion has been cleared up by the establishment of standards for medicinal dyes and food colors in the United States Pharmacopeia and National Formulary and by the Dye Certification Division of the United States Department of Agriculture.

Dyes used to color pharmaceutical preparations and foods must comply with the specifications of the Coal-Tar Color Regulations promulgated under the authority of the United States Food, Drug, and Cosmetic Act.

Triphenylmethane Dyes. The most valuable medicinal derivatives of triphenylmethane dyes are those which result from the introduction of amino groups, forming p-rosaniline and rosaniline.

p-Rosaniline   Rosaniline

Methylrosaniline Chloride, U.S.P. (Gentian Violet, Methyl Violet, Crystal Violet), the most extensively used of the triphenylmethane derivatives, is prepared by the oxidation of a mixture of dimethyl-p-toluidine and dimethyl aniline with a mild oxidizing agent such as cupric sulfate in the presence of sodium chloride or nitrobenzene. Some pentamethylated compound is formed so that

Hexamethyl-p-rosaniline chloride

the end product is a mixture. The commercial dye is often mixed with diluents such as dextrin and should not be used medicinally. Gentian violet is a dark green powder, soluble 1:40 in water and 1:10 in alcohol.

Gentian violet was proposed as a wound antiseptic by Stelling in 1890. Churchman (1914) found that solutions of the dye had a selective action for Gram-positive bacteria, especially *B. pyocyaneus* and *B. diphtheriae*, and had a weak action on the Gram-negative species. It has low toxicity for tissues and penetrates readily. It has been used mainly against staphylococcus infections in pleural empyema and in arthritis in concentrations of 1:10,000 to 1:500. It is used as an antiseptic for infected wounds, mucous membranes, and serous surfaces.

Malachite Green (the chloride of Tetramethyl-di-*p*-amino-triphenylcarbinol)

Malachite Green

is used as a dye in the form of a $ZnCl_2$ double salt. It is a violet-green, crystalline powder, soluble in water and alcohol. The zinc-free compound is used medicinally as a wound antiseptic in about 1:1000 solutions, to treat ulcers and impetigo, in 1 to 2 per cent ointments, and by subcutaneous injection of 1:2000 in 0.9 per cent NaCl solution to treat trypanosomiasis.

Azo Dyes and Compounds. The azo dyes constitute one of the largest and most important classes of commercial dyestuffs. This class of dyes was first prepared by P. Griess in 1860. They all contain the azo group, —N=N—, which is the chromophore group. Dyes of this class are usually made from two components, one of which is always a primary aromatic amine and the other is a phenol, or a primary, secondary, or tertiary amine. The primary amine is diazotized and subsequently coupled with the other component. Coupling of a phenol with a diazonium compound is generally carried out in alkaline solution whereas amines are coupled in faintly acid or neutral solution.

The azo dyes used medicinally are: Scarlet Red, Scarlet Red Sulfonate, and Dimazon.

Scarlet Red, N.F. (Scarlet Red Medicinal, Biebrich Scarlet Red), was introduced into therapy in 1908 after Fischer found that it stimulated the growth of epithelial cells. It is prepared by coupling pure aminoazotoluene with β-naphthol in the presence of an alkali and purification of the reaction product. It is a brownish-red powder, almost insoluble in water, slightly soluble in alcohol, benzene, and acetone, and readily soluble in chloroform, phenols, fixed oils, and mineral oil.

Scarlet Red is used to stimulate the proliferation of epithelial cells in burns, wounds, chronic ulcers, and in skin grafting. It has been given internally for duodenal ulcers. It is generally used externally in 4 to 8 per cent ointments.

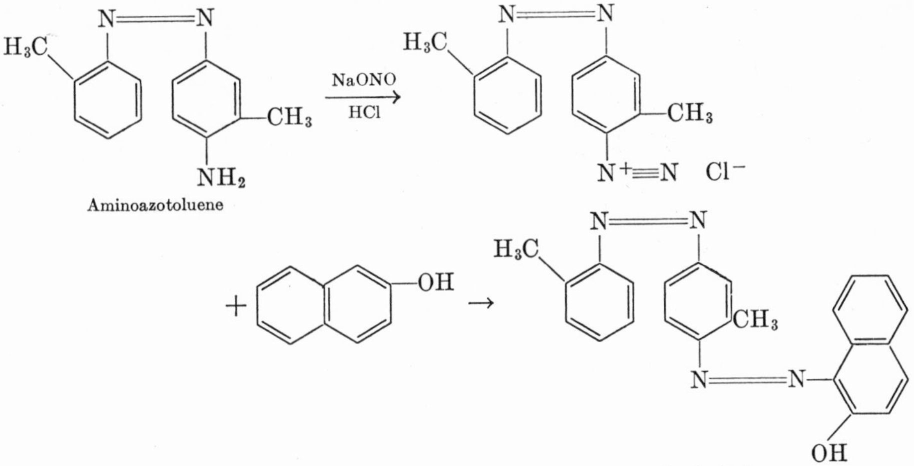

Aminoazotoluene

β-Naphthol

Scarlet Red

Scarlet Red Sulfonate is made by coupling 4-aminoazobenzene-3,4′-disulfonic acid with β-naphthol. Scarlet Red sulfonate is a brownish-red powder. It is soluble in water, slightly soluble in alcohol, acetone, and ether, and very slightly soluble in chloroform, benzene, fixed oils, and mineral oils. Scarlet Red sulfonate is used for the same purposes as Scarlet Red in 4 to 10 per cent ointments and in the form of a 5 per cent emulsion.

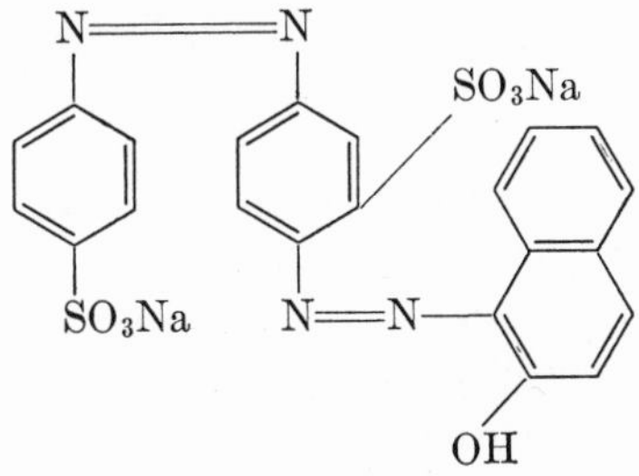

Scarlet Red sulfonate

Amaranth, U.S.P., F.D.C. Red No. 2, Trisodium salt of 1-(4-sulfo-1-naphthyl-azo)-2-naphthol-3,6-disulfonic acid, is a red-brown powder, soluble in water

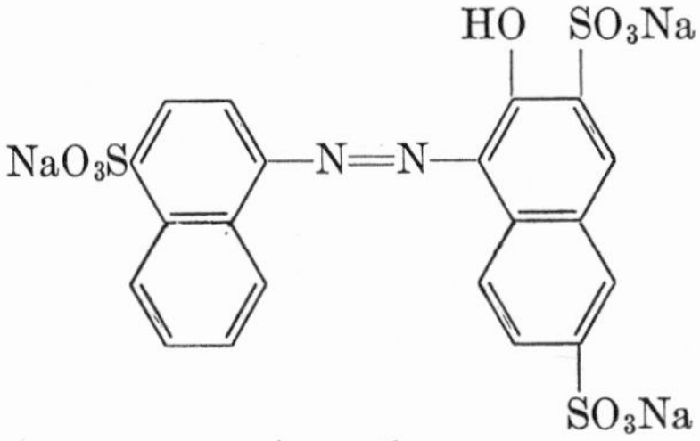

Amaranth

about 1:15 and slightly soluble in ethanol. Amaranth is used to color pharmaceutical preparations and food products.

HALOGENATED ALKYL AMINES

During World War II interest was developed in compounds of general structure $(ClCH_2CH_2)_2NR$. These are nitrogen analogs of mustard gas and are extremely vesicant. Studies with these so-called "nitrogen mustards" have shed considerable light on the mechanism of the action of all mustards with tissues. It has been shown that the cytotoxic action, related in some manner to the proliferative activity of the cell, depends on intramolecular cyclization in a polar solvent to form an onium ion with the liberation of a chloride ion, as indicated; or

$$R_2N—CH_2CH_2—Cl \rightarrow \left[R_2\overset{+}{N} \underset{CH_2}{\overset{CH_2}{\diagup\vert\diagdown}} \right] Cl^-$$

for the analogous thioether, as indicated. Such onium ions are very reactive and

$$R—S—CH_2CH_2—Cl \rightarrow \left[R—\overset{+}{S} \underset{CH_2}{\overset{CH_2}{\diagup\vert\diagdown}} \right] Cl^-$$

attack various uncharged nucleophilic molecules, causing denaturation of the tissue and vesication. The onium ion is capable of alkylating functional groups of biological importance, such as the nitrogen ion, amino acids, peptides, imidazoles, the sulfhydryl and thioether groups, carboxyl groups, and the glycero- and hexosephosphates.[13]

Because mitotic activity is peculiarly sensitive to the action of these compounds, their use in cancer is of more than academic interest. Since they act as "chemical x rays" in producing mutations and changes in somatic chromosomes, e.g., in *Drosophila melanogaster*,[14] *Neurospora crassa*,[15] and *Penicillium notatum*,[16] the geneticist is provided with a promising tool for his studies.

Methchlorethamine Hydrochloride, N.N.R. [*bis*(β-Chloroethyl)methylammonium Hydrochloride], $(ClCH_2CH_2)_2\overset{|}{\underset{CH_3}{N}}H^+ \cdot Cl^-$, has a special affinity for the epithelial cells of the intestine and the cornea and the cells of certain neoplastic growths; hence, it is used as a palliative for the treatment of neoplastic disturbances, particularly those of the lymphoid and hematopoietic tissues. Since there is no known antidote, it must be administered with extreme care.

Cf. triethylene melamine, page 439.

---

[13] Gilman and Philips, *Science*, **103**, 409 (1946).
[14] Auerbach, Robson, and Carr, *Science*, **105**, 243 (1947).
[15] Horowitz, Houlahan, Hungate, and Wright, *Science*, **104**, 233 (1946).
[16] Stahmann and Stauffer, *Science*, **106**, 35 (1947).

Dibenamine (N,N-Dibenzyl-β-chloroethylamine Hydrochloride) is a potent adrenergic-blocking agent which is effective against epinephrine, against sympathin E, and in large doses against adrenergic nerve stimulation. Dibenamine has been tried clinically in such ailments as Raynaud's disease, Buerger's disease, and others but its use has been restricted to experimentation. A disadvantage is the necessity of administering the product intravenously.

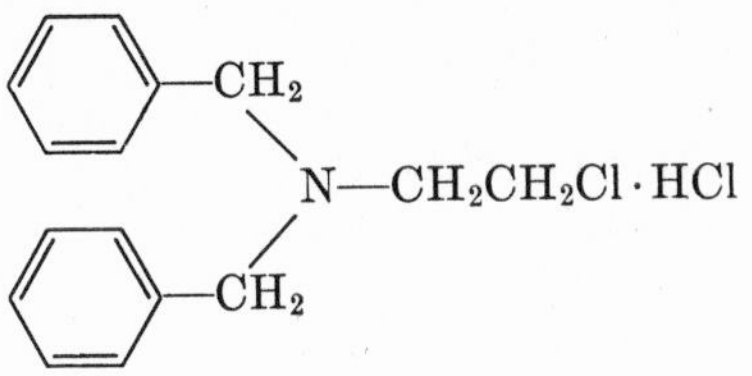

Dibenamine

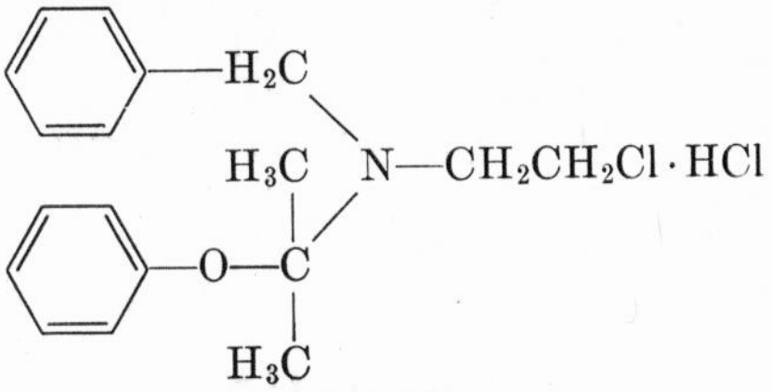

Dibenzyline

Dibenzyline (N-Phenoxyisopropyl-N-benzyl-β-chloroethylamine Hydrochloride) is an adrenergic-blocking agent which is effective orally to increase peripheral blood flow and to raise skin temperature; it relieves causalgic pain and lowers high blood pressure due to excessive secretion of epinephrine. It is used in peripheral vascular disorder and hypertension due to pheochromocytoma.

ALKANOLAMINES

Compounds containing both the amino and hydroxy function are used in the synthesis of a number of important and useful medicinal products. Examples of such intermediates are shown. β-Dimethylaminoethanol shows a cholinelike

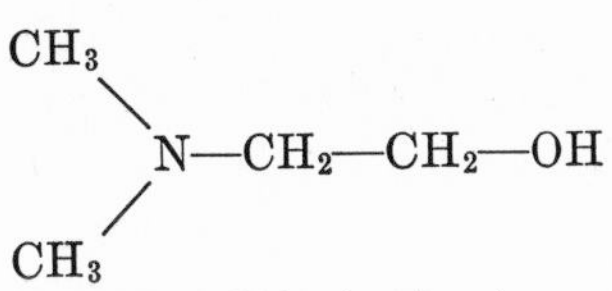

β-Dimethylaminoethanol

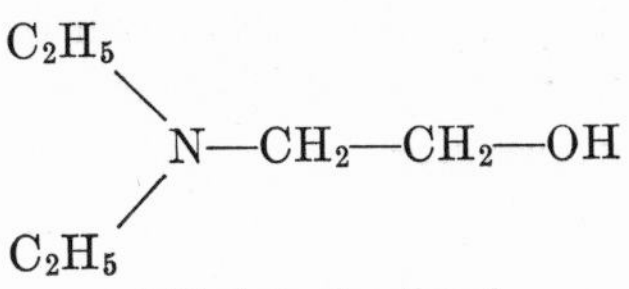

β-Diethylaminoethanol

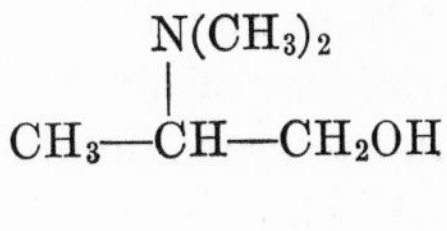

2-Dimethylamino-1-propanol

effect in the prevention of perosis and promotion of growth in chicks maintained on a choline-deficient diet; possibly it is converted to choline by methionine.[17] β-Methylaminoethanol, under similar conditions, prevents perosis but does not support growth.[18] Both β-methylaminoethanol and β-dimethylaminoethanol improve the work capacity of a failing mammalian heart in a manner similar to that exhibited by the digitalis glycosides.[19]

Aminohydroxy compounds of the paraffin hydrocarbons are employed as emulsifying agents in cosmetics and as intermediates for the synthesis of phar-

---

[17] Jukes and Oleson, *J. Biol. Chem.*, **157**, 419 (1945).
[18] Jukes, Oleson, and Dornbush, *J. Nutrition*, **30**, 219 (1945).
[19] Krayer, Farah, and Uhle, *J. Pharmacol.*, **88**, 277 (1946).

maceutical products and surface active agents. The compounds used include
those shown.

$$NH_2$$
$$CH_2OH—\overset{|}{\underset{|}{C}}—CH_2OH$$
$$C_2H_5$$

2-Amino-2-ethyl-1,3-propanediol

$$NH_2$$
$$CH_3—CH_2—\overset{|}{CH}—CH_2OH$$

2-Amino-1-butanol

$$NH_2$$
$$CH_2OH—\overset{|}{\underset{|}{C}}—CH_2OH$$
$$CH_3$$

2-Amino-2-methyl-1,3-propanediol

$$NH_2$$
$$CH_3—\overset{|}{\underset{|}{C}}—CH_2OH$$
$$CH_3$$

2-Amino-2-methyl-1-propanol

Triethanolamine, U.S.P., is a pale yellow, hygroscopic liquid, miscible with
water and alcohol and soluble in chloroform. It consists of a mixture made up of
about 80 per cent triethanolamine, 15 per cent diethanolamine, and 2.5 per cent
monoethanolamine. It is a technical product used only for external application
in medicaments. It combines with fatty acids to form soaps which have excellent
detergent properties. These soaps are soluble in water and also in organic solvents such as kerosene, gasoline, and oils. Emulsions of such soaps are readily
formed by mixing fatty acids dissolved in oil with an aqueous solution of triethanolamine. Incorporated into preparations for external application, such as
ointments and dermatological pastes, they increase the penetration and thus
increase the bacteriostatic effect and also facilitate the removal of such products,
e.g., from the scalp.

Choline and Its Derivatives

Hunt and Taveau in 1906 [20] reported on their discovery of a parasympathetic
stimulant, which Dale in 1914 suspected of being acetylcholine; [21] in 1929 he was
able to prove that he was correct.[22]

Choline is one of the hydrolytic products of the lecithins. It is β-hydroxy-
ethyltrimethylammonium hydroxide, $(HOCH_2CH_2NMe_3)OH$, a quaternary
ammonium base of ethanolamine. It is a marked circulatory depressant, usually
producing a lowering of blood pressure.

Choline is a viscid, colorless liquid, strongly alkaline, soluble in water and
alcohol and insoluble in ether, which possesses vitaminlike activity in that it is
capable of supplying essential transferable methyl groups in biological processes.
Betaine and methionine show similar behavior.

Acetylcholine Chloride (Acetoxyethyltrimethylammonium Chloride),
$[CH_3—COO(CH_2)_2—N(CH_3)_3]Cl$, is a white, very hygroscopic crystalline powder, which dissolves readily in water to form neutral but unstable solutions. Solutions for use must be freshly prepared. It is ineffective when administered orally.

[20] Hunt and Taveau, *Brit. Med. J.*, **2**, 1788 (1906).
[21] Dale, *J. Pharmacol. Exptl. Therap.*, **6**, 147 (1914).
[22] Dale and Dudley, *J. Physiol.*, **68**, 97 (1929).

It is about 1000 times as active as a parasympathetic stimulant as choline. It lowers blood pressure by dilation of the peripheral vessels and relaxes spasm of smooth muscles. It is used for the same purposes as mecholyl, but its action is much briefer since it is destroyed by choline esterase. It is usually administered in sterile aqueous solution by subcutaneous or intramuscular injection, and it is applied locally in such conditions as atrophic rhinitis.

Methacholine Chloride, U.S.P. (Acetyl-β-methylcholine Chloride, Mecholyl), may be prepared by the sequence of reactions indicated. It occurs as white,

$$(CH_3)_3N \xrightarrow[\substack{\text{1. } CH_3-\overset{O}{\overset{\|}{C}}-CH_2-Cl \\ \text{2. catalytic reduction} \\ \text{3. acetylation}}]{} [(CH_3)_3\overset{+}{N}-CH_2-\underset{\underset{CH_3}{|}}{CH}-O-\overset{O}{\overset{\|}{C}}-CH_3]Cl$$

hygroscopic crystals or a crystalline powder and is freely soluble in water and alcohol. Solutions are relatively stable to heat and will keep for two or three weeks. Mold growth may be delayed by refrigeration. The methyl group confers sufficient stability toward cholinesterase as compared to acetylcholine to give a product that in the body exhibits sustained parasympathetic stimulation.

Mecholyl causes stimulation of the parasympathetic nervous system to produce results opposite to those caused by stimulation of the sympathetic nervous system by epinephrine, ephedrine, and related compounds. It causes a fall in blood pressure, slowing of the heart, constriction of the bronchioles, dilation of peripheral blood vessels, constriction of the pupils, increase in intestinal tone and peristalsis, stimulation of the muscles of the bladder, and contraction of the uterine musculature. It has been used to treat paroxysmal tachycardia, Raynaud's disease, diabetic gangrene, varicose ulcers, rheumatoid arthritis, atonic constipation, postoperative abdominal distention, functional dysmenorrhea, and atrophic rhinitis.

The drug may be given orally, with milk to disguise its bitter taste, by iontophoresis, or subcutaneously.

Methacholine Bromide, N.N.R. (Acetyl-β-methylcholine Bromide), $[(CH_3)_3\overset{+}{N}-CH_2-CHCH_3-O-\overset{O}{\overset{\|}{C}}-CH_3]Br^-$, possesses an activity that is similar to that of the chloride. Although it is also hygroscopic, it is less so than the chloride and therefore is preferred for preparing tablets. For injection or iontophoresis the chloride is preferred.

Carbachol, U.S.P. (Carbamylcholine Chloride, Doryl, Lentin), is prepared by reacting β-chloroethyl carbamate with trimethylamine. It is a stable, hy-

$$(CH_3)_3N + Cl-CH_2-CH_2-O-\overset{O}{\overset{\|}{C}}-NH_2 \rightarrow$$

$$[(CH_3)_3\overset{+}{N}-CH_2-CH_2-O-\overset{O}{\overset{\|}{C}}-NH_2]Cl^-$$

groscopic, crystalline powder which readily dissolves in water to form neutral solutions. It is fairly soluble in alcohol. It is reported that the solutions can be heated without causing decomposition. It is also reported that it is not destroyed by the gastric enzymes and fluids.

Carbachol is the most powerful parasympathetic stimulant of the choline type. It is not readily absorbed from the gastrointestional tract where it chiefly exerts its action. Because it is not easily hydrolyzed by cholinesterase, its action is prolonged when injected and is inclined to be more toxic than other products of this type. Its action and uses are very similar to those of mecholyl, but it is much more active on oral administration. It is administered orally in the form of tablets or hypodermically by subcutaneous injection.

Bethanechol Chloride, U.S.P. (Urecholine Chloride), is prepared by treating propylene chlorohydrin with phosgene and then with ammonia. The resultant urethan is then heated with trimethylamine. It is a white, crystalline solid

$$\underset{\substack{|\\ \text{OH}}}{\text{CH}_3-\text{CH}-\text{CH}_2-\text{Cl}} \xrightarrow[\substack{\text{1. phosgene}\\ \text{2. ammonia}\\ \text{3. trimethylamine}}]{} [(\text{CH}_3)_3\overset{+}{\text{N}}-\text{CH}_2-\underset{\substack{|\\ \text{CH}_3}}{\text{CH}}-\text{O}-\overset{\substack{\text{O}\\ ||}}{\text{C}}-\text{NH}_2]\text{Cl}^-$$

which is very soluble in water and freely soluble in alcohol.

Pharmacologically it behaves similar to mecholyl but differs from acetylcholine in that it exhibits little if any ganglionic stimulating action and is not hydrolyzed by cholinesterase. It is less toxic and active than some of the other esters of choline.

It is useful in the prevention and relief of postoperative urinary retention, treatment of chronic or functional urinary retention due to muscular atony without obstruction, postoperative abdominal distention, and other conditions that are relieved by choline ester types of parasympathetic stimulants.

Tridihexethyl Iodide, N.N.R. [Penthilon Iodide, (3-Cyclohexyl-3-phenyl-3-hydroxypropyl)-triethylammonium Iodide], is related to the anticholinergic

$$\left[\underset{\substack{|\\ \text{C}_6\text{H}_5}}{\overset{\substack{\text{OH}\\ |}}{\text{C}}}\text{CH}_2\text{CH}_2\underset{\substack{|\\ \text{CH}_2\text{CH}_3}}{\overset{\substack{\text{CH}_2\text{CH}_3\\ |}}{\text{N}}}-\text{CH}_2\text{CH}_3 \right]^+ \text{I}^-$$

Tridihexethyl iodide

structures; it is used for the treatment of peptic ulcer, for the control of gastric hyperacidity and hypermotility, and for spastic colon.

ESTERS OF ALKANOLAMINES

Among the esters of alkanolamines are found compounds of varied pharmacological activity, including local anesthetic, spasmolytic and antispasmodic, antiparkinson, and antigastric properties. In a broad sense these esters may be considered as being modeled after the tropane alkaloids (see page 385), that is alkanolamine esters of benzoic or substituted benzoic acids or esters of tropic acid and its analogs. The biological properties depend on both the acid and the amino alcohol components. In general the aromatic acids are found in local anesthetics of the procaine type; tropic acidlike esters are spasmolytic; and esters of the benzilic type are more mydriatic.[23]

Esters of Aromatic Acids

Koller, in 1884, reported his results with cocaine in ophthalmological practice, thereby introducing "local" anesthesia. As a medical discovery, anesthesia ranks second to Lister's introduction of the practice of surgical antisepsis and asepsis. Without anesthesia surgery could not have progressed and advanced as it has.

Cocaine, valuable as it is as a local anesthetic, has several clinical and commercial disadvantages. It is a habit-forming drug and as such is restricted under the narcotic laws, and it does produce in the patient undesirable side effects. It cannot be sterilized well in pharmaceutical preparations without undergoing hydrolysis.

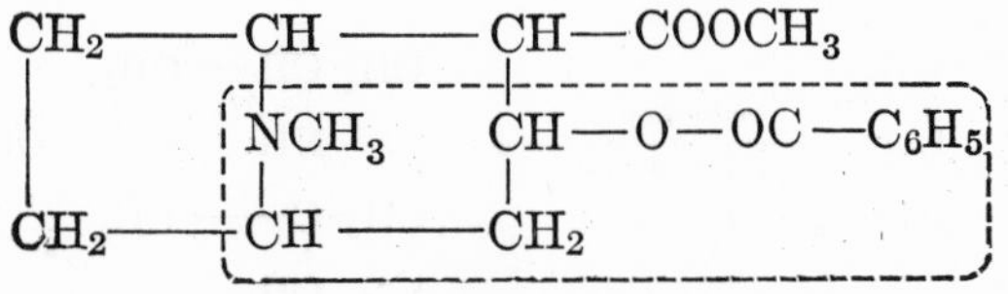

Cocaine showing anesthesiophoric group.

The chemistry of cocaine and its structure are described under the tropane alkaloids. Early in the study of the chemistry of cocaine, the question naturally arose: To what portion of the molecule does the compound owe its activity? As a partial answer to this

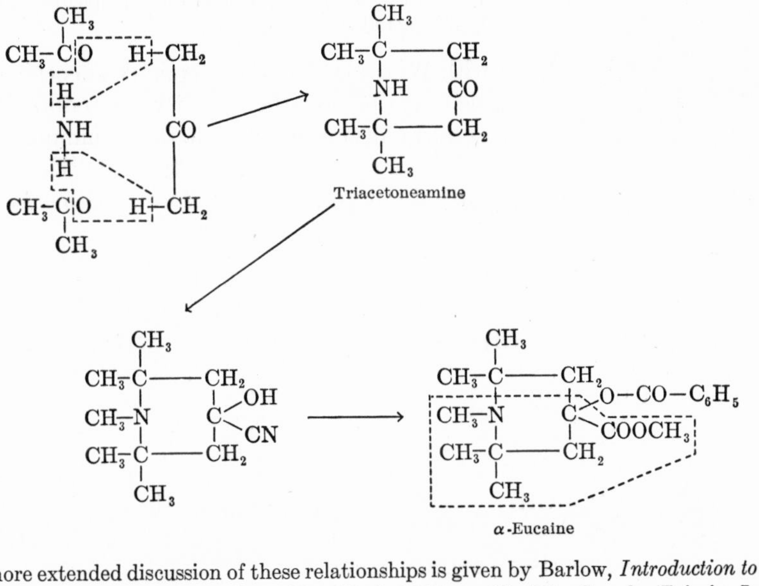

Triacetoneamine

α-Eucaine

---

[23] A more extended discussion of these relationships is given by Barlow, *Introduction to Chemical Pharmacology*, John Wiley & Sons, New York, 1955, pp. 83–179. See also Zaimis, *J. Pharm. Pharmacol.*, **7**, 497 (1955).

question, it was observed that the anesthetic activity was lost if either the methyl ester group or the benzoyl group was removed. Removal of the N-methyl group had no particular effect on the activity. In order to determine whether the pyrrolidine nucleus (the five-membered ring) was necessary, a compound with the piperidine ring (six-membered) analogous to that found in the natural base was synthesized. Three molecules of acetone were condensed with ammonia to form triacetoneamine. This was methylated, converted into the cyanohydrin which was hydrolyzed, the carboxyl group esterified, and the hydroxyl group benzoylated to form α-eucaine, as shown on page 197. This compound is about as strongly anesthetic as cocaine. Since, however, it is somewhat painful and irritant on injection, it was superseded by β-eucaine, which may be prepared in an analogous manner, starting with diacetoneamine and acetaldehyde.[24] β-Eucaine is less toxic and safer in practice than is α-eucaine.

$$\begin{array}{ccccc}
H_2C-H & H \\
| & | \\
CO & NH & + & O=CH-CH_3 & \longrightarrow \\
| & | \\
CH_2\!-\!\!-C-CH_3 \\
& | \\
& CH_3
\end{array}$$

Diacetoneamine

$$\begin{array}{ccc}
CH_3\!-\!CH\!-\!\!-\!\!-CH_2 \\
| \quad\quad | \\
NH \quad\quad CO \\
| \quad\quad | \\
CH_3\!-\!C\!-\!\!-\!\!-CH_2 \\
| \\
CH_3
\end{array}
\quad\xrightarrow[\text{esterification}]{\text{reduction and}}\quad
\begin{array}{ccc}
CH_3\!-\!CH\!-\!\!-\!\!-CH_2 \\
| \quad\quad | \\
NH \quad\quad CHO-OC-C_6H_5 \\
| \quad\quad | \\
CH_3\!-\!C\!-\!\!-\!\!-CH_2 \\
| \\
CH_3
\end{array}$$

β-Eucaine

As information accumulated, it was learned that certain minimum structural requirements are necessary in compounds of this type.

Ritsert[25] had established by 1890 that ethyl p-aminobenzoate possesses anesthetic activity, and the compound which he had prepared from it with p-phenolsulfonic acid, he called "subcutin" because it could be injected subcutaneously.

Einhorn,[26] who had worked with Willstätter on the chemistry of cocaine, made the generalization: "All aromatic esters possess the capacity to produce anesthesia." Other factors might have a modifying effect, but the minimum requirement is that the compound must be an ester of an aromatic acid. Einhorn prepared esters of this type, e.g., orthoform and new orthoform, the methyl esters

$$\begin{array}{ccc}
NH_2 \\
| \\
C \\
\diagup \quad \diagdown\!\!\!= \\
CH \quad\quad C-OH \\
\| \quad\quad \| \\
CH \quad\quad CH \\
\diagdown \quad \diagup\!\!\!= \\
C \\
| \\
COOCH_3
\end{array}
\qquad\qquad
\begin{array}{ccc}
OH \\
| \\
C \\
\diagup \quad \diagdown\!\!\!= \\
CH \quad\quad C-NH_2 \\
\| \quad\quad \| \\
CH \quad\quad CH \\
\diagdown \quad \diagup\!\!\!= \\
C \\
| \\
COOCH_3
\end{array}$$

Orthoform   New orthoform

[24] Harries, Ann., 296, 328 (1897); 299, 346 (1897).
[25] Bodendorf, Deut. Apoth. Ztg., 49, 1642 (1934).
[26] Ann., 371, 125 (1909).

of p-amino-m-hydroxybenzoic acid and of m-amino-p-hydroxybenzoic acid, respectively. This observation led to the synthesis of a large number of analogous esters of which ethyl p-aminobenzoate, anesthesin, and n-butyl p-aminobenzoate, butesin, are finding practical use.

A series of the alkyl p-aminobenzoates, when tested against goldfish, showed increasing potency in the order:[27] methyl, ethyl, allyl, isopropyl, tert-butyl, sec-butyl, n-propyl, isobutyl, n-butyl, and n-amyl. The esters of higher alkyl groups are the most active, and the esters with normal chains are more active than those with the isomeric branched chains.

The next advance was in the recognition that the presence of a basic nitrogen atom in the esterified alcohol was highly desirable; it permitted the formation of neutral soluble salts, solutions of which could be injected, and it also influenced the activity favorably. Thus, it was recognized that in cocaine the "anesthesiophore" group was Ar—CO—O—(C)$_n$—N, shown in the boxed area of the formula for cocaine. It will be observed that the same grouping is present in the eucaine structures.

After Einhorn and Uhlfelder[28] described the synthesis of procaine, or, as they called it, novocaine, which also contains the same anesthesiophoric group as the eucaines and cocaine, there were inaugurated research programs which have

$$H_2N-\underset{}{\bigcirc}-CO-OCH_2CH_2-N(C_2H_5)_2$$

Procaine or novocaine, the p-aminobenzoic acid ester of β-diethylaminoethanol

resulted in the synthesis of literally hundreds of compounds, most of them containing the same anesthesiophoric arrangement. Perhaps no field in the synthesis of medicinal products has been studied more extensively than the domain of compounds related, by homology or analogy, to procaine and cocaine. Unfortunately the evaluation of the products was made by about as many different procedures as there were investigators, and it will be impossible to co-ordinate the available data and summarize completely the effect of chemical structure on physiological activity. Consequently, only general effects and tendencies will be indicated. This may be accomplished by considering three separate structural elements of the anesthesiophoric grouping, namely:

$$Ar-CO-O(C)_n-N=$$

A   B   C

the acid with which the compound is esterified, the alkanol group which is esterified and bears the basic amino nitrogen atom, and the nitrogen atom with particular reference to the substituents which it carries. Such a review is, at best, sketchy and roughly qualitative.

[27] Adams, Rideal, Burnett, Jenkins, and Dreger, *J. Am. Chem. Soc.*, **48**, 1758–1770 (1926).
[28] *Ann.*, **371**, 131–142 (1909).

The "local" action of these esters is attributed to the fact that they inhibit the cholinesterase of the blood.[29]

The Acid (Part A)

The acid may vary within wide limits, e.g., benzoic acid, substituted benzoic acids, and various analogs of benzoic acid. As a rule, which must not be taken too literally, p-aminobenzoates are more effective than simple benzoates.[30] In a series of p-alkoxybenzoates of general structure [31] $p\text{-RO}—C_6H_4—CO—O—(CH_2)_n—N(C_2H_5)_2$ it was observed that anesthetic potency increased with increase in R and that normal alkyl groups were more effective than their isomeric branched-chain alkyl groups. Esters of piperonylic acid, such as Helicaine and Piperothesine, are active, as are also the esters of α- and β-naphthoic

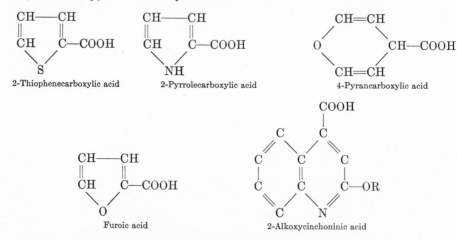

CO—O—CH₂CH₂N(C₂H₅)₂·HCl
Helicaine

CO—O—CH₂CH₂CH₂N(C₂H₅)₂·HCl
Piperothesine

acids.[32, 33] Carboxylic acid esters of heterocyclic compounds are also active. Among these may be mentioned the cocaine and stovaine analogs derived from thiophene-2-carboxylic acid,[34] the procaine analog of pyrrole-2-carboxylic acid,[35, 36] and of pyran-4-carboxylic acid.[37]

2-Thiophenecarboxylic acid

2-Pyrrolecarboxylic acid

4-Pyrancarboxylic acid

Furoic acid

2-Alkoxycinchoninic acid

[29] Ferrari, *Boll. soc. med. chir. Modena*, **45**, 422 (1945); *C.A.*, **42**, 3489 (1948).

[30] Mannich and Hof, *Arch. Pharm.*, **265**, 589, 598 (1927).

[31] Rohmann and Scheurle, *Arch. Pharm.*, **274**, 110 (1936).

[32] Fisk and Underhill, *J. Pharmacol. Exptl. Therap.*, **49**, 329 (1933).

[33] Bjerregaard and Houston, *Proc. Oklahoma Acad. Sci.*, **14**, 77 (1934); *C.A.*, **28**, 6851 (1934).

[34] Steinkopf and Ohse, *Ann.*, **437**, 14 (1924); **448**, 205 (1926).

[35] Kamm, *J. Am. Chem. Soc.*, **42**, 1030 (1920).

[36] Blicke and Blake, *J. Am. Chem. Soc.*, **52**, 235 (1930); **53**, 1051 (1931).

[37] Leffler and Brill, *J. Am. Chem. Soc.*, **55**, 365 (1933).

The esters of furoic acid show increase in anesthetic activity from methyl to amyl.[38] The esters of 2-alkoxycinchoninic acid are active,[39, 40] whereas the esters of the pyridinecarboxylic acids are not.[41]

An interesting variant has been introduced by employing p-aminothiobenzoic acid. This analog of procaine, called Thiocaine, NH_2—C_6H_4—CO—S—CH_2-$CH_2N(CH_2CH_3)_2$, is reported to be four to six times as active as procaine and half as toxic as cocaine.[42, 43]

The Alkyl Chain (Part B)

Few generalizations are permitted as to the effect produced by modification of the hydrocarbon portion between the acid moiety and the basic nitrogen. As a rule propane compounds, C_3, are more active than the homologous ethane esters, C_2.[44, 45] Two compounds of type CH_3O—C_6H_4—CO—O—$(CH_2)_n$—$N(CH_2$-$CH_3)_2$, in which n equals 2 and 5, respectively, were compared with cocaine; to anesthetize the web of a frog's foot, a concentration of the ethane compound 24 times greater was required than for the pentane homolog.[46] A comparison was made of corresponding p-ethoxybenzoates in which n was equal to 2 and 3; the former was about a sixth as active as the latter. Benzoates, p-aminobenzoates, and cinnamates of type Ar—CO—O—CH_2—NR_2, in which R varied from ethyl to pentyl, though showing anesthetic activity, were less active than the homologous esters of structure Ar—CO—O—$CH_2CH_2NR_2$.[47]

Substitution in a chain of 2 or 3 carbon atoms affords excellent anesthetic esters, as may be noted from the structural formulas of the established com-

Larocaine

Tutocaine

Allocaine

Alypin

[38] Phatek and Emerson, *J. Pharmacol. Exptl. Therap.*, **58**, 174 (1936).

[39] Gardner and Hammel, *J. Am. Chem. Soc.*, **58**, 1361 (1936).

[40] Wojahn, *Arch. Pharm.*, **269**, 422 (1931).

[41] Chiang and Hartung, *J. Org. Chem.*, **10**, 26 (1945).

[42] Hansen and Fosdick, *J. Am. Chem. Soc.*, **55**, 2872 (1933); U. S. pat. 2,090,756 (1937).

[43] Lischer and Jordan, *J. Am. Chem. Soc.*, **59**, 1623 (1937).

[44] Meeker, *J. Lab. Clin. Med.*, **11**, 139 (1925); *C.A.*, **20**, 1852 (1926).

[45] McElvain, *J. Am. Chem. Soc.*, **49**, 2835 (1927).

[46] Rohmann and Schuerle, *Arch. Pharm.*, **274**, 110 (1936).

[47] Lynn and Lofgren, *J. Am. Pharm. Assoc.*, **21**, 541, 761 (1932).

pounds shown. In Alypin the chain branches and both terminals have the characteristic dialkylamino groupings. Allocaine will be recognized as the benzoic ester of an ephedrinelike compound.

Closely related compounds with strong anesthetic action were obtained in the synthesis of compounds of the type, shown, in which R_2 is dimethyl, diethyl, or

$$
\begin{array}{c}
NR_2 \\
| \\
Ar\text{—}CH\text{—}CH\text{—}CH_3 \\
| \\
O\text{—}OC\text{—}Ar
\end{array}
$$

pentamethylene and Ar is p-methoxyphenyl, or m,p-dimethoxyphenyl, or m,p-methylenedioxyphenyl.[48] The alkyl may contain a carbethoxy group; e.g., the ester obtained from p-aminobenzoic acid and ethyl α-hydroxy-β-aminobutyrate

$$p\text{-}NH_2\text{—}C_6H_4\text{—}COO\text{—}CH(COOEt)\text{—}CH(NH_2)\text{—}CH_3$$

has pronounced anesthetic action.[49]

The nitrogen and acid moieties may be joined by a cycle. For example, cyclic alkanolamines may be obtained by the hydrogenation of dialkylaminophenols.

The 4-dialkylamino-cyclo-hexanols exist in two forms, *cis* and *trans*, each yielding a different ester with p-aminobenzoic acid. The ester of the *trans* form, when tested on goldfish, was found to be about as active as cocaine and about twice as

active as the ester of the corresponding *cis* isomer. In this compound the esterified portion may be looked upon as a bridge connecting the N to the acid residue. The corresponding 3-dialkylamino-isomer is more active.[50]

Unsymmetrically bridged chains were obtained from cyclohexanone, formaldehyde, and a secondary amine by means of the Mannich reaction, as indicated. Benzoates in which R_2 is dimethyl, diethyl, or pentamethylene are reported to be very strongly anesthetic.[51]

[48] Mannich and Schmitt, *Arch. Pharm.*, **266**, 73 (1928).
[49] Konek and Szasz, *Wien Chem. Ztg.*, **46**, 266 (1943); *C.A.*, **40**, 6064 (1946).
[50] Heckel and Adams, *J. Am. Chem. Soc.*, **49**, 1303–1307 (1927).
[51] Mannich and Hönig, *Arch. Pharm.*, **265**, 598–610 (1927).

$$
\begin{array}{c}
\text{CH}_2 \\
\text{H}_2\text{C} \quad \text{CH}_2 \\
\text{H}_2\text{C} \quad \text{C=O} \\
\text{CH}_2
\end{array}
\;+\; \text{HCHO} + \text{HNR}_2 \;\rightarrow\;
\begin{array}{c}
\text{CH}_2 \\
\text{H}_2\text{C} \quad \text{CH—CH}_2\text{—NR}_2 \\
\text{H}_2\text{C} \quad \text{C=O} \\
\text{CH}_2
\end{array}
\xrightarrow{\text{H}_2}
$$

$$
\begin{array}{c}
\text{CH}_2 \\
\text{H}_2\text{C} \quad \text{CH—CH}_2\text{—NR}_2 \\
\text{H}_2\text{C} \quad \text{CHOH} \\
\text{CH}_2
\end{array}
\;\rightarrow\;
\begin{array}{c}
\text{CH}_2 \\
\text{H}_2\text{C} \quad \text{CH—CH}_2\text{—NR}_2 \\
\text{H}_2\text{C} \quad \text{CH—O—OC—AR} \\
\text{CH}_2
\end{array}
$$

Amino Group (Part C)

Many modifications have been made which involve the substituents on the basic amino nitrogen atom. The primary amine corresponding to allocaine is reported to have activity approaching that of cocaine and to be about a third as toxic. Primary amino esters of this type are stable only as salts, however, for, when an attempt is made to isolate the free ester-base, the acid portion migrates from the oxygen atom to the nitrogen atom, forming the isomeric amide.[52] The

$$
\begin{array}{c}
\qquad\qquad \text{CH}_3 \\
\text{C}_6\text{H}_5\text{—CH—CH—NH}_2\cdot\text{HCl} \\
\qquad\quad | \\
\qquad\quad \text{O—OC—C}_6\text{H}_5
\end{array}
\xrightarrow{\text{alkali}}
\begin{array}{c}
\text{C}_6\text{H}_5\text{—CH—CH—CH}_3 \\
\qquad\quad | \qquad | \\
\qquad\;\, \text{OH} \quad \text{NHCOC}_6\text{H}_5
\end{array}
$$

reversible migration of the acyl group between the oxygen and the nitrogen in amino alcohols of the ephedrine type is discussed by Welsh.[53]

Derivatives of secondary amines have attracted interest. The p-aminoben-zoates were synthesized according to the procedure: [54]

$$
\text{NO}_2\text{—C}_6\text{H}_4\text{—CO—Cl} + \text{HO(CH}_2)_n\text{NH—R} \xrightarrow{\text{NaOH}}
$$
$$
\text{NO}_2\text{—C}_6\text{H}_4\text{—CO—O—(CH}_2)_n\text{—NH—R} \xrightarrow{\text{H}}
$$
$$
\text{NH}_2\text{—C}_6\text{H}_4\text{—CO—O—(CH}_2)_n\text{—NH—R}
$$

and the p-alkoxybenzoates were obtained by allowing the hydrochloride of the aminoalcohol to react with excess of the desired benzoyl chloride.[55] Amylsine and

$$
\text{RO—C}_6\text{H}_4\text{—CO—Cl} + \text{HO—(CH}_2)_n\text{—NHR}'(\text{HCl}) \rightarrow
$$
$$
\text{RO—C}_6\text{H}_4\text{—CO—O—(CH}_2)_n\text{—NHR}'(\text{HCl})
$$

monocaine are examples of useful anesthetics of this series (see page 206).

[52] Hartung, Munch, and Kester, *J. Am. Chem. Soc.*, **54**, 1526 (1932).
[53] Welsh, *J. Am. Chem. Soc.*, **69**, 128 (1947).
[54] Goldberg and Whitmore, *J. Am. Chem. Soc.*, **59**, 2380 (1937).
[55] Pierce, Salisbury, and Fredericksen, *J. Am. Chem. Soc.*, **64**, 1691 (1942).

Tertiary amines have been used almost universally. These represent various types. First, there are the dialkylamino compounds, e.g., the dimethylamino, the diethylamino, etc. In members of this type anesthetic efficiency seems to increase with the weight of the alkyl group. In a series of p-aminobenzoates of —$CH_2CH_2NR_2$ and —$CH_2CH_2CH_2NR_2$ it was found that activity was greater when R was C_3 or C_4. Some of the compounds, however, were quite irritating.[56] The same was true for a series of esters of dialkylaminomethanols.[57, 58]

The substituents on the nitrogen may also be unlike,[59] or the terminal carbons of the two alkyl groups may be joined,[60, 61] thus forming, with the nitrogen, a

$$NH_2-\!\!\!\bigcirc\!\!\!-CO-O-CH_2CH_2N\!\!\!\begin{array}{c} CH_2CH_3 \\ \diagup \\ \diagdown \\ CH_2CH_3 \end{array}$$

Procaine,
diethylaminoethyl p-aminobenzoate

$$NH_2-\!\!\!\bigcirc\!\!\!-CO-O-CH_2-CH_2-N\!\!\!\begin{array}{c} CH_2CH_2 \\ \diagup \\ \diagdown \\ CH_2CH_2 \end{array}$$

Pyrrolidinoethyl p-aminobenzoate

heterocycle. A more common type of cycle occurs in the piperidino derivatives,[62, 63, 64, 65] of which Piperocaine is an excellent example. The effect on activity

$$C_6H_5-CO-O-CH_2CH_2CH_2-N\!\!\!\begin{array}{c} CH_2-CH_2 \\ \diagup \quad \diagdown \\ \quad CH_2 \\ \diagdown \quad \diagup \\ CH-CH_2 \\ | \\ CH_3 \end{array}$$

Piperocaine

of further variations in the fundamental structure of local anesthetics is discussed for a series of 43 new, synthetic compounds by Gilman, Goodman, et al.[66]

As matters now stand, the choice in the clinic for a local anesthetic is not based necessarily upon the potency of the compound, but upon other factors.

[56] Meeker, J. Lab. Clin. Med., 11, 468–474 (1925); C.A., 20, 1852 (1928).

[57] Lynn and Lofgren, J. Am. Pharm. Assoc., 21, 761–764 (1932).

[58] Lynn and Lofgren, J. Am. Pharm. Assoc., 14, 970–972 (1925).

[59] Brill, J. Am. Chem. Soc., 54, 2484–2487 (1932).

[60] Blicke and Blake, J. Am. Chem. Soc., 53, 1015–1025 (1931).

[61] Andrews and McElvain, J. Am. Chem. Soc., 51, 887–892 (1929).

[62] McElvain, et al., J. Am. Chem. Soc., 49, 2835–2840 (1927); 50, 3348–3354 (1928); 52, 1633–1640 (1930); 55, 4625–4629 (1933).

[63] Barnes and Adams, J. Am. Chem. Soc., 49, 1307–1315 (1927).

[64] Marvel and Shelton, J. Am. Chem. Soc., 51, 915–917 (1929).

[65] Leffler and Brill, J. Am. Chem. Soc., 55, 365–370 (1933).

[66] Gilman, Goodman, Thomas, Hahn, and Prutting, J. Pharmacol., 74, 290 (1942).

First of all, the drug should have the minimum of side reactions. Many of the compounds described are reported to produce irritation. This irritation may be caused by the base, or the compound may be too acidic in the form of its salts. A second factor is stability. It is often necessary to sterilize solutions of the anesthetic without producing deterioration. In other words, the drug must be sufficiently stable for pharmaceutical preparation. A third factor, not decisive, is the ease of chemical manufacture.

The esters of the procaine type are inactivated by cholinesterase, which hydrolyzes them.[67]

Products

Procaine Hydrochloride, U.S.P. (Novocaine, β-Diethylaminoethyl p-Aminobenzoate Hydrochloride), $p\text{-}NH_2C_6H_4COOCH_2CH_2\overset{+}{N}H(C_2H_5)_2Cl^-$, is a powerful anesthetic when injected. It is prompt acting, and it is less toxic than cocaine. The anesthetic effect is not well maintained, and so it is usually administered with a solution of epinephrine which through its peripheral action retards the rate of absorption of the procaine. It is not an effective anesthetic when applied to intact mucous membranes.

Procaine salts are used in concentrations varying from about 0.5 to 20 per cent, depending on the type of anesthesia required, and with epinephrine salts in concentrations varying from about 1:20,000 to 1:10,000.

In compounds of the procaine type it is the aliphatic amino portion of the molecule that forms stable salts with acids. The amino group substituted in the benzoic acid portion of the compound is very weakly basic and, in a manner characteristic for aromatic amines, forms salts that are readily hydrolyzed in solution.

Various routes have been developed and patented for the synthesis of procaine. The presently preferred procedure is summarized in the accompanying reactions.

$$HN(C_2H_5)_2 \xrightarrow[\substack{\text{or} \\ CH_2CH_2 \\ \diagdown O \diagup}]{ClCH_2CH_2OH} (C_2H_5)_2CH_2CH_2OH \xrightarrow{p\text{-}NO_2C_6H_4COCl}$$

Diethylaminoethanol

$$(C_2H_5)_2NCH_2CH_2O\text{—}CO\text{—}C_6H_4\text{—}NO_2 \xrightarrow{H_2}$$
Diethylaminoethyl p-nitrobenzoate

$$(C_2H_5)_2NCH_2CH_2O\text{—}CO\text{—}C_6H_4\text{—}NH_2$$
Procaine

Butacaine Sulfate, U.S.P., N.N.R. (Butyn, γ-Di-n-butylaminopropyl p-aminobenzoate), $[H_2NC_6H_4\text{—}CO\text{—}O(CH_2)_3\text{—}N(n\text{-}C_4H_9)_2]_2H_2SO_4$, is a higher homolog of procaine. It has about the same toxicity as cocaine on injection. Since it penetrates mucous membranes readily, it is used extensively as a surface anesthetic replacing cocaine, particularly in eye surgery, because it does not

[67] Foldes, Davis, Shanor, and van Ness, *J. Am. Chem. Soc.*, **77**, 5149 (1955).

cause mydriasis. It is generally used as the sulfate in a 2 per cent solution, which may be sterilized by boiling without decomposition, for eye, ear, nose, and throat surgery, the solution being applied topically.

Tetracaine Hydrochloride, U.S.P. (Amethocaine Hydrochloride, Ponto-caine Hydrochloride, β-Dimethylaminoethyl p-n-butylaminobenzoate Hydro-chloride), $(n)H_9C_4NHC_6H_4$—CO—O—CH_2—CH_2—$N(CH_3)_2 \cdot HCl$, differs from the previously mentioned compounds chiefly because of the alkyl substituent on the nitrogen in the aminobenzoic acid portion of the molecule. The hydro-chloride possesses, in general, the properties of procaine hydrochloride; it is, how-ever, capable of producing corneal anesthesia and is effective on mucous mem-branes. In spinal anesthesia its action is quite prolonged. It is employed as a solution of the hydrochloride, 0.5 to 2 per cent in eye and nose anesthesia and 1 per cent for spinal anesthesia.

Piperocaine [67a] **Hydrochloride, U.S.P.** [Metycaine Hydrochloride, 3-Benz-oxy-1-(2-methylpiperidino)propane Hydrochloride], acts promptly either by in-

$$\text{—CO—O—CH}_2\text{—CH}_2\text{—CH}_2\text{—N} \quad \cdot \text{HCl}$$

$$CH_3$$

Piperocaine hydrochloride

jection or by application to mucous surfaces. Its toxicity is comparable to that of procaine when given subcutaneously, but, when administered intravenously, it is about three times as toxic. It is used in 2 to 10 per cent solutions and in 4 per cent ophthalmic ointment for nose and throat anesthesia; in the genitourinary tract, 0.5 to 4 per cent solutions are used.

Naepaine Hydrochloride, N.F. (Amylsine Hydrochloride, 2-Amylamino-ethyl p-aminobenzoate Hydrochloride), $[H_2N$—C_6H_4—CO—O—CH_2—CH_2—$\overset{+}{N}H_2$—CH_2—CH_2—CH_2—CH_2—$CH_3]Cl^-$, is a white, crystalline powder sol-uble in water and insoluble in organic solvents. It resembles cocaine in activity but does not cause dilation of the pupil when instilled in the eye. It is employed in ophthalmic practice when mydriasis is not desired in aqueous solutions of 2 to 4 per cent concentration.

Butethamine Hydrochloride, N.N.R. (Monocaine Hydrochloride), H_2N—C_6H_4—CO—O—CH_2—CH_2—NH—CH_2—$CH(CH_3)_2 \cdot HCl$, is a white, crystal-line powder, soluble in water and in alcohol. It has local anesthetic properties similar to procaine hydrochloride. It is very useful for nerve block in surgery and dentistry. It is about one-third more anesthetic and toxic than procaine. Its use is not warranted in topical or surface anesthesia of mucous or other membranes.

[67a] The name Piperocaine was originally given to an ester of structure $(CH_2O_2)C_6H_3CH=$ $CHCOOCH_2CH_2N(CH_2CH_3)_2$. See Kuwahata *et al.*, *Folia Pharmacol. Japon.*, **7**, 11 (1928); *C.A.*, **23**, 2499 (1929). It was erroneously given also to the product known as Helicaine (see p. 200). Beginning with N.N.R. 1949, the name Piperocaine was assigned to the substance previously known as Metycaine, N.N.R.

Intracaine Hydrochloride (Diethoxin, 2-Diethylaminoethyl p-ethoxybenzo-ate Hydrochloride), $[C_2H_5OC_6H_4COOCH_2CH_2NH^+(C_2H_5)_2]Cl^-$, is a rapid, effective local anesthetic of low toxicity. It is about two times as potent as procaine, and the duration of action is about twice as great. It is used topically for regional anesthesia, by infiltration or block in the urethra and bladder and in dental anesthesia.

Benoxinate Hydrochloride, N.N.R. (Diethylaminoethyl-m-butyloxy-p-am-inobenzoate Hydrochloride), possesses surface anesthetic activity useful in ophthalmology for short operative procedures involving the cornea and conjunc-tiva. It also exhibits bacteriostatic properties.

Benoxinate hydrochloride

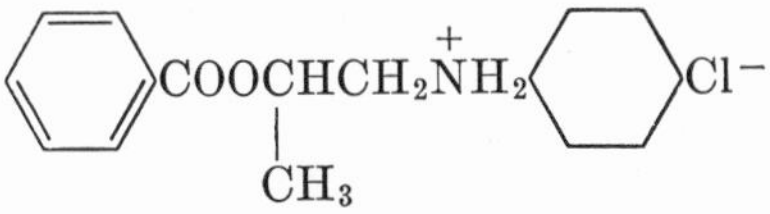

Hexylcaine hydrochloride

Hexylcaine Hydrochloride, N.N.R. (Cyclaine Hydrochloride, 1-Cyclohexyl-amino-2-propyl Benzoate Hydrochloride), is useful for infiltration and spinal anesthesia and nerve block. Applied topically it is as active as cocaine.

Surfacaine (Cyclomethycaine, 3-(2-Methylpiperidino)propyl p-cyclohexyl-oxybenzoate Hydrochloride) is an effective local anesthetic for surface anesthesia

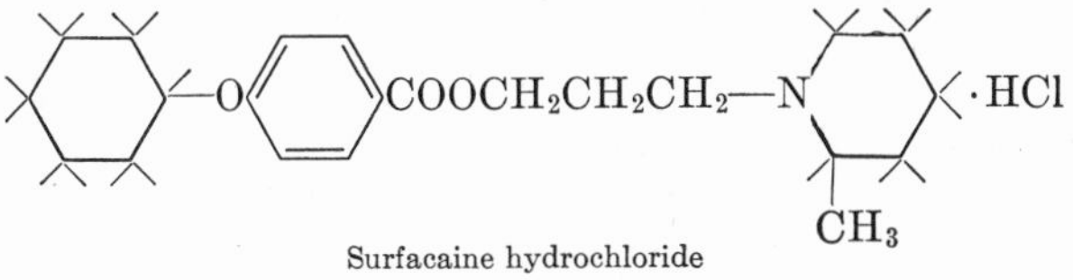

Surfacaine hydrochloride

lasting from 4 to 8 hr., and it has a potent anesthetic effect on rectal, vaginal, urethral, and bladder mucous membrane. It is used in chemical and thermal burns, sunburn and skin abrasions, and in urological, obstetric, gynecological, and other anesthetic procedures.

Structurally related compounds with anesthetic activity include the following alkyl esters of p-aminobenzoic acid. These compounds have already been dis-

$$NH_2—C_6H_4—CO—O—C_2H_5 \qquad NH_2—C_6H_4—CO—O—C_4H_9$$

Benzocaine,
Ethyl p-aminobenzoate, U.S.P.

n-Butyl p-aminobenzoate, U.S.P.

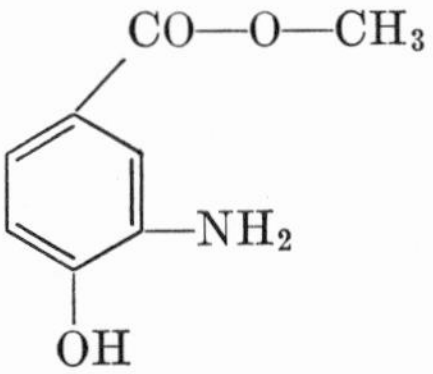

Orthoform, N.N.R.,
methyl m-amino-p-hydroxybenzoate

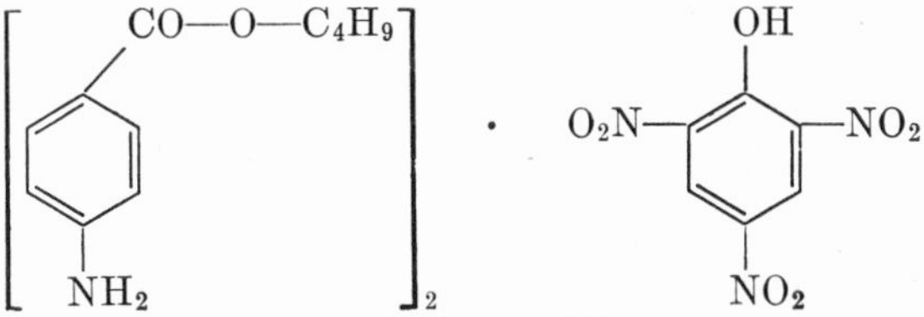

Butesin picrate, N.N.R.

cussed in part in the consideration of the procaine-type anesthetics. All of them are slightly soluble, which limits their use. They are usually employed as dusting powders diluted and intimately mixed with sterile talc. Although they are practically insoluble in water, they are soluble in oils and fats and are often used in oil solutions, ointments, and suppositories. Butesin picrate combines the anesthetic activity of butesin with the antiseptic activity of trinitrophenol. It is used to treat burns and other painful denuded skin surfaces, usually being applied in the form of a 1 per cent ointment.

Ethyl p-aminobenzoate is capable of absorbing those light waves in the ultraviolet region, in the neighborhood of 3100 A, responsible for producing sunburn; therefore, incorporation of this ester into lotions or ointments makes possible the protection against undue exposure to the summer sun.

For other useful anesthetics see Dibucaine (page 247), Procaine Amide (page 249), Diperidon (page 245), Lidocaine (page 249), Phenacaine (page 260), and Pramoxine (page 208).

Esters of Substituted Acetic and Glycolic Acids

Two predominant physiological characteristics of atropine are its mydriatic and spasmolytic properties. Pyman [67b] prepared and examined various esters of tropanol and of tropic acid, thus pointing the way to structural modifications leading to the synthesis of mydriatics, which offer certain clinical advantages over the natural alkaloid, and of spasmolytics in which the unwanted effects of atropine are less pronounced.

As with the local anesthetics, various alkanolamines have been converted into their corresponding esters, but the most favorable activity, apparently, is found in esters of a dialkylaminoethanol. Quaternization tends to accentuate the spasmolytic properties, as is seen also in homatropine methyl bromide (page 387).

The hydrochloride of benzyl β-dimethylamino-α-phenyl-α-ethylpropionate is reported to have an antispasmodic action on smooth muscles of isolated organs. It is more effective and less toxic than papaverine.[68] Dialkylaminoalkyl esters of diarylacetic acids also show spasmolytic action.[69] Examination of a group of 41 such esters showed diethylaminoethyl fluorene-9-carboxylate, depending on the test object, to possess activity from 0.14 to 20 times that of atropine; as an antagonist to the vascular action of acetylcholine it was 0.008 times as active as atropine.[70]

Products

Methantheline Bromide, U.S.P. (Banthine Bromide, 2-Diethylaminoethyl 9-xanthenecarboxylate Methobromide), is an anticholinergic agent used for the

[67b] Pyman, *J. Chem. Soc.*, **1917**, 1103.
[68] Unna, *J. Pharmacol.*, **70**, 179 (1940).
[69] Richardson, U. S. pat. 2,390,555; *C.A.*, **40**, 1970 (1946).
[70] Lehman and Knoefel, *J. Pharmacol.*, **74**, 274 (1942).

control of vagotonia and parasympathotonia of peptic ulcers. It reduces gastric hypermotility and abolishes or reduces excessive acidity.

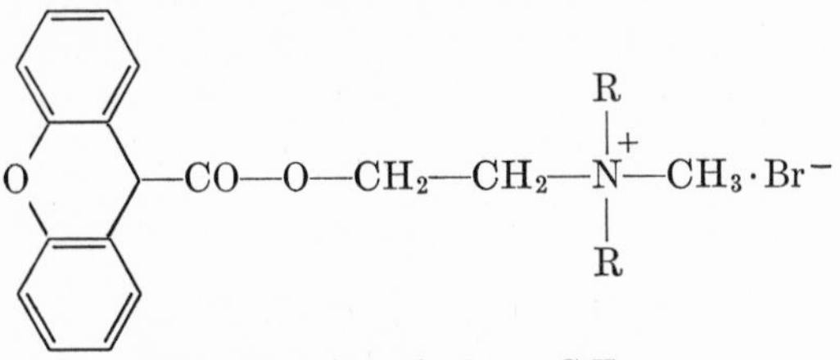

Methantheline bromide, R = —C_2H_5
Propentheline bromide, R = —$CH(CH_3)_2$

Propentheline Bromide, N.N.R. (Probanthine, 2-Diisopropylaminoethyl 9-xanthenecarboxylate Methobromide), is an effective anticholinergic substance which inhibits neural impulses at the ganglia of the sympathetic and parasympathetic systems and at the postganglionic endings of the parasympathetic system. It is used for the treatment of peptic ulcers, gastritis, and other parasympathotonic disorders.

Bentyl Hydrochloride (N,N-Diethylaminoethyl 1-cyclohexyl-1-cyclohexane-carboxylate Hydrochloride) is a non-narcotic antispasmodic with direct smooth muscle and parasympathetic depressant properties. It exhibits practically none of the undesirable effects of atropine or belladonna. It is used to relieve spastic conditions of smooth muscles such as functional disorder of the gastrointestinal tract, irritable colon, spastic constipation, pylorospasm, biliary tract dysfunction, and urethral spasms.

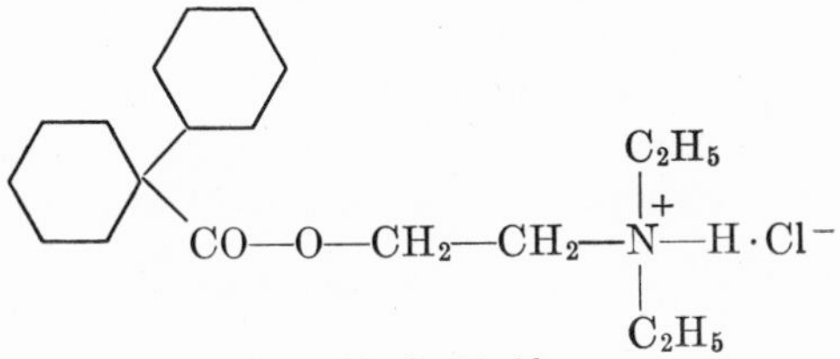

Bentyl hydrochloride

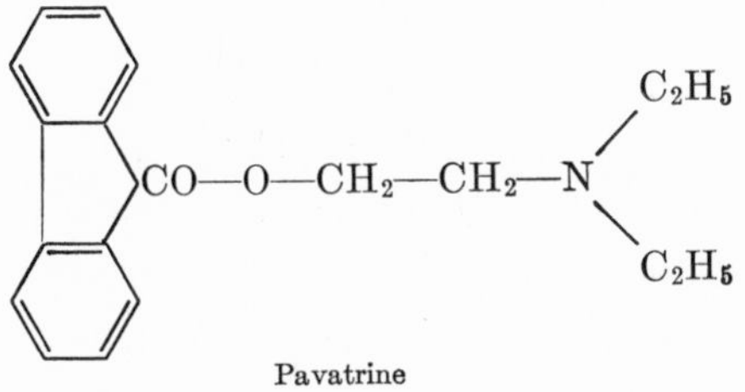

Pavatrine

Pavatrine (2-Diethylaminoethyl 9-fluorenecarboxylate), used as its hydrochloride, is an effective, non-narcotic spasmolytic agent which relaxes smooth muscle spasms by acting directly on the smooth muscle and through the autonomic nervous system. It is relatively free of the side effects of the alkaloids of the belladonna group. It is used to treat gastrointestinal irritability, gastric hypermotility, spastic colitis, dysmenorrhea due to uterine hypertonicity, and other conditions involving smooth muscle spasms.

Cyclopentylate Hydrochloride, N.N.R., is a spasmolytic agent, possessing about half the antispasmodic activity of atropine. It produces rapid, intense cycloplegia and mydriasis of moderate duration and therefore is primarily useful for refraction studies. Because of its mydriatic properties it is also useful in the treatment of iritis and other eye conditions.

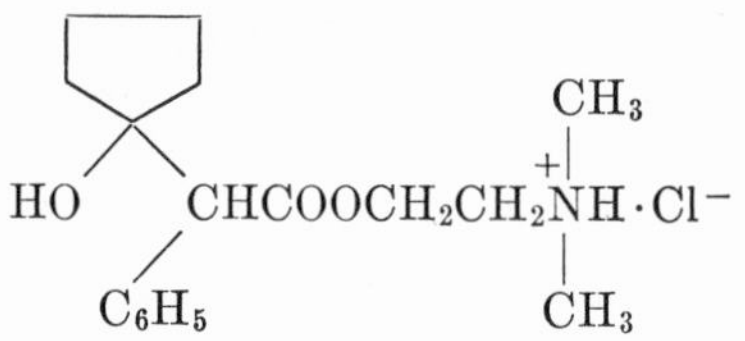

HO   CHCOOCH$_2$CH$_2$NH·Cl$^-$ /C$_6$H$_5$ CH$_3$

Cyclopentylate hydrochloride

H—C—CO—O—CH$_2$—CH$_2$—N(C$_2$H$_5$)$_2$

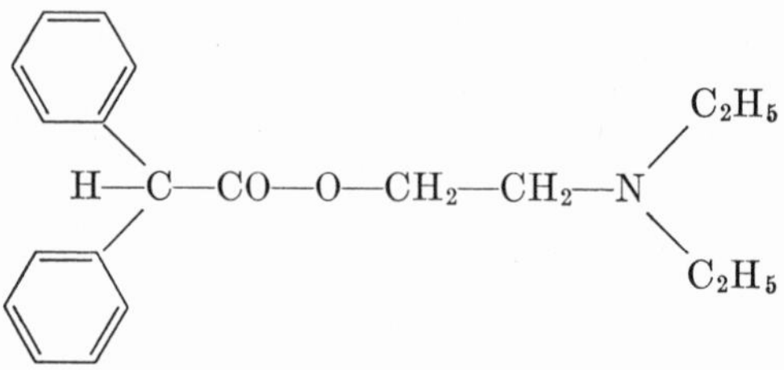

Trasentine

Trasentine (Adiphenine Hydrochloride, 2-Diethylaminoethyl diphenylacetate Hydrochloride) is an effective non-narcotic relaxant of smooth muscle spasms. It acts directly on muscle fibers as well as inhibiting parasympathetic nerve endings. It is used in cardiospasm, pylorospasm, spastic colon, renal and biliary colic, genitourinary spasm and other conditions involving smooth muscle spasms.

Syntropan, N.N.R. (Phosphate of DL-tropic acid ester of 3-Diethylamino-2,2-dimethyl-1-propanol), consists of a white powder, readily soluble in water. It is not used as a mydriatic, being only about 1/1000 as active as atropine, and it does not dry the secretions of the glands as atropine does. It is chiefly employed as an antispasmodic in renal spasm, etc., as a substitute for atropine. It is of interest to compare the structure of this compound with that of larocaine.

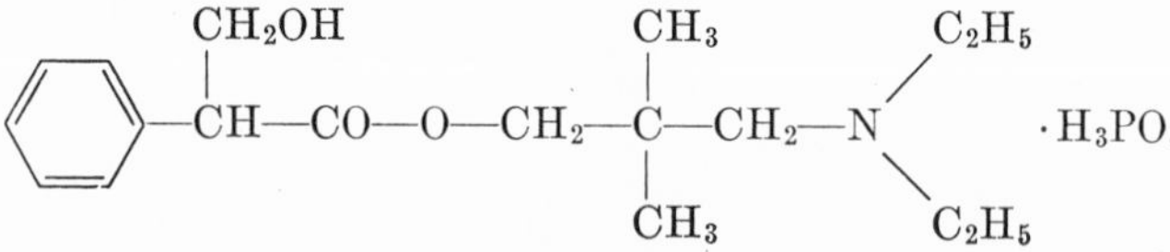

—CH—CO—O—CH$_2$—C—CH$_2$—N(C$_2$H$_5$)$_2$ · H$_3$PO$_4$ CH$_2$OH / CH$_3$ / CH$_3$

Syntropan

Diethylaminethoxyethyl Phenylcyclopentanecarboxylate (Tuclase, UBC 2543) has been used successfully in irritation coughs of mechanical origin,

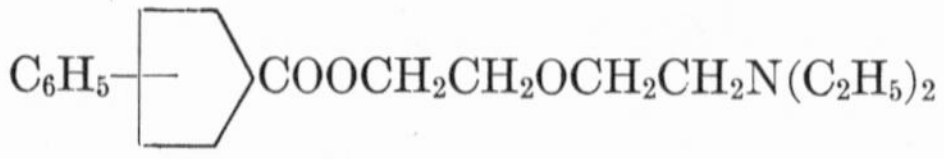

C$_6$H$_5$—[ ]—COOCH$_2$CH$_2$OCH$_2$CH$_2$N(C$_2$H$_5$)$_2$

defensive coughs, and coughs of catarrhal origin. It is reported to be non-narcotizing and nonhabit forming.[71]

[71] Deporter, *Brux.-Med.*, **1954**, 34/10, 422; *Excerpta Med.*, Sec. XV, **8**, 396 (1955).

The quaternary nitrogen may be linked through a double bridge to the acid portion, and the molecule will retain some of the atropinelike properties. An example of such a compound is **N-ethyl-3-pyridyl benzilate methobromide** (Piptal, JB 323), which is a post-ganglionic depressant, useful for the management of ulcers and hypertrophic gastritis.[72]

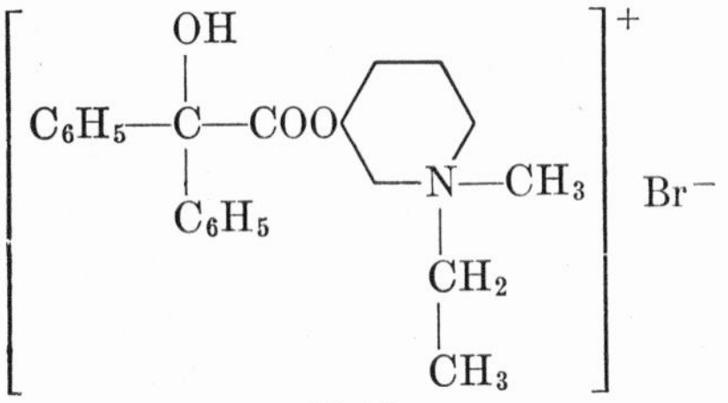

Piptal

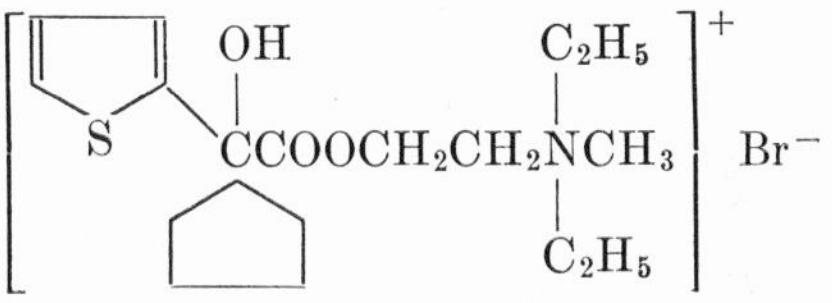

Penthionate bromide

Penthionate Bromide, N.N.R. (2-Diethylaminoethyl cyclopentyl-2-thiopheneglycolate Methobromide), shows that the substitutions on the glycolic acid moiety need not be homocyclic and they may contain fewer than six members, for this ester is anticholinergic, antisecretory, and is a suitable adjunct for the control of peptic ulcer.

ANTIHISTAMINE DRUGS

Since Dale and Laidlaw [73] first pointed out the similarity in the symptoms of histamine shock and anaphylactic shock, a wealth of evidence has accumulated in support of the view that histamine is liberated as a result of the antigen-antibody reaction and is a major factor in allergic conditions.[74, 75, 76] There is less sound evidence incriminating histamine in several other pathologic conditions, such as burns, "radiation sickness," and the toxemias of pregnancy. Consequently there has been an intensive search for means of inactivating histamine or preventing it from reaching the site of action. The synthetic histamine antagonists have been the most successful drugs of this type.

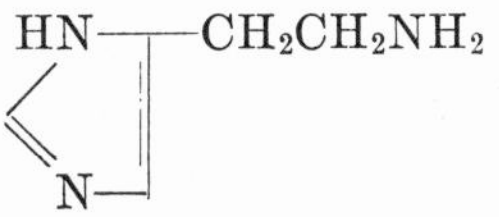

Histamine

The first active compounds of this type were thymoxyethyldiethylamine (929 F) and N-ethyl-N-(β-diethylaminoethyl)aniline (1571 F). These compounds were prepared in Fourneau's laboratory as part of a series of sympatholytics.

[72] Riese, *Am. J. Gastroenterology*, **23**, 223 (1955).
[73] Dale and Laidlaw, *J. Physiol.*, **41**, 318 (1910).
[74] Dragstedt, *J. Allergy*, **16**, 69 (1945).
[75] Rose, *Am. J. Med.*, **3**, 545 (1947).
[76] Selle, *Texas Rep. Biol. Med.*, **4**, 138 (1946).

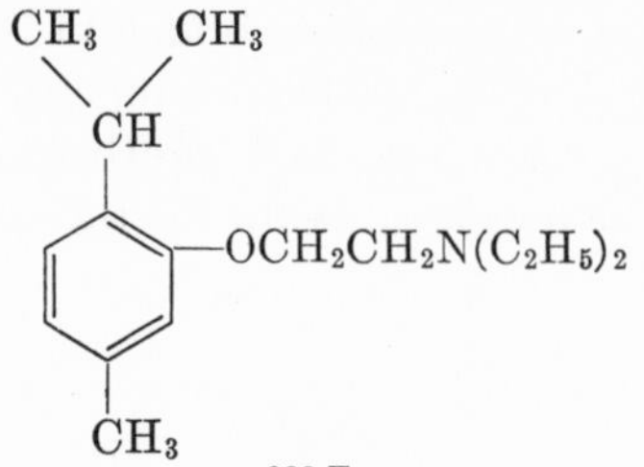

929 F

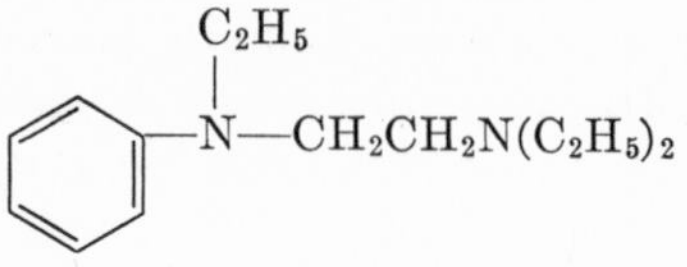

1571 F

Their antihistamine activity was discovered by Bovet and Staub in 1937.[77, 78, 79, 80] Although useful in the laboratory both compounds have toxic effects which prevent their clinical use.

Halpern,[81] in 1942, reported a study of a series of compounds prepared in the Rhône Poulenc laboratories. The most active was Antergan, N-benzyl-N-phenyl-N',N'-dimethylethylenediamine. Antergan was the first compound to find clinical use in the treatment of allergic conditions. Although it has been replaced by more active compounds which are tolerated better, the basic Antergan structure has served as a model for a number of the antihistamine drugs in use today.

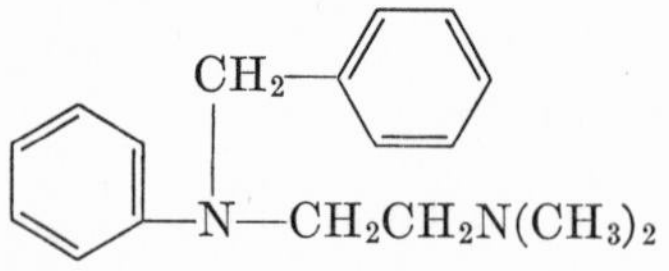

Antergan

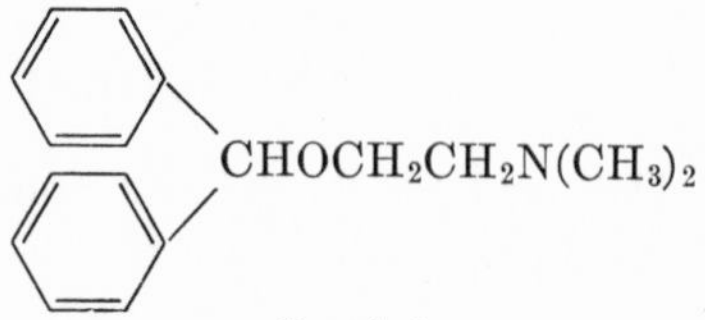

Benadryl

Benadryl was one member of a series of dialkylaminoalkyl ethers of benzhydrol,[82] prepared originally as antispasmodics. Its antihistamine activity was observed by Loew, Kaiser, and Moore.[83]

Through the efforts of several research groups a large number of compounds with antihistamine activity have been discovered.

An examination of the structural formulas of the official substances, listed in Table XVII, reveals that most of the compounds may be considered as having in common a general formula which may be written as $\begin{smallmatrix}A\\B\end{smallmatrix}\!\!>\!X-CH_2CH_2N(CH_3)_2$.

Even Antazoline, Chlorcyclizine, Phenindamine, and Pyrathiazine do not differ radically from that structure.

[77] Bovet and Staub, *Compt. rend. soc. biol.*, **124,** 547 (1937).
[78] Bovet and Staub, *ibid.*, **125,** 818 (1937).
[79] Staub, *Ann. inst. Pasteur*, **63,** 485 (1939).
[80] Staub, *ibid.*, **63,** 485 (1939).
[81] Halpern, *Arch. intern. pharmacodynamie*, **68,** 339 (1942).
[82] Rieveschl, U. S. pat. 2,421,714 (1947).
[83] Loew, Kaiser, and Moore, *J. Pharmacol.*, **83,** 120 (1945).

Typical Syntheses. The synthesis of Tripelennamine, shown below,[84] is typical of the preparation of compounds of the Antergan type. The alkali amide used as the condensing agent prevents the alkylation of the tertiary nitrogen atoms in the pyridine nucleus and the side chain.

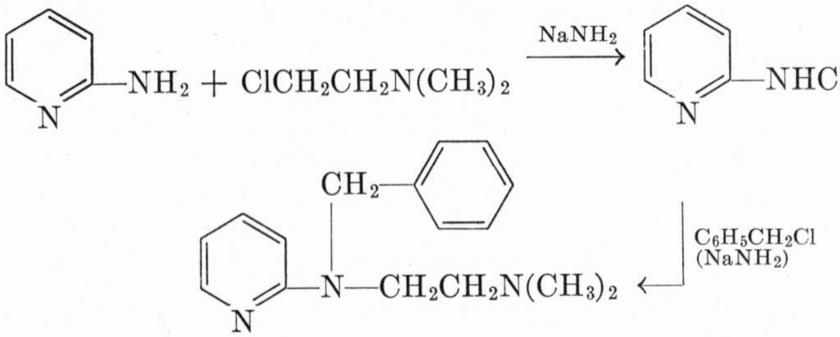

$$\text{pyridyl}-NH_2 + ClCH_2CH_2N(CH_3)_2 \xrightarrow{\text{NaNH}_2} \text{pyridyl}-NHCH_2CH_2N(CH_3)_2$$

$$\text{pyridyl}-N(CH_2C_6H_5)-CH_2CH_2N(CH_3)_2 \xleftarrow[\text{(NaNH}_2)]{\text{C}_6\text{H}_5\text{CH}_2\text{Cl}}$$

Diphenhydramine is prepared from benzhydryl bromide and β-dimethylaminoethanol in the presence of anhydrous sodium carbonate: [85]

$$(C_6H_5)_2CHBr + HOCH_2CH_2N(CH_3)_2 \rightarrow (C_6H_5)_2CHOCH_2CH_2N(CH_3)_2$$

Pheniramine is made from 2-benzylpyridine and dimethylaminoethyl chloride: [86]

$$\text{2-benzylpyridine} + ClCH_2CN_2N(CH_3)_2 \xrightarrow{\text{NaNH}_2} \text{pyridyl}-CH(C_6H_5)-CH_2CH_2N(CH_3)_2$$

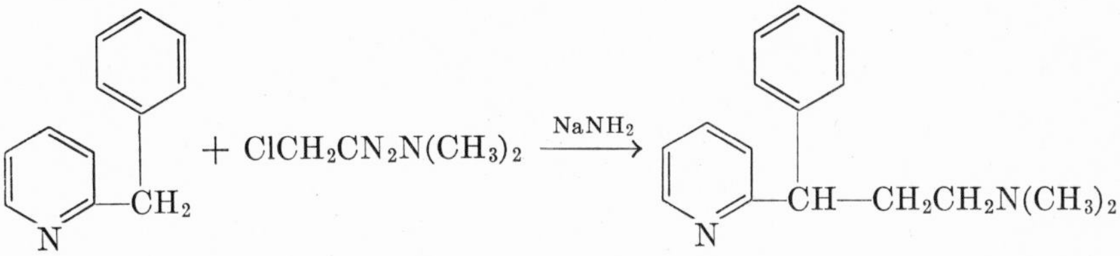

Doxylamine is prepared from acetophenone, pyridine, and dimethylaminoethyl chloride: [86]

$$\text{pyridine} + C_6H_5COCH_3 \xrightarrow[\text{HgCl}_2]{\text{Hg or}} \text{pyridyl}-C(C_6H_5)(OH)-CH_3$$

$$\xrightarrow[\text{(NaNH}_2)]{\text{ClCH}_2\text{CH}_2\text{N(CH}_3)_2} \text{pyridyl}-C(C_6H_5)(OCH_2CH_2N(CH_3)_2)-CH_3$$

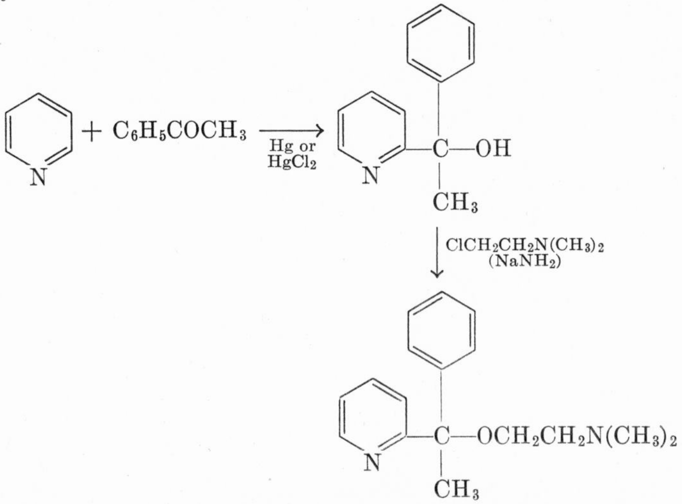

[84] Huttrer, Djerassi, Beears, Mayer, and Scholz, *J. Am. Chem. Soc.*, **68**, 1999 (1946).
[85] Rieveschl, U. S. pat. 2,421,714 (1947).
[86] Sperber, Papa, Schwenk, and Sherlock, *J. Am. Chem. Soc.*, **71**, 887 (1949).

TABLE XVII

STRUCTURAL SIMILARITIES OF ANTIHISTAMINES

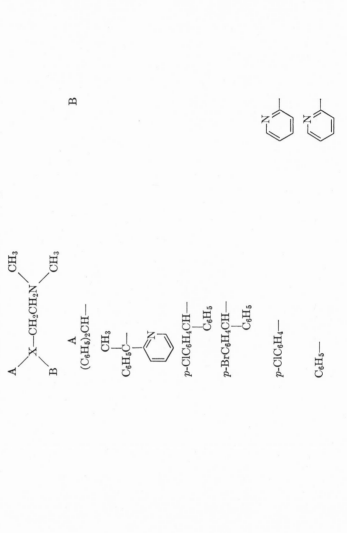

Name	A	B	X
Diphenhydramine Benadryl	$(C_6H_5)_2CH-$		$-O-$
Doxylamine Decapryn	C_6H_5C- with CH_3 and pyridyl		$-O-$
Carbinoxamine Clistin	$p\text{-}ClC_6H_4CH-$ C_6H_5		$-O-$
Bromodiphenhydramine Ambodryl	$p\text{-}BrC_6H_4CH-$ C_6H_5		$-O-$
Chlorpheniramine Chlorprophenpyridamine	$p\text{-}ClC_6H_4-$	pyridyl	$=CH-$
Pheniramine Prophenpyridamine Trimeton	C_6H_5-	pyridyl	$=CH-$
Tripelennamine Pyribenzamine	$C_6H_5CH_2-$	pyridyl	$>N-$

General structure:

$$A-X-CH_2CH_2N\begin{matrix}CH_3\\CH_3\end{matrix}$$
$$B$$

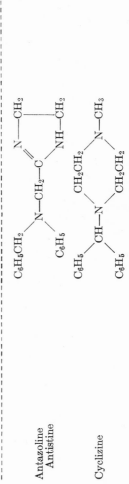

Chlorothen
Chloromethapyrilene

Methapyrilene
Semokin
Thenylene

Methaphenilene
Histadyl
Diatrine

Thenyldiamine

Pyrilamine
Neo-antergan

Thonzylamine

Antazoline
Antistine

Cyclizine

TABLE XVII—*Continued*

STRUCTURAL SIMILARITIES OF ANTIHISTAMINES

Name	
Chlorcyclizine Di-paralene	
Meclizine	
Phenindamine Thephorin	
Promethazine Phenergan	
Pyrathiazine	

Mode of Action. The antihistamine compounds are most active against the smooth muscle effects of histamine, and the pharmacological evaluation of these drugs has centered about measuring their activity against the bronchoconstrictor, spasmogenic (gastrointestinal and uterine), and depressor effects of histamine. Whether the drugs are active against the secretogog actions of histamine is a controversial point, but it is evident that their activity in this respect is of a much lower order.

For detailed and critical reviews of the pharmacology and clinical aspects of the anti-histamine drugs the reader is referred to the articles of Loew [87] Feinberg,[88] and Bovet.[88a]

It has been shown that 929 F and Antergan do not inactivate histamine *in vitro* and have no effect on diamine oxidase (histaminase),[89, 90] the enzyme that is believed to inactivate histamine in the body. Tripelennamine has no effect on the antigen-antibody reaction *in vitro*,[91] and Antergan does not prevent the release of histamine during anaphylactic shock.[90]

Halpern [90] proposed the theory that the drugs compete with histamine for the site of action. Subsequent work supports this theory. Quantitative measurements of the inhibition ratios between histamine and Benadryl on blood pressure in the dog [92] show that per cent inhibition of histamine plotted against concentration of drug gives a curve with the form of the Langmuir adsorption isotherm.[93] A similar relationship is said to hold for the inhibition ratios measured on bronchi and intestinal strips, although extensive quantitative data are lacking. These results are in full accord with the competitive inhibition theory; that is, when the drug combines with the receptor substance, it produces no appreciable effect but prevents histamine from combining with the receptor substance.

The inhibition ratios are different on different systems. Although they vary somewhat from drug to drug, as a crude approximation it can be said that 1 molecule of drug antagonizes between 10 and 100 molecules of histamine on the isolated guinea pig intestine, and between 1 and 0.1 molecule of histamine on the bronchi. In the depressor experiments in the dog 100 to 1000 molecules of drug are required to antagonize 1 molecule of histamine. The fact that the dose-response curves are of the same form in all three experiments argues for the same mechanism.[94]

Uses. The principal use of antihistamine agents is for their therapeutic effect on nasal allergies particularly in seasonal hay fever and to a lesser degree in perennial vasomotor rhinitis. The time and conditions of the season, the weather, and the concentration of the pollen and spore counts play an important

[87] Loew, *Physiol. Reviews*, **27**, 542 (1947).

[88] Feinberg, *Am. J. Med.*, **3**, 560 (1947).

[88a] Bovet, *Minerva Medica*, **41I**, 357 (1950).

[89] Staub, *Ann. inst. Pasteur*, **63**, 485 (1939).

[90] Halpern, *Arch. intern. pharmacodynamie*, **68**, 339 (1942).

[91] Arbesman, Koepf, and Miller, *J. Allergy*, **17**, 203 (1946).

[92] Wells, Morris, Bull, and Dragstedt, *J. Pharmacol.*, **85**, 122 (1945).

[93] Per cent inhibition of histamine is substituted for the amount of material adsorbed, and effective concentration of drug for the concentration of material in solution.

[94] Marsh and Davis, *J. Pharmacol.*, **89**, 234 (1947).

part in the incidence of relief. Relief is most favorably obtained from mild attacks of hay fever and predominantly sneezing symptoms. Advance symptoms and conditions most favorable for allergic reactions diminish the likelihood of relief. The drugs are of little value in the relief of nasal congestion and do not prevent or effectively relieve asthmatic attacks which frequently complicate hay fever. Their effect is entirely palliative.

These drugs are useful in the treatment and prevention of systemic allergic reactions. However, for such conditions the sympathomimetics are more urgently indicated. Usually relief is obtained from antihistamine drugs for allergic reactions, resulting in the use of penicillin, streptomycin, sulfonamides, and other drugs. They find use in the relief of urticaria, angioneurotic edema, and serum sickness.

Most of the antihistamine drugs produce sedation, the individual response depending on the size of the dose and varying with the agent. This property is being used advantageously in several somniferous proprietary preparations.

Diphenhydramine Hydrochloride, U.S.P. [Benadryl Hydrochloride,[95] 2-(Benzohydryloxy)-N,N-dimethylethylamine Hydrochloride], is a white, odorless, crystalline powder which is freely soluble in water and alcohol. It slowly darkens on exposure to light.

In addition to its use as an antihistamine agent, it is used to relieve bronchial spasm. Used in full therapeutic dosage a high incidence of sedation results.

Doxylamine Succinate, N.N.R. (Decapryn Succinate, 2-[α-(2-Dimethyl-aminoethoxy)-α-methylbenzyl] pyridine Succinate), is a cream-to-white powder which is very soluble in water and freely soluble in alcohol.

A high incidence of sedation is evident when it is used in full therapeutic doses.

Carbinoxamine Maleate, N.N.R. [(p-Chlorobenzohydryloxyethyl)dimethyl-ammonium Maleate, Clistin], is a white, odorless powder, slightly soluble in water, and with a bitter taste. It is reported to have potent antihistamine activity with a low incidence of side effects, and it shows no local anesthetic action, nor is it likely to produce cardiovascular or respiratory manifestations.

Bromodiphenhydramine Hydrochloride is the hydrochloride salt of the bromine analog of carbinoxamine and has similar properties.

Chlorpheniramine Maleate, U.S.P. [Chlorprophenpyridamine Maleate, Chlor-Trimeton Maleate, 1-(p-Chlorophenyl)-1-(2-pyridyl)-3-dimethylamino-propane Maleate], is a white, crystalline solid which is freely soluble in water and soluble in alcohol.

It has good therapeutic efficacy in very low dosage, and the incidence of side effects are few. It may be administered intravenously, intramuscularly, or subcutaneously whenever oral administration is not feasible or if absorption is not as rapid as desired.

Pheniramine [Prophenpyridamine, N.N.R., Trimeton, 1-Phenyl-1-(2)pyridyl)-3-dimethylaminopropane] is an oily liquid which is insoluble in water but

---

[95] The structural formulas of the salts of these antihistamines are not given. They may be constructed from the information given in Table XVII.

soluble in alcohol and in dilute acids. **Pheniramine Maleate, N.F.** (Trimeton Maleate), is a white solid which is very soluble in water and in alcohol. Both are active antihistamine agents and are effective in the prevention and treatment of motion sickness. The salt has no therapeutic advantage over the base.

Tripelennamine Hydrochloride, U.S.P. (Pyribenzamine Hydrochloride, N-Benzyl-N',N'-dimethyl-N-2-pyridylethylenediamine Hydrochloride), and **Tripelennamine Citrate, U.S.P.**, are white, crystalline powders which are very soluble in water and freely soluble in alcohol. The hydrochloride darkens slowly on exposure to light.

Both salts have a low incidence of side reactions. Gastrointestinal irritation is common but not severe. Stimulation of the nervous system occurs frequently. The citrate, more palatable than the hydrochloride for oral administration, otherwise has no advantage. The drugs may be administered subcutaneously, intramuscularly, or intravenously when oral medication is not feasible or if a rapid response is desired.

Chlorothen Citrate, U.S.P. [Chloromethapyrilene Citrate, N,N-Dimethyl-N'-(2-pyridyl)-N'-(5-chloro-2-thenyl)ethylenediamine Citrate], is a white solid which is freely soluble in water and alcohol. It possesses properties similar to other antihistamine agents, and no advantage is claimed for it.

Methapyrilene Hydrochloride, U.S.P. [Semikon Hydrochloride, Thenylene Hydrochloride, Histadyl, N,N-Dimethyl-N'-(2-pyridyl)-N'-(2-thenyl)-ethylenediamine Hydrochloride], is a white, crystalline powder which is very soluble in water and freely soluble in alcohol. It possesses properties similar to other antihistamine agents and is claimed to have a low incidence of sedation.

Pyrilamine Maleate, U.S.P. [Neo-Antergan Maleate, N,N-Dimethyl-N'-(p-methoxybenzyl)-N'-(2-pyridyl)ethylenediamine Maleate], is a white, crystalline powder which is very soluble in water and freely soluble in alcohol. It possesses properties similar to other antihistamine agents and is claimed to have a low incidence of sedation.

Methaphenilene Hydrochloride, N.F. [Diatrine Hydrochloride, N,N-Dimethyl-N'-(α-thenyl)-N'-phenylethylenediamine Hydrochloride], is a white-to-pale-yellow, crystalline powder which is soluble in water and sparingly soluble in alcohol.

Methaphenilene hydrochloride is an effective antihistamine agent which possesses a low incidence of side effects. It is reported to have a moderate tendency to cause irritation of the gastrointestinal tract.

Thenyldiamine Hydrochloride, U.S.P. {2-[(2-Dimethylaminoethyl)-3-thenylamino]pyridine Hydrochloride}, occurs as white crystals, is practically odorless, and is soluble to the extent of about 1 gram in 5 ml. each of water, alcohol, and chloroform.

Thonzylamine Hydrochloride, U.S.P. (Neohetramine Hydrochloride, N,N-Dimethyl-N'-(p-methoxybenzyl)-N'-(2-pyrimidyl)-ethylenediamine Hydrochloride), is a white, crystalline powder which is very soluble in water and freely soluble in alcohol.

To produce reasonable incidence and degree of therapeutic effectiveness larger doses are required as compared to most other antihistamine agents. However, it has the advantage that sedation is less frequent and less severe.

Antazoline Hydrochloride, U.S.P. [Antistine Hydrochloride, 2-(N-Benzyl-anilinomethyl)-2-imidazoline Hydrochloride], and **Antazoline Phosphate, N.N.R.** [Antistine Phosphate, 2-(N-Benzylanilinomethyl)-2-imidazoline Phosphate], are white, crystalline compounds with a bitter taste. The hydrochloride is sparingly soluble in water and alcohol. The phosphate is soluble in water and sparingly soluble in alcohol.

The antihistamine activity of these two compounds is weaker than most of the other agents of this class but they have the advantage that they are milder and less irritating to tissues. The hydrochloride may be applied topically to the mucous membranes of the nose to produce some local effect on nasal allergy but immediate relief is rarely obtained. The phosphate is preferred to the hydrochloride for ophthalmic use because it produces less smarting and stinging.

Cyclizine Hydrochloride, N.N.R., and **Cyclizine Citrate, N.N.R.** (salts of 1-Benzhydryl-4-methylpiperazine), are antihistamine drugs, both useful for the treatment of motion sickness.

Chlorcyclizine Hydrochloride, U.S.P. [Di-paralene Hydrochloride, 1-(p-Chlorobenzhydryl)-4-methylpiperazine Hydrochloride], is a white, crystalline solid which is freely soluble in water and soluble in alcohol.

The antihistamine activity of this product is prolonged with a low incidence of toxic effect. However, the systemic activity is more erratic as compared to other antihistamine agents.

Meclizine Hydrochloride, N.N.R. [1-(p-Chlorobenzhydryl)-4-(m-methylbenzyl)piperazine Hydrochloride], is an antihistamine, and it depresses the central nervous system; it has pronounced effect against motion sickness, and it is useful for the treatment of nausea and vomiting associated with vertigo, Ménière's disease, and radiation sickness.

Phenindamine Tartrate, U.S.P. (2-Methyl-9-phenyltetrahydro-1-pyridindene Bitartrate, Thephorin), occurs as a white, creamy powder with a slight odor. It is practically insoluble in chloroform and ether, slightly soluble in alcohol, and soluble 1 g. in 40 ml. of water.

Pyrathiazine Hydrochloride, U.S.P. {10-[2-(1-Pyrrolidyl)-ethyl]phenothiazine Hydrochloride}, occurs as white, or grayish-white, odorless crystals which are quite soluble in water, chloroform, and alcohol.

Promethazine, see under promazine and chlorpromazine, page 436.

PHENYLETHYLAMINE DERIVATIVES

In 1895, Oliver and Schaefer demonstrated that the medulla of the suprarenal gland elaborates a principle that is capable of producing a rise in blood pressure when injected into the blood stream.[96] This was the first time that any physiologically active substance had been shown to be elaborated by a ductless gland.

[96] Oliver and Schaefer, *J. Physiol.*, **18**, 230 (1895).

The principle was subsequently isolated, characterized, and synthesized; it was called by various names, such as Suprarenin, Adrenalin, and Epinephrine. In the years following it was assumed to be the active sympathetic mediator. It was thought to be a single substance. However, after some time Cannon and Rosenblueth [97] suggested that this chemical transmitter, which was both excitatory and inhibitory, depending on the nerve endings, indicated a mixture of what was called Sympathin E (excitatory) and Sympathin I (inhibitory). The former has now been shown to be norepinephrine and the latter epinephrine. In 1949, a chemical separation of the two principles was achieved.[98, 99]

Norepinephrine is the predominating substance liberated into the blood stream following stimulation of the sympathetic nerves of the hepatic, splenic, abdominal, and hypogastric systems; it is the predominant transmitter substance liberated at the adrenergic nerve endings. In fowls and in the whale the gland contains about 80 per cent norepinephrine and 20 per cent epinephrine. The human gland contains about 20 per cent norepinephrine except in cases of certain tumors. Norepinephrine produces bradycardia and has little effect on cardiac output; it raises both systolic and diastolic blood pressure. Epinephrine produces tachycardia, increases cardiac output, and produces a rise only in the systolic blood pressure.[100]

The isolation and recognition of the powerful physiological actions of epinephrine from the medulla of the suprarenal gland and of ephedrine from various species of ephedra stimulated synthetic chemical research. This research has resulted in the production of a number of new organic medicinal agents which, because they have the property of causing results very similar to those caused by stimulation of the sympathetic nervous system, have been called "sympathomimetic" drugs. They have also been called "pressor" drugs becuase they increase the blood pressure.

Structure and Physiological Activity

In this series of amines and aminoalcohols, on the basis of those listed and many others, is found one of the best-known correlations of the effect of chemical structures on physiological activity. Several definite conclusions are indicated, namely:

1. The optimum pressor activity (production of a rise in blood pressure) is found in those compounds in which the aromatic nucleus and the amino group are attached to neighboring or adjacent carbon atoms, thus Ar—C—C—N$\big\langle$. For example, of the three isomeric phenylpropylamines, $C_6H_5CH(NH_2)$—

[97] Cannon and Rosenblueth, *Am. J. Physiol.*, **104**, 557 (1933); Rosenblueth, *The Transmission of Nerve Impulses at Neuroeffector Junctions and Peripheral Synapses*, John Wiley & Sons, N. Y., 1950.

[98] Goldenberg *et al.*, *Science*, **109**, 534 (1949).

[99] Auerbach and Angell, *Science*, **109**, 537 (1949).

[100] West, *J. Pharm. Pharmacol.*, **7**, 81 (1955).

CH_2CH_3, $C_6H_5CH_2CH(NH_2)CH_3$, and $C_6H_5CH_2CH_2CH_2NH_2$, the second, which has the indicated skeleton, is the most active.

2. The alcoholic hydroxyl group either increases the activity or decreases the toxicity or does both. For example, benzedrine has $\frac{1}{4}$ the pressor activity of propadrine and its acute toxicity is three times as great; epinephrine is twelve times as active as is epinine.

3. Propadrine is typically musculotropic, and norhomo-epinephrine is typically sympathicotropic. Structural intermediates are shown. p-Hydroxypro-

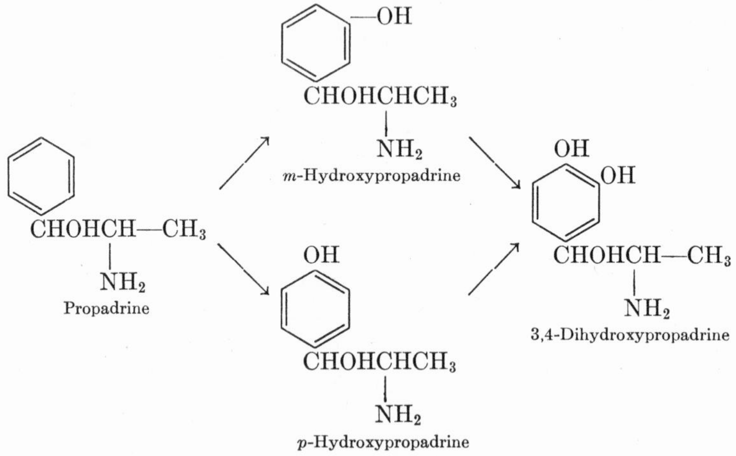

m-Hydroxypropadrine

Propadrine

3,4-Dihydroxypropadrine

p-Hydroxypropadrine

padrine is predominantly musculotropic in its method of action; m-hydroxypropadrine is much more sympathicotropic; complete sympathicotropic activity appears when two phenolic hydroxy groups are present.

The effect of substituents other than hydroxyl in the aromatic nucleus has been abundantly investigated, but, of them all, only the p-amino group seems to hold interest.

4. The primary amines are more active and less toxic, generally, than the corresponding methylated, secondary amines. For example, norepinephrine is about $\frac{10}{7}$ as active as epinephrine with the same configuration; norephedrine is less toxic and somewhat more active as a pressor than is ephedrine. The presence of the N-methyl group seems to confer on epinephrine increased bronchodilator properties.[101] Further alkylation, such as conversion into tertiary amines, or increasing the size of the alkyl in the secondary amines, increases the toxicity and decreases the pressor activity. Yet such compounds may possess other virtues, e.g., isoproterenol, which possesses bronchodilator and vasodepressor properties.[102]

5. Compounds with three carbon atoms in the side chain, such as ephedrine, and norhomo-epinephrine, are much more active on the circulation after oral

[101] Pedden, Tainter, and Cameron, *J. Pharmacol.*, **55**, 242 (1935).

[102] Lands, Rickards, Nash, and Hooper, *J. Pharmacol. Exptl. Therap.*, **89**, 297 (1947).

administration than are the homologs with only two carbon atoms in the side chain. Increasing the length of the chain beyond three carbon atoms affects adversely the pressor activity.[103] However, other desirable physiological properties appear in such long-chain analogs; e.g., stimulants without pressor activity,[104] or an epinephrinelike bronchodilator effect without increase in blood pressure, as is reported with butanefrine.[105]

6. If the aromatic nucleus and the side chain of these pressor compounds are separated, as in ethers of the type Ar—O—$CH_2CH_2NR_2$, they become sympatholytic and in dogs reverse the characteristic action of epinephrine.[106]

It is now possible to correlate to a considerable extent the biochemical reactions of these compounds with their chemical structure and thus, perhaps, to explain the physiological responses they produce.[107] The inactivation or detoxication may be effected in one or several of the following ways:

1. **Monoamine Oxidase System.** This enzyme appearing in the liver promotes the oxidation of primary carbinamines, as ammonium ions, according to the general equations:

$$RCH_2\overset{+}{N}H_3 + O_2 \rightarrow RCH{=}\overset{+}{N}H_2 + H_2O_2$$

$$RCH{=}\overset{+}{N}H_2 + H_2O \rightarrow RCHO + \overset{+}{N}H_4$$

or if the amine is secondary:

$$RCH_2\overset{+}{N}H_2CH_3 + O_2 \rightarrow RCH{=}\overset{+}{N}HCH_3 + H_2O$$

$$RCH{=}\overset{+}{N}HCH_3 + H_2O \rightarrow RCHO + \overset{+}{N}H_3CH_3$$

This system is undoubtedly responsible for the complete and prompt degradation of substances such as isoamylamine and β-phenethylamine, and partly for tyramine. Secondary carbinamines, such as ephedrine and benzedrine, are refractory toward monoamine oxidase and are, except as mentioned below, excreted unchanged.

2. **Cytochrome and Phenolase Systems.** Tyrosinase, for example, will oxidize a compound containing a *para* phenolic hydroxyl group to a catechol derivative. This *o*-dihydroxybenzene is oxidized to the corresponding *o*-quinone, which may, under the influence of the enzymes, act in several ways:

[103] Hartung, *Ind. Eng. Chem.*, **37**, 126 (1945).

[104] Rosenmund and Karg, *Ber.*, **75**, 1850 (1942).

[105] Suter and Ruddy, *J. Am. Chem. Soc.*, **66**, 747 (1944).

[106] Levy and Olszycka, *Compt. rend. soc. biol.*, **119**, 899 (1935); *C.A.*, **29**, 6649 (1935).

[107] For more comprehensive discussions of this subject two reviews may be consulted, *viz.*, Beyer, *Physiological Reviews*, **26**, 169–197 (1946) and Hartung, *Annual Review of Biochemistry*, **15**, 593–616 (1946).

a. e.g., a derivative of primary carbinamine

o-Quinone of tyramine   Indole derivative $\rightarrow$ Melanin

b. The quinone may oxidize a secondary carbinamine:

$$Ar-CH_2-\underset{\underset{NH}{\|}}{C}-CH_3 + H_2O \rightarrow Ar-CH_2-CO-CH_3 + NH_3$$

These mechanisms explain the degradation of many phenolic derivatives and of some nonphenolic secondary carbinamines.

3. **Ascorbic-dehydroascorbic Acid System.** The reaction may be summarized:

Dehydroascorbic acid   Ascorbic acid

This explains the major part of the degradation of secondary carbinamines, i.e., ephedrine, propadrine, benzedrine, etc., observed *in vivo*.

4. **Epinephrine and cobefrine,** suitable substrates *in vitro* for appropriate enzyme systems, are probably detoxified by esterification of a phenolic hydroxyl group with sulfuric acid. This appears to be true for such of these compounds as are administered. It is not unlikely that the epinephrine naturally elaborated by the suprarenal medulla is converted into adrenachrome (see Indole).

Products

Epinephrine, U.S.P. [Adrenalin, Suprarenin, 1-(3,4-Dihydroxyphenyl)-2-methylamino-1-ethanol], may be isolated from adrenal glands or it may be prepared synthetically. It occurs as white-to-light-brown, odorless microcrystals, which are sensitive to light.   In the official product not more than about 4 per cent may be norepinephrine.   The synthesis of epinephrine is summarized in the equation shown.

Chloroacetocatechol

Norepinephrine   Epinephrine

Each product may be resolved into its *dextro-* and *levo*-rotatory forms.

Epinephrine is important historically as the first hormone to be isolated and the first of which the structure was proved by synthesis.   By means of C^{14} it has been possible to show that it is formed *in vivo* from phenylalanine.[108]

The levo and racemic compounds are the only ones used in medicine.   Dilute aqueous solutions deteriorate with the formation of red-to-brown color and loss of activity.   Such solutions are partially stabilized by chlorobutanol and by reducing agents, e.g., sodium bisulfite.

Epinephrine is used to cause a rise in blood pressure from stimulation of the vasoconstrictor mechanism of the systemic vessels and of the accelerator mechanism of the heart.   It is used locally to arrest hemorrhage and to enhance the activity of local anesthetics.   It is used hypodermically to relax the bronchial muscle in asthma and in anaphylactic reactions, and intravenously to tide the patient over acute circulatory collapse.

The action of epinephrine upon intravenous injection is of short duration since it is rapidly destroyed in the body.   It is practically inactive when administered orally.   Epinephrine is employed in solutions of from 1:15,000 to 1:1000 in water or oil of the hydrochloride or free base, respectively.   It is also used in the form of ointments and suppositories in 1:1000 parts.

Norepinephrine, also known as **Arterenol,** as already mentioned, occurs along with natural epinephrine and has been identified with Sympathin E. Excessive amounts have been identified in certain tumors, as in the glia tumor of the brain [109] and in pheochromocytoma.[10, 11]   As a pressor agent it is about $\frac{5}{8}$ as active as epinephrine, but its action on the rat uterus is much feebler.

[108] Gurin and Delluva, *Federation Proc.*, **6,** 257 (1947).

[109] Bülbring, Philpot, and Bosanquet, *Lancet*, **264,** 865 (1953); *C.A.*, **47,** 7639 (1953).

[110] v. Euler, Lund, Olsson, and Sandblom, *Scand. J. Clin. & Lab. Invest.*, **5,** 122 (1953); *C.A.*, **47,** 11469 (1953).

[111] Head and West, *J. Comp. Pathol.*, **65,** 366 (1955); *C.A.*, **50,** 2814 (1956).

Levarterenol Bitartrate, U.S.P. [Levophed Bitartrate, (−)Arterenol Bitartrate], is synthesized according to the reactions indicated.[112]   It is a white, crystalline powder which is freely soluble in water and slightly soluble in alcohol.

Its action differs clinically from that of epinephrine in that it functions as a sympathetic mediator of peripheral vasoconstriction whereas epinephrine acts as an overall vasodilator but raises blood pressure by increasing cardiac output. It is similar in activity to Phenylephrine and other synthetic pressor amines which are preferred to epinephrine in hypotensive states caused by central vasomotor failure and peripheral circulatory collapse.

Levarterenol bitartrate is used to maintain blood pressure in acute hypotensive states resulting from surgical and nonsurgical trauma, central vasomotor depression and hemorrhage.   It is administered intravenously by infusion in isotonic sodium chloride, 5 per cent dextrose, human plasma, or whole blood.

Isoproterenol Hydrochloride, U.S.P. [Aludrine Hydrochloride, Isuprel Hydrochloride, 1-(3,4-Dihydroxyphenyl)-2-isopropylamino-1-ethanol Hydrochloride], is the salt of a sympathomimetic amine in which the presence of a larger alkyl group on the nitrogen atom substantially eliminates circulatory effects, except possibly for tachycardia.   It may be administered sublingually or by oral inhalation for treatment of asthma.   It is effective in epinephrine-fast patients.   Its principal effect is on the bronchi.   It has less pronounced action on the smooth muscles than does epinephrine.

Isoproterenol hydrochloride X⁻ = Cl⁻
Isopropylarterenol sulfate X = ½(SO₄·2H₂O)⁻²

Isopropylarterenol Sulfate, N.N.R. (Isonorin Sulfate, Norisodrine Sulfate), forms white, hygroscopic crystals which are freely soluble in water and slightly soluble in alcohol.   It is used for the same purposes as is the corresponding hydrochloride.

Methadren (Methyladrenalin, N-methylepinephrine) like its racemate requires 0.125 to 0.150 mg. per kg. (in nembutalized rabbits) to produce a rise in blood pressure equivalent to that obtained with epinephrine at a dose level of 0.005 mg. per kg.   Intravenously to dogs it was $\frac{1}{40}$ as active as epinephrine.   In inhibiting gastrointestinal activity it was from $\frac{1}{50}$ to $\frac{1}{80}$ as effective as epinephrine.   Its glycogenolytic activity is only slightly less than that of epinephrine. The lethal dose was 5–6 mg. per kg. intravenously to rats, and 2.5–3.7 mg. per kg. intravenously to rabbits.[113]

[112] Langenbeck and Fischer, *Pharmazie*, **5**, 56 (1950).
[113] Stutzman and Orth, *J. Pharmacol. Exptl. Therap.*, **69**, 1 (1940).

Phenylephrine Hydrochloride, U.S.P. (Neo-Synephrine Hydrochloride, Isophrin Hydrochloride, (−)1-*m*-Hydroxyphenyl-2-methylaminoethanol Hydrochloride), is prepared by the sequence of reactions shown. It occurs as white, or

nearly white, crystals which are freely soluble in water and in alcohol. It is relatively stable in alkaline solution and is unharmed by boiling for sterilization.

It is an active vasoconstrictor and a vasopressor when administered orally. It is relatively nontoxic and when applied to mucous membrane reduces swelling and congestion.

It is used to relieve nasal congestion resulting from disorders of the respiratory tract such as sinusitis, vasomotor rhinitis, and hay fever. It may be used also for certain hypotensive states due to circulatory collapse, as a mydriatic for the eye preliminary to fundoscopic examination, and for its pressor and antiallergic effect.

Halostachine (1-Phenyl-2-methylamino-1-ethanol), C_6H_5—CHOH—CH_2—$NHCH_3$, m.p. 43–45°, has been isolated from *Halostachis caspica*.[114]

Ephedrine, U.S.P. (D-*erythro*-1-Phenyl-2-methylamino-1-propanol), C_6H_5—CHOH—CH—CH_3, was first isolated from various species of Ephedra.

$\quad\quad\quad\;$ |
$\quad\quad\quad$ $NHCH_3$

An interesting synthesis of (−)-ephedrine, of the same configuration as that found in the plant, depends, first, on the synthesis of (−)-phenylacetylcarbinol, C_6H_5—CHOH—CO—CH_3, by the fermentation of sugar through the action of the enzyme carboligase of yeast in the presence of benzaldehyde; second, the keto-alcohol is allowed to react with methylamine, and the product is reduced catalytically by means of an activated aluminum or platinum catalyst.[115]

$$C_6H_5CHO + sugar \xrightarrow{\text{yeast}} C_6H_5—CHOH—COCH_3$$
$$\text{D}(-)\text{Phenylacetylcarbinol}$$

$$C_6H_5—CHOH—CO—CH_3 + NH_2CH_3 \xrightarrow[\text{(catalyst)}]{H_2} C_6H_5—CHOH—CH—CH_3$$
$$\quad\quad\quad\quad\quad\quad\quad\quad\quad\quad\quad\quad\quad\quad\quad\quad\quad\quad\quad\quad NHCH_3$$
$$\text{(−)Ephedrine}$$

Ephedrine simulates epinephrine in action. Its pressor effects and its local constrictor effects are more lasting than epinephrine. It is active when given orally or systemically. It is used to cause a rise in blood pressure, to dilate the

[114] Menshikov and Rubinstein, *J. Gen. Chem.* (*U.S.S.R.*), **13**, 801 (1943); *C.A.*, **39**, 1172 (1945).

[115] U. S. pat. 1,956,950; *C.A.*, **28**, 4072 (1934); U. S. pat. 1,962,476; *C.A.*, **28**, 4834 (1934). Neuberg, Hirsch, and Heinz, *Biochem. Z.*, **115**, 282 (1921); **128**, 610 (1922).

bronchi and pupils, and to contract the capillaries on mucous membranes in rhinitis, sinusitis, asthma, hay fever, and urticaria. Salts of ephedrine are active when given orally, intramuscularly, intravenously, or by other means. The base or its salts may be used in oil or aqueous solution as a spray in $\frac{1}{2}$ to 2 per cent solution. The base, hydrochloride, and sulfate, and several preparations containing these salts are official.

Racephedrine Hydrochloride, N.F. (Racemic Ephedrine Hydrochloride), may be prepared by the catalytic reduction of 1-phenyl-1,2-propanedione in the presence of methylamine.[116] It occurs as white crystals or powder which is

$$C_6H_5{-}CO{-}CO{-}CH_3 + CH_3NH_2 \xrightarrow[\text{(PtO}_2)]{\text{H}_2 \text{ in MeOH}} C_6H_5{-}CHOH{-}CH{-}CH_3$$
$$\underset{\text{NHCH}_3}{\big|}$$

Racemic ephedrine

affected by light. It is freely soluble in water and soluble in alcohol.

The differences in pharmacodynamic properties of DL-ephedrine and its component D(−)-ephedrine are not too great, producing peripheral effects similar to those of ephedrine. It is used locally to dilate the pupil of the eye and to relieve congestion of the nasal passage in rhinitis and sinusitis. In some instances it is useful in asthma, and it may be used in hay fever and urticaria. It may be useful also in certain types of hypotension but is of no benefit in shock, circulatory collapse or hemorrhage.

Phenylpropanolamine Hydrochloride, N.N.R. (Propadrine Hydrochloride, DL-1-Phenyl-2-amino-1-propanol Hydrochloride, Norephedrine Hydrochloride), is prepared according to the reaction sequence shown. It is a pressor drug which acts similarly to ephedrine. Applied locally to shrink swollen mu-

$$C_6H_5COCH_2CH_3 \xrightarrow[\text{(H}^+)]{\text{RONO}} C_6H_5{-}CO{-}C{-}CH_3 \xrightarrow[\text{(HCl)}]{\text{H}_2 \text{ with Pd-C}}$$
$$\underset{\text{NOH}}{\big\|}$$

Propiophenone   Isonitrosopropiophenone

$$C_6H_5{-}CHOH{-}CH{-}CH_3$$
$$\underset{\text{NH}_3\text{Cl}}{\big|}$$

(±)Propadrine hydrochloride

cous membranes, its action is more prolonged than that of ephedrine. It is less toxic than ephedrine, with less stimulation of the anxiety complex. It is used as a 1 per cent solution, as a 0.66 per cent jelly locally, in solution as a spray and in drops. It is active when given orally.

Nylidin Hydrochloride, N.N.R. [Arlidin, Dilator, Dilatal, 1-(p-Hydroxyphenyl)-2-(1-methyl-3-phenylpropyl)amino-1-propanol], p-HOC$_6$H$_4$—CHOH—CH—NH—CHCH$_2$CH$_2$C$_6$H$_5$, is reported to be a superior vasodilator, useful
|
CH$_3$ CH$_3$
for the treatment of patients with peripheral vascular diseases.[117]

---

[116] Sunagawa and Okuda, *J. Pharm. Soc. Japan*, **72**, 117 (1952); *C.A.*, **46**, 11146 (1952).
[117] *Chem. Eng. News*, **33**, 2896 (1955).

Metraminol Bitartrate, N.N.R. [Aramine Bitartrate, $(-)$-1-m-Hydroxy-phenyl-2-amino-1-propanol Bitartrate], a sympathomimetic, is employed as a nasal decongestant and for the treatment of nasal edema caused by the common cold. The synthesis starts from an optically active acyloin prepared by the fermentation of sugar in the presence of m-hydroxybenzaldehyde.

HO

CHO + sugar $\xrightarrow{\text{yeast}}$ HO CHOHCOCH$_3$ $\xrightarrow[\substack{\text{2. catalytic} \\ \text{hydrogenation} \\ \text{and hydrogenolysis}}]{\text{1. benzylamine}}$

Levorotatory acyloin

HO CHOH—CH—CH$_3$
|
NH$_2$

Metraminol
D$_g$-$erythro$-1-m-hydroxyphenyl-2-amino-1-propanol

Amphetamine (Benzedrine, 1-Phenyl-2-aminopropane) is synthesized from phenylacetic and acetic acids according to the reaction sequence shown. It is a

$$C_6H_5CH_2COOH + CH_3COOH \xrightarrow[\text{(vapor phase)}]{MnO_2} C_6H_5CH_2COCH_3 \xrightarrow{HCONH_2 + HCOOH}$$

$$\underset{CH_3}{C_6H_5CH_2-\overset{\displaystyle CH_3}{CHNH}-CHO} \xrightarrow[\text{(acid)}]{HOH} C_6H_5CH_2-\overset{\displaystyle CH_3}{CH}-NH_2$$

Amphetamine

colorless, mobile liquid which volatilizes slowly at ordinary temperature. It absorbs carbon dioxide from the air to form the carbonate and its solutions are alkaline to litmus. The free base and its carbonate are volatile and are used by inhalation to shrink the nasal mucosa and relieve congestion in such conditions as the common cold, hay fever, asthma, and to decrease secretions in rhinitis.

Amphetamine Sulfate, U.S.P., and **Amphetamine Phosphate, N.N.R.,** are two salts of amphetamine which share the action and uses of the base. The sulfate is used orally as the powder, elixir, or tablets to stimulate the central nervous system in narcolepsy, in treating certain psychogenic depressive conditions, alcoholism, etc. Its most extensive use therapeutically is to treat certain depressive conditions, in particular those characterized by apathy and psychomotor retardation. It is also used in the management of obesity.

Amphetamine phosphate has the same activity and is used for the same purpose as amphetamine sulfate. Its only advantage is that it has greater solubility, and this property is useful only in the preparation of solutions for injection.

Dexedrine Sulfate (D-Amphetamine Sulfate, d-Benzedrine Sulfate) is the dextroisomer of *Amphetamine Sulfate, U.S.P.* The two optical isomers possess marked differences in physiological activity. The levo form possesses better pressor activity but poorer analeptic activity; the dextro form has opposite effects; that is, it is a better analeptic agent and a poorer pressor agent. Thus, Dexedrine sulfate is used primarily for conditions requiring central nervous system stimulation.

Methamphetamine Hydrochloride, U.S.P. (Desoxyephedrine Hydrochloride, (+)1-Phenyl-2-methylaminopropane Hydrochloride), is prepared as shown.

$$C_6H_5CH_2COCH_3 + H_2NCH_3 \xrightarrow[\text{(catalytic)}]{H_2} C_6H_5CH_2\overset{\overset{\displaystyle CH_3}{|}}{C}H-NHCH_3$$

Racemic methamphetamine, resolved through tartrate salt

It occurs as white crystals or crystalline powder which is freely soluble in water and alcohol.

The activity of methamphetamine is qualitatively similar to that of amphetamine, but differs in degree; its circulatory activity is slightly less but its stimulating properties slightly greater. It is used orally to treat narcolepsy and mild depression. It is used also as an adjunct in the treatment of obesity by allaying hunger pains and in the treatment of alcoholism.

(−)-Desoxyephedrine is reported to have about equal circulatory activity as the (+)isomer but to be less stimulating on the central nervous system.

Hydroxyamphetamine Hydrobromide, U.S.P. [Paredrine Hydrobromide, 1-(p-Hydroxyphenyl)-2-aminopropane Hydrobromide], $p\text{-}HOC_6H_4CH_2CHCH_3$,

$$\overset{\displaystyle |+}{NH_3Br^-}$$

is a white, crystalline solid which is very soluble in water and freely soluble in alcohol.

Paredrine Hydrobromide has general properties similar to other sympathomimetic amines. Studies in animals indicate that it is less toxic than epinephrine and amphetamine. It lacks the ephedrinelike central stimulation. For topical application it is about twice as active as ephedrine, quicker in its response, and less irritating.

Phenylpropylmethylamine, N.N.R. (Vonedrine, 1-Methylamino-2-phenylpropane), $C_6H_5-\overset{\overset{\displaystyle}{|}}{C}H-CH_2-NHCH_3$, is a colorless-to-pale-yellow liquid

$$CH_3$$

which is very soluble in alcohol and sparingly soluble in water.

Vonedrine is a volatile base and thus may be inhaled to produce nasal constriction. It is claimed to produce no irritation, central nervous system or cardiovascular stimulation. It is primarily used for nasal constriction by inhalation.

Phenylpropylmethylamine Hydrochloride, N.N.R. (Vonedrine Hydrochloride), is used chiefly in isotonic solutions for topical application as a local vasoconstrictor.

Mephenteramine, N.N.R., and **Mephenteramine Sulfate, N.N.R.,** are the free base and the sulfate, respectively, of 1-phenyl-2-methyl-2-methylaminopropane (Wyamine). They are sympathomimetic agents, reported to be less toxic than amphetamine.

Mephenteramine may be synthesized by the accompanying sequence of reactions:

$$C_6H_5CH_2Cl + (CH_3)_2CHCOC_6H_5 \xrightarrow{NaNH_2} C_6H_5CH_2\overset{\overset{\displaystyle CH_3}{|}}{\underset{\underset{\displaystyle CH_3}{|}}{C}}COC_6H_5 \xrightarrow{NaNH_2}$$

$$C_6H_5CH_2\overset{\overset{\displaystyle CH_3}{|}}{\underset{\underset{\displaystyle CH_3}{|}}{C}}CONH_2 \xrightarrow[NaOH]{Br_2} C_6H_5CH_2\overset{\overset{\displaystyle CH_3}{|}}{\underset{\underset{\displaystyle CH_3}{|}}{C}}NH_2 \xrightarrow[HCOOH]{HCHO} C_6H_5CH_2\overset{\overset{\displaystyle CH_3}{|}}{\underset{\underset{\displaystyle CH_3}{|}}{C}}NHCH_3$$

Mephenteramine

Methoxyphenamine Hydrochloride, N.N.R. (Orthoxine Hydrochloride, 2-(o-Methoxyphenyl)isopropylmethylamine Hydrochloride), is a sympathomimetic whose predominant actions are bronchodilation and inhibition of smooth muscle spasm. It has very little effect on the blood vessels, and its pressor activity is considerably less than that of ephedrine or epinephrine. It is useful in the treatment of asthma and effective in allergic rhinitis, acute urticaria, and gastrointestinal allergy.

Methoxyphenamine hydrochloride

Methoxamine hydrochloride

Methoxamine Hydrochloride, U.S.P. [Vasoxyl Hydrochloride, 2-(2,5-Dimethoxyphenyl)-1-amino-2-propanol Hydrochloride], is a sympathomimetic agent which exhibits peripheral vasoconstriction characteristic of other amines of this group, but unlike other pressor amines it decreases heart rate as the blood pressure increases. It tends to slow ventricular rate but it does not produce ventricular tachycardia, fibrillation, or increased sinoauricular rate. It is free of cerebral-stimulating action.

It is used primarily in conjunction with spinal anesthesia during surgery to maintain or restore adequate blood pressure. It is also used as an adjunct in the treatment of hypotension associated with hemorrhage, trauma, and surgery.

Since simple aliphatic amines exhibit vasoconstrictor properties (page 182), similar effects may be expected from hydroaromatic derivatives of the amphetamine type and from their analogs.

Cyclopentamine Hydrochloride, N.N.R. (Clopane Hydrochloride, 1-Cyclopentyl-2-methylaminopropane Hydrochloride), is a sympathomimetic agent with uses and actions characteristic of other pressor amines. It produces vasoconstrictor activity and systemic pressor effect similar to ephedrine but with only slight cerebral excitation. Orally, it is more effective than ephedrine.

It is used topically for temporary relief of nasal congestion. It is administered by injection as an adjunct for maintenance of blood pressure in operative procedure and cardiovascular collapse where drugs of this type are not contraindicated.

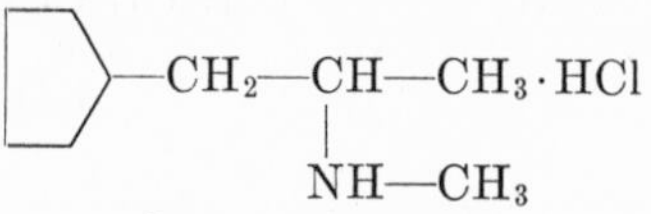

$$\text{[cyclopentyl]}-CH_2-CH-CH_3 \cdot HCl$$
$$\underset{\displaystyle NH-CH_3}{|}$$

Clopane hydrochloride

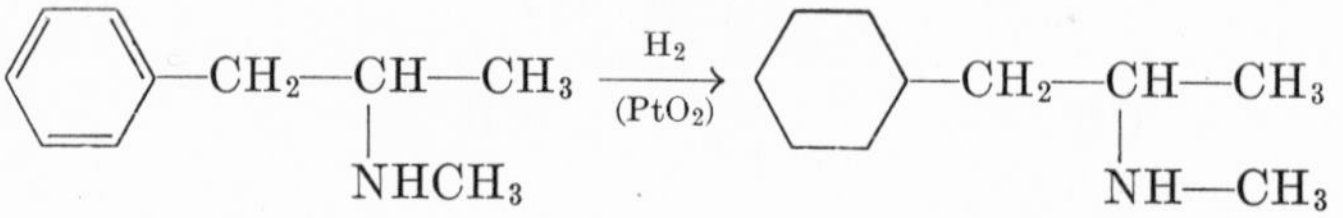

$$\text{[phenyl]}-CH_2-CH-CH_3 \xrightarrow[\text{(PtO}_2)]{\text{H}_2} \text{[cyclohexyl]}-CH_2-CH-CH_3$$
$$\underset{\displaystyle NHCH_3}{|} \qquad\qquad \underset{\displaystyle NH-CH_3}{|}$$

Benzedrex

Propylhexedrine, U.S.P. (Benzedrex, 1-Cyclohexyl-2-methylaminopropane), shares the uses and actions of similar volatile sympathomimetic amines. It has only one-half the pressor effect of amphetamine but produces decidedly less effect on the central nervous system.

It is used primarily by inhalation for its local shrinking effect on the nasal mucosa to relieve nasal congestion. It is useful in common cold, allergic rhinitis, or sinusitis.

Hydroaromatic compounds of this type may be prepared by the hydrogenation of the corresponding aromatic amines.[118]

Mecamylamine (Inversine, 3-Methylaminoisocamphane) is a ganglionic blocking agent which is reported to be active after oral administration against hypertension.[119]

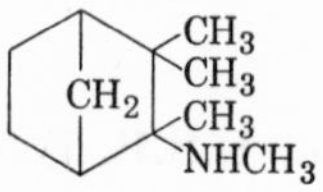

$$\begin{array}{c} CH_2 \\ \end{array} \begin{array}{c} CH_3 \\ CH_3 \\ CH_3 \\ NHCH_3 \end{array}$$

AMINO ETHERS

See: Diphenhydramine, page 218; Doxylamine, page 218; Carbinoxamine, page 218; Benztropine, page 391.

Gallamine Triethiodide, N.N.R., is a trisquaternary ammonium compound and triether of pyrogallol of the structure shown. It possesses curarelike prop-

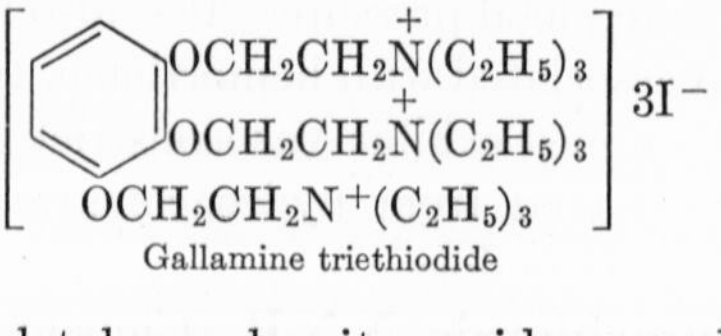

$$\left[\text{[benzene ring]} \begin{array}{l} OCH_2CH_2\overset{+}{N}(C_2H_5)_3 \\ OCH_2CH_2\overset{+}{N}(C_2H_5)_3 \\ OCH_2CH_2N^+(C_2H_5)_3 \end{array} \right] 3I^-$$

Gallamine triethiodide

erties and relaxes the skeletal muscles; it provides complete muscular relaxation during such procedures as surgery and intubation.

---

[118] Zenitz, Macks, and Moore, *J. Am. Chem. Soc.*, **69**, 1117 (1947).
[119] Moyer *et al.*, *Proc. Soc. Exptl. Biol. Med.*, **90**, 402 (1955).

Pramoxine, (Tronothane, 4-n-Butoxyphenyl-morpholinopropyl Ether),

$$p\text{-}n\text{-}C_4H_9OC_6H_4OCH_2CH_2CH_2N \underset{CH_2CH_2}{\overset{CH_2CH_2}{\diagup\diagdown}} O,$$ is an effective local anesthetic for

local applications. It is recommended for treatment of pain in rectal, vaginal, and other mucous membranes and for a variety of dermal conditions, such as itching.

Compounds of type $R_2NC_6H_4O(CH_2)_nO(CH_2)_nOC_6H_4NR_2$ are schistosomicidal, showing greatest activity when $n = 7$ or 8; they make parasites more amenable to phagocytosis.[120]

AMINO ALDEHYDES AND KETONES

It was assumed that the oxidation of choline with concentrated nitric acid formed an aldehyde, $(CH_3)_3\overset{+}{N}CH_2CHO$, which was mistakenly identified with the toxic principle of the toadstool, *Agaricus muscarius;* hence it was called muscarine. Acetals of this aldehyde have now been prepared and found to exhibit muscarinelike action. The most active of a large series of such acetals was that prepared with propylene glycol, $\left[(CH_3)_3\overset{+}{N}CH_2CH{\diagup}^{OCHCH_3}_{OCH_2} \right] I^-$; the iodide administered to a dog at dosage levels of 0.002 mg. usually proved fatal, and 0.001 mg. produced considerable lowering of blood pressure.[121]

An unstable, natural poison from mushrooms was later isolated and found to give for the salt the formula $C_8H_{18}O_2NCl$; $[\alpha]_D^{20} = +1.57°$. Its properties are best explained by an aldehydic quaternary ammonium structure [122] as shown.

$$CH_3CH_2-CH-CH-CHO$$
$$\quad\quad\quad | \quad\quad |$$
$$\quad\quad OH \quad +N(CH_3)_3$$

Methadone Hydrochloride, U.S.P. (Adanon Hydrochloride, dl-6-Dimethylamino-4,4-diphenyl-3-heptanone Hydrochloride) is prepared as shown on page 234. The hydrochloride is a white, crystalline powder which is soluble in water and freely soluble in alcohol. It is incompatible with alkaline solutions and with *Syrup of Wild Cherry, U.S.P.* The racemate has been resolved; it and its isomers have about the same toxicity in laboratory animals, but the analgesic and morphinelike activity are exhibited chiefly by the (−)-isomer. Methadone is 3 to 10 times more toxic than morphine and 2 to 3 times more than demerol, the toxicity varying with different species of animals, but its analgesic effect is about

---

[120] Raison and Standen, *Brit. J. Pharmacol.,* **10,** 191 (1955); *C.A.,* **49,** 13525 (1955).

[121] Fourneau *et al., Ann. pharm. franç.,* **3,** 114 (1945); *C.A.,* **41,** 92 (1947).

[122] Kögl, Duisberg, and Erxleben, *Ann.,* **489,** 156 (1931).

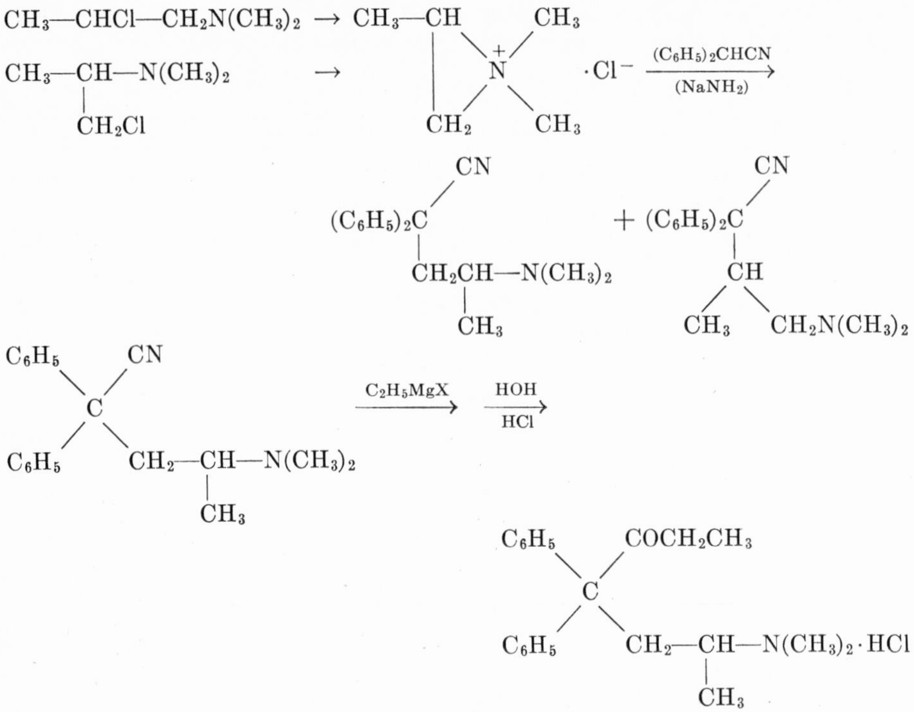

$CH_3—CHCl—CH_2N(CH_3)_2$ →

$CH_3—CH—N(CH_3)_2$
|
CH_2Cl

→

(reaction scheme forming the quaternary ammonium chloride)

$CH_3—CH$ CH_3
         N$^+$ ·Cl^- $\xrightarrow{\substack{(C_6H_5)_2CHCN \\ (NaNH_2)}}$
CH_2 CH_3

(C_6H_5)_2C with CN
|
$CH_2CH—N(CH_3)_2$
|
CH_3

$+$ (C_6H_5)_2C with CN
|
CH
CH_3 $CH_2N(CH_3)_2$

C_6H_5 CN
       C
C_6H_5 $CH_2—CH—N(CH_3)_2$
              |
              CH_3

$\xrightarrow{C_2H_5MgX}$ $\xrightarrow[HCl]{HOH}$

C_6H_5 $COCH_2CH_3$
        C
C_6H_5 $CH_2—CH—N(CH_3)_2·HCl$
               |
               CH_3

Methadone

2 to 10 times greater than that of morphine and demerol, respectively, so that it has a reasonably wide margin of safety.

The levorotatory isomer of methadone, $[\alpha]_D^{23.5} = -128°$, possesses fifty times the analgesic action of the dextroisomer in man; it produces greater narcosis, is 25 times as depressant to the respiration, and 65 times more stimulating to the duodenum.[123]

Methadone is administered orally in the form of the syrup or tablets or by intramuscular or intravenous injection of an aqueous solution to control pain and suppress coughing. The drug may cause addiction in man, and it is classified as a narcotic.

Methadone, after subcutaneous or intramuscular administration, is probably completely absorbed. By using the drug labeled with C^{14} it was found that about a third is eliminated via the urinary tract and the remainder in the feces.[124]

Amino Sugars

Amino sugars are widely distributed in nature, appearing as components in the mucoproteins, in bacterial polysaccharides, in hyaluronic acid, in heparin, in chitin, in various blood group substances, and even in antibiotics.[125] Usually they

[123] Scott, Robbins, and Chen, J. Pharmacol. Exptl. Therap., 93, 282 (1948).
[124] Elliott, Chang, Abdou, and Anderson, J. Pharmacol. Exptl. Therap., 95, 494 (1949).
[125] Kent and Whitehouse, Biochemistry of the Aminosugars, Academic Press, New York, 1955.

are aminohexoses and space isomers of CH_2OH—$(CHOH)_3$—$CHNH_2$—CHO, and they exhibit many of the properties that characterize sugars.

Chitosamine (D-Glucosamine) is a hydrolytic product of chitin. It is also found as a component of the carbohydrate portion of blood group A specificity.[126]

Chondrosamine (Galactosamine) is a constituent of cartilage.[127]

L-N-Methylglucosamine has been isolated from streptomycin (see page 488).

α-D-Glucosamine has been identified as a hydrolytic product of streptothricin and streptolin B.[127a]

Heparin Sodium, U.S.P., is an anticoagulant usually obtained from the lungs or livers of domesticated animals. Its anticoagulant action seems to be produced in conjunction with thrombin.

Purified heparin has been isolated as the barium salt. It has a molecular weight of about 20,000. It is polysaccharide in nature, and is characterized by the fact that half of the hexose units are D-glucosamine. The chemical structure is a repetition of the four hexose units as shown.[128]

Sodium heparinate

Chitosan,
a polyglucosamine

The sulfamic acid groups in heparin are essential for anticoagulant activity, for it is found that sulfamation of chitosan confers upon this polyglucosamine anticoagulant properties.[129]

AMINO ACIDS

Compounds containing both an amino and a carboxylic acid function are most important from a vital point of view; this is true especially of the α-amino acids. They are the building blocks from which proteins are formed. As far as their chemical properties are concerned, these amino acids exhibit the properties characteristic of both the carboxyl and the amino group; these need not be reviewed here. Some amino acids which have been isolated from natural sources are listed in Table XVIII.

Because of the complex nature of proteins and the difficulty in separating the individual components it was quite impossible to learn much about the dispensability and indispensability of the individual amino acids. Beginning in 1930,

[126] Bray, Henry, and Stacy, *Biochem. J.*, **40**, 124 (1946).

[127] James, Smith, Stacy, and Wiggins, *Nature*, **156**, 308 (1945).

[127a] van Tamelen, Dyer, Carter, Pierce, and Daniels, *J. Am. Chem. Soc.*, **78**, 4817 (1956).

[128] Wolfrom, Montgomery, Karabinos, and Rathgeb, *J. Am. Chem. Soc.*, **72**, 5796 (1950).

[129] Doczi, Fischman, and King, *J. Am. Chem. Soc.*, **75**, 1512 (1953).

TABLE XVIII

SOME NATURALLY OCCURRING α-AMINO ACIDS

Structure	Name	Melting Point °C.	Boiling Point of Ethyl Ester °C.	$[\alpha]_D^{20°}$ in Water
NH_2—CH_2COOH	Glycine, aminoacetic acid	230 (d)	52.10	inactive
CH—CH—COOH | NH_2	(+)-Alanine, α-aminopropionic acid	297 (d)	48.11	+2.7
Me_2CH—CH—COOH | NH_2	(+)-Valine, α-aminoisovaleric acid	315 (d)	63.5_8	+6.42
Me_2CHCH_2—CH—COOH | NH_2	(−)-Leucine, α-aminoisocaproic acid	293 (d)	83.5_{12}	−10.35
Et \\ CH—CH—COOH / | Me NH_2	(+)-Isoleucine, α-amino-β-methyl-valeric acid	280 (d)	90–92_{15}	+11.3
$CH_3(CH_2)_3$—CH—COOH | NH_2	Nor-leucine, α-aminocaproic acid	—	—	—
$NH_2(CH_2)_4$—CH—COOH | NH_2	(+)-Lysine, α-amino-ϵ-amino-caproic acid	—	—	+14–15
HO—CH_2—CH—COOH | NH_2	(−)-Serine, α-amino-β-hydroxy-propionic acid	228 (d)	—	−6.83
$CH_3CH(OH)CH(NH_2)COOH$	Threonine, α-amino-β-hydroxy-butyric acid	—	—	—
$C_6H_5CH_2$—CH—COOH | NH_2	(−)-Phenylalanine, α-amino-β-phenyl-propionic acid	283 (d)	143_{10}	−35.1
p-HO—$C_6H_4CH_2$ | NH_2—CH—COOH	(−)-Tyrosine, α-amino-β-(p-hy-droxyphenyl)-pro-pionic acid	315 (d)	—	−8.64
HOOC—CH_2—CH—COOH | NH_2	(−)-Aspartic, aminosuccinic acid	271 (d)	126.5_{11}	−2.37

TABLE XVIII—*Continued*

SOME NATURALLY OCCURRING α-AMINO ACIDS

Structure	Name	Melting Point °C.	Boiling Point of Ethyl Ester °C.	$[\alpha]_D^{20°}$ in Water
HOOC—CH₂CH₂—CH—COOH | NH₂	(+)-Glutamic, α-aminoglutaric acid	213 (d)	140.10	+30.0
HOOC—CH₂—CHOH | NH₂—CH—COOH	(+)-Hydroxyglutamic, α-amino-β-hydroxyglutaric acid	135	—	+0.8
CH₂—CH(NH₂)—COOH | S | S—CH₂—CH(NH₂)—COOH	(−)-Cystine, di-α-amino-β-thiopropionic acid	258 (d)	—	−215.5
CH₃—S—CH₂CH₂—CH—COOH | NH₂	(−)-Methionine, α-amino-γ-methylthiolbutyric acid	283 (d)	dec.	−7.2
H₂N–C–NH–(CH₂)₃–CH–COOH ‖ | NH NH₂	(+)-Arginine, α-amino-δ-guanidinovaleric acid	207 (d)	—	26.5
C—CH₂—CH(NH₂) ... COOH (indole structure)	(−)-Tryptophan, α-amino-β-indolepropionic acid	298 (d)	—	−32.1
HC═C—CH₂—CH—COOH | | | N NH NH₂ ＼／ CH	(−)-Histidine, α-amino-β-imidazolepropionic acid	155 (d)	—	−39.7
H₂C———CH₂ | | H₂C CH—COOH ＼ ／ NH	(−)-Proline, pyrrolidine-α-carboxylic acid	210 (d)	78.10	−84.9

TABLE XVIII—*Continued*

SOME NATURALLY OCCURRING α-AMINO ACIDS

Structure	Name	Melting Point ° C.	Boiling Point of Ethyl Ester ° C.	$[\alpha]_D^{20°}$ in Water

HO—CH——CH$_2$
  | |
H$_2$C   CH—COOH
   \ /
    NH
	(−)-Hydroxypyroline, γ-hydroxypyrroli-dine-α-carboxylic acid	270 (d)	—	−80.6

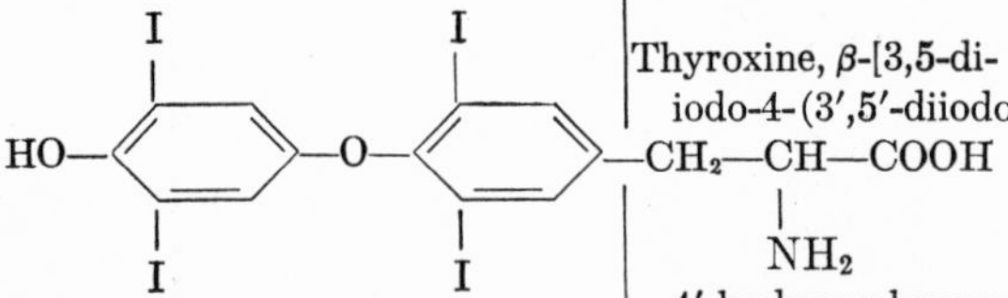 HO—⟨ ⟩—O—⟨ ⟩—CH$_2$—CH—COOH (with I substituents) NH$_2$	Thyroxine, β-[3,5-di-iodo-4-(3′,5′-diiodo-4′-hydroxyphenoxy)phenyl]-α-amino-propionic acid	—	—	—

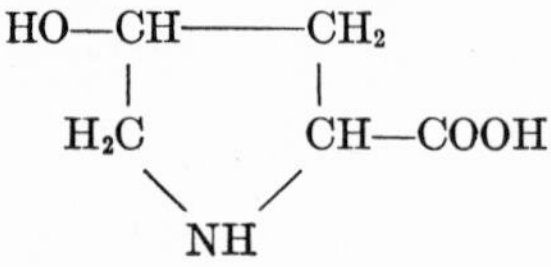

however, Rose and his co-workers [130] resorted to feeding experiments in which the proteins were completely replaced by the individual acids, employed in known amounts. In this manner it has been possible to obtain some indication about the requirements of the single components. Table XIX is constructed from the the data submitted by Rose and indicates the minimum amounts necessary for normal life. The minimum is expressed in parts per hundred of the total ration.

TABLE XIX

ESSENTIAL AMINO ACIDS

Name	Minimum Amount Necessary, Per Cent of Total Ration
Lysine	1.0
Tryptophan	0.2
Histidine	0.4
Phenylalanine	0.7
Leucine	0.9
Isoleucine	0.5
Threonine	0.6
Methionine	0.6
Valine	0.7
Arginine*	0.2

* The animal organism can synthesize part of its own requirement of arginine, but not sufficient for its normal requirement.

[130] *Science*, **86**, 298 (1937).

A tryptophan-deficient diet in growing rats gives rise to a variety of lesions, e.g., vascularization of the cornea and development of cataract; alopecia about the head and back; abnormal, brittle, misshapen, and discolored incisor teeth; atrophy of the testis and aspermiogenesis in the growing male.[131]   In the same animal the deficiency symptoms for phenylalanine include changes in the testes, accessory genital tissues, adrenal and pituitary glands, and bone; these changes are reversible.[132]   Threonine deficiencies show loss in weight, changes in reproductive tissues, and alterations in the chromophilic cells of the anterior pituitary; these manifestations are relieved by feeding threonine.[133]   The absence of histamine from the diet results in regressive changes in the pituitary, sex organs, thymus, adrenal cortex, and bone; these changes, too, are reversible.[134]   Kwashiorkor, a nutritional deficiency disease associated with low animal protein diets, results presumably from inadequate consumption of lysine, tryptophan, methionine, and, perhaps, threonine.[135]   Vitamin B_4 may be identical with a mixture of arginine and lysine; at least the deficiency produced by the lack of these two acids in chicks resembles deficiency ascribed to vitamin B_4.[136]

If the deficiency symptoms resulting from the absence of these essential amino acids had been recognized before the acids were known, or if the symptoms had not been experimentally associated with the compounds in question, it is possible that each of these acids would have been identified as a vitamin to relieve the symptoms of specific dietary deficiencies.   Threonine was in fact recognized by its deficiency manifestations before it was isolated from natural sources; the symptoms prompted the search for it.   These essential amino acids differ from the usual conception of the term vitamin in that they also supply energy or serve as structural material for the tissues.   It has been suggested that substances of this nature be called *vitagens*.[137]

Properties

The amino acids act both as acids and as amines.   In solution, the mono-aminomonocarboxylic acids are neutral.   This property is accounted for by the double ionization, and internal neutralization, as indicated.   This amphoteric

$$
\begin{array}{c}
\text{CO—OH} \\
| \\
\text{CH}_2\text{—NH}_2
\end{array}
+ \text{HOH} \leftrightarrow
\begin{array}{c}
\text{CO—O}^- \\
| \qquad + \text{H}^+ \\
\text{CH}_2 \\
| \\
\text{NH}_3{}^+ \qquad + {}^-\text{OH}
\end{array}
$$

arrangement is called a zwitter ion.   In concentrated alcohol the tendency to form an internal salt is somewhat restricted, and the acid may be titrated with

[131] Albanese and Buschke, *Science*, **95**, 584 (1942).

[132] Schwartz, Scott, and Ferguson, *Anat. Record*, **110**, 313 (1951).

[133] Scott and Schwartz, *Proc. Soc. Exptl. Biol. Med.*, **84**, 271 (1953).

[134] Scott, *Arch. Pathol.*, **58**, 129 (1954).

[135] *Chem. Eng. News*, **34**, 1188 (1956).

[136] Hegsted, Briggs, Elvehjem, and Hart, *J. Biol. Chem.*, **140**, 191 (1940).

[137] Rosenberg, *Chemistry and Physiology of the Vitamins*, Interscience Publishers, New York, 1942, p. 5.

standard alkali, phenolphthalein being used as an indicator. The high melting points of the amino acids (most of them decompose at the fusion point) may be due to this inner saltlike character.

Most of the simple amino acids have a sweet taste. If the carboxyl group is masked, e.g., by esterification, the compound assumes definitely basic properties. If the amino group is masked, as by acylation, the compound becomes definitely acidic.

The van Slyke amino acid determination depends on the reaction of the amino group with nitrous acid which converts the amino acid into an α-hydroxy acid and liberates nitrogen quantitively.

The Sörensen formol titration of amino acids depends on the formation of the N-blocked derivative; this derivative is strongly acidic and may be titrated.

Products

Aminoacetic Acid, N.F. (Glycine, Glycocoll), H_2N—CH_2—COOH, crystals, having a sweet taste, soluble in water 1:2 and slightly soluble in alcohol, is used as a diuretic and as a muscle stimulant; it is said to affect muscle retention of creatine. It is usually administered in solution in water or milk or as the elixir.

Glycine Hydrochloride is a salt of glycine. It is used as a convenient method of administering HCl. It is used in gastric hypoacidity and serves the same purpose as the administration of diluted hydrochloric acid. About 0.2 g. of glycine hydrochloride is equivalent to more than 10 drops of Diluted Hydrochloric Acid, N.F.

Betaine Hydrochloride (Acidol), $[(CH_3)_3N^+$—CH_2—$COOH]Cl^-$, is a crystalline compound readily soluble in water. It is used in hypoacidity, yielding about 24 per cent HCl. It is a convenient form for the administration of hydrochloric acid; 0.5 g. is equivalent to about 18 minims of Diluted Hydrochloric Acid, N.F.

Diglycocoll Hydroiodide-Iodine, N.N.R. (Bursoline), $[HI(NH_2CH_2CO-OH)_2]_2 \cdot I_2$, is a ready source for free iodine for disinfecting drinking water.

Dihydroxy Aluminum Aminoacetate (Alminate), NH_2—CH_2—$COOAl(OH)_2$, is a basic aluminum salt of glycine used as an antacid and reported to have a buffer value about six times that of aluminum hydroxide. It is used in tablet form to treat hyperacidity in such conditions as duodenal or gastric ulcer.

Glutamic Acid Hydrochloride, N.F., like glycine hydrochloride, is used for the convenient administration of hydrochloric acid. It is practically tasteless and does not injure the teeth. It is used to treat hypoacidity due to pernicious anemia, gastric cancer, chronic dyspepsia, etc.

Glutamic acid was fed to mentally retarded patients, 16 months to 17.5 years of age, in doses of 6 to 24 g. per day; although there were some instances of convulsive disorders, tests showed definite improvement in verbal, motor, and personality responses.[138]

[138] Zimmerman, Burgemesiter, and Putnam, *Arch. Neurol. Psychiat.*, **56**, 489 (1946); *C.A.*, **41**, 2805 (1947).

Thyroxin (Thyroxine) is an active principle prepared synthetically or obtained from the thyroid gland. See Table XVIII for formula and chemical nomenclature. The synthetic product is identical with the natural thyroxine. Thyroxine is used to stimulate general metabolism, increase the pulse rate and blood pressure, and bring about an increase in the excretion of nitrogenous products. The purified hormone is used for the same purposes as thyroid gland extracts, namely, to treat all conditions due to thyroid deficiencies, such as cretinism, myxedema, retarded mental development, and obesity. It is usually administered orally in the form of tablets.

Sodium Levothyroxine, N.N.R., the salt of L-thyroxine, about twice as potent as racemic thyroxine, is useful in replacement therapy in diminished or totally absent thyroid function. Overdosage may produce symptoms of hyperthyroidism.

3,3′,5-Triiodothyronine occurs in thyroglobulin along with thyroxine;[139] and it appears in the serum of patients treated with iodine, as shown in subjects receiving I^{131}.[140] Assayed by preventing goiter in rats treated with thiouracil, it is 3 to 4 times as active as thyroxine.[141,142] 3,3′-Diiodothyronine is found in marine algae,[143] and in the rat it accounts for at least a fourth of the thyroxinelike compounds present in the blood stream.[144] Change in the position of the iodine atoms interferes with its activity.[145]

Histidine Monohydrochloride, N.F. (β-4-Imidazolyl-α-aminopropionic acid Hydrochloride), is used in about 4 per cent solution intramuscularly for the treatment of peptic ulcer and postoperative jejunal ulcer.

p-Aminobenzoic Acid (PABA, Vitamin H), $p\text{-}NH_2C_6H_4COOH$, was originally known only from synthetic sources. The initial interest for the medicinal chemist was in its value for preparing esters of the procaine type (see page 197).

More recently it has come into prominence because of its vitaminlike properties. Woods [146] observed an antisulfanilamide activity *in virto* with p-aminobenzoic acid which he had isolated from yeast and other substances that had similar activity. Rubbo and Gillespie [147] isolated p-aminobenzoic acid from yeast concentrate and showed that it is a growth factor for *Clostridium acetobutylicum*. Selbie [148] found that it inhibited the action of sulfanilamide in mice infected with *Streptococcus hemolyticus*. Individuals who are readily cured of

[139] Roche, Lissitzky, and Michel, *Biochim. et Biophys. Acta*, **11**, 220 (1953); *C.A.*, **47**, 10047 (1953).

[140] Benua, Dobyns, and Nimmer, *J. Clin. Endocrinol. and Metabolism*, **15**, 1367 (1955); *C.A.*, **50**, 2036 (1956).

[141] Gross and Rivers, *Lancet*, **262**, 593 (1952); *C.A.*, **46**, 6268 (1952).

[142] Barker, *Proc. Soc. Exptl. Biol. Med.*, **90**, 109 (1955); *C.A.*, **50**, 2785 (1956).

[143] Scott, *Nature*, **173**, 1098 (1954).

[144] Roche, Michel, Nunez, and Wolf, *Compt. rend. soc. biol.*, **149**, 884 (1955); *C.A.*, **50**, 2785 (1956).

[145] Lerman, Harington, and Means, *J. Clin. Endocrinol. and Metabolism*, **12**, 1306 (1952); *C.A.*, **47**, 11561 (1953).

[146] Woods, *Brit. J. Exptl. Path.*, **21**, 74 (1940); *C.A.*, **34**, 7408 (1940).

[147] Rubbo and Gillespie, *Nature*, **146**, 838 (1940).

[148] Selbie, *Brit. J. Exptl. Path.*, **21**, 90 (1940); *C.A.*, **34**, 7408 (1940).

gonorrhea yield cultures with low p-aminobenzoic acid synthesis, and the organism is sensitive to sulfanilamide; clinically resistant individuals yield cultures with a high rate of p-aminobenzoic acid synthesis.[149] Ansbacher [150] identified p-aminobenzoic acid as the achromotrichia factor in the rat and as a growth-promoting factor for the chick. Sieve [151] reported that in man nutritional achromotrichia is favorably influenced by the use of p-aminobenzoic acid.

It is likely that the biochemical activity of p-aminobenzoic acid depends on its incorporation into the folic acid molecule (see page 426). p-Aminobenzoic acid appears to act as a hydrogen transfer agent for *E. coli* and other facultative anaerobes, a function with which the sulfa drugs interfere.[152] It seems to have a favorable effect in certain types of asthma, probably because of its sparing action on epinephrine.[153] It has been found highly effective as a detoxicant for lethal doses of carbarsone and other benzenearsonates in rats without inhibiting trypanocidal activity. It is reported to be useful in the treatment of rheumatic fever.[154]

In man p-aminobenzoic acid is conjugated with glycine and largely excreted by the kidney as p-aminohippuric acid, p-$NH_2C_6H_4CONHCH_2COOH$.

Other antagonist to p-aminobenzoic acid are 5-nitrothiophene-2-carboxamide, methyl 2-(5-acetylaminothienyl) ketone, and 6-aminonicotinic acid; these compounds exhibit antibacterial properties similar to sulfanilamide.[155]

p-Aminobenzoic acid absorbs light rays in the ultraviolet region and may, therefore, be incorporated in suitable bases as an effective screen against sunburn.

p-Aminosalicylic Acid, N.N.R. (Para-Pas, Parasal, Propasa), is prepared essentially by the Kolbe synthesis as illustrated.[156] It is a white, or nearly white,

bulky powder which is slightly soluble in water and soluble in alcohol.

It is used principally as a supplement with the streptomycins in the treatment of tuberculous infections for the purpose of postponing bacterial resistance or the treatment of infections that have become resistant to the antibiotics.

Sodium p-Aminosalicylate, N.N.R. (Para-Pas Sodium, Parasal Sodium, Pasera Sodium, Padem Sodium, Pasmed Sodium), is a white-to-pale-yellow,

[149] Landy and Gerstung, *J. Immunol.*, **51**, 269 (1945); *C.A.*, **40**, 2194 (1946).

[150] Ansbacher, *Science*, **93**, 164 (1941).

[151] Sieve, *Science*, **94**, 257 (1941).

[152] Baumgärtel, *Deut. med. Wochschr.*, **69**, 748 (1943); *C.A.*, **38**, 4002 (1944).

[153] Rosenberg, *Chemistry and Physiology of the Vitamins*, Interscience Publishers, New York, 1942, p. 286.

[154] *Proc. Soc. Exptl. Biol. Med.*, **65**, 178 (1947).

[155] Johnson, Green, and Pauli, *J. Biol. Chem.*, **153**, 37 (1944).

[156] Yoshimura, Jap. pat. 3022, June 12, 1951. Rosdahl, Swed. pat. 135,135, April 8, 1952; *C.A.*, **47**, 4914 (1953).

crystalline powder which is freely soluble in water and sparingly soluble in alcohol. It is used for the same purpose as p-aminosalicylic acid, the sodium salt being more soluble in water.

Edathamil, N.N.R. (Ethylenediaminetetracetic Acid, Sequestrene A), and **Edathamil Tetrasodium** (Tetrasodium Ethylenediaminetetracetate, Versene) are excellent sequestering and chelating agents. There is increasing use for

$$CH_2N(CH_2COOH)_2$$
$$|$$
$$CH_2N(CH_2COOH)_2$$

Edathamil

compounds that form stable complexes with multivalent cations, such as Ca^{+2}, Cu^{+2}, Hg^{+2}, Fe^{+3}, Cr^{+3}, and Pb^{+2}. Such agents find use for heavy metal detoxification, e.g., chrome ulcers in the skin, and for the removal of corneal calcium. The acid, if given too rapidly, may cause a serious imbalance of biological calcium, which may lead in extreme cases to hypocalcemic convulsions or even cardiac arrest. It is suggested that these agents may prove useful for removing from the system even the radioactive products of nuclear fission. The chelating properties of Edathamil have been investigated as an approach to the solution of the problem resulting from atherosclerosis.[157]

Edathamil Calcium-Disodium, N.N.R. (Calcium Disodium Ethylenediaminetetracetate), is a chelate of calcium in which the calcium atom is exchanged

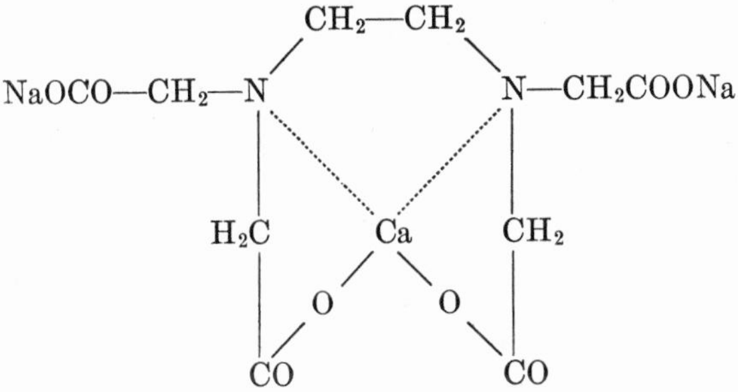

for an even more firmly bound lead ion; the lead complex is virtually soluble in water and is excreted intact in the urine; hence, the calcium complex is useful in treating lead poisoning.

AMIDES

See acetanilid (page 186), phenacetin (page 187), and carbamylcholine (page 195).

Amides contain the characteristic group —CO—N=. They may be considered as ammonia or an amine in which an N— hydrogen atom is replaced by an acyl group or radical; or as acids in which the hydroxyl group of the acidic carboxyl group is replaced by the NH_2— or a substituted amido group.

[157] Clark, Clark, and Neosher, *Am. J. Med. Sci.*, **229**, 142 (1955).

The introduction of an acyl group into ammonia or an amine results in the loss of the basic characteristics; e.g., amides do not react with acids to form stable salts. Since amides are the ammono-analogs of the acids, they may assume

$$R—CO—OH \quad\quad and \quad\quad R—CO—NH_2$$

acidic properties; this may be noted especially in the sulfonamides, in phthali-mide, and in the barbituric acids, in which the amido hydrogen is acidic.

The acid amides act as hypnotics and sedatives. Numerous compounds of this type have been introduced but they have been largely replaced by more effective agents. Examples of active compounds are shown.

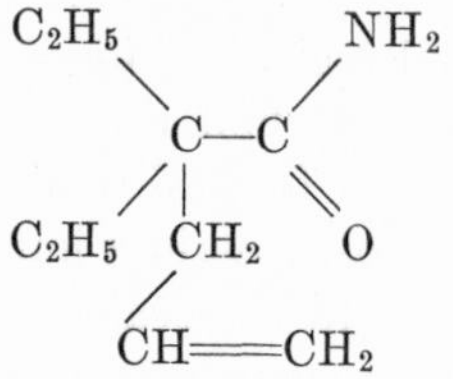

Novonal,
diethylallylacetamide

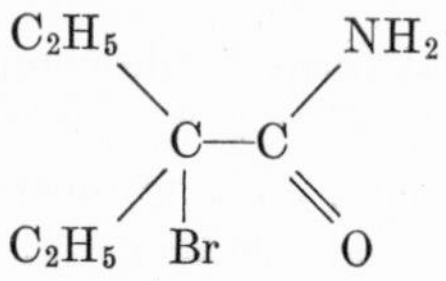

Neuronal,
α-bromodiethylacetamide

Urethanes

The amides of carbonic acid are particularly interesting, both because of their chemical structure and properties and their physiological and medicinal uses.

Carbamic acid, $NH_2—CO—OH$, is unstable and is known only by its various derivatives, such as the salts, called carbamates, and as its esters, called urethanes. Urethanes have been introduced as hypnotics and sedatives; they have been largely replaced by more efficient products.

Urethan, U.S.P. (Ethyl Carbamate), consists of colorless crystals, m.p. 48°, soluble in water 1:0.5 and readily soluble in alcohol. It can be prepared by adding ethyl chloroformate to ammonia,

$$ClCOOC_2H_5 + 2NH_3 \rightarrow NH_2COOC_2H_5 + NH_4Cl$$

It is a mild hypnotic and a feeble diuretic usually administered in solution or as the powder in capsules. Urethan with quinine hydrochloride is used as a scleros-ing agent for the treatment of varicose veins. Ethyl carbamate causes temporary but significant retardation of growth of spontaneous Walker carcinoma 256 in rats, a decrease in the leucocyte count of myelogenous leukemia in the mouse, and exerts an inhibitory effect on prostatic cancer.[158]

Other urethanes that have at one time or another been used include:

Aponal, the carbamate of tertiary amyl alcohol, $NH_2COOC{—}CH_3$.   **He-**
$\qquad\qquad\qquad\qquad\qquad\qquad\qquad\qquad\qquad\qquad\qquad CH_3$
$\qquad\qquad\qquad\qquad\qquad\qquad\qquad\qquad\qquad\qquad\qquad C_2H_5$

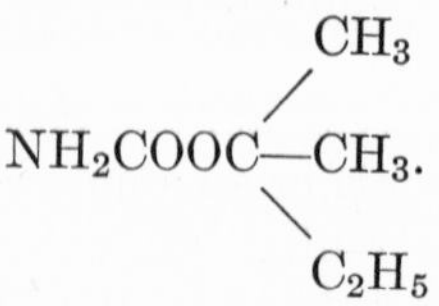

[158] Oertly and Myers, *J. Am. Chem. Soc.*, **41**, 855 (1919). Lorang, *Rec. trav. chim.*, **47**, 179 (1928). Thate, *Rec. trav. chim.*, **48**, 116 (1929).

donal, the carbamate of secondary amyl alcohol, $NH_2COOC\begin{matrix} / CH_3 \\ \backslash CH_2CH_2CH_3 \end{matrix}$. **Aleudrin,** the ester of 1,3-dichloro-2-propanol, $NH_2COOCH(CH_2Cl)_2$. **Voluntal,** trichloroethyl carbamate, $NH_2COOCH_2CCl_3$. They are more toxic and depressant than Urethan.

N-substituted urethanes have been studied for their local anesthetic properties. Thus diurethanes of the general structure $\begin{matrix} CH_2\text{—}NHCOOR \\ | \\ CH_2\text{—}NHCOOR \end{matrix}$ in which R varies from ethyl to isoamyl produce corneal anesthesia.[159] Phenyl naphthyl urethane, $\begin{matrix} \alpha\text{-}C_{10}H_7 \backslash \\ NCOOR \\ C_6H_5 / \end{matrix}$, is reported to be strongly active.[160] A useful N-phenylurethane is found in Diothane.

Diperodon Hydrochloride, N.N.R. (Diothane Hydrochloride, 3-(1-Piperidyl)-1,2-propanediol dicarbanilate Hydrochloride), is a useful anesthetic; it pos-

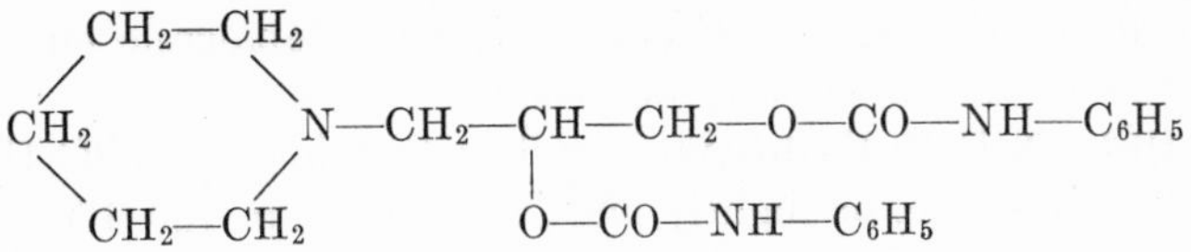

sesses properties similar to those of cocaine but the effect is reported to last somewhat longer.

Mepromate, N.N.R. (Equanil, Miltown, 2-Methyl-2-*n*-propyl-1,3-propandiol Dicarbamate), is proposed for the treatment of anxiety and tension, and for the treatment of insomnia caused by worry and muscle spasm.[161]

Mephenesin Carbamate, N.N.R. (2-Hydroxy-*o*-tolyloxy-3-carbamoxypropane), exhibits action like that of mephenesin but is somewhat more potent.

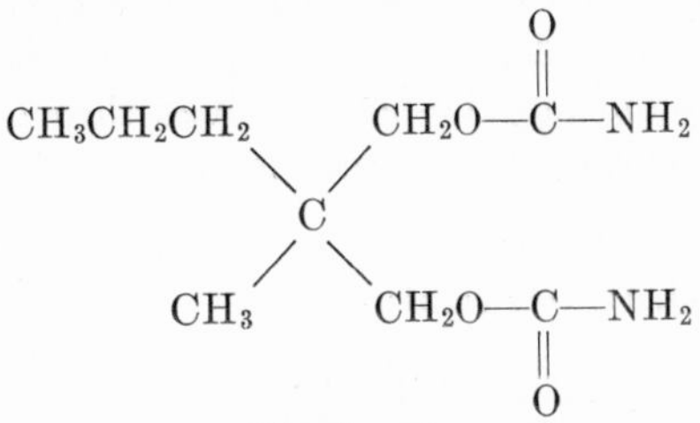

Meprobamate

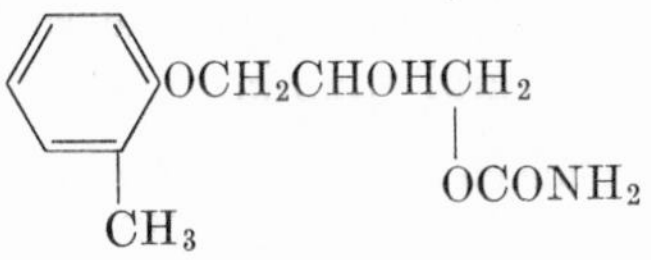

Mephenesin carbamate

159 Ma and Shriner, *J. Am. Chem. Soc.*, **58,** 1630 (1936).
160 Boese and Major, *J. Am. Chem. Soc.*, **57,** 175 (1935).
161 *J. Am. Pharm. Assoc.* (*Pract. Pharm. Ed.*), **16,** 643 (1955).

Neostogmine bromide, X = Br⁻ (rendered below)

Neostigmine bromide, $X = Br^-$
Neostigmine methyl sulfate, $X = CH_3SO_4^-$

Ethinamate

Ethinamate, N.N.R. (Valmid, Ethynylcyclohexyl Carbamate), is suggested as a hypnotic for the prompt induction of sleep in simple insomnia.

Neostigmine [Prostigmine, 3-(Dimethylcarbamoxy)phenyltrimethylammonium Salt] is a synthetic substitute for physostigmine used in the treatment of the symptoms of myasthenia gravis. Numerous carbamates of this type have been studied.[162, 163]

Neostigmine is used chiefly for its action on skeletal muscle, the bowel, and the bladder, e.g., in atony of the bladder and in myasthenia gravis. *Neostigmine Bromide, U.S.P.*, is used in the form of tablets for oral administration. *Neostigmine Methylsulfate, U.S.P.*, is used in solution for subcutaneous or intramuscular injections.

Salicylamide exerts slightly deeper and quicker analgesic effects than aspirin, and of about the same order of toxicity.[164]

Salicylanilide, N.F. (o-Hydroxybenzanilide, Salinidol), o-HOC$_6$H$_4$CONHC$_6$-H$_5$, forms odorless, white, or slightly pink, crystals, m.p. 136–138°. It is used as an antifungal agent.

Pantothenic Acid (Chick Antidermatitis Factor, Vitamin B Filtrate Factor) was one of the filtrate factors of the vitamin B complex. The name is derived from the Greek word meaning "from everywhere." Williams *et al.*[165, 166] established its constitution [167] by synthesis through condensation of α-hydroxy-β,β-dimethyl-γ-butyrolactone with β-alanine. Good sources of pantothenic acid are dried yeast, liver, rice polishings, and whole grain cereals.

Pantothenic acid may play an integral part in the activity of coenzyme A. Human beings show no symptoms that characterize the deficiency of this vitamin.

The synthesis of pantothenic acid from isobutyraldehyde and β-alanine is indicated. The racemic synthetic compound may be best resolved through the optically active methoquinine salt.[168] The dextrorotating isomer is identical with the natural vitamin.

[162] Aeschlimann and Reinert, *J. Pharmacol.*, **43**, 413–444 (1931).

[163] Stedman, *Biochem. J.*, **20**, 719–734 (1926).

[164] Ichniowski and Hueper, *J. Am. Pharm. Assoc.*, **35**, 225 (1946).

[165] *J. Am. Chem. Soc.*, **55**, 2912 (1933).

[166] *Ibid.*, **60**, 2719 (1938).

[167] Williams and Major, *Science*, **91**, 246 (1940).

[168] Stiller, Harris, Finkelstein, Keresztesy, and Folkers, *J. Am. Chem. Soc.*, **62**, 1785 (1940). Stiller and Wiley, *J. Am. Chem. Soc.*, **63**, 1237 (1941).

$$\begin{array}{c} CH_3 \\ \diagdown \\ CH-CHO + HCHO \rightarrow HOCH_2-\overset{\overset{\displaystyle CH_3}{|}}{\underset{\underset{\displaystyle CH_3}{|}}{C}}-CHO \xrightarrow{HCN} \xrightarrow{HOH} \\ \diagup \\ CH_3 \end{array}$$

$$\left[HOCH_2-\overset{\overset{\displaystyle CH_3}{|}}{\underset{\underset{\displaystyle CH_3}{|}}{C}}-CHOH-COOH \right] \xrightarrow{-HOH} \underset{\underset{\displaystyle O}{\diagdown \diagup}}{(CH_3)_2C\text{------}CHOH} \xrightarrow{NH_2CH_2CH_2COOCH_2C_6H_5}$$

α-Hydroxy-β,β-dimethyl-γ-butyrolactone

$$(CH_3)_2C\text{------}\underset{\underset{\displaystyle NH-CH_2CH_2COOCH_2C_6H_5}{CH_2 \quad C}}{\overset{\overset{\displaystyle CHOH}{\quad OH}}{}} \rightarrow$$

$$HOCH_2-\overset{\overset{\displaystyle CH_3}{|}}{\underset{\underset{\displaystyle CH_3}{|}}{C}}-CHOH-CO-NH-CH_2CH_2COOH$$

Pantothenic acid,
α,γ-dihydroxy-β,β-dimethylbutyryl-β'-alanide

Pantothenic acid seems to possess considerable specificity. Small changes in structure, even esterification, make it inactive. The (−) isomer is inactive. The need in man for this vitamin has not been demonstrated. In the chick deficiency produces dermatosis, unhatchability of eggs, etc.[169,170]

Calcium Pantothenate $[(C_9H_{16}O_5N)_2Ca]$ is a white powder, readily soluble in water and glycerin and slightly soluble in alcohol. Its aqueous solutions are dextrorotatory. It is slightly hygroscopic, stable in air, and not readily decomposed by light.

Ammono Analogs of Anesthetic Esters

Most of the locally active anesthetic compounds are of the ester type, but there are some compounds of different structure which also are endowed with activity. An example of this type is *Nupercaine.*

Dibucaine Hydrochloride, U.S.P. (Nupercaine Hydrochloride), acts like cocaine when applied to mucous surfaces and like procaine when injected, the action being relatively prolonged. Although it is more toxic, following injection, than cocaine, its activity is also correspondingly greater. In preparing solutions alkali-free glass should be used.

[169] Rosenberg, *Chemistry and Physiology of the Vitamins*, Interscience Publishers, New York, 1942, p. 268.

[170] Pollock, *J. Am. Chem. Soc.*, **65**, 1335 (1943).

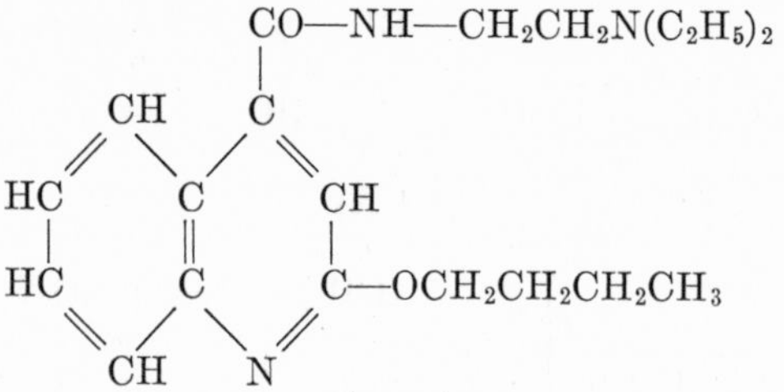

$$CO-NH-CH_2CH_2N(C_2H_5)_2$$

Nupercaine

Structurally Nupercaine is an amide of 2-butoxycinchoninic acid with β-di-ethylaminoethylamine. If the —NH— were replaced by an oxygen atom, the compound would be one of the familiar esters containing the anesthesiophoric group.

Refer to Franklin's *The Nitrogen System of Compounds*. This amide would, according to Franklin's system, be called an *ammono* ester, and as such it is entirely analogous to the *aquo* esters. From this point of view it is not surprising that Nupercaine possesses anesthetic properties. The really surprising thing is that more amides of the procaine analogs have not been investigated. In other words, the anesthesiophoric groups are quite analogous, or at least should be,

$$Ar-CO-O-(C)_n-N=$$

for the *aquo* type, and

$$Ar-CO-N-(C)_n-N=$$

for the *ammono* type.

The effect of structure on activity of Nupercaine analogs has been investigated by Wojahn.[171] He found that esters of the 2-alkoxycinchoninic acids are active, as are also the amides of dialkylamines.

Here again the analogy between the *aquo* and *ammono* system holds perfectly. Secondary amines are considered as *ammono* alcohols by Franklin's system, and hence the amides must naturally be *ammono* esters.

In a series of *aquo* analogs it was observed that as R increased from ethyl to

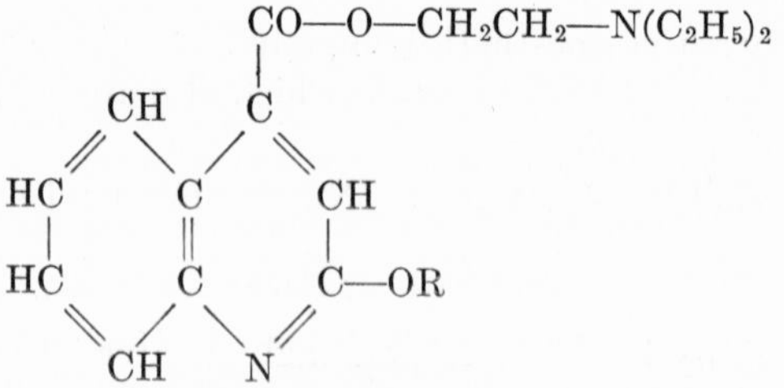

$$CO-O-CH_2CH_2-N(C_2H_5)_2$$

Nupercaine analog

butyl the activity increased, but that the pentoxy derivative was less active. It is not necessary to retain the alkoxy group in position 2; in other positions it pro-

[171] Wojahn, *Arch. Pharm.*, **274**, 83–106 (1936).

duces much the same effect. Its presence in the 2 position in Nupercaine is largely a matter of ease of synthesis.[172]

Procainamide Hydrochloride, U.S.P. (Pronestyl Hydrochloride, N′-p-Aminobenzoyl-N,N-diethylethylenediamine Hydrochloride). In 1936 Mautz [173] observed that the direct application of procaine to the myocardium elevated the sensitivity of the ventricular muscle to electrical stimulation; however, the anti-fibrillatory and antiarrhythmic activities were of short duration, for procaine is hydrolyzed to inactive components by means of enzymes. The search for more suitable agents led to the preparation and study of procainamide, which has pharmacological properties similar to those of procaine. It is excreted up to 60 per cent in the urine.

The synthesis of procainamide is summarized in the accompanying equations.[174]

$$p\text{-}NO_2C_6H_4COCl + NH_2CH_2CH_2N(CH_2CH_3)_2 \rightarrow$$

$$p\text{-}NO_2C_6H_4CONHCH_2CH_2N(CH_2CH_3)_2 \xrightarrow[\text{electrolytic}]{\text{catalytic or}}$$

$$\underset{\text{reduction}}{}$$

$$p\text{-}NH_2C_6H_4CONHCH_2CH_2CH_2N(CH_2CH_3)_2$$
$$\text{Procainamide}$$

Lidocaine Hydrochloride, N.F. (Xylocaine Hydrochloride, α-Diethylamino-2,6-aceto-xylidide Hydrochloride), is a potent local anesthetic agent. Compared with equal concentrations of procaine hydrochloride it produces a more prompt, intense, and extensive anesthesia.

It is used for infiltration and block anesthesia in dental as well as in general surgical procedures. It is also used topically for anesthesia of accessible mucous membranes.

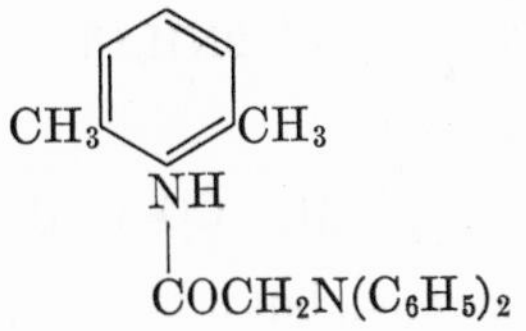

Lidocaine

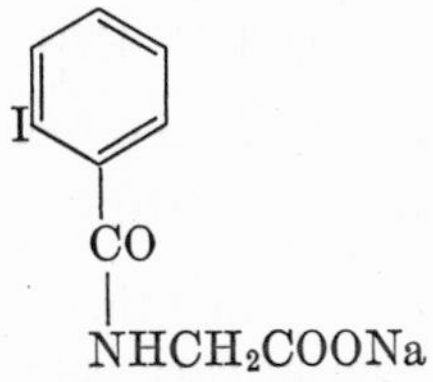

Iodohippurate sodium

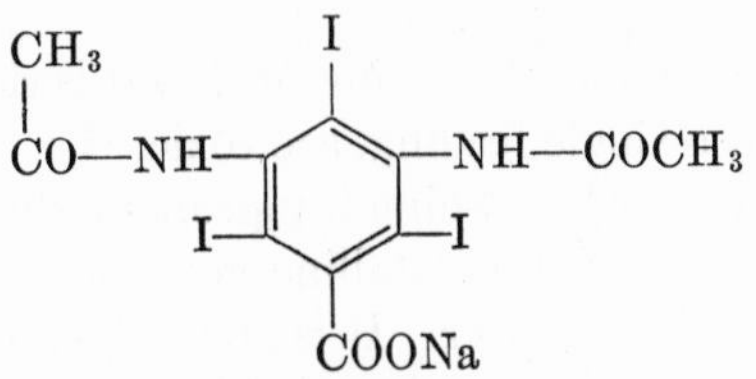

Diatrizoate sodium

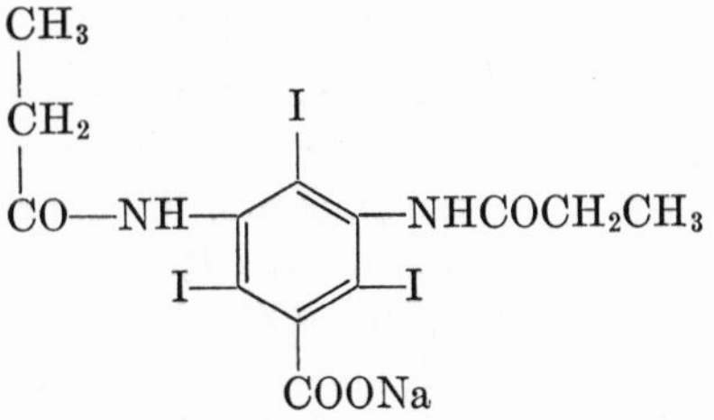

Sodium diprotrizoate

[172] Wojahn, *Arch. Pharm.*, **269**, 422–427 (1931).

[173] Mautz, *J. Thoracic Surg.*, **5**, 612 (1936).

[174] Yamazaki *et al.*, *J. Pharm. Soc. Japan*, **73**, 294 (1953); Tashika and Kuranari, *ibid.*, 1069; *C.A.*, **48**, 2003 (1954).

Iodohippurate Sodium, N.N.R. (Hippuran, Sodium o-iodohippurate), is a white, crystalline powder, soluble in water, alcohol, and dilute alkali. It is used as a contrast medium in urography.

Diatrizoate Sodium, N.N.R. (Sodium 3,5-Diacetamido-2,4,6-triiodobenzoate), is a useful roentgenographic medium, administered intravenously, for urography.

Sodium Diprotrizoate, N.N.R. (Miokon Sodium, Sodium 3,5-Dipropionamido-2,4,6-triiodobenzoate), because of its high iodine content is radio-opaque and is used intravenously for kidney urography.

Urea and Derivatives

Urea, U.S.P. (Carbamide), $NH_2—CO—NH_2$, colorless and odorless crystals, soluble in water 1:1.5 and in alcohol 1:10, may be synthesized in several ways.

1. By the rearrangement of ammonium isocyanate:

$$NH_4N{=}C{=}O \rightarrow NH_2—CO—NH_2$$

This will be remembered as the classical urea synthesis by Whöler, an experiment that started organic chemistry on its great development in 1828. Ammonium salts of cyanic and isocyanic acids are unstable and spontaneously undergo the indicated shift in structure.

2. By dehydration of ammonium carbamate:

$$NH_4O—CO—NH_2 \xrightarrow{-HOH} NH_2—CO—NH_2$$

The ammonium carbamate is prepared directly from gaseous ammonia and carbon dioxide. The dehydration is carried out in closed vessels at 130°. This is the commerical method for the preparation of urea.

3. By the reaction of phosgene (carbonyl chloride) with ammonia:

$$COCl_2 + 4NH_3 \rightarrow NH_2—CO—NH_2 + 2NH_4Cl$$

4. The reaction of dialkyl carbonates with ammonia:

$$RO—CO—OR + 2NH_3 \rightarrow 2ROH + NH_2—CO—NH_2$$

Urea is a nontoxic diuretic that is rapidly excreted, but it is reported to have no solvent action on urinary calculi. As a diuretic it is administered usually in solution or in cachets. Incorporated into creams and jellies, it is used to stimulate cell proliferation and tissue growth in varicose and diabetic ulcers, infected heat and x-ray burns, etc.

Urea is a useful source of nitrogen for ruminants receiving feed that is rich in starch.[175] Large amounts, 100 g. or more at a single feeding, are toxic.[176]

Bromisovalum, N.N.R. (Bromural, α-Bromo-β,β-dimethylpropanoylurea), $(CH_3)_2CH—CHBr—CO—NH—CO—NH_2$, a white, crystalline powder, soluble in alcohol, ether, and alkalies but insoluble in cold water. It is an effective hypnotic and sedative. It is claimed to be noncumulative and nonhabit-forming. It is usually administered in the form of tablets.

[175] *Chemistry & Industry*, **1955**, 1733.

[176] Wahhab, Hussain, Ali, and Muhammad, *Pakistan J. Sci. Research*, **7**, No. 1,22 (1955); *C.A.*, **50**, 3537 (1956).

Carbromal, N.F. (Adalin, Bromo-α,α-diethylacetylurea), $(C_2H_5)_2CBr$—CO—NH—CO—NH_2, an odorless crystalline powder, soluble in alcohol 1:18 and in water about 1:3000. It is a prompt-acting hypnotic and sedative used to reduce excitement and promote sleep in conditions where a powerful hypnotic is not required. It is usually administered as tablets.

Sedormid (Allylisopropylacetyl Urea), with properties similar to those of carbromal, is an effective sedative more prompt and strong in action than the bromides but not so strong as the barbiturates. It is used in mild conditions of nervousness and excitement usually being administered in the form of tablets.

$$CH_3$$
$$\diagdown$$
$$CHCH-\overset{O}{\overset{\|}{C}}-NH-\overset{O}{\overset{\|}{C}}-NH_2$$
$$\diagup \quad \mid$$
$$CH_3 \quad CH_2-CH{=}CH_2$$

Phenacemide, N.N.R. (Phenylacetylurea, Phenurone), $C_6H_5CH_2CONH$-$CONH_2$, is a white-to-creamy-white, odorless, crystalline solid. It is used as an anticonvulsant in epilepsy and in the control of mixed seizures.

Suramin Sodium, N.N.R. [Naphuride Sodium, Bayer 205, Germanin, Hexasodium *bis*-(*m*-aminobenzoyl-*m*-amino-*p*-methyl-benzoyl-1-naphthylamino-4,6,8-trisulfonate) carbamide], is a white, odorless, tasteless, crystalline compound, readily soluble in water and insoluble in alcohol. It is employed as a trypanosomacide in African sleeping sickness, being administered by intravenous or other routes of injection.

IMIDES

See Milontin (page 324) and Mysalol (page 350).

PROTEINS

The proteins are nitrogenous organic substances produced by and associated with living matter. The importance of protein constituents of protoplasm is evidenced by the fact that the name protein is derived from the Greek word, *proteios*, which means "pre-eminence" or "of first importance." When hydrolyzed by acids, they are resolved into α-amino acids, the component units from which they are synthesized in nature. The elemental constitution of the protein varies with the source.

The chief structural characteristic of proteins is the manner in which the component amino acids are joined, namely by means of an amide of one amino acid with another, which is also spoken of as a peptide bond. This may be illustrated in a simple formula such as —NHCHRCO—NHCHR'CO—NHCHR"CO—NH—. Thus, an amide composed of two amino acids is called a dipeptide, one of three amino acids, a tripeptide, and so on. A protein with more than 2000 units must perforce be large and complex.

Protein Therapy

The daily protein requirements for adults are usually based on Sherman's standard of 1 gram per kg. of body weight. This quantity is generally accepted and used to provide a reasonable margin of safety. Inadquate intake, faulty digestion and absorption, loss of blood through surgery or hemorrhage, disease, and heightened metabolism as in fevers, tuberculosis, hyperthyroidism, pregnancy, and lactation are factors that may lead to protein deficiency, which is made evident from a determination of the nitrogen balance. A negative nitrogen balance exists when excretion of nitrogen, chiefly in the urine, is greater than the intake. A positive nitrogen balance indicates that the protein is being utilized for energy and not for building body tissue and implies a greater intake than output of nitrogen. Ordinarily there is no retention of nitrogen in the adult body, the intake as protein being equivalent to the nitrogen eliminated; thus a nitrogen equilibrium is established.

In the process of digestion the complex protein molecules are cleaved to polypeptides and ultimately to amino acids. The amino acids are absorbed into the circulation and serve to meet metabolic requirements. Since the body cannot synthesize the essential amino acids, disease or inadequate intake may cause a deficiency of protein or of amino acids. There is evidence that a specific amino acid deficiency may exist and cause certain symptoms. However, laboratory methods suitable for the simple detection of such deficiencies have not been developed. Furthermore, the hypothesis that deficiency disorders seldom occur singly and that nutritive imbalance cannot be corrected permanently by the administration of a single chemical substance seems to be borne out by the success attained by multi-vitamin and multi-amino acid therapy.

Synthetic amino acids are available commercially but their use with few exceptions is impracticable at this time because of their cost. Protein hydrolysates, i.e., a mixture of natural amino acids prepared by the splitting of protein with acids or enzymes or both, are suitable for administration after removal of the hydrolyzing agent. The processes are relatively inexpensive and practical. The amino acid preparations formed by enzymatic hydrolysis of protein contain about 70 per cent of the potential amino acid nitrogen in the amino form and about 30 per cent as peptide nitrogen. Acid hydrolysis yields almost 100 per cent of the nitrogen in the form of amino acids, but tryptophan is destroyed in the process and must be replaced. It has been demonstrated clinically that protein hydrolysates containing amino acids and peptides, when given in sufficient amounts, can maintain nitrogen balance effectively and cause regeneration of serum proteins.

A large number of protein hydrolysates have been introduced as drugs. The products differ greatly in source of protein, protein equivalency, taste, admixed substances, solubility, etc. Amigen and parenamine are representative of the enzymatic and acid hydrolysates, respectively.

Aminopeptodrate, N.N.R. (Caminoids), is a mixture of amino acids and polypeptides derived by an enzymatic digest of liver and beef muscle extract, wheat gluten, soya, yeast, casein, and lactalbumin with dextrose, maltose, and sucrose. It is used as a diet supplement in conditions where a high protein intake is desired.

Plasma Hydrolysate, N.N.R. (Travamin), is a protein hydrolysate in which more than half of the total nitrogen is present in the form of α-amino nitrogen. It is obtained from an artificial digest of proteins derived from bovine blood plasma. It is used for maintenance of positive nitrogen balance in conditions where there is interference with ingestion, digestion, or absorption of foods.

Protein Hydrolysates, N.N.R. (Amigen, Aminonat, Aminosol, Hyprotigen, Parenamine, Protolysate), are products obtained by artificial digests of proteins such as casein, lactalbumin, or amino acids. The α-amino acid content represents more than half of total nitrogen.

These products are used parenterally to maintain a positive nitrogen balance in conditions that result in deficient nitrogen intake.

Protein Products

A. Isolated proteins:
   1. *Gelatin, U.S.P.* An albuminoid used in the preparation of galenicals and protein derivatives.
   2. Hemoglobin derivatives have been administered by mouth in the treatment of pernicious anemia.
   3. Casein. A phosphoprotein, used in the preparation of pharmaceuticals and as a protein food.

B. Egg proteins:
   1. Fresh egg yolk contains the phosphoprotein, vitellin, and a small amount of another protein, livetin. Is used in the preparation of galenicals.
   2. Fresh egg is used in the preparation of galenicals.

C. Protein foods: With the exception of casein and caseinate, these are mixtures. They are used chiefly in the diets of infants, undernourished adults, and diabetics.

D. Metallic derivatives of proteins:
   1. Mercurol contains 20 per cent mercury combined with nucleic acid, and is used chiefly as a local antiseptic.
   2. Peptonized iron. Prepared from peptone and iron oxide. This compound and the galenicals made from it are used chiefly for their nutritional value.
   3. Calomelol is a mercurous protein compound having the same therapeutic use as calomel.
   4. *Strong Silver–protein, N.F.*, *Protargol, N.N.R.*, and Protargentum contain between 7.5 and 8.5 per cent silver. They are antiseptics which stand between silver nitrate and the mild silver proteinates in both germicidal and irritant action.

5. *Mild Silver–protein, N.F.*, Argyn, Solargentum, Silvol, and Cargentos, contain 19 to 25 per cent of silver. They are nonirritant antiseptics.
6. Collargol belongs to the class of mild silver proteinates, but contains 78 per cent of silver.

E. Nonmetallic derivatives of proteins:
   1. Albumin tannate, composed of albumin and tannic acid, is used as an intestinal astringent.
   2. Ovogal is composed of egg albumin and bile acids, and is recommended chiefly as a laxative.
   3. Iodalbin and iodo–casein contain iodine combined with protein and have the same therapeutic action as the soluble iodides.

F. Allergenic extracts are for the most part protein preparations used for the diagnosis (determination of the sensitivity) and prophylaxis (desensitization) in conditions due to allergy or hypersensitiveness. They are made by the extraction of single and mixed pollens, bacteria, food, hair, fungi, and many other substances. For a more complete description of the products and their uses, see N.N.R.

G. Thromboplastic substances, N.N.R. These substances contain a lecithoprotein called tissue fibrinogen, which promotes blood coagulation.

H. *Thrombin, N.N.R.*, is a sterile, hemostatic powder consisting of sucrose and the thrombin isolated from bovine plasma. It is applied topically as the dry powder or in sterile, isotonic salt solution to control capillary bleeding as well as bleeding in certain surgical conditions. It reacts with blood fibrinogen to form fibrin, resulting in an adherent clot.

The capacity of thrombin when applied topically to clot the blood and plasma speedily and firmly finds wide application in control of capillary bleeding, fibrin sutures of tissues, and skin graft fixation.

I. Enzymes and hormones: Although nonprotein substances belonging to these two groups have been isolated, a number of enzymes and hormones appear to be conjugated protein compounds.

Immune Serum Globulin (Human), U.S.P. (Human Immune Globulin), is a solution of antibodies extracted from the placentae and placental blood of humans. Each lot represents at least ten individuals. It is injected as a prophylactic against measles and also to modify the disease.

Many other substances such as citrated **Normal Human Plasma, U.S.P., Normal Human Serum, U.S.P.**, antitoxins, toxins, serums, and vaccines, may be regarded as protein products.

Surgical Gut, U.S.P., Surgical Sutures, U.S.P., and **Surgical Silk, U.S.P.**, are examples of products that do or may consist largely of proteins.

Glutathione is a tripeptide widely distributed in both plant and animal tissues, and it is extremely important in tissue oxidation. It is composed of glutamic acid, cysteine, and glycine linked in the manner shown. In oxidation-

$$\text{HOOC—CH—CH}_2\text{CH}_2\text{—CO—NH—CH—CO—NH—CH}_2\text{—COOH}$$
$$\underset{\text{NH}_2}{\vert} \qquad\qquad\qquad \underset{\text{CH}_2\text{—SH}}{\vert}$$

reduction processes the reversible reaction may be represented

$$2\text{G—SH} \leftrightarrow \text{G—S—S—G}$$

This formation relative to the disulfide linkage is suggestive of a similar linkage in the oxidation of thiosulfate to tetrathionate.

$$2NaO—SO_2—SH \rightarrow NaO—SO_2—S—S—SO_2—ONa$$
Sodium tetrathionate

The official posterior pituitary preparations contain mixtures of hormones. These comprise oxytocin, the milk-ejecting hormone, and vasopressin. Both are octapeptides, and their structure has been established as indicated.[177]

CONH₂
|
C₆H₄OH   CH₂   CONH₂   CH₂
| | | / \
CH₂   R   CH₂   CH₂   CH₂ CH₂   R'
| | | \ |
NH₂CHCO—NHCHCO—NHCHCO—NHCHCO—NHCHCO—N—CHCO—NHCHCO—NHCH₂CONH₂
| |
CH₂S————————————————————————————————————SCH₂

CH₃
|
Oxytocin, R = —CHCH₂CH₃, R' = —CH₂CH(CH₃)₂

NH
‖
Pitressin, R = —CH₂C₆H₅, R' = —CH₂CH₂CH₂NHCNH₂

Insulin is the active principle or hormone of the pancreas. It is used as *Insulin Injection, U.S.P., Globin Zinc Insulin Injection, U.S.P., Isophane Insulin Injection, U.S.P.,* and *Protamine Zinc Insulin Injection, U.S.P.* It is a protein molecule with a molecular weight of about 12,000, and degradation reactions show that it is composed of four fragments, two of Fraction A made up of twenty-one amino acids and two of Fraction B made up of thirty amino acids. Sanger and his co-workers [178] have established the sequence of amino acids in each of these fractions as shown on page 256.

In pork insulin, components at 8, 9, and 10 are threonine-serine-isoleucine, and in sheep insulin they are alanine-glycine-valine.[179]

On the assumption that the four fractions are linked together through di-sulfide bonds as $(A + B)_2$ there are numerous hypothetical combinations that may be constructed. However, in view of Pauling's α-helix hypothesis for the structure of proteins,[180] many of these may be ruled out. Several likely formulas for the total structure of insulin have been advanced,[181, 182] but the correctness of any of them remains to be established.

Insulin Injection, U.S.P. (Insulin, Iletin, Insulin Hydrochloride), is an aqueous solution of the active principle of the islet tissue of the pancreas, purified to remove reaction-producing substances, adjusted to a pH of about 3 by the addition of hydrochloric acid, and stabilized by the addition of about 0.2 per cent phenol or cresol and about 1.6 per cent of glycerol.

[177] du Vigneaud *et al., J. Am. Chem. Soc.,* **75,** 4480, 4879 (1953).

[178] Sanger and Tuppy, *Biochem. J.,* **49,** 463, 481 (1951); Sanger and Thompson, *ibid.,* **53,** 372 (1953).

[179] Brown, Sanger, and Kitai, *Biochem. J.,* **60,** 556 (1955).

[180] Pauling, Corey, and Banson, *Proc. Natl. Acad. Sci. U. S.,* **37,** 205 (1951).

[181] Robinson, *Nature,* **172,** 27 (1953).

[182] Arndt and Riley, *Nature,* **172,** 245 (1953).

Fraction A

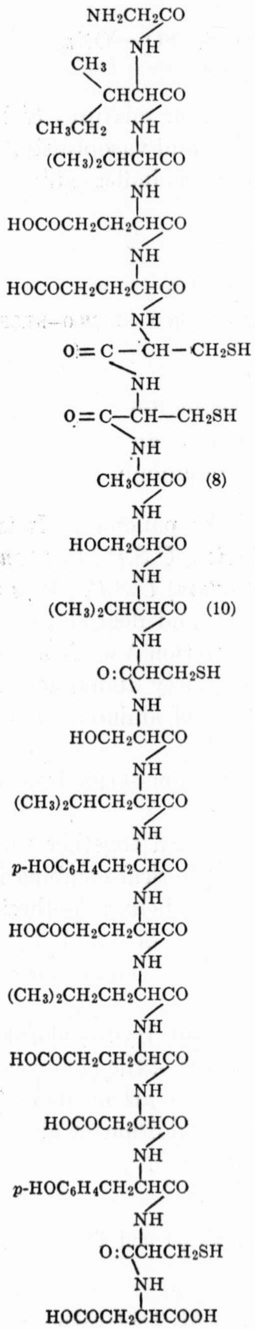

NH₂CH₂CO
      NH
CH₃
  CHCHCO
CH₃CH₂ NH
(CH₃)₂CHCHCO
      NH
HOCOCH₂CH₂CHCO
      NH
HOCOCH₂CH₂CHCO
      NH
O=C—CH—CH₂SH
      NH
O=C—CH—CH₂SH
      NH
CH₃CHCO (8)
      NH
HOCH₂CHCO
      NH
(CH₃)₂CHCHCO (10)
      NH
O:CCHCH₂SH
      NH
HOCH₂CHCO
      NH
(CH₃)₂CHCH₂CHCO
      NH
p-HOC₆H₄CH₂CHCO
      NH
HOCOCH₂CH₂CHCO
      NH
(CH₃)₂CH₂CH₂CHCO
      NH
HOCOCH₂CH₂CHCO
      NH
HOCOCH₂CHCO
      NH
p-HOC₆H₄CH₂CHCO
      NH
O:CCHCH₂SH
      NH
HOCOCH₂CHCOOH

Fraction B

C₆H₅CH₂CH(NH₂)CO
(CH₃)₂CHCH(NH)CO
HOCOCH₂CH(NH)CO
HOCOCH₂CH₂CH(NH)CO
N—CH   NH
‖   CCH₂CHCO
CH—NH   NH
(CH₃)₂CHCH₂—CH—CO
      NH
O:CCHCH₂SH
NHCH₂CO
HOCH₂CH(NH)CO
N—CH   NH
‖   CCH₂CHCO
CH—NH   NH
(CH₃)₂CHCH₂CHCO
(CH₃)₂CHCH(NH)CO
HOCOCH₂CH₂CH(NH)CO
CH₃CH(NH)CO
(CH₃)₂CHCH₂CH(NH)CO
p-HOC₆H₄CH₂CH(NH)CO
(CH₃)₂CHCH₂CH(NH)CO
(CH₃)₂CHCH(NH)CO
      NH
O:CCHCH₂SH
NHCH₂CO
HOCOCH₂CH₂CH(NH)CO
NH
‖
NH₂CNHCH₂CH₂CH₂CH(NH)CO
CH₂(NH)CO
C₆H₅CH₂CH(NH)CO
C₆H₅CH₂CH(NH)CO
p-HOC₆H₄CH₂CH(NH)CO
CH₃CHOHCH(NH)CO
CH₂—N
        CHCO
CH₂—CH₂
      NH
NH₂CH₂CH₂CH₂CH₂CHCO
CH₃CH(NH)COOH

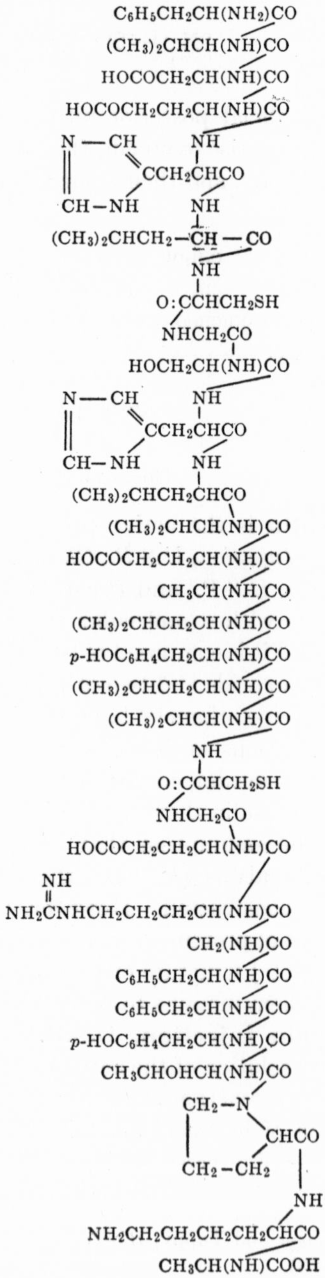

The potency of insulin is expressed in terms of U.S.P. insulin units. Crystalline zinc insulin is used as the reference standard.

Insulin is used to control the blood sugar level in diabetes; it makes possible the normal utilization of carbohydrates. It is estimated that each unit on the average makes possible the utilization of 2 g. of carbohydrate. It is usually administered subcutaneously about 15 to 30 min. before meals, the dose being calculated according to the requirements for each individual.

Protamine Zinc Insulin Injection, U.S.P., N.N.R. (Protamine Zinc and Iletin), is a uniform suspension of insulin with the protamine, derived from the sperm or testes of certain species of fish, and zinc chloride. Each cubic centimeter contains 40 or 80 units of insulin. About 0.125 mg. of protamine and 0.2 mg. of zinc are present for each 100 units of insulin.

This preparation has the same effects as insulin, but because it is more slowly absorbed the blood sugar level lowering effect is from three to six times as prolonged. The total dosage is about two-thirds that of unmodified insulin, and the greatest effect appears about 18 to 24 hr. after administration. It is administered like insulin after shaking the vial to ensure uniform suspension of the precipitate.

Corticotropin (Adrenocorticotropic Hormone, ACTH) is a polypeptide elaborated by the anterior lobe of the pituitary gland. It stimulates the suprarenal cortex to secrete its entire group of hormones, notably hydrocortisone, some cortisone, and corticosterone. The activity of corticotropin is attributed to the elaborated corticosteroidal hormones.

The structure of corticotropin had been determined to the extent that the identity and amounts of the constituent amino acids have been established. However, the complete sequence is not yet known.[183, 184]

Related to corticotropin, and present in the posterior lobe of the pituitary gland, is a melanocyte-stimulating hormone, intermedin, more simply abbreviated MSH. It is a peptide composed of eighteen amino acids with the sequence as indicated on page 257.[184a]

A striking feature in this sequence is that of the seven components, methionine-glutamic acid-histidine-phenylalanine-arginine-tryptophan-glycine; this is also found in the corticotropins. It is suggested that this specific order may account for the intrinsic melanocyte-stimulating activity of corticotropin, and the different order of the amino acids on either end of this sequence may account for the adrenal-stimulating activity of the corticotropins.

AMIDINES

Amidines have the characteristic structure, as shown. They may, according

$$R-C\diagupstack{NH_2}{\diagdown NH}$$

to the ammonia system of compounds, be looked upon as the complete ammono analogs of the carboxylic acids.

Diamidines of structure $R-\underset{\|}{\underset{NH}{C}}-NH-(CH_2)_n-NH-\underset{\|}{\underset{NH}{C}}-R$ have been proposed for use as disinfectants.[185] Symmetrical diamidines of the general structure, as shown, exhibit activity against protozoal infections.[186]

$$NH_2-\underset{\|}{\underset{NH}{C}}-C_6H_4-K-C_6H_4-\underset{\|}{\underset{NH}{C}}-NH_2$$

K = —CH:CH—, 4,4′-Stilbenediamidine, Stilbamidine
K = O(CH₂)₃O—, 4,4′-Diamidinodiphenoxypropane, Propamidine
K = O(CH₂)₅O—, 4,4′-Diamidinodiphenoxypentane, Pentamidine

Propamidine, active against *S. aureus*, was used in the treatment of war wounds without causing hemolysis or phagocytosis,[187] and in the treatment of secondary infections caused by hemolytic streptococci. **Pentamidine,** active

[183] Brink *et al.*, *J. Am. Chem. Soc.*, **75**, 1960 (1953).
[184] Pernis, Essellier, and Morandi, *Klin. Wochschr.*, **32**, 204 (1954).
[184a] Geschwind, Li, and Barnafi, *J. Am. Chem. Soc.*, **78**, 4494 (1956).
[185] Kaufmann, Budwig, and Lohnke, *Ber.*, **75**, 1585 (1942).
[186] Bowesman, *Ann. Trop. Med. Parasitol.*, **34**, 217 (1940).
[187] Thrower and Valentine, *Lancet*, **244**, 133 (1943).

in vitro against *Leishmania Donovani*,[188] has been suggested for the treatment and prevention of trypanosomiasis.[189]

Stilbamidine Isethionate, N.N.R. The salt of stilbamidine with hydroxyethanesulfonic acid, $HOCH_2CH_2SO_3H$, is useful for the treatment of protozoan and fungal infections.

Chloroguanide Hydrochloride, U.S.P. (Paludrine, Guanatol Hydrochloride, Proguanil Hydrochloride), may be prepared by the accompanying sequence of reactions.[190] It occurs as colorless crystals or white, crystalline powder which

$$Cl\text{—}C_6H_4\text{—}NH\text{—}CN \xrightarrow[\substack{(pressure \\ at\ 120°)}]{NH_3} ClC_6H_4NH\text{—}C\overset{NH_2}{\underset{NH}{\diagup\diagdown}} \xrightarrow{(CH_3)_2CHNHCN}$$

p-Chlorophenyl-cyanamide

$$Cl\text{—}C_6H_4\text{—}NH\overset{1}{\text{—}}C\overset{3}{\text{—}}NH\text{—}C\overset{5}{\text{—}}NH\text{—}CH(CH_3)_2$$
$$\qquad\qquad\quad \|\qquad\quad\ \|$$
$$\qquad\qquad\quad NH\qquad\ NH$$

Paludrine

is stable in air but darkens on exposure to light. It is sparingly soluble in water and soluble in alcohol.

Chloroguanide hydrochloride is used to prevent, suppress, or treat *Plasmodium falciparum* or to suppress or treat *Plasmodium vivax*. It is only partially effective as compared to chloroquine or quinacrine in vivax malaria.

Chloroazodin, N.F. (Azochloramide, N,N′-Dichloroazodicarbonamide), may be prepared by the sequence of reactions shown. It consists of yellow crystals

$$\overset{H_2N}{\underset{HN}{\diagdown\diagup}}C\text{—}NH_2 \xrightarrow[H_2SO_4]{HNO_3} \overset{H_2N}{\underset{HN}{\diagdown\diagup}}C\text{—}NHNO_2 \xrightarrow[H_2SO_4]{Zn} \overset{H_2N}{\underset{HN}{\diagdown\diagup}}C\text{—}NHNO \xrightarrow{H_2NNH_2\cdot H_2O}$$

$$\overset{H_2N}{\underset{HN}{\diagdown\diagup}}C\text{—}NH\text{—}NH_2 \xrightarrow{H_2N(NH)C\text{—}NHNO} \overset{H_2N}{\underset{HN}{\diagdown\diagup}}C\text{—}N\text{=}N\text{—}C\overset{NH_2}{\underset{NH}{\diagup\diagdown}} \xrightarrow{NaOCl}$$

$$\overset{H_2N}{\underset{N}{\diagdown}}C\text{—}N\text{=}N\text{—}C\overset{NH_2}{\underset{N}{\diagup}}$$
$$\qquad |\qquad\qquad\qquad\ |$$
$$\qquad Cl\qquad\qquad\qquad Cl$$

Chloroazodin

---

[188] Adler *et al.*, *Ann. Trop. Med. Parasitol.*, **39**, 14 (1945); *C.A.*, **40**, 621 (1946).

[189] Van Hoof, Henrard, and Peel, *Trans. Roy. Soc. Trop. Med. Hyg.*, **37**, 271 (1944); *C.A.*, **38**, 5307 (1944).

[190] Curd and Rose, *Chemistry & Industry*, **1946**, 75.

which are slightly soluble in water, alcohol, vegetable oils, and glyceryl triacetate. It is used as a chlorine-liberating antiseptic and germicide, being reported to be active over prolonged periods in the presence of pus and organic matter. It is used in solutions of about 1:3000 to 1:500 in glyceryl triacetate for wet dressings and topical application.

Phenocaine Hydrochloride, N.F. (Halocaine Hydrochloride, N,N'-*bis*-(*p*-Ethoxyphenyl)acetamidine Hydrochloride), is prepared from *p*-phenetidin and phenacetin.

Phenocaine

It is more toxic than cocaine, and hence it is used only by application to the eye. A 1 per cent solution of the hydrochloride instilled into the eye produces anesthesia in from 1 to 10 min. Although the solutions are permanent, the salt is so readily decomposed that even glass vessels should be avoided in preparing them.

Cyanides and Nitro Compounds

CYANIDES

Cyanides or nitriles have the general structure R—C≡N. Chemically they are of major importance as solvents and intermediates in synthesis. However, only a few medicinal products contain the cyano group; cyanocobalamin or vitamin B_{12} (see page 432) is one of these. Nitriles are considered here merely to complete the chemical classification of the text.

The first member of the nitrile series is formonitrile, HCN, hydrogen cyanide. It possesses the characteristic properties of both a weak acid and an acid nitrile. It is extremely toxic, producing its effect in part by forming a stable complex with hemoglobin. It is used in lethal gas chambers and for exterminating plague-infested vermin and rodents.

p-Aminoacetophenone and **p-Aminopropiophenone,** producing methemoglobinemia, protect experimental animals against the lethal action of hydrogen cyanide and cyanogen chloride. Dogs receiving up to four LD_{50} doses of hydrogen cyanide may be saved by the intravenous administration of p-aminopropiophenone.

The organic cyanides, RCN, are less toxic than HCN, and many of them possess a pleasant odor.

Isomeric with the nitriles are the isonitriles, related to each other as are hydrogen cyanide and its tautomer. The isonitriles, also called carbylamines, are

H—C≡N	H—N⇌C	R—C≡N	R—N⇌C
Hydrocyanic acid	Tautomer	Nitrile	Isonitrile

obtained in small amounts in the synthesis of nitriles, especially when an alkyl halide is allowed to react with an alkali cyanide. They are very toxic, and it is not improbable that the toxicity of the nitriles is largely caused by the isonitrile present as an impurity. The isonitriles are characterized by their objectionable odor. They serve to identify primary amines according to the reaction:

$$R—NH_2 + CHCl_3 + 3KOH \rightarrow R—NC + 3KCl + 3HOH$$

The cyanohydrins are hydroxynitriles. Hydrogen cyanide will react with a carbonyl group to form a cyanohydrin or hydroxynitrile, e.g.:

$$C_6H_5—CHO + HCN \rightarrow C_6H_5—CHOH—CN$$
Mandelonitrile

The importance of such a synthesis is apparent (see also the Cyanophoric Glycosides, page 115).

ESTERS OF NITRIC AND NITROUS ACIDS

The esters of nitric and nitrous acids have identical types of action in the body. It is generally assumed that the nitrate esters act after being reduced to nitrites. The nitrites cause a prompt but transient fall of blood pressure through vasodilation. The nitrate esters act more slowly, but their effect is maintained for as long as 3 or 4 hours.

Glyceryl Trinitrate (Nitroglycerin, Trinitrin, Glonoin) was discovered in 1847 by Sobrero who called it pyroglycerin. Its chemical composition was determined by Williamson in 1854.

Glyceryl trinitrate is manufactured by spraying glycerol into a well-agitated mixture of nitric and sulfuric acids while cooling the mixture to maintain the temperature at about 20°. After all the glycerol has been added the mixture is cooled to 15°, when the nitroglycerin separates as an oily layer on the surface of the acid. The reaction, although more complex, may be represented by the accompanying equation. The glyceryl trinitrate is

$$
\begin{array}{ccc}
CH_2OH & & CH_2—ONO_2 \\
| & 3HNO_3 & | \\
CHOH & \xrightarrow{} & CH—ONO_2 \\
| & & | \\
CH_2OH & & CH_2—ONO_2
\end{array}
$$

separated, is washed repeatedly with water, dilute sodium carbonate solution, and then with water again, and is dried over anhydrous sodium sulfate. It is a colorless or pale yellow oil, readily soluble in water or alcohol and miscible with ether or chloroform. It explodes with great violence when heated to 180° or on percussion. Consequently, if the spirit is spilled, it should be hydrolyzed at once with a solution of sodium or potassium hydroxide.

Glyceryl trinitrate is a colorless liquid which has a burning taste and produces a headache on tasting. It is only slightly soluble in water but very soluble in alcohol. It is employed in medicine usually in the form of the spirit or *Glyceryl Trinitrate Tablets, U.S.P.,* as a vasodilator to reduce arterial tension in diseases associated with aortic dysfunction. It has also been employed as a diuretic and it diminishes albuminuria. Its action is similar to that of amyl nitrite though slower and more prolonged.

Erythrityl Tetranitrate (Tetranitrol, Erythrol Tetranitrate) is prepared by reacting erythritol with nitric acid in the presence of sulfuric acid. The product

$$
\begin{array}{l}
CH_2\text{---}OH \\
| \\
CH\text{---}OH \\
| \qquad + 4HNO_3 \xrightarrow{H_2SO_4} \\
CH\text{---}OH \\
| \\
CH_2\text{---}OH
\end{array}
\qquad
\begin{array}{l}
CH_2\text{---}O\text{---}NO_2 \\
| \\
CH\text{---}O\text{---}NO_2 \\
| \\
CH\text{---}O\text{---}NO_2 \\
| \\
CH_2\text{---}O\text{---}NO_2
\end{array}
$$

occurs as leaflets which are soluble in alcohol and glycerol. It is insoluble in water. It is very explosive.

Physiologically, erythrityl tetranitrate behaves similar to nitroglycerin but the onset of action is somewhat slower and the duration of action is longer. The time required to reduce the nitro groups to nitrite probably explains the delayed activity. It is used to produce a mild, gradual, and prolonged vasodilation. It is used to reduce arterial hypertonia and as a prophylaxis and treatment against angina pectoris.

Pentaerythritol Tetranitrate, N.N.R. (Peritrate Tetranitrate), is prepared by reacting pentaerythritol with nitric acid in the presence of sulfuric acid. For medicinal purposes it is diluted with an inert ingredient, such as lactose, as a precaution against explosion. It is a slow-acting vasodilator, and its properties are ascribed to the release of nitrite in the body over longer periods.

$$
\begin{array}{cc}
O_2NOCH_2 & CH_2ONO_2 \\
 & \diagdown \quad \diagup \\
 & C \\
 & \diagup \quad \diagdown \\
O_2NOCH_2 & CH_2ONO_2
\end{array}
\qquad
\begin{array}{l}
CH_2ONO_2 \\
| \\
O_2NO\text{---}C\text{---}H \\
| \\
O_2NO\text{---}C\text{---}H \\
| \\
H\text{---}C\text{---}ONO_2 \\
| \\
H\text{---}C\text{---}ONO_2 \\
| \\
CH_2ONO_2
\end{array}
$$

Pentaerythritol
tetranitrate

Mannitol hexanitrate

Mannitol Hexanitrate, N.N.R. (Nitromannite, Mannitol Nitrate), is the hexanitrate ester of mannitol. It is prepared by reacting mannitol with nitric acid in the presence of sulfuric acid. The product occurs as long needles in regular clusters which are soluble in alcohol but insoluble in water. It is explosive. Diluted with nine parts of carbohydrate to one part of the nitrate, it forms a nonexplosive mixture which is the form employed for pharmaceutical preparations.

Mannitol hexanitrate causes a persistent relaxation of smooth muscle, particularly those of the smaller blood vessels, causing a fall in blood pressure which is not permanent. The action is too slow for relief in angina pectoris, and it has not proved useful as in prophylaxis. It does not benefit most cases of essential hypertension.

Pyroxylin, U.S.P. (Nitrocellulose), $C_{12}H_{16}O_6(ONO_2)_4$, is prepared by nitrating cellulose. It contains about two nitrate groups for each glucose unit. A solution of 4 g. pyroxylin in 75 ml. ether and 25 ml. alcohol is *Collodion, U.S.P.* The addition of castor oil and camphor to collodion forms *Flexible Collodion, U.S.P.*, which is used extensively as a protective covering for minor cuts and the like. *Salicylic Acid Collodion, U.S.P.*, prepared by the addition of salicylic acid to flexible collodion, is used to remove corns. *Styptic collodion* is prepared with tannic acid.

Ethyl Nitrite (Nitrous Ether), CH_3CH_2—ONO, at ordinary temperature is a gas and is prepared by the action of sulfuric acid on a mixture of alcohol and sodium nitrite in the cold. It is little used in therapy because it is unstable and unreliable. Freshly prepared ethyl nitrite behaves like other nitrites but when taken orally along with water the nitrite escapes rapidly and produces little effect. It is used in a 4 per cent alcoholic solution and known in that form by the common name of *Ethyl Nitrite Spirit, N.F.*

Amyl Nitrite, U.S.P. (Isoamyl Nitrite), $C_5H_{11}ONO$, is a pale yellow liquid which is prepared by the addition of sulfuric acid to a cold mixture of amyl alcohol, sodium nitrite, and water. It is a volatile, flammable liquid having a characteristic ethereal odor and a pungent taste. It is very slightly soluble in water, but it is miscible with alcohol and with ether.

Amyl nitrite is used as an antispasmodic in angina pectoris and as a depressomotor and vasodilator. It is employed as a restorative in cardiac failure during chloroform or nitrous oxide anesthesia. It is usually administered by inhalation or internally in hydroalcoholic solution. It is usually sold in "pearls" which are small, thin-walled glass capsules that can be easily broken so that the vapors may be inhaled.

Octyl Nitrite [Octrite, 1(2-Ethylhexyl) nitrite], $CH_3CH_2CH_2CH_2CH$-(C_2H_5)—CH_2—ONO, has been studied by Krantz, Carr, and Forman. The product does not possess the disagreeable properties of amyl nitrite and the action on the coronary flow is just as prompt.[1]

NITRO COMPOUNDS

Organic compounds in which a hydrogen atom is replaced by the group $-N\langle^O_O$, also written $-N\langle^O_O$, are called nitro derivatives. Examples of this class of compounds are nitromethane, $CH_3-N\langle^O_O$, nitrobenzene, $C_6H_5N\langle^O_O$, etc.

[1] Krantz, Carr, and Forman, *J. Pharmacol. Exptl. Therap.*, **64**, 302 (1938).

These compounds should not be confused with the esters of nitrous acid, with which they are isomeric. Thus nitromethane, CH_3—NO_2, is quite different from methyl nitrite, CH_3—O—N=O. Nitromethane possesses none of the properties of an ester.

These compounds should also be distinguished from the esters of nitric acid, e.g., glyceryl trinitrate which mistakenly has been called nitroglycerin.

The aliphatic nitro hydrocarbons, more commonly known as the nitro paraffins, are prepared by other methods than are the aromatic nitro hydrocarbons, and they also possess different properties; hence it is always necessary to make a distinction between the nitro paraffins and the nitro aromatics.

One property possessed in common by both the nitro paraffins and the nitro aromatics is their explosibility; this is especially true for the polynitrated compounds. Thus, trinitrotoluene, the TNT of war fame, and picric acid have long been known for this characteristic. The polynitro paraffins may be equally adaptable for explosive purposes.

The mononitro paraffins are irritating and toxic, the effects increasing with the size of the molecule. Concentrations in the atmosphere of 0.05 per cent of nitromethane were tolerated by monkeys; 0.10 per cent proved dangerous. Nitroethane administered to rabbits was only partially excreted by the lungs, and much of it was destroyed in the tissues.[2]

Chloropicrin (Trichloronitromethane, Nitrochloroform), Cl_3C—NO_2, is obtained when many hydrocarbons are treated simultaneously with nitric acid and a chlorinating agent, e.g., chlorinated lime. It may be readily prepared by treating chloroform with concentrated nitric acid:

$$Cl_3CH + HO—NO_2 \rightarrow HOH + Cl_3C—NO_2$$

This compound, an agent used in chemical warfare as a lung irritant, is a heavy liquid, boiling at 112°, but with a relatively high vapor pressure; its odor is described as that of flypaper or anise. It produces severe coughing, lachrymation, and vomiting; a concentration of 1 ppm. causes a copious flow of tears.

Aromatic Nitro Compounds

The nitro group is introduced into the aromatic nucleus by reaction with nitric acid, frequently in the presence of sulfuric acid. All known nitro compounds are prepared synthetically except chloramphenicol (page 495).

Aromatic nitro compounds depress life processes and produce hemorrhage in the alimentary canal; death is caused by respiratory paralysis. Nitro compounds are of no direct or particular interest in pharmaceutical chemistry; they are, however, of great value in the chemical industry, being used to a large extent as intermediates.

Nitrobenzene (Oil of Mirbane), C_6H_5—NO_2, like aniline, is highly toxic. It has no usage in medicines, but it is important from a toxicological standpoint

[2] Machle, Scott, and Treon, *J. Ind. Hyg. Toxicol.*, **22**, 315 (1940); **24**, 5 (1942); *C.A.*, **35**, 805 (1941); **36**, 2021 (1942).

and as a hazardous industrial poison. It has been used in shoe polishes (but is now forbidden because of its toxic effects), and sometimes as a perfume in soaps.

The **nitrophenols** are readily prepared by the direct nitration of the phenols. The introduction of the nitro group into phenols does not reduce their antiseptic activity.

As shown *o*- and *p*-nitrophenol may exist in two forms, the phenol form and the aci-quinone form.

Nitrophenol form,
colorless

aci-Quinone form,
colored

Because it is capable of forming the quinonoid, chromophoric arrangement nitrophenol may be employed as an indicator in acid-base titrations.

The mononitrophenols are toxic, causing stimulation followed by depression of the central nervous system and the formation of methemoglobin. The *para* compound is reported to be the most and the *ortho* isomer the least toxic. The dinitrophenols also are toxic; they accelerate oxygen metabolism and cause an increase in body temperature. They may cause many other toxic effects, e.g., cataract formation, liver and kidney injury, agranulocytosis, and dermatitis. The 2,4-, 2,5-, and 2,6-dinitrophenols are reported to be more toxic than the 2,3-, 3,4-, and 3,5-isomers. It seems that the hyperthermic activity is dependent on at least one nitro group being *para* to the hydroxyl and that methemoglobin formation is augmented by the *ortho* and *meta* isomers; e.g., 2,4-dinitrophenol is an active hyperthermic agent but causes little methemoglobinemia, but the less toxic 2,3- and 3,6-dinitrophenols cause hemoglobinemia and are relatively inactive as hyperthermic agents. The toxicity of tri- and higher polynitro phenols is less than that of the dinitrophenols. Alkylation, as in the nitro cresols, yields compounds that have qualitative and quantitative activities like those of the dinitrophenols, but the toxicity is decreased.

Dinitrophenol (2,4-Dinitrophenol) exerts a remarkable stimulating effect on fat metabolism, and the metabolism is sufficient to produce hyperthermia.

2,4-Dinitrophenol has been tried extensively for the clinical reduction of obesity; it is very effective. Unfortunately, its action is not always reliable and toxic manifestations, frequently with fatal results, appear unexpectedly. Occasionally also it has been reported to give rise to the growth of cataract in the eyes.

Trinitrophenol (Picric Acid, 2,4,6-Trinitrophenol) is used as an antiseptic in the treatment of burns and exudative wounds. Its coagulant action on the tissues serves to develop a natural protective covering of the wound under which the normal healing processes may be carried out. It is usually applied in a 1 per cent solution. A 5 per cent solution is sometimes used in the treatment of certain types of eczema.

Silver Picrate, N.N.R. (Silver Trinitrophenoxide), combines the antiseptic activity of silver with that of picric acid. It is used to treat urethritis, vaginitis caused by *Trichomonas vaginalis,* etc. It may be administered as a dusting powder containing 1 per cent silver picrate with sterile talc, or in the form of suppositories.

$$O—Ag \cdot H_2O$$

$$O_2N— \quad —NO_2$$

$$NO_2$$

Nitro derivatives of aminophenols and aminophenolic ethers are of interest because of their sweet taste. Compared to sucrose as 1, the sweetening powers reported are:[3]

1-hydroxy-2-amino-4-nitrobenzene	120
1-methoxy-2-amino-4-nitrobenzene	220
1-ethoxy-2-amino-4-nitrobenzene	350
1-*n*-propoxy-2-amino-4-nitrobenzene	4100
1-*n*-butoxy-2-amino-4-nitrobenzene	1000
1-isopropoxy-2-amino-4-nitrobenzene	600
1-allyloxy-2-amino-4-nitrobenzene	2000

These compounds are claimed to have a sweet taste without the secondary bitter taste commonly associated with saccharin. On the other hand, their high order of toxicity [4,5] has rendered the group essentially useless, at least in this country. The *n*-propoxy derivative has been examined most extensively and has the greatest sweetening effect; it also possesses considerable local anesthetic activity.[6]

The ethoxy analog is known as **Neo-Douxan** [7] which has apparently found use on an industrial scale in Germany.

The ethers of the isomeric 2-nitro-4-aminophenols are tasteless.

Dinitro-*o*-cresol, used as its sodium salt under the name of Sinox, is toxic to broad-leaved weeds. By its use the yield of flax per acre has been more than doubled.

[3] Verkade, van Dijk, and Meerburg, *Proc. Nederland. Akad. Wetensch.,* **45,** 630 (1942); *C.A.,* **38,** 4093 (1944).

[4] Hannig, *Arzneimittel-Forsch.,* **6,** 310 (1953); *C.A.,* **47,** 10131 (1953).

[5] Fitzhugh, Nelson, and Frawby, *J. Am. Pharm. Assoc.,* **40,** 583 (1951).

[6] Frisch, *Chemistry in Can.,* **2,** 22 (1950); *C.A.,* **46,** 9259 (1952).

[7] Lehman, *Assoc. Food & Drug Officials U. S.,* **40,** 82 (1951).

CHAPTER
9

Sulfur Compounds

The role and reactions of organic sulfur compounds, more particularly of the —SH or sulfhydryl group, in vital processes is coming to be better understood. The behavior of the —SH group in such substances as coenzyme A, in glutathione and other peptides, and in thioctic acid as an intermediary in capturing energy from the sun during photosynthesis [1] serves to give emphasis to its importance. Interference with or modification of the normal reactions of the sulfhydryl group, e.g., inhibition of the vital oxidation-reduction reaction from sulfhydryl to disulfide,

$$2\text{—SH} \underset{H_2}{\overset{O_2}{\rightleftharpoons}} \text{—S—S—}$$

or oxidation to sulfonic acid,

$$\text{—SH} \rightarrow \text{—SO}_3\text{H}$$

or complexing with heavy metals to form unreactive mercaptides, which explains metal poisoning,

$$2\text{—SH} + \text{Hg}^{++} \rightarrow \text{—S—Hg—S—}$$

have profound physiological effects. Thus alloxan, for example, which is an —SH reagent, inhibits insulin formation by combining with the sulfhydryl groups of the hormone precursors in the pancreas and thus produces experimental diabetes. Ionizing radiations produce from water agents that oxidize sulfhydryl groups, thus explaining at least in part the biological effects of such radiations.[2]

[1] Barltrop, Hayes, and Calvin, *J. Am. Chem. Soc.*, **76,** 4348 (1954).
[2] Barron, *Texas Repts. Biol. and Med.*, **11,** 651 (1953).

Other sulfur-containing compounds, such as thiophenols, Ar—SH, thioethers, R—S—R′, thioaldehydes, RCH:S, thioketones, R—CS—R′, thioacids, RCO—SH, have at various times received the attention of the medicinal chemist; the sulfonamides, however, are the best known.

The following compounds are of interest here.

Divinyl sulfide, $(CH_2=CH)_2S$, b.p. 101°, is the chief constituent of the oil of *Allium ursinum*.

β,β'-Dichlorodiethyl sulfide, $ClCH_2CH_2$—S—CH_2CH_2Cl, is the vesicant war gas known as "yellow cross" or "mustard gas," b.p. 215°.

A comparison of the vesicant properties of the halogenated derivatives of diethyl sulfide reveals the following:[3]

CH_3CH_2—S—CH_2CH_3	inactive
CH_3—CHCl—S—CHCl—CH_3	inactive
CH_3—CH_2—S—CH_2—CH_2Cl	active
CH_2Cl—CH_2—S—CH_2—CH_2Cl	"mustard," most active
CH_2Cl—CH_2—S—CHCl—CH_2Cl	weakly active
CH_2Cl—CH_2—S—CCl_2—CH_2Cl	weakly active
CH_2Cl—CH_2—S—CCl_2—$CHCl_2$	weakly active

To shed light on the possible modes of action of mustard gas on the tissues, its various reactions have been investigated. Its reactions with water are summarized as shown. The disulfonium salt $S[CH_2CH_2\overset{+}{S}(CH_2CH_2OH)_2]_2$ is of con-

siderable interest because of its toxicity. The LD_{50} for mice is 50 to 100 mg. per kg.; at doses above 250 mg. per kg., death occurs rapidly with flaccid paralysis and respiratory failure. With cysteine the compound reacts according to the equation shown. Although there is no evidence for the formation of the sul-

$$S[CH_2CH_2\overset{+}{S}(CH_2CH_2OH)_2]_2 + 2HSCH_2CH(NH_2)COOH \rightarrow$$

$$S(CH_2CH_2SCH_2CHNH_2COOH)_2 + 2S(CH_2CH_2OH)_2$$

[3] Mameli, *Boll. chim. farm.*, **68**, 587 (1929).

fonium compounds indicated *in vivo*, such formations may play a part in the overall toxicity of mustard gas.[4]

Mustard gas shaken with carboxylic acids forms diesters of thiodiglycol.[5] With methionine a sulfonium compound of structure $S(CH_2CH_2\overset{+}{S}CH_2CH_2-\underset{\underset{CH_3}{|}}{})$

$CHNH_2COOH)_2$ is formed; with proteins the reaction may be more complex.[6,7]

Applied to pigskin much of the mustard compound cannot be recovered; the fixed sulfur is attached to insoluble proteins. Horse serum treated with mustard gas becomes more basic; since potentiometric titration shows that the decrease in acidity parallels the increase in the sulfur content of the protein, denaturation is explained by esterification of the free carboxyl groups. Hemoglobin, known to contain large amounts of histidine, is presumed to react through the imidazole nucleus to form quaternary ammonium ions such as that shown.[8]

$$\begin{array}{c} H_2C \quad CH{=\!=}C{-} \\ \diagup \;\; \backslash \;\; | \qquad | \\ H_2C \qquad {}^+N \qquad N \\ | \qquad\quad \backslash \;\; \diagup\!\!\diagdown \\ | \qquad\qquad CH \\ | \qquad\qquad \\ S \qquad CH_2 \\ \backslash \quad\; \diagup \\ CH_2 \end{array}$$

The mustard gases owe their activity to the formation of onium ions, as indicated. The onium ion reacts readily with various anions and with various un-

$$RSCH_2CH_2Cl \;\rightarrow\; R{-}\overset{+}{S}{\underset{\diagdown}{\overset{\diagup}{\Big|}}}{\begin{array}{c} CH_2 \\ \\ CH_2 \end{array}} \;\; \cdot Cl^-$$

charged nucleophilic molecules. Hence, there are numerous possibilities of biological reaction, which contribute to the death of the cell.[9]

In 1934, it was observed that mustard gas retarded the development of tumors experimentally stimulated by 1,2,5,6-dibenzanthracene. Since then many studies have been made respecting the susceptibility of living cells toward this agent, and it develops that it is a strong mutagen and is also likely to be a potent carcinogen. The nitrogen mustards have received perhaps more attention,[10]

[4] Stein, Moore, and Bergmann, *J. Org. Chem.*, **11**, 664 (1946).

[5] Moore, Stein, and Fruton, *J. Org. Chem.*, **11**, 675 (1946).

[6] Stein and Moore, *J. Org. Chem.*, **11**, 681 (1946).

[7] Wood, Rachele, Stevens, Carpenter, and du Vigneaud, *J. Am. Chem. Soc.*, **70**, 2547 (1948).

[8] Davis and Ross, *J. Am. Chem. Soc.*, **69**, 1177 (1947).

[9] Gilman and Philips, *Science*, **103**, 409 (1946).

[10] Heston and Schneiderman, *Science*, **117**, 109 (1953); Klopp and Bateman, *Advances in Cancer Research*, **2**, 255 (1954).

and useful modifications of these highly active compounds are mentioned under halogenated alkylamines, page 192.

The sulfhydryl or —SH grouping is of vital biological significance. For example, the cysteine-cystine oxidation-reduction system is of elemental importance in biochemistry.

$$2HSCH_2-CH-COOH \xrightarrow{O} \underset{H_2 \leftarrow}{} S-CH_2-CH-COOH$$

$$\underset{NH_2}{|} \qquad \underset{NH_2}{|}$$

$$S-CH_2-CH-COOH$$

$$\underset{NH_2}{|}$$

Cysteine   Cystine

Advantage is taken of this oxidation-reduction system in the use of sodium thioglycolate, $HSCH_2COONa$, as a reducing agent in hair waving. [11]

Compounds containing the sulfhydryl group inactivate many antibiotics. Thioglycolic acid, cysteine, ethanthiol, and thiosulfate inhibit or suppress the antifungal activity of menadione.[12] It is suggested that many antibiotics depend on their ability to combine with essential —SH groups in bacterial metabolism for their fundamental mode of action. A type reaction is that of cysteine with angelica lactone, for which one of two possible mechanisms is postulated.[13] A

$$CH_2-CH + HSCH_2CH-COOH \xrightarrow[\text{(Preferred)}]{A} CH_2-CH_2$$

$$CO \quad C-CH_3 \quad NH_2 \qquad CO \quad C-SCH_2CH-COOH$$

$$O \qquad\qquad O \quad CH_3 \; NH_2$$

$$\xrightarrow{B} \qquad\qquad CH_2-CH_2$$

$$CO \quad C-CH_3$$

$$NH \quad O$$

$$HSCH_2-CH-COOH$$

further study shows that, whatever the mechanism, many thiols react with and inactivate many types of antibiotics.[14]

With the quinone type of antibiotic an analogous addition is postulated, since activity is inhibited by monothioglycol, by thioglycolic acid, and by cysteine.[15] For antibiotic hydroquinones there may be preliminary or simultaneous oxidation. However, such mechanisms do not explain the antibiotic activity of 2-

[11] Reed, Tennenbaum, and Den Beste, U. S. pat. 2,405,166; *C.A.*, **40**, 6225 (1946).
[12] Colwell and McCall, *J. Bact.*, **51**, 659 (1946); *C.A.*, **40**, 5800 (1946).
[13] Cavallito and Haskell, *J. Am. Chem. Soc.*, **67**, 1991 (1945).
[14] Cavallito, *J. Biol. Chem.*, **164**, 29 (1946); *C.A.*, **41**, 94 (1947).
[15] Geiger, *Arch. Biochem.*, **11**, 23 (1946).

methyl-3-methoxynaphthoquinone or of trimethoxytoluquinone (spinulosin trimethyl ether), the latter being one of the strongest bacteriostats in the quinone group. Hence, it is likely that the mechanism is more complex than postulated.[16]

MERCAPTANS

Dimercaprol, U.S.P. (BAL, British Anti-Lewisite, 2,3-Dimercapto-1-propanol), CH_2SH—$CHSH$—CH_2OH, illustrates the ability of the —SH group to react with heavy metals, much like hydrogen sulfide. It is prepared by the addition of bromine to allyl alcohol, and the resultant 2,3-dibromo-1-propanol is allowed to react with sodium hydrosulfide under pressure. The product is a colorless, or

$$CH_2{=}CH_2{-}CH_2OH \xrightarrow[\text{2. NaHS + H}_2\text{O}]{\text{1. Br}_2} CH_2SH{-}CHSH{-}CH_2OH$$

almost colorless, viscid liquid with an offensive, mercaptanlike odor. It is soluble in vegetable oils. It was developed during the war as a protective agent against arsenical gases. It has been found effective as an antidote in arsenic, mercury, and other heavy-metal poisoning. In arsenic poisoning BAL forms stable, relatively nontoxic thioarsenites which tend to remove the arsenic from the tissues and hasten their excretion. A 10 per cent solution of BAL in peanut oil with 20 per cent benzyl benzoate is administered by intramuscular injection. Benzyl benzoate is added because the product is more stable in the mixture than in peanut oil alone.

Bismuth Sodium Thioglycollate, N.N.R. (Thio-Bismol), is the salt formed by the reaction of sodium thioglycollate and bismuth hydroxide and contains approximately 38 per cent bismuth. The structural formula is $Bi(S{-}CH_2{-}COONa)_3$ but the product may deviate slightly from this. It is a yellow, hygroscopic, granular product which is freely soluble in water. Aqueous solutions are unstable.

It is used intramuscularly in the treatment of syphilis by virtue of the bismuth present. It is readily absorbed and produces little local injury upon injection.

SULFONES

See also glucosulfone and sulfoxone, page 290.

Thioalcohols react with the aldehydic or ketonic carbonyl group to form the thio-analogs of acetals, which are known as mercaptals.

$$\underset{\text{R}'}{\overset{\text{R}}{|}}C{=}O + 2R''SH \rightarrow HOH + \underset{\substack{\diagup \diagdown \\ R'\quad S{-}R''}}{\overset{\substack{R\quad S{-}R'' \\ \diagdown \diagup}}{C}}$$

Mercaptal

[16] Hoffman-Osterhoff, *Science*, **105**, 549 (1947).

The thioethers may be oxidized to the disulfone compounds as indicated.

$$R''-\overset{\overset{\displaystyle R}{|}}{\underset{\underset{\displaystyle R'}{|}}{S-C-S}}-R'' \xrightarrow{\text{KMnO}_4} R''-\overset{\overset{\displaystyle O}{\uparrow}}{\underset{\underset{\displaystyle O}{\downarrow}}{S}}-\overset{\overset{\displaystyle R}{|}}{\underset{\underset{\displaystyle R'}{|}}{C}}-\overset{\overset{\displaystyle O}{\uparrow}}{\underset{\underset{\displaystyle O}{\downarrow}}{S}}-R''$$

Several members of the disulfone series possess hypnotic properties; especially notable are sulfonal, trional, and tetronal. These compounds were introduced as

CH₃ — SO₂—C₂H₅ \ C / CH₃ — SO₂—C₂H₅ (Sulfonal)   C₂H₅ — SO₂—C₂H₅ \ C / CH₃ — SO₂—C₂H₅ (Trional)   C₂H₅ — SO₂—C₂H₅ \ C / C₂H₅ — SO₂—C₂H₅ (Tetronal)

therapeutic agents by Bauman and Kast in 1888. For many years they were the most frequently used hypnotics but they have been almost completely replaced by more efficient products, e.g., the barbiturates. The only ones still used are sulfonal and trional, and they are no longer official.

Sulfonmethane (Sulfonal, Diethylsulfon-dimethylmethane) is a white, crystalline powder, m.p. 124–126°, soluble in water 1:365 and soluble in alcohol 1:60. Its uses are similar to those of sulfonethylmethane.

Sulfonethylmethane (Trional, Diethylsulfon-methylethylmethane) consists of colorless crystals, soluble in water 1:200 and soluble in alcohol, m.p. 75°; it is employed as a hypnotic and antispasmodic. It is not certain in its action and is of little value in insomnia accompanied by pain. It is reported to be habit forming. The margin of safety between the effective and the toxic dose is not large. Toxic symptoms are manifested by the appearance of hematoporphyrin in the urine. It is usually administered with large quantities of warm liquids.

The activity of the compounds of the disulfone series increases as the number of ethyl groups increases. Tetronal, with four ethyl groups, is more active and more toxic than trional.

THIOCYANATES AND ISOTHIOCYANATES

Potassium Thiocyanate, N.F. (Potassium Sulfocyanate), KSCN, is used to relieve high blood pressure. It is usually administered in the form of enteric coated tablets, the dosage being governed by the concentration of thiocyanate, which is determined colorimetrically, in the blood.

Allyl Isothiocyanate (Allyl Sulfocyanate, Volatile Oil of Mustard), $CH_2=$ $CH—CH_2—N=C=S$, is present in the seed of black mustard in the form of the glycoside, sinigrin, from which it may be obtained by hydrolysis. It may be prepared from allyl iodide and potassium isothiocyanate.

$$CH_2=CH—CH_2—I + KNCS \rightarrow CH_2=CH—CH_2—N=C=S + KI$$

It is a colorless oil with a very pungent, irritating odor. It is soluble in alcohol and slightly soluble in water.

It is a powerful rubefacient.

SULFONIC ACIDS

Compounds that have the general structure R—$\overset{\overset{\text{O}}{\uparrow}}{\underset{\underset{\text{O}}{\downarrow}}{\text{S}}}$—OH are known as sulfonic

acids. Structurally they may be looked upon as hydrocarbons in which a hydrogen atom is replaced by the sulfonic acid group, —SO_3H, or as sulfuric acid in which one hydroxyl group is replaced by a hydrocarbon residue. A number of sulfonated esters and products derived from them are used commercially as wetting, emulsifying, and detergent agents.

The sulfonic acid group, —SO_3H, confers acidic properties. It is also a solubilizing group, making the molecule in which it is substituted more soluble in water. Physiologically it seems to decrease the toxicity of the molecule.

Methanesulfonic Acid, CH_3SO_3H, is employed for making salts of active bases, e.g., phentolamine methanesulfonate. The dimethanesulfonate of 1,4-butanediol, **Busulfan, N.N.R.** (Myleran), $CH_3SO_3CH_2CH_2CH_2CH_2OSO_2CH_3$, is an active alkylating agent, but unlike the "mustard" compounds, its cytotoxic action does not affect the germinal or lymphatic tissues, or intestinal epithelium, but is largely confined to the bone marrow. Hence, it is used to control the symptoms of granulocytic leukemia;[17] it is reported to be as effective as x-ray therapy or treatment with radiophosphorus.[18]

The sodium salts of dialkyl sulfosuccinates are known as Aerosols. They are prepared according to the general equation

$$
\begin{array}{c}
\text{CH—COOH} \\
\| \\
\text{CH—COOH}
\end{array}
+ 2\text{ROH} \rightarrow
\begin{array}{c}
\text{CH—COOR} \\
\| \\
\text{CH—COOR}
\end{array}
\xrightarrow{\text{NaHSO}_3}
\begin{array}{c}
\text{NaO}_3\text{S—CH—COOR} \\
| \\
\text{CH}_2\text{—COOR}
\end{array}
$$
$$\text{Aerosols}$$

Dioctyl Sodium Sulfosuccinate, U.S.P. (Aerosol O.T.), the ester of 2-ethylhexanol, is a white, waxlike plastic solid. It is usually sold in the form of pellets, which may be dissolved in alcohol or glycerol. It is soluble in water 1:70. Strong bases decompose the ester, but it is moderately stable in acids and dilute alkali. It is used to increase the solubility of cresol in water, to enhance the bactericidal properties of antiseptics, to prepare hydrophilic ointment bases, and as a detergent for cleansing glassware.

Dibutyl Sodium Sulfosuccinate (Aerosol IB), the ester of n-butyl, isobutyl, or sec-butyl, or a mixture of esters, is a white, powderlike material, stable in acid or neutral media, but is hydrolyzed in alkaline solution.

[17] Haddow and Timmis, *Lancet*, **1953** (i), 207.
[18] Haut, Altman, Cartwright, and Wintrobe, *Arch. Internal Med.*, **96**, 451 (1955).

Diamyl Sodium Sulfosuccinate (Aerosol AY) is the *n*-amyl or 1-methylbutyl ester; it is available as hard pellets or as a powder.

Dihexyl Sodium Sulfosuccinate (Aerosol M.A.) is a mixture of the mono- and diesters of 1-methylpentanol; it is supplied in slightly hygroscopic, waxlike pellets which are soluble in water after preliminary soaking.

Sulfocolaurate is the potassium salt of the β-(α-sulfoacetamido)ethyl ester of lauric acid.

$$CH_3-(CH_2)_{10}-COO-CH_2-CH_2-NH-CO-CH_2-SO_3K$$

It is a white powder which is sparingly soluble in cold water. It is used as a foaming agent in dentrifices in concentrations of 1 to 2 per cent at which dilution it does not irritate the tissues of the mouth.

Zinc Phenolsulfonate, N.F. (Zinc Sulfocarbolate), $(C_6H_4-OH-SO_3, 1:4)_2Zn$, is an efflorescent crystalline compound, soluble in water about 1:1.6 and in alcohol about 1:1.8. It is used as an astringent antiseptic internally and externally.

Ichthammol, N.F. (Ammonium Ichthosulfonate, Hirathiol, Ichthynate, Ichthyol, Isarol), is a mixture of sulfides, sulfones, and sulfonates obtained from bituminous shales. It has a high sulfur content, the sulfur compounds occurring as "sulfoichthiolic acids" which are neutralized with ammonia. It is a brownish-black, thick fluid, soluble in water and in glycerin and miscible with fats. It is an emollient and demulcent with some antiseptic value used as such or in combination with other antiseptics for the treatment of various skin disorders, such as psoriasis, eczema, and erysipelas; it is also used to promote the healing of chronic ulcers and other inflammations. It is usually applied as the *Ichthammol Ointment, N.F.*

Potassium Guaiacolsulfonate, N.F. (Thiocol), $C_6H_3-OH-OCH_3-SO_3K$, 1:2:6, is a colorless, crystalline, practically neutral compound, soluble in water and slightly soluble in alcohol. It is employed as a sedative expectorant in the treatment of colds, coughs, and other inflammatory conditions of the respiratory tract. It is reported to have advantages over guaiacol in that it is practically tasteless and nontoxic and is not a gastric irritant. It is administered in the form of tablets and as a syrup.

Chloramine-T, N.F. (Chloramine, Sodium *p*-Toluenesulfonechloramide), is prepared by the accompanying sequence of reactions. It is a crystalline powder,

$$CH_3-C_6H_5 \xrightarrow{H_2SO_4} p\text{-}CH_3-C_6H_4-SO_2-OH \xrightarrow{PCl_5} p\text{-}CH_3-C_6H_4-SO_2Cl \xrightarrow{NH_3}$$

$$p\text{-}CH_3-C_6H_4-SO_2-NH_2 \xrightarrow[\text{(NaOCl)}]{Cl_2} p\text{-}CH_3-C_6H_4-SO_2-N \begin{smallmatrix} Na \\ \diagup \\ \diagdown \\ Cl \end{smallmatrix}$$

Chloramine-T

soluble about 1:7 in water and insoluble in organic solvents. It contains about 12 per cent of active chlorine. It slowly decomposes in solution with liberation of the chlorine. It is used in 1 to 2 per cent aqueous solutions for the irrigation and dressing of wounds and in about 0.1 per cent solutions for mucous membrane applications.

Dichloramine-T (Dichloramine, p-Toluenesulfonedichloramide) is prepared by chlorinating p-toluenesulfonamide.

$$p\text{-}CH_3\text{---}C_6H_4\text{---}SO_2\text{---}NH_2 \rightarrow p\text{-}CH_3\text{---}C_6H_4\text{---}SO_2\text{---}NCl_2$$
$$\text{Dichloramine-T}$$

It is a white or yellow, crystalline solid, slightly soluble in water and alcohol; the solutions gradually decompose with the liberation of chlorine. It is used as an antiseptic and disinfectant like the inorganic hypochlorites, but it is more convenient to use and is less irritant. It is employed in 1 to 2 per cent solution in chlorinated paraffin for application to mucous surfaces and in about a 5 per cent solution for dressing wounds.

Halazone, N.F., is prepared by oxidation of p-toluenesulfonamide, followed by treatment with hypochlorite; it may be looked upon as dichloramine-T with the methyl group oxidized to a carboxyl group, forming the dichloramide of p-sulfobenzoic acid. It occurs as a white, crystalline powder which melts with de-

$$p\text{-}CH_3\text{---}C_6H_4\text{---}SO_2\text{---}NH_2 \rightarrow C_6H_4 \Big\langle {{\text{COOH}} \atop {\text{SO}_2\text{NH}_2}} \quad \xrightarrow[\text{2. H}^+]{\text{1. NaOCl}} \quad C_6H_4 \Big\langle {{\text{COOH}} \atop {\text{SO}_2\text{---}NCl}_2}$$

composition at 195°. It has a characteristic chlorinelike odor. It is slightly soluble in water but dissolves readily in alkali hydroxide and carbonates by virtue of the formation of the alkali salt. It is affected by light and is best preserved in a tight light-resistant container.

The sodium salt, soluble in water, is used to sterilize drinking water.

Saccharin, U.S.P. (Gluside, Benzosulfimide), is the imide of o-sulfobenzoic acid. It is about four hundred times sweeter than cane sugar. It is synthesized according to the reactions shown.

$$CH_3\text{---}C_6H_5 + HO\text{---}SO_2\text{---}Cl \rightarrow o\text{-}CH_3\text{---}C_6H_4\text{---}SO_2\text{---}Cl \xrightarrow{NH_3}$$

$$CH_3\text{---}C_6H_4\text{---}SO_2\text{---}NH_2 \xrightarrow{O_2} C_6H_4 \Big\langle {{\text{COOH}} \atop {\text{SO}_2\text{NH}_2}} \quad \rightarrow$$

$$C_6H_4 \Big\langle {{\text{CO}} \atop {\text{SO}_2}} \Big\rangle NH \xrightarrow{NaOH} C_6H_4 \Big\langle {{\text{CO}} \atop {\text{SO}_2}} \Big\rangle N\text{---}Na$$
$$\text{Saccharin} \qquad\qquad \text{Soluble saccharin}$$

In actual practice the o- and p-Toluenesulfonyl chlorides are obtained simultaneously. The o-isomer is converted into saccharin as indicated; the p-isomer is employed in the synthesis of the chloramines.

Since it does not enter into the metabolic processes of the body it is employed as a sweetening agent in the diet of diabetics.

The structure of the saccharin molecule may not be modified extensively without the loss of its sweet taste. Almost any change other than the introduction of an amino or hydroxyl group into the 6 position causes loss of the sweet taste.[19]

Saccharin Sodium, U.S.P. (Soluble Gluside, Soluble Saccharin), is a white, crystalline powder, soluble in water about 1:1.2 and in alcohol about 1:50. It is about four hundred times as sweet as sugar when tasted in dilute solution. It is used as a sweetening agent in concentrations of about 1:10,000. Tablets of soluble saccharin are used to sweeten the beverages of diabetics and others who must restrict the intake of carbohydrate in the diet.

SULFATE ESTERS

Sodium Lauryl Sulfate, U.S.P. (Duponol), is the product obtained from sulfating long-chain alcohols derived by high-pressure hydrogenation of coconut oil and other fatty glycerides, using copper-chromium oxide as catalyst or by sodium-alcohol reduction and then neutralizing the acid with sodium hydroxide. It consists chiefly of sodium lauryl sulfate, $CH_3—(CH_2)_{10}—CH_2—OSO_3Na$. It is a white or light yellow, crystalline product, readily soluble in water. It is compatible with alkali and soap. It is not affected by dilute acid, calcium, or magnesium ions. For example, 0.1 per cent solutions exhibit detergent properties in the presence of 2500 p.p.m. of calcium. The solution has excellent detergent properties. It is an anionic wetting agent used in soapless shampoos, brushless shaving creams, liquid dentifrices, and in the so-called washable ointment bases which form oil-in-water emulsions. It is also used as a lubricant in tablet manufacture.

Hydroxystearin Sulfate, N.F., prepared by sulfating hydrogenated castor oil, is an unctuous mass, miscible with glycerol, propylene glycol, petrolatum and fixed oils and dispersible in water and alcohol. It is used to form hydrophilic ointments.

Sulfamic Acids

Cyclamate Calcium, N.N.R. (Sucaryl Calcium, Calcium Cyclohexylsulfamate Dihydrate), is the product obtained by sulfonation of cyclohexylamine and the resultant compound treated with calcium hydroxide. It is a white, crystal-

Cyclamate calcium

line, practically odorless powder which is freely soluble in water and insoluble in alcohol.

[19] Finzi and Colonna, *Gazz. chim. ital.*, **68**, 132 (1938).

Cyclamate calcium is about 30 times sweeter than sugar, and as a result it is used as a sweetening agent by individuals on a restricted carbohydrate diet. It is essentially nontoxic but an excessive use of the product may produce a laxative effect.

Cyclamate Sodium, N.N.R. (Sucaryl Sodium, Sodium Cyclohexylsulfamate), is prepared by treating cyclohexylammonium N-cyclohexylsulfamate with sodium hydroxide. It is a white, crystalline powder which is freely soluble in water and insoluble in alcohol. Like the calcium salt, it is a stable, nonnutritive sweetening agent and used by individuals on a restricted carbohydrate diet. Excessive intake may produce laxative effects. The percentage of sodium present is a factor that must be considered when this product is administered to individuals with renal damage complications.

Disulfiram, N.N.R. [Antabuse, Abstinyl, *Bis*(diethylthiocarbamyl) Disulfide], $(CH_3CH_2)_2N-C-S-S-C-N(CH_2CH_3)_2$, originally designed as an

$$(CH_3CH_2)_2N\underset{\underset{S}{\parallel}}{C}-S-S-\underset{\underset{S}{\parallel}}{C}N(CH_2CH_3)_2$$

antioxidant for the rubber industry, has been found to inhibit the *in vivo* oxidation of ethyl alcohol beyond the acetaldehyde stage; the accumulation of acetaldehyde makes the imbiber ill, and, if the administration of the drug is properly controlled, he becomes conditioned against alcoholic beverages.

SULFONAMIDE DERIVATIVES

A most important development in the history of chemotherapy was the discovery of the antibacterial powers of *p*-aminobenzenesulfonamide and its derivatives. This compound is better known as sulfanilamide, a name long recognized in dye chemistry. The great contribution of the "sulfa" drugs to modern medicine may be judged by the amounts produced in the United States alone. United States Tariff Commission figures show that in 1943 production reached the staggering figure of more than 10 million pounds. This maximum was reached before the advent of the antibiotics, but that the sulfas are still important is indicated by the production of 4.67 million pounds in 1953.[20]

It is necessary to understand the system of nomenclature for these compounds. The names of the fundamental radicals and their derivation from the parent compound, sulfanilic acid, may be seen in the accompanying structural formulas.

OH	$NH_2(N^1)$		NH—
$O{\leftarrow}S{\rightarrow}O$	$O{\leftarrow}S{\rightarrow}O$	$O{\leftarrow}S{\rightarrow}O$	$O{\leftarrow}S{\rightarrow}O$
NH_2	$NH_2(N^4)$	NH_2	NH_2
Sulfanilic acid	Sulfanilamide	Sulfanilyl-	Sulfanilamido-

[20] *Encyclopedia of Chemical Technology*, The Interscience Encyclopedia, Inc., New York, Vol. XIII, 1954, p. 281.

The numbering is indicated in the formula for sulfanilamide where the sulfonamide group, being the principal functional group and the one on which the name of the compound is based, occupies the 1 position on the benzene ring. Substituents attached to the amido nitrogen are therefore designated by the prefix N^1, to distinguish from substituents attached to the amino nitrogen, N^4. The compound having the structure, NH_2—⟨ ⟩—SO_2NH—⟨ ⟩—SO_2NH_2, is correctly named N^4-sulfanilylsulfanilamide. Unfortunately, it was named disulfanilamide when originally described in the literature, but should not be confused with true disulfanilamide, $(NH_2$—⟨ ⟩—$SO_2)_2NH$, which has also been made. This latter compound might be called N^1-sulfanilylsulfanilamide. Correct chemical names for additional compounds will be indicated.

It has become a practice to give nonproprietary names to new sulfanilamide derivatives by shortening the prefixes "sulfanilamido-" and "sulfanilyl-" to "sulfa-" and omitting the number which identifies the particular isomer. The nonproprietary names thus often bear a close resemblance to correct chemical nomenclature.

Synthesis. The fundamental intermediate common to all the derivatives of sulfanilamide is N-acetylsulfanilyl chloride:

$$CH_3CONHC_6H_5 + HOSO_2Cl \rightarrow CH_3CONHC_6H_4SO_2Cl$$

1 mole	5 moles	N-Acetylsulfanilyl
Acetanilid	Chlorosulfonic	chloride
	acid	

On treatment with excess ammonia and hydrolysis of the acetyl group with excess mineral acid or base, sulfanilamide is produced, as indicated. By reaction

$$\xrightarrow[NH_3]{\text{excess}} CH_3CONHC_6H_4SO_2NH_2 \xrightarrow[\substack{\text{water} \\ \text{heat}}]{HCl} HCl \cdot NH_2C_6H_4SO_2NH_2$$

N^4-Acetylsulfanilamide   Sulfanilamide hydrochloride

$$\downarrow \substack{NaOH \\ Heat} \qquad\qquad \downarrow NaOH$$

$$NH_2C_6H_4SO_2NHNa \xrightarrow{HCl} NH_2C_6H_4SO_2NH_2$$

Sodium sulfanilamide   Sulfanilamide

of acetylsulfanilyl chloride with almost every conceivable compound having the structure, $HN{\Large\langle}\begin{smallmatrix}R \\ R'\end{smallmatrix}$, where R is a radical and R' is hydrogen or an organic radical, followed by hydrolysis of the acetyl group by the methods described, over a thousand N^1-substituted derivatives of sulfanilamide have been prepared. The choice of base or acid for hydrolysis depends on the nature of the compound. Where the compound has the structure, —SO_2NHR, it forms a very soluble salt with strong bases. Alkaline hydrolysis is then preferred, because many of the derivatives, especially where R is a heterocyclic radical, undergo hydrolytic cleavage by boiling with aqueous mineral acids, giving sulfanilic acid and the aminoheterocycle. On the other hand, if the compound has the struc-

ture $-SO_2N\overset{R}{\underset{R'}{<}}$, or $-SO_2N{=}R_2$, it will not form a salt with bases, and there

is danger, particularly with the second structure, of hydrolysis to sulfanilamide and the oxygen derivative of R. Hydrolysis with dilute hydrochloric acid with formation of the hydrochloride of the N^4-amino group is to be preferred in this case. All N^1-sulfanilamide derivatives may be hydrolyzed to sulfanilic acid by boiling with 60 to 80 per cent sulfuric acid.

For synthesis of especially sensitive N^1-substituted sulfanilamides, p-nitro-benzenesulfonyl chloride may be used and the resulting p-nitrobenzenesulfon-amide may be reduced to the corresponding amino compound by neutral iron reduction. Exposure to the hydrolytic effects of strong acids or bases is thus avoided.

Synthesis of N^4-substituted derivatives of sulfanilamide may start with sulfanilamide itself. Most N^1-substituted sulfanilamides undergo the same reactions. As examples, the amino group may be reacted with acid chlorides or anhydrides to give N^4-acylsulfanilamides; or the amino group may be diazotized and coupled with a wide variety of aromatic hydroxy and amino compounds

giving rise to azo dyes, RN$=$N$-\langle\bigcirc\rangle-SO_2NH_2$. Historically, it was such

an azo dye that led to the discovery of the miraculous properties of the sulfon-amide drugs.

History. Sulfanilamide was first synthesized by Gelmo in 1908. It attracted the attention of Hörlein of the I. G. Farbenindustrie, the great German dye trust, about 1910 as an intermediate for azo dyes. A number of such dyes were made and were found to have superior fastness properties as wool dyes. Later Mietzsch and Klarer synthesized a number of azo dyes which were tested by Gerhard Domagk as bactericides. It was found that mice infected with a virulent strain of β-hemolytic streptococci survived if treated with some of these dyes, but that untreated mice died. This discovery was made in 1932 and, as a result, clinical use of one of the dyes, named Prontosil, was started in Germany about 1934. It was not until late 1935 that the information really reached the scientific world, where it touched off a tremendous amount of research in the field by every large pharmaceutical firm and medical research organization in the world. The news apparently first reached the Pasteur Institute in Paris, where Tréfouël, Mme. Tréfouël, Nitti, and Bovet reasoned that since Prontosil was not active on streptococci in a test tube, although it was highly active *in vivo*, it must be changed or broken down in the body to give an active form. A consideration of the structure showed that reduction of the azo linkage would give sulfanilamide. This was therefore tested and found to be active both *in vivo* and *in vitro*. Later Prontosil was shown definitely to give sulfanilamide in the body. From France the exciting news spread to England, then to America and the rest of the world.

Relationship between Structure and Activity. By the study of more than three thousand sulfanilamides and related derivatives, some important generalizations on the relationship of structure to chemotherapeutic activity may be drawn.

1. The structure necessary to activity is NH_2—⟨benzene⟩—SO_2—, or the sulfanilyl radical.

2. Substitution or replacement of the N^4-amino group by a substituent which cannot be reconverted to free NH_2 by the animal body destroys the activity *in vivo*. Many of the groups that can be changed to amino in the animal body cannot be changed by bacteria, and the derivative is, therefore, inactive *in vitro*. Examples of groups that are more or less readily converted to amino groups in the animal body are RCONH—, RN=N—, R=N—, NO_2—, HONH—, N_3—, CH_3NH—, $(CH_3)_2N$—, $C_6H_5CH_2NH$—,

$$RCHNH—, \text{ and } RCHNH—.$$
$$\underset{SO_3Na}{|} \qquad \underset{SO_2Na}{|}$$

Groups that are not converted to free NH_2 groups in the animal body are ⟨benzene⟩—NH—, long-chain alkylamino groups, certain acylamino groups, and RSO_2NH—.

3. Replacement of the N^4-amino group by such groups as CH_3—, HO—, HO_3S—, HOOC—, Cl—, etc., destroys the activity.

4. Shifting the N^4-amino group to the 2 or 3 position on the ring gives inactive compounds; i.e., derivatives of orthanilamide and metanilamide are inherently inactive, since they are well absorbed into the animal organism but offer no antibacterial action.

5. Introduction of additional groups onto the benzene nucleus destroys the activity or greatly diminishes it.

6. Substitution of the amido, or N^1-nitrogen, by various groups produces wide fluctuation in activity. Substitution by various heterocyclic rings on this position has given compounds of much greater potency than the parent sulfanilamide, and with a more favorable ratio of toxic to therapeutic dose.

7. 4,4'-Diaminodiphenylsulfone having the structure

$$NH_2—⟨\text{benzene}⟩—SO_2—⟨\text{benzene}⟩—NH_2$$

is highly active but is also much more toxic than sulfanilamide. It seems probable that many of its derivatives, formed by substitution of the amino groups, are active by reason of conversion in the body to the parent structure.

Products

The sulfonamide drugs that have been authorized for sale in the United States by the Food and Drug Administration are the following: (These drugs may be sold only on prescription.)

Sulfanilamide, N.F. (*p*-Aminobenzenesulfonamide, Colsulanyde, Prontosil Album, Prontylin, Sanamide, Stramide, Streptal, Streptocide), H_2N—C_6H_4—SO_2NH_2, is a white, odorless, crystalline compound with a slightly sweet taste, melting range 164.5–166.5°, soluble in water 1:125 at 25°, forming a neutral solution. It is very soluble in boiling water, hot alcohol, cold hydrochloric acid, cold dilute sodium hydroxide, and cold acetone. It is insoluble in ether, chloroform, and benzene. It is assayed by solution in hydrochloric acid and diazotization with standard sodium nitrite solution, starch-iodide paste being used to determine the end point. This same method of assay is used for all N^1-substituted sulfanilamides. Diazotization followed by coupling to aromatic amines is used for colorimetric determination of blood levels of the drug and derivatives in therapy.

Sulfanilamide has been very widely used in the following conditions: (1) All β-hemolytic streptococcal infections of the ear, nose, throat, other body organs, and blood stream, e.g., mastoiditis, otitis media, sinusitis, tonsillitis, laryngitis, pharyngitis, meningitis, peritonitis, puerperal sepsis, osteomyelitis, pleurisy, empyema, streptococcal pneumonia, ulcers, and septicemia. (2) Meningococcal infections. (3) Gonococcal infections. (4) Urinary tract infections caused by the above organisms, or by *E. coli*. (5) Skin infections such as impetigo and erysipelas. (6) Trachoma and gonococcal ophthalmia. (7) Lymphogranuloma venereum. (8) Ludwig's angina. (9) Surgical use in preventing infection in surgical incisions, resections, war wounds, etc. For this use the sterile crystalline powder is used.

Sulfanilamide is usually given in the form of tablets. In both mild and severe infections, the usual dose is calculated as 0.1 g. per kg. of body weight per day, divided into six parts and given at intervals of 4 hr., day and night, until the temperature of the patient is normal for 5 days. The drug exhibits a number of toxic reactions such as nausea, dizziness, cyanosis, hemolytic anemia, psychoses, acidosis, fever, and rash. Adequate care by a physician is, therefore, essential in the use of the drug. Sodium bicarbonate is commonly given to counteract acidosis.

It has been found that p-aminobenzoic acid in relatively small amounts overcomes the antibacterial action of sulfanilamide and its derivatives. The administration of local anesthetics derived from this compound, such as procaine, monocaine, etc., therefore, must be avoided.

Sulfapyridine, U.S.P. (N^1-2-Pyridylsulfanilamide), was made by Ewins and

Phillips [21] in England, and its outstanding effect in curing pneumonia was first published by Whitby.[22] The compound had been independently synthesized by several groups in the United States, Russia, and India. It is white, crystalline, odorless, and tasteless; soluble in water 1:3500, in alcohol 1:440, and in acetone 1:65 at 25°. It is freely soluble in dilute mineral acids and aqueous solutions of sodium and potassium hydroxide. It melts between 191° and 193°.

Sulfapyridine was the first drug to have an outstanding curative action on pneumonia. Its use reduced the mortality of this dread disease from about 30 per cent to 10 per cent. In addition, sulfapyridine is a considerably more potent

[21] May and Baker Ltd., British pat. 512,145.
[22] Whitby, *Lancet*, **1**, 1210 (1938).

drug than sulfanilamide in the treatment of streptococcal and gonococcal infections. It is also effective in staphylococcal infections. Its use in this country has been supplanted largely by sulfathiazole and sulfadiazine, because of the lower toxicity of these compounds. Sulfapyridine causes severe nausea in a majority of patients and, in addition to the other toxic symptoms of sulfanilamide, may cause kidney damage varying from mild hematuria to fatal anuria as a result of crystallization of acetylsulfapyridine in the tubules of the kidney.

The usual dose of sulfapyridine in adult pneumonias is 4 g. initially, followed by 1 g. every 4 hr. until the temperature is normal for 72 hr.

Sulfapyridine Sodium, N.F., is a white, odorless, crystalline compound very soluble in water and alcohol, giving highly alkaline solution (pH 11–12) which absorbs carbon dioxide readily with precipitation of sulfapyridine. It is used for intravenous injection, as a 5 per cent solution in sterile water, for critically ill patients requiring an immediate high blood level of the drug. It must not be given intramuscularly or subcutaneously because its high alkalinity will cause tissue damage.

Sulfathiazole, N.F. (N^1-2-Thiazolylsulfanilamide), was synthesized independently by at least 12 different laboratories in the United States, England, Germany, Denmark, Switzerland, Russia, Hungary, and India. The first publication was by Fosbinder and Walter in 1939.

Sulfathiazole is white, crystalline, odorless, and tasteless, soluble in water 1:1700 and in alcohol 1:200 at 25°. It is freely soluble in acetone, dilute mineral acids, or aqueous sodium hydroxide. It melts between 200° and 203°.

Sulfathiazole is more potent than sulfapyridine in streptococcal, staphylococcal, pneumococcal, and gonococcal infections and has the decided advantage of causing less nausea, dizziness, and cyanosis. However, drug fever occurs in about 10 per cent of patients and rash in about 5 per cent. Hematuria occurs in 2.5 per cent of patients as compared to 8 per cent with sulfapyridine. It has been supplanted for many uses by the less toxic sulfadiazine. The oral dosage is the same as for sulfapyridine.

Sulfathiazole Sodium, N.F., is a white, odorless, crystalline compound readily soluble in water or alcohol, giving highly alkaline solutions (pH 9.5–10.5), which absorb carbon dioxide readily with precipitation of sulfathiazole.

Sulfadiazine, U.S.P. (2-Sulfanilamidopyrimidine, 2-Sulfanilamido-1,3-diazine, N^1-2-Pyrimidylsulfanilamide), was first described by Roblin, Williams, Winnek, and English in 1940, but was independently synthesized by at least five other laboratories. It occurs as a white, odorless, tasteless, crystalline powder, soluble in water 1:8100 at 37°, sparingly soluble in alcohol and acetone. It is readily soluble in dilute mineral acids and in moderately strong bases, including aqueous ammonia. The melting range is 252–256°.

Sulfadiazine has about the same potency against susceptible organisms as sulfathiazole. However, it exhibits fewer toxic reactions than any other of the sulfa drugs and as a result is most generally useful. Nausea, dizziness, cyanosis, acidosis, fever, and rash are rarely observed. Hematuria occurs in about 1 per cent of the cases, and anuria has also been reported but is less common than with sulfathiazole. Kidney complications can be avoided by giving sufficient sodium bicarbonate to maintain slight alkalinity in the urine.

Sulfadiazine is now recognized as the drug of choice in the treatment of most types of infection for which the sulfonamide drugs are indicated, with the possible exception of certain staphylococcal infections where sulfathiazole has slightly greater potency. Sulfadiazine was highly important in war medicine where it was given prophylactically by mouth, to supplement the effect of sulfanilamide applied locally, in prevention of infections in wounded personnel. Sulfadiazine is also incorporated in ointment bases for local application.

Sulfadiazine Sodium, U.S.P., is an anhydrous, white, odorless, crystalline powder readily soluble in water and alcohol, giving strongly alkaline solutions (pH 9–10), which tend to absorb carbon dioxide with precipitation of sulfadiazine. Its uses are the same as the sodium salts of sulfapyridine and sulfathiazole.

Sulfamerazine, U.S.P. [2-Sulfanilamido-4-methylpyrimidine, N^1-(4-Methyl-2-pyrimidyl)sulfanilamide], melting range 235–238°, is similar in its physical,

chemical, and therapeutic properties to sulfadiazine but is more slowly excreted; hence a given blood level of the drug may be maintained through a smaller or less frequent dosage. This advantage is offset by a somewhat higher incidence of toxic reactions, however.

Sulfamerazine Sodium, U.S.P., has properties similar to sulfadiazine sodium.

Sulfamethazine, U.S.P. [2-Sulfanilamido-4,6-dimethylpyrimidine, N^1-(4,6-Dimethyl-2-pyrimidyl)sulfanilamide, Sulfamethazine] may be synthesized by a novel route, using sulfaguanidine as an intermediate. Although sulfamethazine

$$H_2N-\underset{\text{Sulfaguanidine}}{\bigcirc}-SO_2NH-\overset{\overset{\text{NH}}{\|}}{\underset{\underset{\text{NH}_2}{|}}{C}} + \underset{\text{2,4-Pentandione}}{\overset{\overset{\text{COCH}_3}{|}}{\underset{\underset{\text{COCH}_3}{|}}{CH_2}}} \xrightarrow{-2H_2O}$$

$$H_2N-\bigcirc-SO_2NH-\overset{N—CCH_3}{\underset{N=CCH_3}{C \quad CH}}$$

Sulfamethazine

appears to be handled unpredictably by the human body and has not found favor in this country in human medicine, it is so well absorbed and slowly excreted by domestic animals and poultry that it appears to be the most generally useful drug in the veterinary field where low cost of treatment through small and infrequent dosage is an important advantage. It is used extensively in combination sulfa therapy.

Sulfapyrazine, N.N.R. (2-Sulfanilamidopyrazine, 2-Sulfanilamido-1,4-diazine, N^1-2-Pyrazylsulfanilamide), melting range 250–254° with decomposition,

$$NH_2-\bigcirc-SO_2NH-C\underset{HC}{\overset{N}{\diagup}}\underset{N}{\overset{CH}{\diagdown}}CH$$

is similar to sulfadiazine in physical, chemical, and therapeutic properties, but it is even less soluble in water and may cause a higher incidence of kidney damage. Other toxic reactions are as low or lower than those exhibited by sulfadiazine, but this may be because toxic blood levels of the drug are difficult to reach except by intravenous injection of the sodium salt. Problems of commercial synthesis have prevented extensive use of the drug.

Sulfapyrazine Sodium, N.N.R., occurs as the monohydrate; it has uses similar to sulfadiazine sodium.

Sulfaguanidine, N.F. (Sulfanilylguanidine Monohydrate), is a white, odorless, crystalline powder soluble in water 1:450 at 37° and 1:10 at 100°. It is less soluble in hot alcohol and acetone and insoluble in benzene, ether, and chloroform. Sulfaguanidine is readily soluble in cold mineral acids but insoluble in cold dilute bases. Hot, strongly alkaline solutions decompose the compound to sulfanilamide with the evolution of ammonia.

$$H_2N-\bigcirc-SO_2NH-\overset{\overset{\text{NH}}{\|}}{C}-NH_2 \cdot H_2O$$

Sulfaguanidine is unique among sulfanilamide derivatives in that large quantities may be given by mouth without the development of high blood levels and consequent toxic reactions. This was considered an advantage in the treatment of intestinal diseases where high concentration in the intestinal contents is necessary to inhibit bacteria. The drug was used in large quantities by the armed forces of World War II for the treatment of bacillary dysentery. Sulfadiazine is now thought superior for this use because it maintains an adequate concentration of drug in the intestinal wall as well as in the intestinal contents.

Sulfaguanidine has been used extensively in veterinary medicine, especially for treatment of coccidiosis in chickens.

Sulfisoxazole, U.S.P. (N^1-3,4-Dimethyl-5-isoxazolylsulfanilamide, 5-Sulfanilamido-3,4-dimethylisoxazole, Gantrisin), is an antibacterial agent that some evidence indicates is the drug of choice against proteus infection. The product is prepared by reacting p-acetamidobenzenesulfonyl chloride with 3,4-dimethyl-5-aminoisoxazole, and then deacetylizing the resultant product. It is a white, odorless, tasteless, crystalline powder which melts at 192–195°. It is more soluble in water than sulfanilamide, and solutions are acid to litmus. At pH 5–7 the solubility is so high in body fluids that neither the product nor its acetyl derivative is likely to produce crystalluria and renal blocking in concentrations at which other sulfonamides employed singly do.

It possesses the action, uses, and toxic manifestations of other sulfonamide derivatives.

Sulfisoxazole, R = H—
Acetylsulfisoxazole, R = CH₃CO—

Acetylsulfisoxazole, N.N.R., shares the properties and uses of sulfisoxazole, the acetyl group being removed in the intestine.

Sulfisoxazole Diethanolamine, N.N.R. (2,2′-Iminodiethanol salt of N^1-3,4-dimethyl-5-isoxazolylsulfanilamide, Gantrisin Diethanolamine), is the product obtained by adding enough diethanolamine to a solution of sulfisoxazole to bring the pH of the solution to about 7.5. This salt is more soluble at the physiological pH range of 6.0 to 7.5 than is Gantrisin.

The product is administered by intravenous, intramuscular, or subcutaneous injection to obtain blood levels that cannot be attained by oral administration. It is also used in 4 per cent solution in the form of eye drops for topical treatment of susceptible infections.

Succinylsulfathiazole, U.S.P. [Sulfasuxidine, p-(2-Thiazolylsulfamyl)succinanilic Acid Monohydrate, 2-(N^4-Succinylsulfanilamido)thiazole Monohydrate], is for use in intestinal infections, where its low absorption from the intestine into the blood stream is advantageous. Probably the compound is slowly cleaved to sulfathiazole as the active form, since it is inactive *in vitro*.

$$\text{HC} \diagup{\text{S}}\diagdown \text{C—NH—SO}_2$$

NHCOCH$_2$CH$_2$COOH · H$_2$O

Phthalylsulfathiazole, U.S.P. [Sulfathalidine, p-(2-Thiazolylsulfamyl)-phthalanilic Acid, 2-(N^4-Phthalylsulfanilamido)thiazole], has properties similar

to succinylsulfathiazole and is claimed to be somewhat more potent. Its use has been restricted to veterinary medicine.

Sulfacetamide, U.S.P. (Sulfacet, Sulamyd, Albucid, Region, N^1-Acetyl-sulfanilamide, N-Sulfanilylacetamide), is a white, crystalline powder, soluble in water 1:62.5 at 37°, very soluble in hot water and alcohol; the aqueous solution is acid. It melts between 182° and 185°. Sulfacetamide has been used largely for treatment of gonorrhea and other urinary-tract infections, where its high solubility and ready elimination permit high urinary concentrations to be maintained without danger of kidney complications. Sulfacetamide forms a very soluble, neutral sodium salt which has the advantage of lacking the caustic properties of the more active sodium salts of sulfathiazole and sulfadiazine.

$$\text{H}_2\text{N—}\bigcirc\text{—SO}_2\text{NHCOCH}_3$$

Sodium Sulfacetamide, U.S.P. (Sulamyd Sodium), is the monohydrated sodium salt of N-sulfanilylacetamide. It is a white, odorless, bitter, crystalline powder which is soluble in 2.5 parts of water. It is highly soluble at the physiological pH of 7.4. Aqueous solutions must be refrigerated and protected from light to avoid deterioration.

It is very useful because of its high solubility for repeated topical application of ophthalmic infections responding to sulfonamide therapy. It is usually employed for this purpose in a 30 per cent aqueous solution or 10 per cent ointment.

Prontosil [Prontosil Flavum, Streptozon, p-(2,4-Diaminophenylazo)benzenesulfonamide Hydrochloride] was the first sulfanilamide derivative to be used clinically. It is a red, crystalline powder, soluble in water 1:400. This compound has no apparent advantages over sulfanilamide, to which it is cleaved in the animal body.

$$HCl \cdot H_2N\text{—}\langle\quad\rangle\text{—}N{=}N\text{—}\langle\quad\rangle\text{—}SO_2NH_2$$
$$\overset{|}{NH_2}$$

Azosulfamide [Neoprontosil, Prontosil S, Streptozon S, Disodium 2-(4′-sulfamylphenylazo)-7-acetamido-1-hydroxynaphthalene-3,6-disulfonate] is much more soluble than Prontosil. It is used for intravenous injections but has largely been supplanted by newer derivatives.

$$CH_3CONH\text{—}\overset{OH}{\underset{NaO_3S}{\bigcirc\bigcirc}}\text{—}N{=}N\text{—}\langle\quad\rangle\text{—}SO_2NH_2$$
$$SO_3Na$$

Other sulfonamide drugs that have been sold outside of the United States are:
Irgafen [N^1-(3,4-Dimethylbenzoyl)sulfanilamide, N-Sulfanilyl-3,4-Dimethylbenzamide, N-Sulfanilyl-3,4-xylamide] has been studied clinically in Europe

$$NH_2\text{—}\langle\quad\rangle\text{—}SO_2NHCO\text{—}\langle\quad\rangle\overset{CH_3}{\underset{CH_3}{<}}$$

where it is claimed to have potency against organisms susceptible to other sulfa drugs and to be so slowly excreted that comparatively small doses are sufficient to maintain effective blood concentrations.

Sulfamethylthiazole (4-Methyl-2-Sulfanilamidothiazole, N^1-4-Methyl-2-thiazolylsulfanilamide) was tried clinically and appeared to be somewhat more active than sulfathiazole; however, about 2 per cent of patients developed peripheral neuritis, so that further use was discontinued in this country.

$$\overset{\displaystyle S}{HC\diagup\quad\diagdown C}\text{—}NHSO_2\text{—}\langle\quad\rangle\text{—}NH_2$$
$$CH_3\text{—}C\text{——}N$$

Sulfaethylthiadiazole [5-Ethyl-2-sulfanilamido-1,3,4-thiadiazole, N^1-(5-Ethyl-1,3,4-thiadiazol-2-yl)sulfanilamide, Globucid] has been investigated in

$$NH_2\langle\quad\rangle\text{—}SO_2NH\text{—}\overset{\displaystyle S}{\underset{N\text{——}N}{\diagup\quad\diagdown}}\text{—}C_2H_5$$

Europe and appears slightly less active than sulfathiazole. Insufficient case histories have been reported to compare the incidence of toxic reactions with the sulfa drugs in common use. The corresponding drugs with hydrogen or methyl groups in the 5 position have also been investigated clinically but are so rapidly excreted that they are impractical to administer. Substitution of higher alkyl groups appeared to reduce the antibacterial activity.

Marfanil (*p*-Aminomethylbenzenesulfonamide Hydrochloride, Homosulfanilamide, Sulfamylon) was used during World War II by the German Army for

$$\text{HCl}\cdot\text{NH}_2\text{CH}_2\text{—}\underset{}{\bigcirc}\text{—SO}_2\text{NH}_2$$

prophylaxis of wounds, as a dusting powder usually mixed with sulfanilamide or sulfathiazole. The drug is specific for anaerobic organisms such as cause tetanus and gas gangrene. It is not effective when taken by mouth and differs from sulfa drugs in its mechanism of action by not being antagonized by *p*-aminobenzoic acid.

Disulon (Diseptal C, N^4-Sulfanilylsulfanilamide) is much less soluble than sulfanilamide. Conflicting opinions on its effectiveness are found in the literature. Cases of peripheral neuritis are reported following its use.

$$\text{NH}_2\text{—}\underset{}{\bigcirc}\text{—SO}_2\text{NH—}\underset{}{\bigcirc}\text{—SO}_2\text{NH}_2$$

Uleron (Uliron, Diseptal A, N^1-N^1-Dimethyl-N^4-sulfanilylsulfanilamide) was used extensively in Europe for treatment of gonorrhea but caused a high incidence of peripheral neuritis and has been superseded by more recent drugs.

$$\text{NH}_2\text{—}\underset{}{\bigcirc}\text{—SO}_2\text{NH—}\underset{}{\bigcirc}\text{—SO}_2\text{N(CH}_3)_2$$

N^4-Benzylsulfanilamide (Proseptazine, Septazine, Setazine, M. & B. 125) was one of the early sulfanilamide derivatives, used chiefly in England. It owes its activity to slow cleavage to sulfanilamide.

$$\text{H}_2\text{NO}_2\text{S—}\underset{}{\bigcirc}\text{—NHCH}_2\text{—}\underset{}{\bigcirc}$$

Rubiazol [3,5-Diamino-2-(4-sulfamylphenylazo)benzoic Acid] is a French version of Prontosil and, like the other azo dyes, owes its activity to cleavage to sulfanilamide. It is said to be more toxic than azosulfamide.

$$\text{NH}_2\text{—}\underset{\underset{\text{COOH}}{|}}{\overset{\overset{\text{NH}_2}{|}}{\bigcirc}}\text{—N}=\text{N—}\underset{}{\bigcirc}\text{—SO}_2\text{NH}_2$$

Rodilone [1399 F, *bis*(4-Acetamidophenyl)-sulfone] has been used in France. It is claimed to be less toxic than *bis*(4-aminophenyl)-sulfone but probably owes its activity to hydrolysis to the parent compound.

$$CH_3CONH-\langle\bigcirc\rangle-SO_2-\langle\bigcirc\rangle-NHCOCH_3$$

Promizole (2-Amino-5-sulfanilylthiazole) is a heterocyclic isostere of *bis*(4-

$$NH_2-\langle\bigcirc\rangle-SO_2-\langle\text{thiazole}\rangle-NH_2$$

aminophenyl)-sulfone. It has been used experimentally in tuberculosis and leprosy.

Glucosulfone Sodium, N.N.R. (Promin, Sodium 4,4'-diaminodiphenylsulfone-N,N'-didextrose Sulfonate), has been used clinically in the treatment of tuberculosis, but the possible benefits of the treatment are not conclusive. It is sold for treatment of leprosy.

Sulfoxone Sodium, U.S.P. (Diasone Sodium, Disodium[(sulfonyldi-*p*-phenylene)diimino]-dimethanesulfonate), is a derivative of *bis*(4-aminophenyl)-sul-

$$NaO_2SCH_2NH-\langle\bigcirc\rangle-SO_2-\langle\bigcirc\rangle-NHCH_2SO_2Na\cdot4H_2O$$

fone which probably owes its activity to breakdown in the body to the parent compound. It has been studied for use in tuberculosis and leprosy.

N-(2-Thiazolyl)-phenolsulfonamide (Phenosulfazole, Darvisul) has been employed with success in the treatment of mice against experimentally induced infection with western equine encephalomyelitis virus. It produced three types of results: it cured the animals in the early stages of the disease; the mice that survived were immune to reinfection; and when the drug was given in a single oral dose it prevented infection. It is effective in a mouse against as many as 100 times the lethal dose of poliomyelitis virus when given 24 hr. after administration of the virus.[23]

Mechanism of Action. The most satisfactory explanation for the action of the sulfonamide drugs, and the one best fitting the known facts, was the theory developed by Woods, Fildes, McIlwain, and others. *p*-Aminobenzoic acid has been found to be an essential growth factor for most of the bacteria susceptible to the sulfonamide drugs. According to theory, structurally similar sulfanilamide (and its N^1-derivatives) substitute for *p*-aminobenzoic acid in the metabolism of the bacteria but cause bacteriostatis because they do not fulfill the requirements of the bacteria for growth and reproduction. Once rapid growth of bacteria is stopped, the normal defense mechanisms of the host can mobilize and cope with the infection. This theory explains the antagonistic effects of small amounts of

[23] *Chem. Eng. News,* **26,** 2710 (1948).

p-aminobenzoic acid on the action of sulfanilamide drugs, since, if p-aminobenzoic acid is present in sufficient amounts, the bacteria can obtain their requirements and continue growth.

The theory has been applied by the synthesis of many compounds analogous to known metabolites, e.g., 3-sulfamylpyridine which causes inhibition of the

growth of bacteria requiring nicotinic acid as essential growth substance. How-

ever, it is now believed that the sulfonamides affect bacterial oxidation-reduction systems in some manner.

Mixed Sulfonamide Therapy. Although the sulfa drugs have declined somewhat in extent of usage through replacement by the antibiotics, they have become indispensable in modern therapeutics. Their use has been extended through the development of the concept of mixed sulfonamide therapy. The basic principle underlying this concept, which has been demonstrated *in vitro* and by clinical studies, is that two or more sulfonamides, when present simultaneously in the urine, have little or no influence on each other with respect to their individual solubilities.[24, 25, 26, 27, 28, 29] For example, a sample of urine already saturated with sulfathiazole will still dissolve the normal quantity of sulfadiazine and then will further dissolve a normal quantity of sulfamerazine. This is illustrated by Lehr's total solubility data for sulfonamides and sulfonamide mixtures in water at 20°

Sulfadiazine	7.3 mg. per 100 cc.
Sulfamerazine	20.2 mg. per 100 cc.
Sulfathiazole	34.4 mg. per 100 cc.
Sulfadiazine plus sulfamerazine	25.6 mg. per 100 cc.
Sulfadiazine plus sulfathiazole	38.3 mg. per 100 cc.
Sulfamerazine plus sulfathiazole	50.7 mg. per 100 cc.

The chief clinical advantage of this development is the practical elimination of the danger of intrarenal precipitation of the sulfonamides at normal total dosage levels. Under mixed sulfonamide therapy the danger of intrarenal precipitation is only as great as if each compound were administered alone, and in the partial dosage contained in the mixture.

[24] Lehr, *Proc. Soc. Exptl. Biol. Med.*, **58**, 11 (1945).

[25] Lehr, *J. Urol.*, **55**, 548 (1946).

[26] Lehr, Slobody, and Greenberg, *J. Pediat.*, **29**, 275 (1946).

[27] Lehr, *Proc. Soc. Exptl. Biol. & Med.*, **64**, 393 (1947).

[28] Flippin and Reinhold, *Ann. Int. Med.*, **25**, 433 (1946).

[29] Frisk, Hagerman, Helander, and Sjogren, *Brit. Med. J.*, **1**, 7 (1947)

Clinical studies in which the use of adjuvant alkali therapy was intentionally omitted have demonstrated the value of mixed sulfonamides by the absence of renal complications and the low incidence of only mild crystalluria. Exceptionally high doses were used in certain cases without untoward effect. In routine therapy the use of mixed sulfonamides, accompanied by alkalization of the urine and maintenance of adequate fluid intake, reduces the danger of renal precipitation to a minimum.

The various combinations include sulfadiazine-sulfamerazine, sulfadiazine-sulfathiazole, and sulfadiazine-sulfamerazine-sulfathiazole, in the form of tablets and also as microcrystalline suspensions.

Hypoglycemic Action. It was observed as long ago as 1941 that a variety of sulfonamides produced hypoglycemia in experimental animals. In 1955, Franke and Fuchs [30] reported that in many patients the symptoms of diabetes may be controlled by the oral administration of 1-butyl-3-sulfanilylurea, CH_3-$CH_2CH_2CH_2NHCONHSO_2C_6H_4NH_2$, Carbutamide, also designated as BZ 55. Bertram, Bendfeldt, and Otto,[31] reported equally encouraging results with 1-butyl-3-toluenesulfonylurea, $C_4H_9NHCONHSO_2C_6H_4CH_3$-$p$, also known as Orinase. These experimental results have been repeated, and the outlook is encouraging for oral replacement therapy for insulin, at least for the milder cases of diabetes.[32]

Caronamide (4′-Carboxyphenylmethanesulfonanilide, Staticin) is one of a

Caronamide

large number of compounds synthesized and examined for reversible inhibition of the renal excretion of penicillin. It is prepared by allowing phenylmethanesulfonyl chloride to react with p-aminobenzoic acid. Experiments in dogs receiving penicillin show that administration of this compound, orally or parenterally or by stomach tube, causes an increase in the penicillin concentration in the plasma and a delay in its excretion by the kindeys.

Probenecid [p-(Di-n-propylsulfamyl)-benzoic Acid], p-HOOC–$C_6H_4SO_2N$-$(CH_2CH_2CH_3)_2$, decreases metabolism and elimination of such useful and active compounds as p-aminosalicylic acid and p-aminobenzoic acid by inhibiting their conjugation with glycine.

[30] *Deut. med. Wochschr.*, **80**, 1449 (1955).

[31] *Ibid.*, 1455.

[32] Mirsky, Diengott, and Dolger, *Science*, **123**, 583 (1956); Miller and Dulin, *ibid.*, 584; Kinsell, Brown, Friskey, and Michaels, *ibid.*, 585.

Compounds of Phosphorus, Arsenic, and Antimony

Reference to the periodic table of the elements will show that directly under nitrogen, Group V, come phosphorus, arsenic, and antimony. These elements form compounds analogous to the nitrogen compounds. For example, analogous to ammonia there are found and known phosphine, PH_3, arsine, AsH_3, and stibine, SbH_3. As there are known organic substituted ammonias (amines) there are also known organic substituted phosphines, arsines, and stibines. There is considerable parallelism in these series of compounds. Analogous to the nitro compounds are found the phosphonic acids, arsonic acids, and stibonic acids.

$R\!-\!P\!\rightarrow\!O$ with OH, OH	$P\!\rightarrow\!O$ with R, R, OH	$Ar\!-\!As\!\rightarrow\!O$ with OH, OH	$Ar\!-\!Sb\!\rightarrow\!O$ with OH, OH
Monoalkyl-phosphonic acid	Dialkyl-phosphonic acid	Monoaryl-arsonic acid	Monoaryl-stibonic acid

The analogy of these compounds to the nitro compounds is better seen if one assumes that in the series the nitro group exists in a hydrated form. Further

analogies will appear in the individual compounds to be discussed.

PHOSPHORUS COMPOUNDS

Esters of Phosphoric Acid

The role of phosphorus in the biochemistry of man and animals is one of extraordinary importance. It has long been known that phosphorus in the form of phosphoric acid is present in phospholipids and phosphoproteins. Such biologically important compounds as lecithin and nuclein are regarded as complex organic phosphate esters. Today, phosphorus is known to play an essential function in many metabolic transformations involving a number of enzyme systems. The biochemistry of phosphorus is a field unto itself. Suffice it to say here that organic phosphorus esters are concerned with carbohydrate metabolism, fatty acid oxidation, and a host of other enzymatic physiological processes. Phosphates provide the energy-rich bonds in compounds such as adenosine triphosphate (ATP) and phosphocreatine, the sources of immediate energy for muscle contraction. Phosphoric acid is an important component of the nucleic acids.

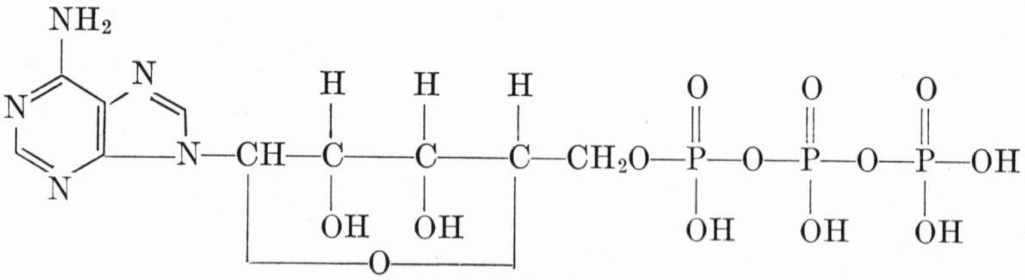

Adenosine triphosphate

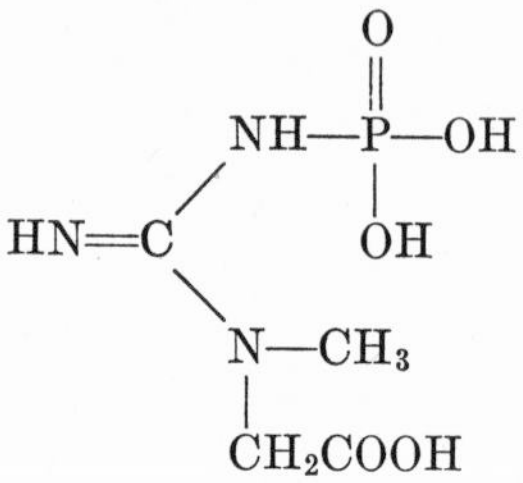

Phosphocreatine

Other esters of phosphoric acid are extremely important in biological processes. In phospholipids two hydroxyls of phosphoric acid are esterified, one with glycerol and the other with an amino alcohol, examples of which are shown. Hydrolysis

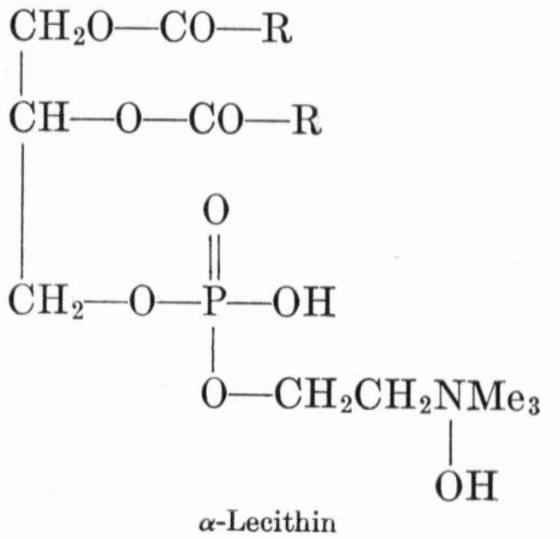

α-Lecithin

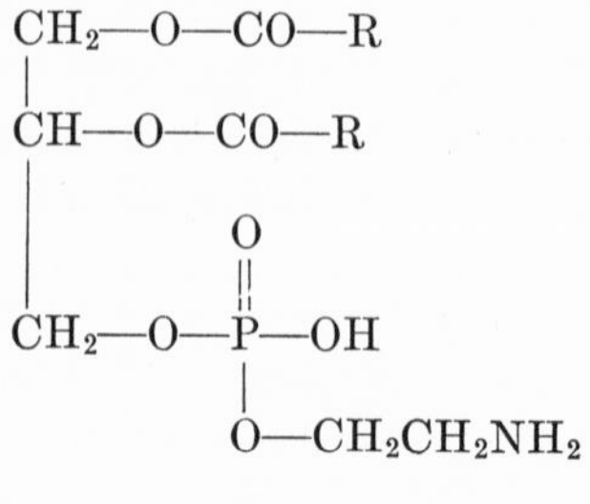

Cephalin

$$\begin{array}{l} CH_2-O-COR \\ | \\ CH-O-CO-R \\ | \\ O \\ || \\ CH_2-O-P-OH \\ | \\ O-C_{17}H_{32}(OH)NH_2 \end{array}$$

Sphingomyelin

$$\begin{array}{l} CH_2-O-CO-R \\ | OH \\ | / \\ CH-O-P-O-CH_2CH_2NMe_3 \\ | \backslash\backslash \\ | O OH \\ CH_2-O-CO-R \end{array}$$

β-Lecithin

of the lecithins yields one molecule of glycerol, two molecules of fatty acid, one molecule of phosphoric acid, and one molecule of choline. Cephalin is an analogous compound, but instead of choline it forms ethanolamine on hydrolysis. The amino alcohol in sphingomyelin is sphingosin, a dihydroxyamine. A compound analogous to the phospholipids is also present in plants as the calcium salt, the metal taking the place of the alkanolamine; these compounds are salts of phosphatidic acid.

The phosphoric ester of riboflavin coupled with a specific protein is know as *yellow enzyme*. The diphosphoric ester of thiamin (vitamin B_1) is a heat-stable coenzyme know as *cocarboxylase*. In the phosphoproteins, of which casein is a good example, the phosphorus is present as an ester of phosphoric acid.

It was assumed that lecithin splits into glycerophosphates in the intestine and that the administration of the cheaper synthetic glycerophosphates, such as the calcium salts, might accomplish the same results. It has been shown that the glycerophosphates are not well metabolized, and there is little evidence to justify their use. If glycerol is heated with phosphoric acid, it is possible on prolonged heating to obtain the glyceryl orthophosphate. Shorter periods of heating produce less loss of water.

$$\begin{array}{l} CH_2OH \\ | \\ CHOH + H_3PO_4 \xrightarrow{-3HOH} \\ | \\ CH_2OH \end{array} \qquad \begin{array}{l} CH_2-O \\ | \backslash \\ CH-O-P=O \\ | / \\ CH_2-O \end{array}$$

Glyceryl orthophosphate

Tetraethyl Pyrophosphate (TEPP) and **Hexaethyl Tetraphosphate** [1] are newly developed insecticides, useful for the control of pests not affected by DDT. Laboratory tests show that they are active against aphids and mites. Bladan, a mixture of 60 per cent hexaethyl tetraphosphate, 20 per cent toluene, and 20 per cent emulsifier, is useful for the control of aphis on cabbage.[2]

Alteration of the simple phosphoric acid ester by one of several methods produces very powerfully active compounds. Thus, Saunders [3] has shown that replacement by fluorine of one of the alkoxy groups in a trialkyl phosphate produces a series of compounds having profound physiological effects. These

[1] *Chem. Eng. News*, **24**, 1954 (1946).

[2] Bronson and Hall, *Agr. Chemicals*, **1**, 19 (1946); *C.A.*, **41**, 2692 (1947).

[3] Saunders, *Chemistry & Industry*, **1947**, 117.

dialkyl fluorophosphates were found to be potent cholinesterase inhibitors; that is, they prevent the hydrolysis of acetylcholine by enzyme action. Of the various esters diisopropyl fluorophosphate or DFP was found to be the most active compound tested.

Although the dialkyl fluorophosphates have assumed considerable importance as pharmacological tools, their therapeutic possibilities have been disappointing. Because of a low therapeutic index, the compounds are considered too dangerous for medicinal purposes. It was early thought that herein might lie the cure for myasthenia gravis. However, the low activity of diisopropyl fluorophosphate against this malady indicated a more complex causative factor involved than cholinesterase.

Other structural variations in the alkyl phosphates have resulted in a lowering of toxicity but with an accompanying loss of activity.

Isoflurophate, U.S.P., Diisopropyl Fluorophosphate, DFP, $[(CH_3)_2CHO]_2$-$P(O)F$, is an extremely toxic liquid which on exposure to moisture forms hydrogen fluoride. It is a potent miotic and has had its principal use as a pharmacological tool for the inhibition of cholinesterase. It is characterized as an ophthalmic parasympathomimetic. Its synthesis [4] is indicated.

$$2(CH_3)_2CHOH \xrightarrow[Cl_2]{PCl_3} [(CH_3)_2CHO]_2P(O)Cl \xrightarrow{NaF} [(CH_3)_2CHO]_2P(O)F$$

Other variations of the basic alkyl phosphate structure have resulted in products of considerably greater economic importance. Organic phosphorus insecticides and ascaricides have achieved well-deserved recognition in the fields of agriculture and public health as well as some promise as medicinal agents. They may be divided into three classes, alkyl pyrophosphates, alkyl thiophosphates, and the phosphoramides.

The alkyl pyrophosphates are partial phosphoric anhydrides and are best exemplified by:

Tetraethyl Pyrophosphate (TEPP) is the most active component of a mixture of organic phosphates known as hexaethyl tetraphosphate. The latter mixture is prepared by adding phosphorus pentoxide to triethyl phosphate.

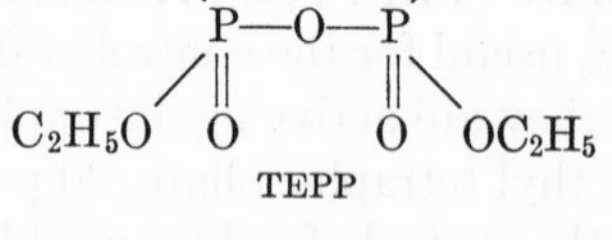

TEPP

Tri-o-tolyl phosphate, commerically used in plasticizers and in motor fuels as an anti-knock (TCP), has inadvertently figured in poisoning of humans.[5] Such triaryl esters exhibit little *in vitro* antiesterase activity; it appears that in animal tissue they are converted into very active inhibitors.[6]

[4] Hardy and Kosolapoff, U. S. pat. 2,409,039, Oct. 8, 1946; *C.A.*, **41**, 1233 (1947).

[5] Weber, *Med. Bull. Veterans Admin.*, **13**, 228 (1937); *C.A.*, **31**, 2287 (1937).

[6] Myers, Rebel, *et al.*, *Nature*, **176**, 259 (1955).

Parathion, diethyl p-nitrophenyl thiophosphate, whose synthesis is indicated, is an important ester of thiophosphoric acid.[7]

$$PCl_3 + S \rightarrow PSCl_3 \xrightarrow{C_2H_5OH} (C_2H_5O)_2PSCl$$

Parathion

The high insecticidal activity of Parathion coupled with its greater stability over the pyrophosphates has made for the widespread popularity of this compound as an agricultural insecticide throughout the world. Its effectiveness has stimulated the search for analogous alkyl thiophosphates having lower mammalian toxicity while maintaining high insecticidal activity.[8]

The phosphoramides constitute a group of organophosphorus insecticides. They are first absorbed by the plants on which they are sprayed. The plants are then rendered toxic to the insects that attack them. For this reason, the phosphoramides are considered *systemic* insecticides and are limited to applications to nonedible vegetation.

Octamethyl Pyrophosphoramide (OMPA) has been accepted as an agricultural insecticide with these limitations.

OMPA

Interestingly, the pyrophosphates and thiophosphates are active inhibitors of cholinesterase *in vivo* as well as *in vitro*, whereas the phosphoramides exert their effects mainly on peripheral tissue without marked stimulatory action on the central nervous system. Thus, octamethyl pyrophosphoramide exhibits no appreciable anticholinesterase activity *in vitro* but is converted by plants as well as the mammalian liver into a strong cholinesterase inhibitor.

The organic phosphorus insecticides have had consideration as therapeutic agents against myasthenia gravis. The exact nature of this disease, which is characterized by a weakness of skeletal muscles, is unknown, but it has been demonstrated that increasing the concentration of acetylcholine in the tissues by administration of cholinesterase inhibitors relieves the symptoms. Rider and his co-workers [9] have had encouraging results with OMPA in the treatment of myasthenia gravis.

[7] Fletcher *et al.*, *J. Am. Chem. Soc.*, **70**, 2943 (1948).
[8] Du Bois, *Bull. Am. Soc. Hosp. Pharm.*, **9**, 168 (1952).
[9] Rider, Schulman, Richter, Moeller, and Du Bois, *J. Am. Med. Assoc.*, **145**, 967 (1951).

All the organophosphorus insecticides have one important physiological action in common. All of them are anticholinesterases *in vivo* and thus produce symptoms similar to those resulting from excessive stimulation of the parasympathetic nervous system. Attempts have been made to relate insecticidal activity to the capacity for inhibiting cholinesterase.[10] Indeed, Du Bois and Coon [11] have tabulated data comparing *in vitro* toxicities and molar concentrations for 50 per cent inhibition of cholinesterase for the alkyl pyrophosphates, thiophosphates, and phosphoramides. Although these data show excellent correlation for these activities, there are sufficient other factors that must be considered before deciding that cholinesterase inhibition is the sole mechanism of action of the organic phosphorus insecticides.[12]

Organic phosphorus compounds in which the phosphorus atom is directly linked to a carbon atom as is the nitrogen atom in a nitro compound have not found significant therapeutic usage. Some aromatic phosphines have been investigated for use as toxic war gases. Isolated reports have indicated an antibacterial activity of phosphorus analogs of the *p*-aminodiphenylsulfones and the sulfonamide drugs. Bauer and Rosenthal of the National Institute of Health report that an organic phosphorus compound of the accompanying structure has a high antistreptococcal activity in mice. There is considerable evidence that

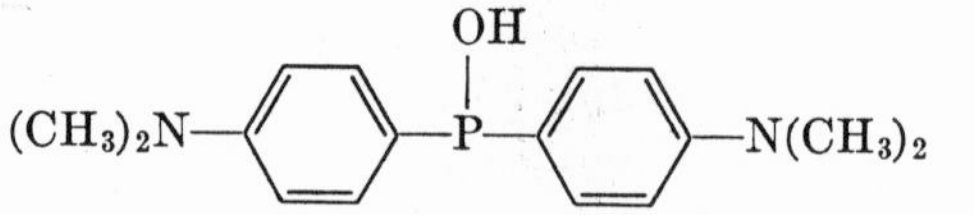

$$(CH_3)_2N-\!\!\!\bigcirc\!\!\!-\overset{\overset{\displaystyle OH}{|}}{P}-\!\!\!\bigcirc\!\!\!-N(CH_3)_2$$

bis-(4-Dimethylaminobenzene)phosphinous acid

Phosphanilic Acid, *p*-aminobenzenephosphonic acid, possesses chemotherapeutic properties similar to the sulfa drugs and acts on bacteria by antagonizing *p*-aminobenzoic acid.[13] An analogous compound in which the phosphorus is trivalent, *p-aminobenzenephosphonous acid*, is only slightly less active than sulfanilamide against *E. coli*, and it is antagonized by *p*-aminobenzoic acid in concentrations about equal to those which inactivate sulfanilamide.[14]

Preliminary results [15] have indicated several **phosphanilamide** derivatives to be superior to phosphanilic acid in antibacterial properties *in vitro*.

ARSENIC COMPOUNDS

Inorganic arsenic compounds have been known since ancient times. Early use was made of the two native sulfides, realgar (As_2S_2) and orpiment (As_2S_3), as depilatories and as a dressing for wounds and internally as tonics and for the

[10] Sexton, *Chemical Constitution and Biological Activity*, 2nd ed., Van Nostrand Company, New York, 1953, p. 328.

[11] Du Bois and Coon, *Arch. Ind. Hyg. and Occupational Med.*, **6**, 9 (1952).

[12] Davies, *J. Pharm. and Pharmacol.*, **6**, 1 (1954).

[13] Kuhn, Möller, and Wendt, *Ber.*, **76**, 405 (1943); Thayer, Magnusen, and Gravett, *Antibiotics & Chemotherapy*, **3**, 256 (1953).

[14] Klotz and Morrison, *J. Am. Chem. Soc.*, **69**, 473 (1947).

[15] Doak and Freedman, *J. Am. Chem. Soc.*, **76**, 1621 (1954).

treatment of intermittent fever. The oxides, arsenic trioxide (As_2O_3) and arsenic pentoxide (As_2O_5), and compounds derived from them were used extensively as poisons in the sixteenth and seventeenth centuries. Later, preparations such as solution of arsenic and mercuric iodides (Donovan's Solution) and solution of potassium arsenite (Fowler's Solution) were employed as tonics in anemia and pulmonary diseases and as remedial agents in malaria and syphilis.

Arsonic Acids

The first organic compound of arsenic was discovered in 1760 by Louis Claude Cadet, a pharmacist in the French army. Upon distilling arsenous acid and potassium acetate, he obtained a fuming liquid of repulsive and garliclike odor which burned on contact with air. Bunsen showed that Cadet's fuming arsenical liquid was composed of carbon, hydrogen, arsenic, and oxygen and that the arsenic-carbon group remained intact in all reactions. Berzelius gave this radical, $(CH_3)_2As$—, the name "cacodyl" which is derived from the Greek word for "stinking." Cahours and Riche established the constitution of cacodyl in 1842. The main constituent of Cadet's fuming liquid is cacodyl oxide:

$$4CH_3COOK + As_2O_3 \rightarrow (CH_3)_2As-O-As(CH_3)_2 + 2K_2CO_3 + 2CO_2$$
Cacodyl oxide

Many of the cacodyl compounds on oxidation form cacodylic acid, an example of which is shown.

$$Me_2As-O-AsMe_2 \xrightarrow[HOH]{HgO} 2$$

Cacodylic acid

There are two series of cadodyl derivatives, namely, those in which the radical behaves as if it were monovalent (trivalent arsenic) and those in which it behaves as if it were trivalent (pentavalent arsenic). Compounds belonging to the first series may be regarded as derivatives of arsine obtained by replacing the hydrogen atoms by other groups, as shown. All the alkyl arsines, e.g., the ethyl,

Arsine   Methyl-arsine   Dimethyl-arsine   Trimethyl-arsine

Dicacodyl (cacodyl)   Cacodyl chloride   Cacodyl cyanide butyl, and amyl compounds, are very toxic. Replacement of the arsine hydrogen by halogen, e.g., methyldichloroarsine, dimethylchloroarsine, increases the toxicity particularly when the halogen is chlorine. These compounds differ from the corresponding compounds of nitrogen in that the primary, secondary, and tertiary arsines have practically no basic properties. None of the compounds of this series is employed as a therapeutic agent since all of them are highly toxic.

Lewisite (Chlorovinyldichloroarsine), $CHCl=CH—AsCl_2$, and ethyldichloroarsine, $CH_3CH_2AsCl_2$, are vesicants used for chemical warfare. Lewisite has a geraniumlike odor and produces irritation to the nasal passages, respiratory tract, eyes, and skin. Ethyldichloroarsine produces a pungent, pepperlike sensation in the nostrils. It causes blisters, paralysis of the hands, and vomiting.

The second series includes compounds of the type shown.

$$CH_3 \diagdown \diagup O$$
$$As$$
$$CH_3 \diagup \diagdown OH$$

Cacodylic acid

$(R)_4AsI$

Tetraalkylarsonium
compounds

$(R)_5As$

Pentaalkylarsonium
compounds

The cacodylate compounds are the only members of this series used medicinally. Cacodyl oxide, obtained by distilling potassium acetate with arsenous acid, is the initial compound from which other cacodyl derivatives are prepared.

Sodium Cacodylate, N.F., is the sodium salt of dimethylarsonic acid, crystallizing with three molecules of water of crystallization, $(CH_3)_2AsO_2Na \cdot 3H_2O$. Cacodylic acid is a stable, water-soluble, crystalline compound; it is amphoteric, forming stable salts with alkalies and unstable compounds with strong acids.

Sodium cacodylate and cacodylic acid were introduced as therapeutic agents by Armand Gautier in 1896 after Bunsen and Kirchner found that cacodylic acid was relatively nontoxic. He employed these substances as tonics in anemias and other debilitating diseases and also empirically in syphilis and malaria. Later, it was established that the effects produced by the cacodylates are much the same as those given by inorganic arsenicals to which they are partly reduced in the body. Because the reduction occurs slowly, the action is prolonged. When given by mouth, the cacodylates impart a garliclike odor to the breath, sweat, and urine, owing to the excretion of cacodyl oxide.

Sodium cacodylate has been replaced by more effective agents in the treatment of protozoan infections. It is now used to a limited extent in the same conditions as the inorganic compounds of arsenic.

Solarson is the trade name of a 1 per cent solution of monoammonium chloroheptenarsonate (Chloroarsenol). The active ingredient of this solution is prepared by treating heptyne with arsenic trichloride, hydrolysis to the arseno compound, and oxidation to the arsonic acid with hydrogen peroxide and conversion to the monoammonium salt, as indicated.

$$CH_3(CH_2)_4C\equiv CH + AsCl_3 \rightarrow CH_3(CH_2)_4CCl=CH—AsCl_2 + H_2O \rightarrow$$

Heptyne

$$CH_3(CH_2)_4CCl=CH—AsO + H_2O_2 \rightarrow$$

$$CH_3(CH_2)_4CCl=CH—AsO(OH)_2 + NH_4OH \rightarrow$$

$$CH_3(CH_2)_4CCl=CH—AsO(OH)(ONH_4)$$

Chloroarsenol

Solarson is reported to be less toxic than arsenic acid upon intravenous or subcutaneous administration when the dosage is computed on the basis of arsenic content. It is used to obtain the tonic effects of arsenic in anemias, malaria, skin diseases, etc.

The aromatic arsenic compounds include some of the most valuable known therapeutic agents because they are effective against protozoan infections. The first compound of this type, known as "atoxyl," the sodium salt of arsanilic acid, was prepared by Béchamp [16] by heating aniline and arsenic acid together. Béchamp believed that this compound was the anilid of arsenic acid. Ehrlich and Bertheim [17] proved the structure of the compound to be that of p-aminobenzenearsonic acid; they named it arsanilic acid by analogy with sulfanilic acid.

NH—AsO₃HNa

NH₂

ONa

As→O

OH

Atoxyl,
Béchamp's formula

Atoxyl (arsanilic acid),
Ehrlich and Bertheim formula

This discovery was of great importance since it showed that arsanilic acid could undergo all the transformations of aniline. Consequently, arsanilic acid became the starting point for the synthesis of many other aryl arsenic compounds.

The studies of Ehrlich and Shiga [18] of the effects of various substances, including arsanilic acid, on trypanosomes indicated that the organic compounds containing pentavalent arsenic were quite inert *in vitro*. Thomas in 1905, however, showed that atoxyl was definitely trypanocidal *in vivo*. Ehrlich and his co-workers then initiated a systematic study of atoxyl and other organic arsenicals. Ehrlich explained the activity of atoxyl *in vivo* and its inactivity *in vitro* by the reduction of the pentavalent arsenic to trivalent arsenic in the body.

The organoarsenicals had become important for the treatment of venereal diseases. They have now, to a considerable extent, been replaced by penicillin and other antibiotics.

[16] *Compt. rend.*, **56**, 1173 (1863).
[17] *Ber.*, **40**, 3292 (1907).
[18] *Klin. Wochschr.*, **41**, 329, 362 (1904).

The aryl arsenical compounds now in use medicinally are generally classified into pentavalent arsenicals represented by the arsonic acids and trivalent arsenicals, examples of which are the arsenobenzene and the arsenosobenzene derivatives. The synthesis of these organoarsenicals is dependent upon the linkage of carbon to arsenic by one of two general methods. The first of these is the Béchamp reaction which involves the direct arsonation of amines or phenols with arsenic acid.

Aniline, for example, heated with excess arsenic acid undergoes the following reactions:

$$C_6H_5-NH_2 + H_3AsO_4 \rightarrow C_6H_5-NH_2 \cdot H_3AsO_4 \xrightarrow[\text{heat } 190°]{-HOH}$$

Aniline arsenate

$$[C_6H_5NH-AsO_3H_2] \xrightarrow{\text{rearranges}} p\text{-}NH_2C_6H_4-AsO_3H_2$$

Arsanilid,   Arsanilic acid
probable intermediate

The second method is the Bart synthesis which depends upon the reaction of an aryldiazonium halide with sodium arsenite. This method permits the prepara-

$$Ar-N_2-X + Na-AsO_3HNa \rightarrow NaX + Ar-N_2-AsO_3HNa \rightarrow$$

$$Ar-AsO_3HNa + N_2$$

tion of a wide variety of aromatic arsenic compounds. Both of these synthetic procedures have been thoroughly reviewed.[19] The arsonic acids prepared in this way can be reduced to arsenobenzenes, or arsenosobenzenes.

The aromatic arsonic acids have been studied quite extensively. Benzene-arsonic acid is more toxic than the methyl compound, and diphenylarsonic acid is more toxic than its monophenyl analog. The effect of substitution into the phenyl group of benzenearsonic acid has led to a number of interesting obser-vations. The introduction of hydroxyl groups into the phenyl nucleus lowers the toxicity.

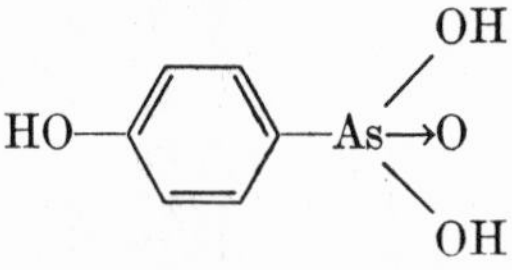

4-Hydroxybenzenearsonic   3-Hydroxybenzenearsonic   2-Hydroxybenzenearsonic
acid   acid   acid

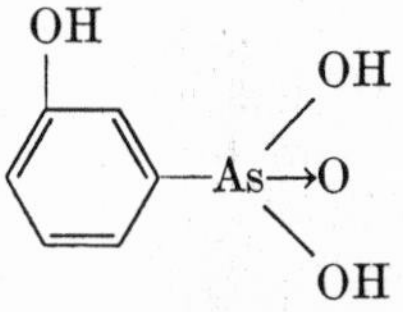

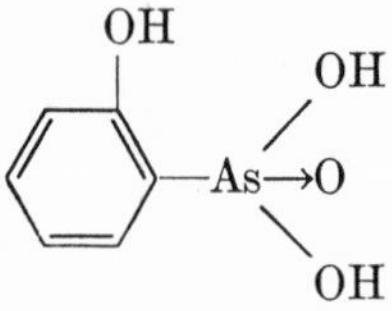

The substitution of a methyl group increases the toxicity, but the same group in hydroxy compounds such as o- and p-cresylarsonic acids decreases the activity against trypanosomes and lowers the toxicity. Nitro and nitroso substitution yields compounds that are almost inactive. Halogenation causes an increase in toxicity, e.g., 3,5-dichlorobenzenearsonic acid is much more toxic than benzene-arsonic acid and causes other undesirable physiological effects.

The introduction of an amino group (atoxyl) decreases the toxicity and gives a compound that has some action against spirillae *in vivo* and slight action *in vitro*. Monomethylation of the amino group of atoxyl causes a considerable increase in

[19] Hamilton and Morgan, *Organic Reactions*, Vol. 2, Wiley & Sons, New York, 1944, Chapter 10.

toxicity without any increase in the spirillicidal action, and dimethylation further increases the toxicity and reduces the activity. On the other hand, acetylation (arsacetin) reduces the toxicity by two-thirds and increases the activity so that the therapeutic index is increased by a factor of 9. Acyl derivatives such as formyl, butyl, chloroacetyl, malonyl, and phthalyl have been made and found to increase in toxicity as the molecular weight of the acyl group is increased without increasing the spirillicidal or trypanocidal action.

Tryparsamide, U.S.P. (Sodium Salt of p-Arsonophenylglycineamide),

$$\underset{\underset{\underset{O}{\downarrow}}{|}}{OH}$$

p-NaO—As—C_6H_4—NHCH$_2$CO—NH$_2$, is of little value in primary and sec-

ondary syphilis. It has been used with considerable success in the treatment of sleeping sickness, in general paresis, and in tabes.

Carbarsone, U.S.P. (p-Carbamidobenzenearsonic Acid), H$_2$N—CO—NH—C$_6$H$_4$—AsO$_3$H$_2$, is a white, crystalline, stable powder, containing about 28.5 per cent As, slightly soluble in water but soluble in alkalies and alkali carbonates. It is used to treat amebiasis, and is usually administered by mouth.

Acetarsone, N.F. (Stovarsol, N-Acetyl-4-hydroxy-m-arsanilic Acid), is a white powder containing about 27 per cent As. It is not readily soluble in water or alcohol, but it dissolves readily in alkalies to form stable solutions at room temperature. It has been successfully used in the treatment of syphilis, yaws, amebiasis, and malaria. It is claimed that stovarsol was the first compound to be successfully administered by mouth in the treatment of syphilis. It is also reported to be a specific in the treatment of agalactia in sheep and goats. It may be synthesized by nitrating p-hydroxybenzenearsonic acid, reducing the nitro to the amino group, and acetylating.

Treparsol is the formyl analog of stovarsol; that is, a formyl group replaces the acetyl group.

Phenarsone Sulfoxylate, N.N.R. (Sodium 4-Hydroxy-m-arsanilate-N-methanal Sulfoxylate), is the compound formed from the reaction of 4-hydroxy-m-arsanilic acid with sodium formaldehyde sulfoxylate. Although it has some value in the treatment of syphilis of the central nervous system, its greatest use is in the treatment of trichomonas vaginitis.

Bismuth Glycolylarsanilate, N.N.R., is an amebicide recommended for the treatment of intestinal amebiasis, having the indicated formula.

$$\begin{array}{c} O \\ \| \\ NH—C—CH_2OH \end{array}$$

HO—As—O—Bi→O

A variety of heterocyclic arsonic acids have been synthesized and found to be active *in vitro* against parasitic organisms. However, they have found little acceptance clinically.

Arsenobenzene Derivatives

The discovery of the therapeutic value of the arsenobenzene derivatives constitutes one of the great advances made in the treatment of syphilis and in the field of chemotherapy. This discovery resulted from Ehrlich's concept that pentavalent arsenicals like atoxyl are reduced in the body to the actively parasiticidal trivalent form. He and his co-workers studied various compounds obtained by the reduction of arsonic acid derivatives.

Arsenobenzene derivatives are readily formed by the reducing action of hypophosphorous acid in methyl alcohol, sodium amalgam, or sodium hydrosulfite on arylarsonic acids. Some doubt still exists regarding the structures of the arsenobenzenes.

Arsphenamine (3,3'-Diamino-4,4'-dihydroxyarsenobenzene Dihydrochloride) is the name adopted in the United States for the product introduced in Germany under the trade name Salvarsan, in Great Britain as Kharsivan, and in France as Arsenobenzol. It is also known as "606" because 605 other preparations were made before this product was elaborated.

It is synthesized by reducing 4-hydroxy-3-nitrophenylarsonic acid with sodium hydrosulfite and magnesium chloride at 40–50°. The essential reactions are indicated.

Arsphenamine

Arsphenamine is a light yellow, hygroscopic powder. It is readily soluble in water, alcohol, or glycerol. It is oxidized readily on exposure to air as such or in solution, becoming darker in color and more toxic. To prevent oxidation, it is marketed in glass containers sealed under a vacuum or filled with an inert gas such as nitrogen. Each manufactured lot must be tested for toxicity and comply with the requirements of the United States Public Health Institute.

Sodium Arsphenamine (Sodium Salvarsan, Sodium Diarsenol) is the disodium salt of 3,3'-diamino-4,4'-dihydroxyarsenobenzene. It is prepared by mixing equimolar amounts of sodium methoxide and a suspension of arsphenamine base in methyl alcohol and by precipitating the product by the addition of absolute alcohol and ether.

Sodium arsphenamine is a pale yellow powder, readily soluble in water and slightly soluble in alcohol. It has the advantage that, unlike arsphenamine, it does not require neutralization before use. It is very unstable. Solutions for administration should be prepared immediately before use without the aid of heat and without shaking.

Silver Arsphenamine (Sodium Silver Arsphenamine) is the disodium salt of silver 3,3'-diamino-4,4'-dihydroxyarsenobenzene. It is prepared by treating arsphenamine dissolved in methyl alcohol with an equimolar solution of a silver salt and adding sodium hydroxide. The sodium silver arsphenamine can then be precipitated by the addition of ether. The structure of the resulting compound is not known with certainty. It contains from 12 to 14 per cent of nonionizable silver and not less than 19 per cent of arsenic. Binz and his collaborators report that, since arseno compounds containing no amino groups do not form complexes with metallic salts, the silver is attached to the nitrogen in silver arsphenamine.

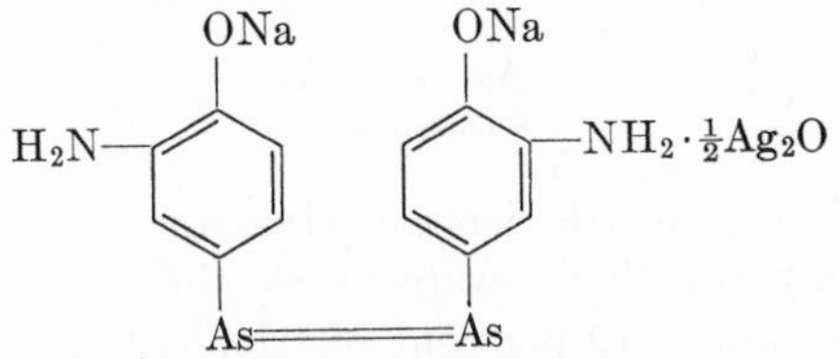

Silver arsphenamine is readily soluble in water. It is usually administered parenterally as a 0.5 per cent solution which must be freshly prepared to guard against oxidation. It is used for the same purposes as arsphenamine. The introduction of silver is said to improve the chemotherapeutic index, owing to the activity of the silver component of the molecule.

Neoarsphenamine (Neosalvarsan, Neokharsivan, Neoarsenobenzol, Neodiarsenol, "914" of Ehrlich's series) is sodium 3,3'-diamino-4,4'-dihydroxyarsenobenzene-N-methanal sulfoxylate. It is prepared by mixing arsphenamine with sodium formaldehyde sulfoxylate and adding sodium bicarbonate solution.

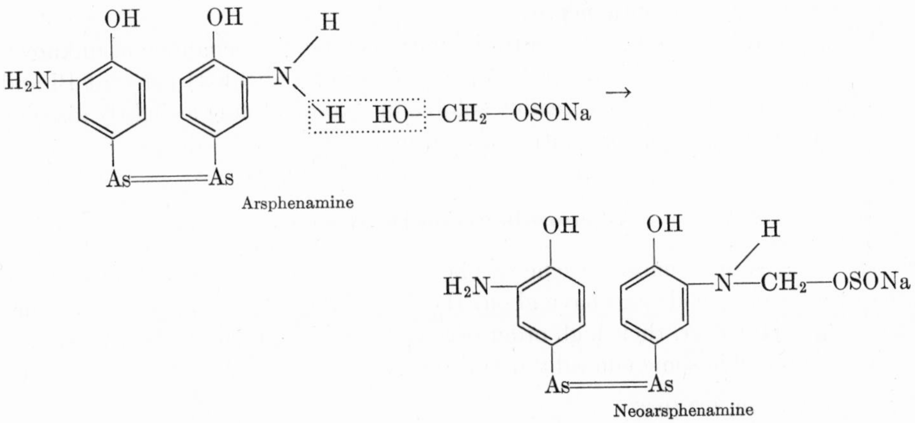

Arsphenamine

Neoarsphenamine

Neoarsphenamine is a yellow powder, very soluble in water, slightly soluble in alcohol, and practically insoluble in absolute alcohol, acetone, chloroform, and ether. It contains about 20 per cent As.

Silver Neoarsphenamine is a derivative of neoarsphenamine similar to silver arsphenamine. It is a grayish-black soluble powder containing 6 to 7 per cent of Ag and about 20 per cent of As. It is used in the same manner as silver asphenamine.

Sulfarsphenamine (Disodium 3,3'-diamino-4,4'-dihydroxyarsenobenzene-N,N'-dimethylene Sulfonate) is prepared from arsphenamine and an excess of sodium formaldehyde bisulfite solution. It was developed by Voegtlin *et al.* of

Sulfarsphenamine

the United States Public Health Service, Hygienic Laboratory. It is a light yellow powder, readily soluble in water with the formation of slightly acid solutions. It contains about 19 per cent of trivalent As. It is more resistant to oxidation than the arsphenamine compounds. The chief advantage of sulfarsphenamine is that it can be administer intramuscularly.

A heterocyclic analog of the salvarsan compounds is 2-pyridon-5-arseno-(3'-amino-4'-hydroxybenzene). It is considerably less toxic than tryparsamide. In

animals it showed promise against neurosyphilis, and in man it was tolerated without affecting the optic nerve.[20]

Bismarsen is a complex bismuth derivative of sulfarsphenamine of unknown constitution. It contains about 13.5 per cent As and about 24 per cent Bi and is a brownish-yellow powder, readily soluble in water, forming a slightly alkaline solution. It is administered intramuscularly.

Arsenosobenzene Derivatives

Derivatives of arsenosobenzene or phenylarsenoxide are generally more toxic than the arsonic acids and have about the same range of toxicity as the arsenobenzenes. However, their high order of activity against many parasitic diseases has made possible some clinically useful products.

[20] Binz, *Ber.*, **70**, 127 (1937).

Mild reducing agents such as phenylhydrazine or a combination of sulfur trioxide and hydriodic acid reduce the arsonic acid group to the trivalent arsenoxides.

Arsenosobenzene, phenylarsenoxide (Arzene), C_6H_5AsO, has found valuable use in poultry feeds against chicken coccidiosis.

Oxophenarsine Hydrochloride, U.S.P. (3-Amino-4-hydroxyphenylarsinoxide Hydrochloride, Mapharsen), $1,3,4\text{-}C_6H_3\text{---}AsO\text{---}NH_2\text{---}OH$, was first prepared by Ehrlich, who found it to be quite toxic. Reexamination of the compound showed that the ratio of the effective to the toxic dose is very favorable. Mapharsen is used in the treatment of syphilis, usually being administered intravenously.

γ-(p-Arsenosophenyl)butyric Acid, $O:As\text{---}C_6H_4\text{---}CH_2CH_2CH_2COOH$, is effective against trypanosomes, even against so-called arsenic-resistant strains. Early field tests indicate that it is highly active as a trypanocidal agent with reasonable freedom from toxic action.[21]

Dichlorophenarsine Hydrochloride, U.S.P. (3-Amino-4-hydroxyphenyl dichloroarsine Hydrochloride), is a white, crystalline powder soluble in water. It was studied many years ago and rejected as too toxic for use in therapy. Later studies have revealed that, when suitably buffered with agents such as sodium citrate and sodium carbonate, it is useful in the treatment of syphilis. Admixed with dry buffering agents it is sealed in ampules. When the contents are dissolved in water the dichlorophenarsine is probably converted to the corresponding arsenoxide.

Dichlorophenarsine

Mechanism of Action of Aromatic Arsenicals

The mechanism of action of aromatic arsenicals has been the subject of discussion since the early work of Ehrlich, who introduced the concept of the reduction of pentavalent arsenic to the more active trivalent arsenic *in vivo*. Sexton[22] has reviewed the considerations of various authors as applied to the trypanocidal activity of these compounds. It is believed that the toxic action of arsenicals on trypanosomes may be explained by the combination of the arsenic with the sulfhydryl groups in such peptides as glutathione. During World War II, the search for an antidote for the arsenic war gases focused considerable attention on the ability of arsenic to combine with thiol groups and gave rise to 2,3-dimercaptopropanol or British Anti-Lewisite (B.A.L.). It is thought that

[21] Eagle, *Science*, **101**, 69 (1945).

[22] Sexton, *Chemical Constitution and Biological Activity*, 2nd ed., Van Nostrand Company, New York, 1953, p. 303.

best antidotal effects to the toxic action of arsenic were achieved with dithiols wherein a stable ring structure was formed. The pyruvate oxidase system [23] is believed to be the one concerned with the vesicant action of the war gases and B.A.L. (see page 272) has been found to counteract the effect of various therapeutic arsenicals on this system. Despite progress in this regard, many questions remain unanswered. For example, the interaction of arsenical drugs with B.A.L. does not always result in loss of therapeutic activity.[24]

Arsthinol, N.N.R., the product from N-acetylmapharsen and B.A.L., has been demonstrated to be effective against intestinal amebiasis and yaws.

Organoarsenic in Feeds

Arsenic compounds have long been used in veterinary medicine to improve the appearance and well-being of animals. Arsenic trioxide and the less toxic cacodylates have been prescribed as general tonics in the treatment of anemias as well as various infections. Derivatives of benzenearsonic acid were first used in 1944 in the feeds of poultry and swine to combat various parasitic diseases paralleling those of humans. For example, 4-nitrobenzenearsonic acid was found to be effective as a preventative against blackhead in turkeys, and arsanilic acid and 3-nitro-4-hydroxybenzenearsonic acid served to control chicken coccidiosis and bloody dysentery in hogs.

In 1946, Morehouse and Mayfield [25] reported the surprising finding that 3-nitro-4-hydroxybenzenearsonic acid has remarkable growth-stimulating properties for poultry when given in the drinking water at very low doses. This report has been confirmed, and arsanilic acid as well as the above compound are now recognized as effective growth stimulators for chickens, turkeys, and hogs. Presumably, the mode of action is similar to that of certain antibiotics in altering the bacterial growth in the gastrointestinal tract to aid improved nutrition in the animal.[26] This dual role of organoarsenic compounds as feed additives has made them commercially of great importance in bulk chemical sales.

ANTIMONY COMPOUNDS

Organometallic antimony compounds with the antimony atom linked directly to a carbon atom have been synthesized and examined for activity comparable to that of the compounds of arsenic. They compare unfavorably as to ease of preparation, stability, and effectiveness. Whereas the effectiveness of the arsenic compounds in which the arsenic atom is linked to carbon seems to be increased through a decrease in toxicity and an increase in specificity for certain organisms, this does not seem to be true of the antimony compounds. Thus the antimony analog of arsphenamine has been prepared, but it is extremely sen-

[23] Peters, *J. Roy. Inst. Public Health and Hyg.*, **15**, 89 (1952); *C.A.*, **46**, 9195 (1952).
[24] Friedheim, *Proc. Soc. Exptl. Biol. Med.*, **64**, 418 (1947).
[25] Morehouse and Mayfield, *J. Parasitol.*, **32**, 20 (1946).
[26] Frost, *Poultry Sci.*, **32**, 217 (1953).

sitive to oxidation and has no practical use. No true organometallic compounds of antimony are used at the present time as medicinal agents.

The use of antimony and potassium tartrate is discussed, page 517. Other compounds of trivalent antimony used medicinally are indicated.

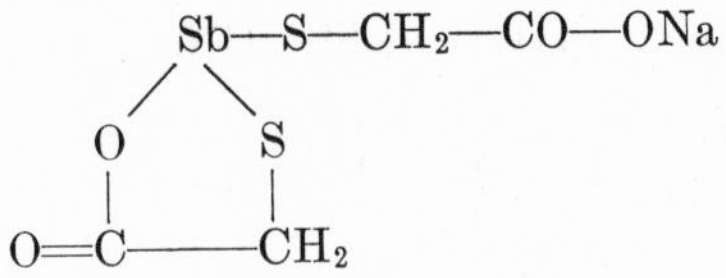

Antimony sodium thioglycolate

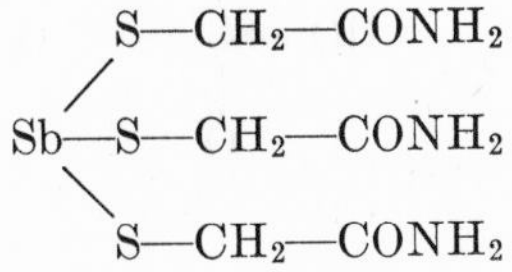

Antimony thioglycolamide

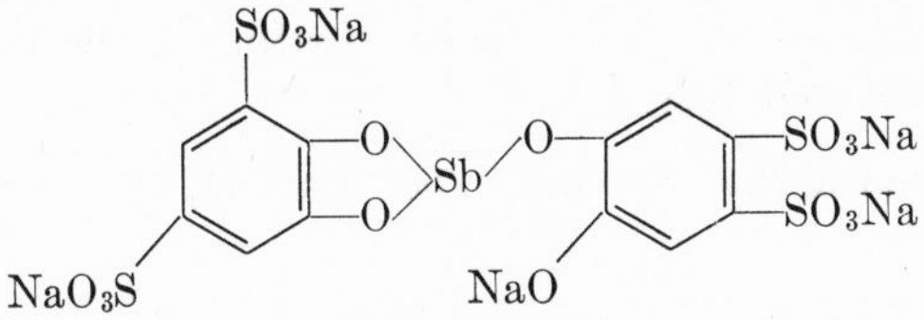

Fuadin, stibophen

Antimony thioglycolamide and antimony sodium thioglycolate are used in the treatment of certain tropical diseases, namely, granuloma inguinale (tumor of granular tissue), trypanosomiasis, kala azar (an epidemic fever caused by small parasites found in the liver and spleen), and as anthelmintics in the treatment of filariasis (parasitic disease caused by various species of flukes). Sterile solutions of the compounds are usually injected intramuscularly and sometimes intravenously.

Pentavalent antimony compounds are reported to be more effective than the trivalent compounds in the treatment of kala azar and trypanosomiasis. They are reported to be less toxic, causing fewer side reactions, but they are more difficult to prepare and are more expensive. Compounds of this type are shown.

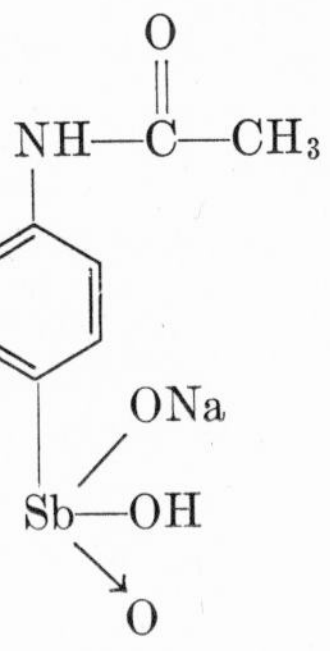

Stibosan

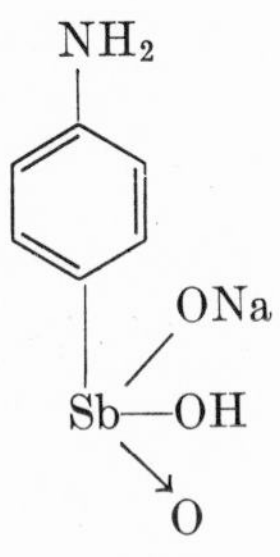

Stibamine

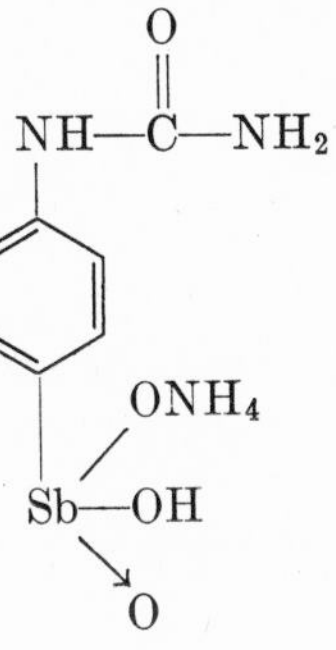

Urea stibamin

$$NHC_6H_{11}O_5 \qquad NHC_6H_{11}O_5 \qquad NHC_6H_{11}O_5$$

HO—Sb————O————Sb————O————Sb—ONa

Neostam

Stibamine Glucoside, N.N.R. [Polymerized p-(2,4-Diamino-1,3,5-triazin-6-ylamino)benzenestibonic Acid], employed as its sodium salt, cures an infection of *Trypanosoma equiperdum* with a single treatment; the dose required is but $\frac{1}{200}$ that of the tolerated dose.[27]

[27] Friedheim and Berman, *Proc. Soc. Exptl. Biol. Med.*, **62**, 131–132 (1946); *C.A.*, **40**, 5837 (1946).

Cycles Containing
One Heteroatom

OXYGEN HETEROCYCLES

The simplest oxygen-containing heterocycle is ethylene oxide, b.p. 10.7° soluble in water. It may be prepared in yields of 90 per cent by adding concentrated sodium hydroxide solution to a boiling solution of ethylene chlorohydrin.

$$
\begin{array}{ccc}
CH_2OH & & CH_2 \\
| & \xrightarrow{\text{NaOH}} & |\quad\diagdown \\
| & & |\qquad O \\
CH_2Cl & & CH_2 \diagup
\end{array}
$$

As a three-membered ring ethylene oxide is very reactive; it will add in good yield to a variety of organic compounds such as alcohols, amines, Grignard reagents, etc., to form many useful products. In addition to its use in organic syntheses, it has been used as a fumigant for foods and textiles. Ethylene oxide has shown considerable value in the sterilization of many drug products in the pharmaceutical industry.

Substituted ethylene oxides possess properties analogous to those of the unsubstituted compound. Where R is an alkyl group, attack of an organic base frequently occurs at the primary position, as shown. However, where R is

$$
\begin{array}{cc}
R{-}CH{-\!-\!-}CH_2 + B^- & R{-}CH{-}CH_2B \\
\quad\diagdown\;\diagup & \qquad| \\
\quad O & \qquad OH
\end{array}
$$

aromatic, as in styrene oxide, reaction may occur at either position, depending on the nature of the attacking anion.

Trimethylene Oxide, or its derivatives, are not well known, and no member of this group seems to have become of importance in medicinal or pharmaceutical chemistry.

$$
\begin{array}{c}
CH_2\!-\!CH_2 \\
|\qquad | \\
CH_2\!-\!O
\end{array}
$$

Trimethylene oxide

$$
\begin{array}{c}
CH_2\!-\!CH_2 \\
|\qquad\quad \backslash \\
\qquad\qquad O \\
|\qquad\quad / \\
CH_2\!-\!CH_2
\end{array}
$$

Tetramethylene oxide

$$
\begin{array}{c}
CH\!=\!CH \\
|\qquad\quad \backslash \\
\qquad\qquad O \\
|\qquad\quad / \\
CH\!=\!CH
\end{array}
$$

Furan

Furan Derivatives

Tetramethylene Oxide, or tetrahydrofuran, is an ether, and it exhibits all the properties characteristic of an ether. The cycle composed of four carbon atoms and one oxygen atom is quite important. Derivatives of tetramethylene oxide may be divided into three groups:

(a) γ-Lactones which are really intramolecular esters (see page 176).

(b) Anhydrides of succinic acid, or derivatives of succinic acid. These compounds have been discussed (see page 164).

(c) Unsaturated tetramethylene oxide or furan, some derivatives of which are especially well known and abundantly available.

The resemblance of tetrahydrofuran to diethyl ether was early recognized, and its possibilities as an anesthetic agent were explored.[1] Its toxic side effects militated against its use for this purpose.

Furan, b.p. 31–32°, is a colorless liquid, possessing an odor resembling that of chloroform. It is stable to alkali but unstable to acids.

Furan may be looked upon as an isoster of benzene, a relationship which is borne out by its resonance energy of 23 kg.-cal. per molecule and by the chemical properties of certain of its derivatives as compared to the correspondingly substituted benzenes.

α-Methylfuran, b.p. 63°, also known as sylvan, is found in beechwood oil. The alcohol, known as furfuryl alcohol, is found in cloves and in roasted coffee. It distils at 170–171°.

$$
\begin{array}{c}
\beta'CH_4\!\!-\!\!{}_3CH\beta \\
\|\qquad\quad \| \\
\alpha'CH^5\quad {}^2C\!-\!CH_2OH \\
\diagdown O \diagup {}_\alpha
\end{array}
$$

Furfuryl alcohol

Furfuraldehyde (Furfural) is the most abundant of the furan compounds. It is obtained by the dehydration of the naturally occurring pentoses, the commercial sources being oat hulls and corncobs. A similar dehydration of glucose

$$
\begin{array}{c}
CH\!-\!\!-\!\!CH \\
\|\qquad\quad \| \\
CH\qquad C\!-\!CHO \\
\diagdown\quad\diagup \\
O
\end{array}
$$

Furfuraldehyde

[1] Stoughton and Robbins, *J. Pharmacol. Exptl. Therap.*, **58**, 171 (1936).

to form the substituted furfuraldehyde is the basis of the Molisch reaction. The aldehyde with α-naphthol layered over concentrated sulfuric acid forms a characteristic violet ring.

Furfuraldehyde, b.p. 162°, behaves much like benzaldehyde in that it will undergo reactions typical of aromatic aldehydes. The Cannizzaro reaction on furfural produces furfuryl alcohol and furoic acid.

Nitrofurazone, N.F. (Furacin, 5-Nitro-2-furfural Semicarbazone), is an odorless, yellow-colored, crystalline powder, soluble in water about 1:4200, slightly soluble in alcohol, propylene glycol, and polyethylene glycols, and insoluble in ether. It is used for its bacteriostatic and bactericidal properties in a hydrophyllic ointment base applied directly or on dressings against infections in wounds, burns, and skin diseases. As an anhydrous solution in polyethylene glycol, it is recommended for control of purulent otitis.

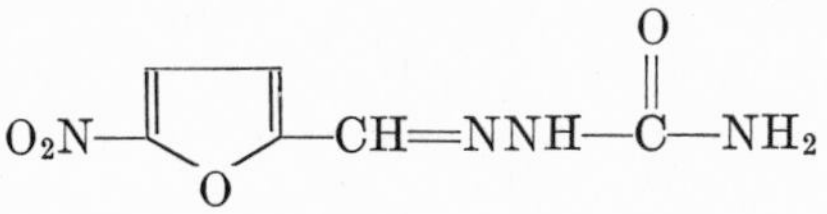

Nitrofurazone

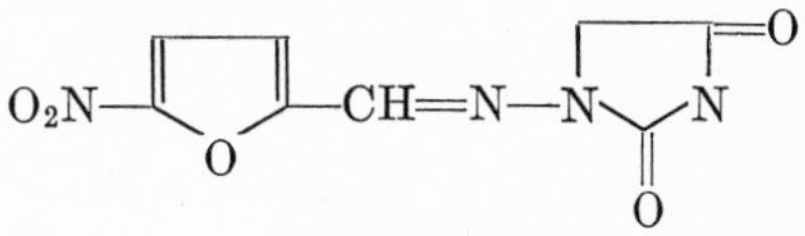

Nitrofurantoin

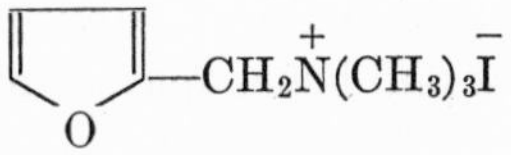

Furmethide

Nitrofurantoin, N.N.R. [Furadantin, N-(5-Nitro-2-furfurylidene)-1-aminohydantoin], is a yellow powder slightly soluble in water having antibacterial activity against both Gram-positive and Gram-negative microorganisms. It is recommended for the treatment of a variety of bacterial infections of the urinary tract by oral administration in tablet form.

Furtrethonium Iodide (Furmethide Iodide, Furfuryltrimethylammonium Iodide) is a parasympathetic stimulant having muscarinelike action. Like prostigmine, it is recommended in glaucoma and in postoperative intestinal peristalsis.

Thiophene

Thiophene and **Benzothiophene** are the sulfur analogs of furan and benzofuran, respectively. Thiophene is more isosteric with benzene than with furan.

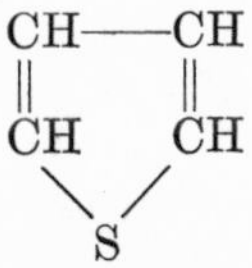

Thiophene

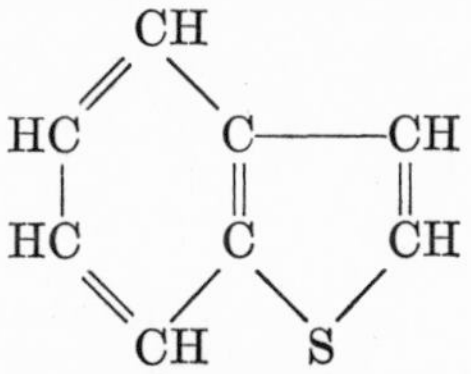

Benzothiophene

It possesses many physical properties that are very close to those of benzene, and, since it is obtained in coal distillation products, it is difficult to remove. As an isostere to benzene, it appears in the structures of several antihistamine drugs, e.g., Methapyrilene, Diatrin, Bromothen, and Chlorothen (page 219). The pressor activities of α-thienylaminoalkanes parallel those of the corresponding phenylaminoalkanes. The thiophene and benzothiophene isosteres of phenylalanine are microbiological antagonists to this amino acid in certain systems.

Pyran Derivatives

Pyran is the unsaturated pentamethylene oxide. **Benzopyran** is particularly important as the parent substance of many plant pigments.

Pyran   Benzopyran

The pyran ketones, called γ-pyrones, are unusual in that the heterooxygen atom possesses basic properties and hence may form oxonium salts as indicated.

Such oxonium salts are widely distributed in nature (see page 318).

Maltol (3-Hydroxy-2-methyl-4-pyrone), found in pine needles and in the bark of the larch, has been obtained as an alkaline degradation product of streptomycin salts.[2]

Maltol   Kojic acid   Meconic acid

Kojic Acid (5-Hydroxy-2-hydroxymethyl-4-pyrone) is an antibiotic substance produced by *Aspergilli*.

[2] Schenck and Spielman, *J. Am. Chem. Soc.*, **67**, 2276 (1945).

Meconic Acid has been isolated from opium.

Anhydro - 3 - hydroxymethylenetetrahydro - 1,4 - pyrone - 2 - carboxylic Acid, m.p. 109.5–110.5°, is an antibiotic which may be isolated from the cultures of various organisms.[3]

Butopyronoxyl, U.S.P. (Indalone, Butyl mesityl Oxide), is one of the active ingredients of insecticide preparations. It is synthesized from mesityl oxide and dibutyl oxalate.

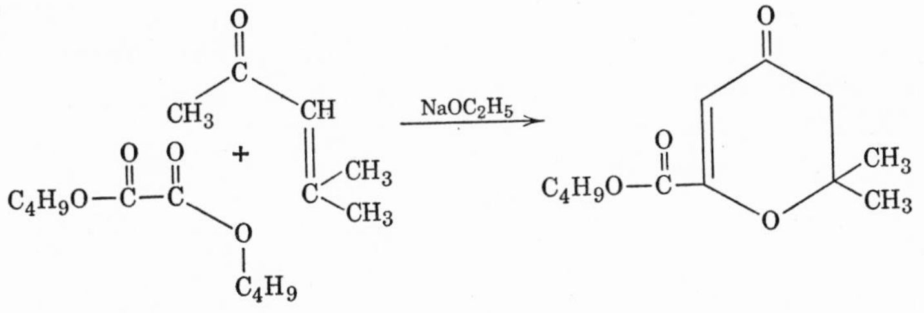

Dibutyl oxalate   Mesityl oxide   Butopyronoxyl

Coumarin, N.F., is the odoriferous principle of the tonka bean and of new-mown hay. It is the lactone of *cis-o*-hydroxycinnamic acid. It may be prepared from phenol by the following reactions:

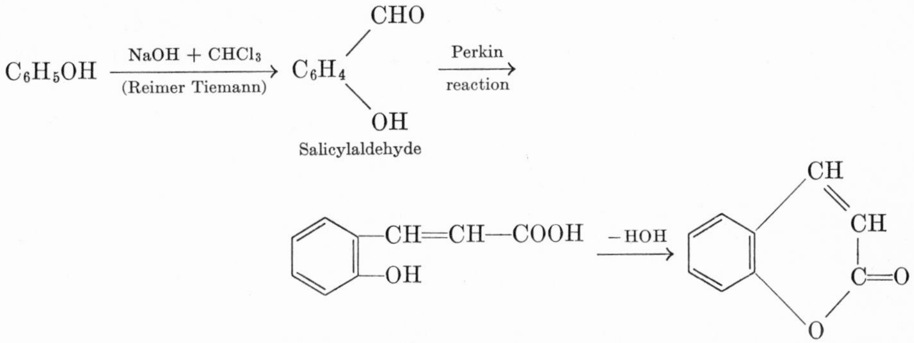

Salicylaldehyde

o-Hydroxycinnamic acid   Coumarin

Coumarin is also found to an appreciable extent in sweet clover. In improperly cured sweet-clover hay this substance is probably first oxidized to 4-hydroxy-coumarin, and this then condenses with formaldehyde to form 3,3′-methylenebis-(4-hydroxycoumarin) or dicoumarin.

Bishydroxycoumarin, U.S.P. (Dicoumarin, Dicumarol), is the agent that produces hemorrhagic sweet-clover disease in stock that is fed spoiled hay. As little as 0.0026 per cent of dicoumarin in dried hay has deleterious or lethal effects. The synthesis of this hemorrhagic agent in the laboratory has been accomplished.[4]

[3] Bergel, Morrison, Moss, and Rinderknecht, *J. Chem. Soc.*, **1944**, 415.

[4] Stahmann, Huebner, and Link, *J. Biol. Chem.*, **138**, 513 (1941).

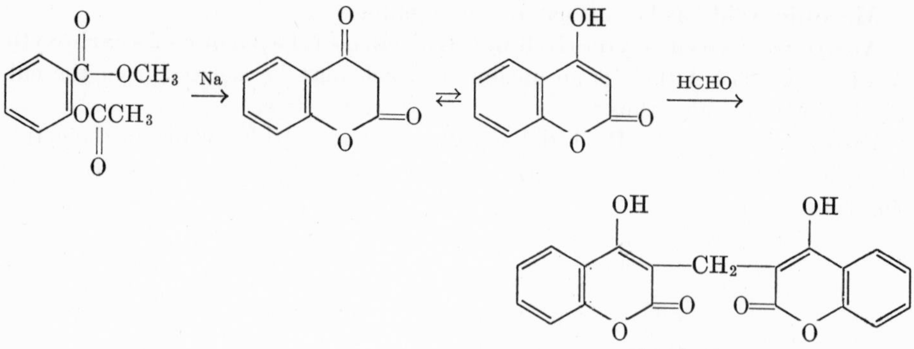

Bishydroxycoumarin

In six patients repeated doses of 200 to 300 mg. daily prolonged prothrombin and clotting time. Vitamin K counteracted this effect.[5]

Dicumarol is an orally effective anticoagulant which serves to prolong the clotting time of blood by decreasing the prothrombin concentration. Such agents are useful in the prophylaxis and treatment of intravascular clots, being particularly indicated as an adjunct in the treatment of coronary thrombosis. The disadvantage of such agents is the long lag period between administration and action as well as the possibility of hypoprothrombinemia occurring with overdosage.

Cyclocumarol, N.N.R. (3,4-Dihydro-2-methoxy-2-methyl-4-phenyl-2H,5H-pyrano[3,2-c][1]-benzopyran-5-one, Cumopyran), is a synthetic anticoagulant having properties similar to Dicumarol. It is about two to three times as active as Dicumarol, and its onset of action is considered to be more rapid and duration of action somewhat longer.

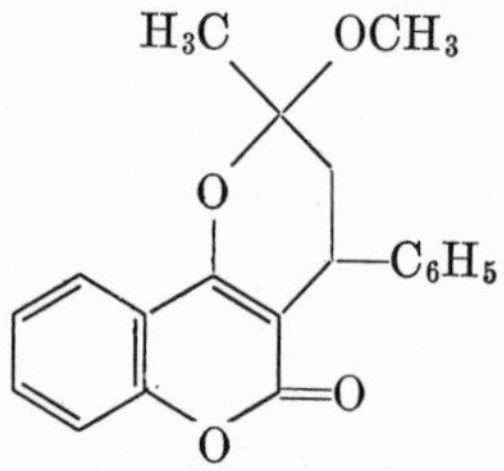

Cyclocumarol

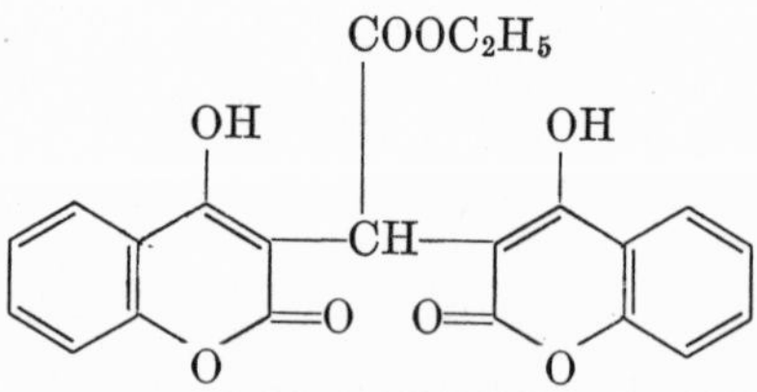

Ethyl biscoumacetate

Ethyl Biscoumacetate, N.N.R. [3,3'-Carboxymethylene Bis-(4-hydroxy-coumarin)-ethyl Ester, Tromexan Ethyl Acetate], is a synthetic anticoagulant prepared form 4-hydroxycoumarin.

Ethyl Biscoumacetate is more rapidly absorbed and excreted than Dicoumarol, and its shorter action reduces the danger of hemorrhagic complications.

Further efforts to find anticoagulant properties in variations of the 4-hydroxycoumarin structure resulted in **Warfarin, N.N.R.** (3-α-phenyl-β-acetylethyl-4-hydroxycoumarin). This compound is considerably more potent than Bis-

[5] Townsend and Mills, *Can. Med. Assoc. J.*, **46**, 214 (1942); *C.A.*, **36**, 2926 (1942).

hydroxycoumarin and was found to produce fatal hemorrhages in experimental animals. Its principal use is as a rodenticide, but it is used medicinally as an anticoagulant. Warfarin is synthesized as follows: [6]

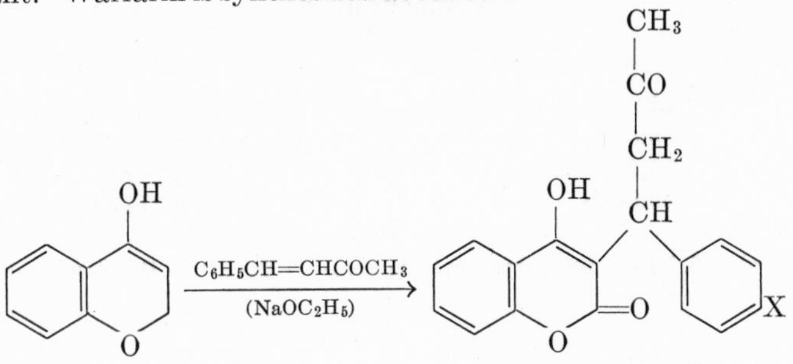

Warfarin, X = H
Tomorin, X = Cl

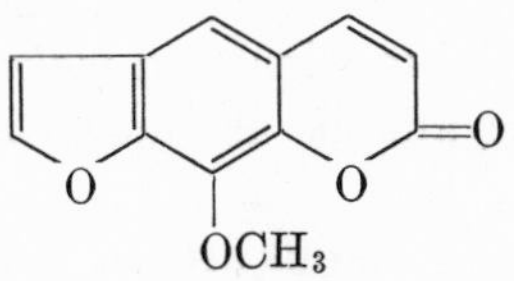

Methoxsalen

Tomorin (3-α-p-Chlorophenyl-β-acetylethyl-4-hydroxycoumarin) is also a potent anticoagulant with lethal properties in the rat. Other coumarins under scrutiny for their anticoagulant properties are **Marcoumar** [7] [3-(1^1-Phenyl-propyl)-4-hydroxycoumarin] and **Sinthrom** [8] (α-Nitrophenyl-p-acetylethyl-4-hydroxycoumarin).

Methoxsalen, N.N.R. [δ-Lactone of 3-(6-hydroxy-7-methoxybenzofuranyl)-acrylic Acid], is used in the treatment of idiopathic vitiligo; it increases production of the melanin pigments in the skin on exposure to ultraviolet light.

Umbelliferone (7-Hydroxycoumarin) is the aglycone of skimmin, a glycoside found in the bark of *Skimmia japonica*. Umbelliferone is used in many lotions and creams as a protective agent against the ultraviolet rays of the sun.

The anthocyanins, natural plant pigments, are glycosides. The sugars most commonly combined with them are glucose, galactose, and rhamnose. The aglycons, known as anthocyanidins, are derivatives of 2-phenylbenzopyran. The

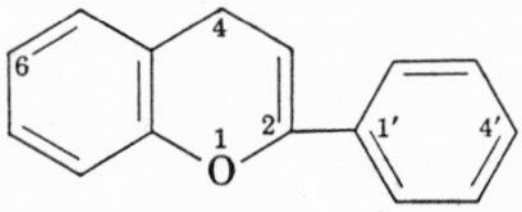

2-Phenylbenzopyran

oxonium salts of this compound are known as flavylium compounds. They are the hydroxyl substituted flavylium salts which occur as aglycons in the anthocyanins.

[6] Stahmann, Ikawa, and Link, U. S. pat. 2,427,578 (1947).
[7] Prior, *Brit. Med. J.*, **1955,** 944.
[8] Polhemus *et al., Clin. Research Proc.*, **3,** 196 (1955).

TABLE XX

ANTHOCYANIDINS

Aglycon	Chemical Name	Occurrence
Pelargonidin	3,5,7,4'-Tetrahydroxyflavylium chloride	Found in asters and dahlias. Present in orange-red to scarlet flowers
Cyanidin	3,5,7,3',4'-Pentahydroxyflavylium chloride	Found in roses and cornflowers. Present in crimson to bluish-red flowers
Apigeniden (rare)	5,7,4'-Trihydroxyflavylium chloride	Occurs in the flowers of *Gesnera fulgens*

In addition to the above, many flowers and berries contain methyl ethers of these anthocyanidins. These include *peonidin*, the blue pigment of the peony; *syringidin*, the coloring material in wine; and *malvidin*, the pigment of the blue mallow. Most of the anthocyanidins are linked in the glycoside through the 3-hydroxyl group.

Closely related to the anthocyanidins are the flavones [9] or 2-phenylchromones which are derivatives of 2-phenylbenzopyrone. Flavone is found in the flower, stalk, leaves, and seed capsules of many varieties of the primula. Derivatives are tabulated in Table XXI.

TABLE XXI

FLAVONES

Aglycon	Chemical Name	Occurrence
Chrysin	5,7-Dihydroxyflavone	Present in poplar buds
Apigenin	5,7,4'-Trihydroxyflavone	Present in celery and parsley
Luteolin	5,7,3',4'-Tetrahydroxyflavone	Present in Dyer's weed
Quercitin	3,5,7,3',4'-Pentahydroxyflavone	Present in quercitron bark

Catechins, the parent substance of many natural tannins, have been isolated as crystalline, colorless compounds from many plants. They have been shown to be hydrogenated anthocyanidins:

Cyanidin   Catechin

[9] For a review of the anthocyanins and flavones see Gilman, *Organic Chemistry*, John Wiley & Sons, New York, 1943, **2**, 1315–1340.

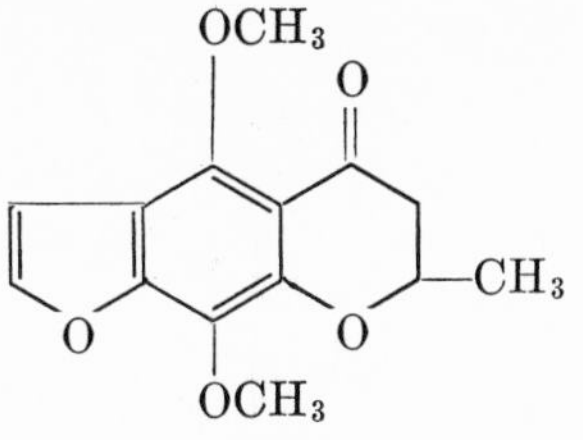

Khellin

Khellin (Visammin, 2-Methyl-5,8-dimethoxyfurochromone) occurs in the seeds of the plant *Ammi visnaga* and may be in general classified as an antispasmodic drug. It has been used to relieve bronchial asthma and for the relaxation of a variety of smooth-muscle organs. More particularly, it is thought to be effective as a coronary vasodilator in the relief of the pain of angina and related heart diseases. Its structure is indicated.

Studies on scurvy more than a century ago demonstrated that lemon juice corrected all the symptoms associated with this disease, including the capillary hemorrhages. It was later believed that vitamin C in the citrus juices was the curative factor. When synthetic vitamin C became available, however, it was found ineffective in alleviating all the scorbutic symptoms related to capillary weakness. This led Szent-Györgyi and his associates to seek for a substance in lemon that had an activity and importance similar to vitamin C. The flavanone glycosides of lemon were accordingly isolated in 1936 and termed vitamin P by Szent-Györgyi (P for permeability factor).

Many flavanol and flavanone glycosides have been examined for their relationship to vitamin P [10] and for their use in treating capillary fragility and permeability. Some of these are: hesperidin, eriodictyol, quercitrin, rutin, epicatechin,[11] and dried lemon peel infusion. Structural formulas for some of the known compounds indicate the type involved.

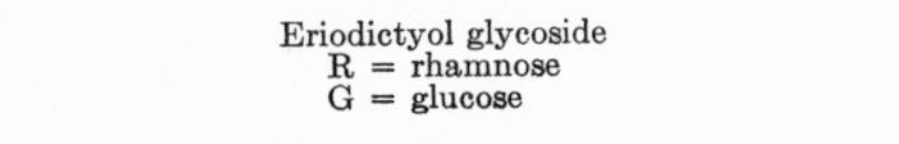

Eriodictyol glycoside
R = rhamnose
G = glucose

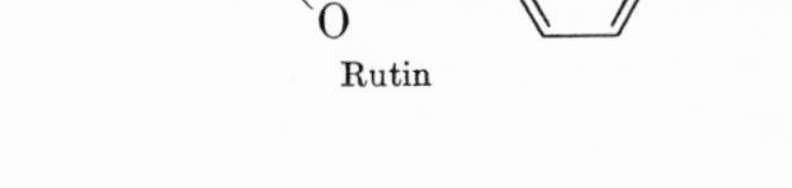

Rutin

[10] Scarborough and Bacharach, *Vitamins and Hormones*, Academic Press, New York, 1949, Vol. VII, pp. 1–55.

[11] Higby, *J. Am. Pharm. Assoc.*, **32**, 76 (1943).

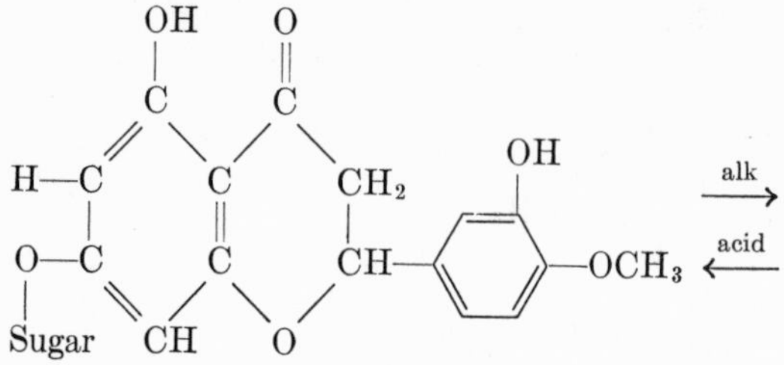

Hesperidin

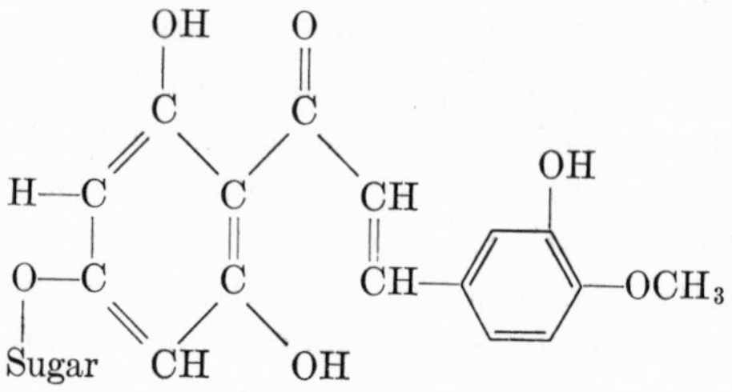

Hesperidin chalcone

Rutin (Rhamnoglycoside of Quercetin, Citrin) is a flavanol glycoside widely distributed in nature which upon hydrolysis yields quercitrin and rutanose. The pure substance isolated from buckwheat has at least ten times the activity of crude hesperidin. First used clinically in 1944 [12] it is reported to be effective against the recurrent hemorrhages caused by or related to decreased capillary fragility. It is usually administered in tablet form. It is believed that rutin is effective, at least in part, in overcoming the results of overexposure to radio-activity.

Vitamin E, the so-called antisterility vitamin, was first suspected in 1922 when it appeared that some then unknown factor was necessary for reproduction in the rat. In the female showing the deficiency, normal pregnancy is followed by fetal death and resorption. Evans and Burr observed that unsaponifiable fractions of wheat germ oil relieved these symptoms, and they applied the name vitamin E to the unknown factor. In 1936, Evans and his co-workers isolated allophanates (NH_2CONH—COOH is allophanic acid) of two compounds from wheat germ oil, both of which were active, and known as α- and β-tocopherol, respectively. Within a very short space of time, the structures of both compounds were determined, and both were prepared synthetically.

The synthesis of vitamin E is achieved by condensing phytyl bromide with trimethylquinol in petroleum ether and in the presence of anhydrous zinc chloride or acidic condensing agents: [13]

[12] Griffith, Couch, and Lindauer, *Proc. Soc. Exptl. Biol. Med.*, **55**, 228 (1944).
[13] Karrer and Isler, U. S. pat. 2,411,967; *C.A.*, **41**, 1713 (1947).

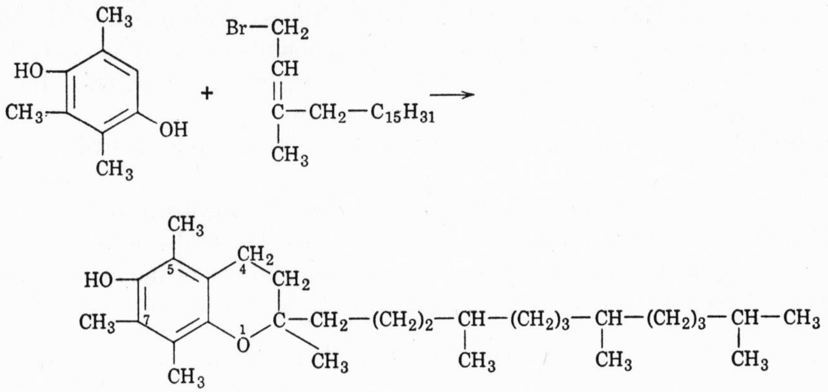

α-Tocopherol

β-Tocopherol is a lower homolog of the α-compound, the methyl in position 7 being absent. γ-Tocopherol is an isomer of β-tocopherol, the 5 position in the aromatic ring being free. δ-Tocopherol, with the methyl groups in both positions 5 and 7 absent, is one of the more abundant members of the vitamin E complex; it constitutes about 30 per cent of the mixed tocopherols in soybean oil.[14]

Only α-tocopherol is considered [15] a source of vitamin E activity for animals and humans.

The role of vitamin E in the human is not yet certain. Its value in the treatment of sterility or habitual abortion is questionable. Despite claims of its importance in the treatment of a variety of diseases, substantiating evidence is lacking. Its role as an activator of cytochrome C reductase has been reviewed by Nason and Lehman.[16]

Rotenone is the name given to a complex ketonic compound derived from many leguminous plants growing in the tropics and subtropics. The search for

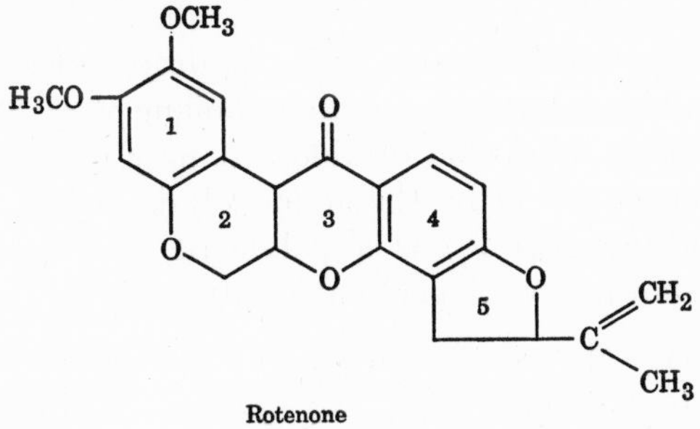

Rotenone

insecticides that would be nontoxic to warm-blooded animals resulted in the isolation of a number of principles, especially from derris and cubé root. La Forge

[14] Stern, Robeson, Weisslerand, and Baxter, *J. Am. Chem. Soc.*, **69**, 869 (1947).
[15] Quaife, *Ann. Rev. Biochem.*, **23**, 223 (1954).
[16] Nason and Lehman, *Science*, **122**, 19 (1955).

et al.[17] established the structure and worked out the stereochemical relationships of the isomeric compounds. The rotenoid compounds are used as contact insecticides and as stomach poisons for lice, aphids, beetles, fleas, etc. Lotions containing rotenone are employed as parasiticides.

Deguelin is dihydrorotenone; that is, the isopropenyl group is hydrogenated to isopropyl.

Elliptone is a lower homolog of deguelin; ring 5 is unsubstituted.

Miracil D (1-Methyl-4-β-diethylaminoethylaminothioxanthone) is used in the treatment of schistosomiasis. It is orally effective and one of the most valuable drugs available for the treatment of human and animal infections of the disease.

Miracil D

NITROGEN HETEROCYCLES—FIVE MEMBERS

Pyrrolidine and Pyrrole

Isosteric with furan is the nitrogen analog with four carbon atoms and one nitrogen atom in a cycle. This type of cycle is very abundant in nature.

Pyrrole   Pyrrolidine   Pyrrolidone

Pyrrolidine (Tetramethyleneimine, Tetrahydropyrrole) possesses all the properties of a secondary amine. It is a liquid boiling at 87–88°; it forms a solid carbonate with atmospheric carbon dioxide. It may be synthesized either by the hydrogenation of pyrrole or by the ammonolysis of furan.

Polyvinylpyrrolidone (P.V.P.) is a polymeric material synthesized from γ-butyrolactone as shown. A 3.5 per cent solution of P.V.P. in water contain-

γ-Butyrolactone   Pyrrolidone   Vinylpyrrolidone   P.V.P.

ing various salts is known as Periston and is used as a blood plasma extender.

[17] La Forge, Haller, and Smith, *Chem. Revs.*, **12**, 181 (1933).

Proline (Pyrrolidine-2-carboxylic Acid), an α-amino acid, is found as the L-configuration as a component of proteins. The racemic modification may be synthesized as indicated. Its N-methyl derivative is known as hygrinic acid, a

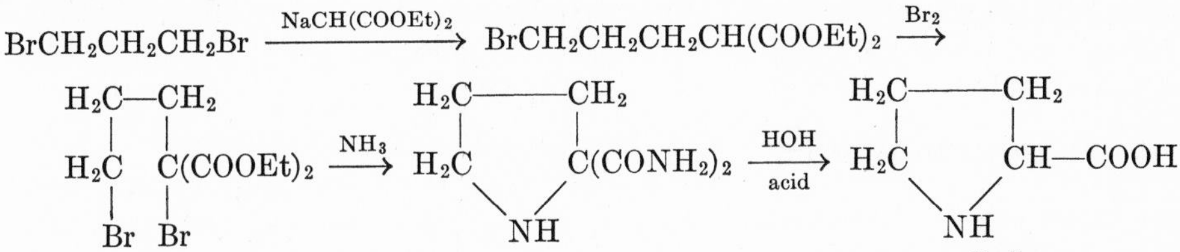

$$BrCH_2CH_2CH_2Br \xrightarrow{\text{NaCH(COOEt)}_2} BrCH_2CH_2CH_2CH(COOEt)_2 \xrightarrow{\text{Br}_2}$$

Proline

product obtained by the oxidation of hygrine and cuskohygrine. Its betaine, known as stachydrine, has been isolated from the roots of the *Stachys tuberifa*.

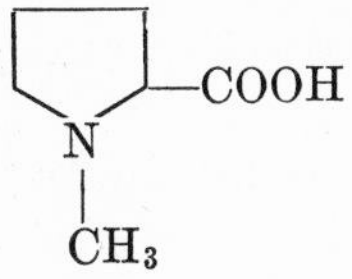

Hygrinic acid

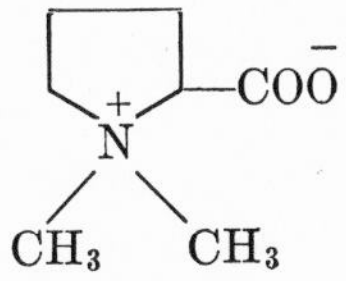

Stachydrine

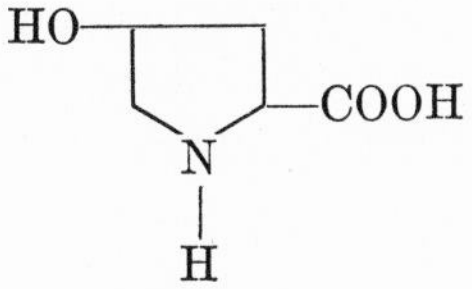

4-Hydroxyproline

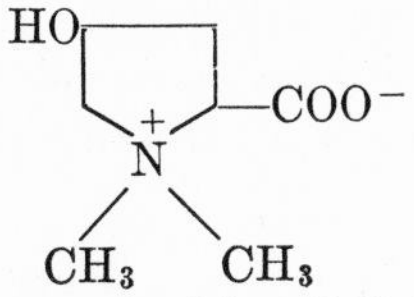

Betonecine, $[\alpha]_D -36.6°$
Turecine, $(+)$ isomer

4-Hydroxyproline, also an amino acid, is also found as a constituent of proteins. With two centers of asymmetry it is capable of existing in four stereoisomeric forms, all of which have been synthesized and isolated. Two isomeric betaines of hydroxyproline, betonecine and turecine, occur in *Betonica officionalis* L.

Hygrine, $C_8H_{15}NO$, **Hygroline,** $C_8H_{17}NO$, and **Cuskohygrine,** $C_{13}H_{24}N_2O$, are three related pyrrolidine alkaloids which occur together in Peruvian coca.

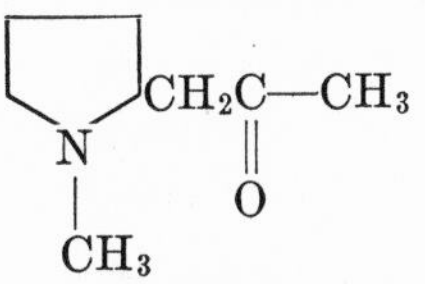

Hygrine

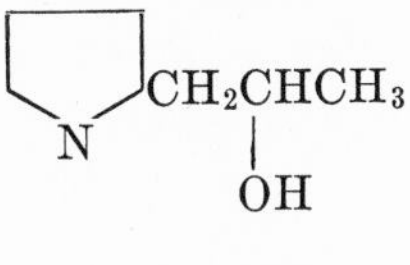

Hygroline

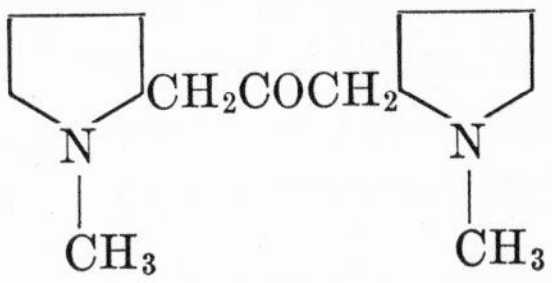

Cuskohygrine

Pentolinium Tartrate, N.N.R. [Pentamethylene-1,1'-*bis*-(1-methylpyrrolidinium Bitartrate)], is a potent ganglionic blocking agent, useful for the management of malignant stages of hypertension. It is active after oral administration. Animal experiments show it to be about five times more potent than hexamethonium bromide.[18]

[18] Wien and Mason, *Lancet*, **264**, 454 (1953); Smirk, *ibid.*, 457.

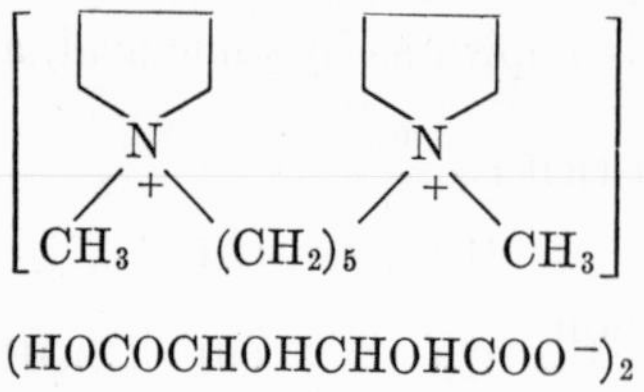

Pentolinium tartrate

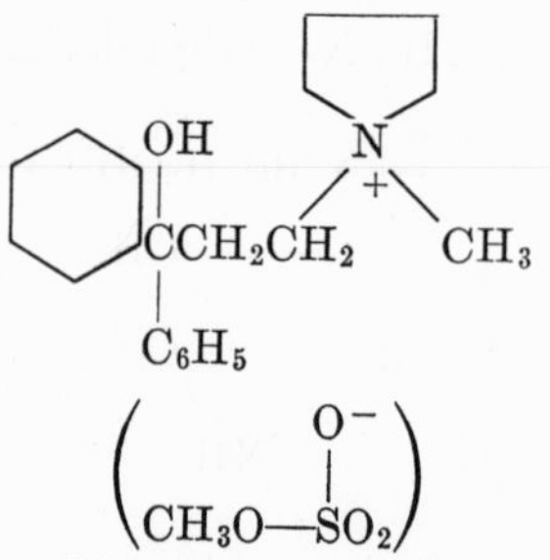

Tricyclamol methyl sulfate

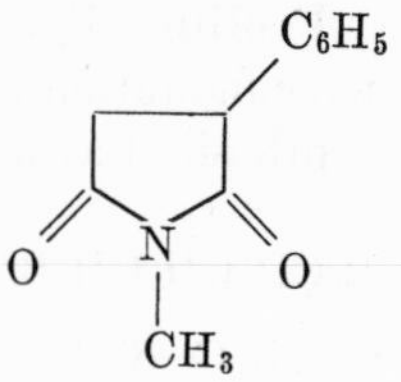

Milontin

Tricyclamol Methyl Sulfate, N.N.R. [Elorine Methyl Sulfate, 1-Cyclo-hexyl-1-phenyl-3-(1-pyrrolidino)-1-propanol Dimethyl Sulfate], is an anticholin-ergic agent, used in the clinic to control functional spasm in the gastrointestinal tract.

Milontin (N-Methyl-α-phenylsuccinimide, 1-Methyl-2-phenylpyrrolidine-2,5-dione) is one of a series of related imides found to be effective in controlling Metrazol-induced seizures in rats, and it is reported to be effective in controlling petit mal epilepsy in humans. It is excreted partly by ring opening and partly by hydroxylation in the *para* position of the phenyl substituent,[19] much as is the case with phenyl substituted barbituric acids or hydantoins.

Pyrrolizidine Alkaloids

The genus *Senecio*, representatives of which once enjoyed reputed medicinal value as crude drugs,[20] contains alkaloids which possess hepatotoxic properties. Since the plants are poisonous to animals, their alkaloids are of interest even though they no longer find therapeutic application. A representative of these alkaloids is *monocrotaline*, for which the following structure has been established.[21]

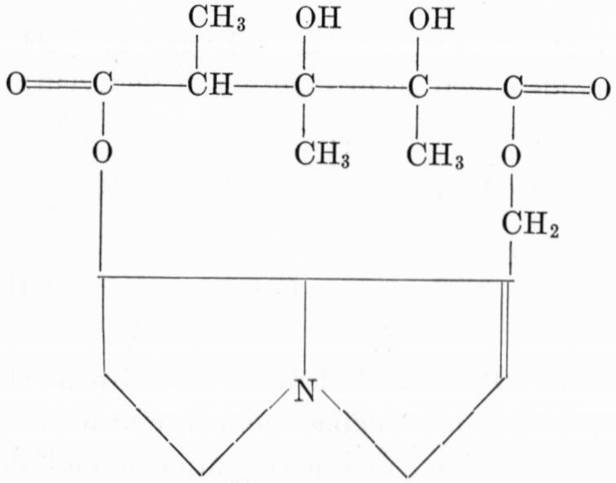

Monocrotaline

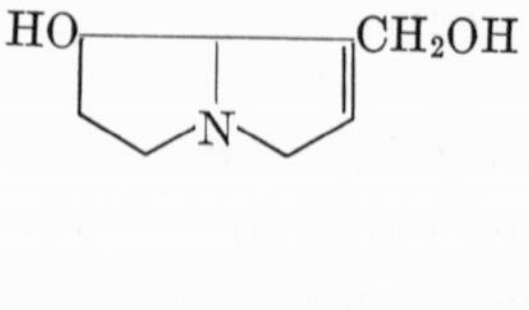

Retronecine

[19] Glazko et al., J. Pharmacol. Exptl. Therap., **111**, 413 (1954).

[20] Dragendorf, Die Heilpflanzen der verschiedenen Voelker und Zeiten, Stuttgart, Ferdinand Enke, 1898.

[21] Adams et al., J. Am. Chem. Soc., **74**, 5612 (1952).

The basic portion of the molecule, *retronecine,* is common to most of the Senecio alkaloids.

Pyrrole is the nitrogen analog of furan and of thiophene. It was first isolated from "bone oil"; substituted pyrroles are present in many natural products, particularly hematin and chlorophyll.

A pine splinter moistened with hydrochloric acid produces with pyrrole and pyrrole derivatives a fiery red color; hence, the name pyrrole.

Pyrrole may be looked upon as a divinylamine, yet it is not a strong base. In fact pyrrole possesses several chemical properties that are characteristic of acids; for example, metallic potassium reacts with pyrrole to liberate hydrogen and to form potassium pyrrole.

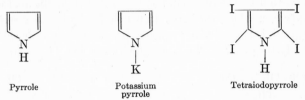

Pyrrole   Potassium   Tetraiodopyrrole
            pyrrole

Tetraiodopyrrole has been used as a substitute for iodoform. It may be synthesized by the direct iodination of pyrrole in the presence of alkali.

Porphins

For vitamin B_{12}, see page 433.

Common to several plant and animal pigments is the porphin molecule, a complex pyrrole heterocycle. It has been synthesized from 2-pyrrolealdehyde [22] or from pyrrole and formaldehyde [23] and has the accompanying structure.

Porphin

Derivatives of porphin occur in hemoglobin, chlorophyll, bilirubin, and vitamin B_{12}.

[22] Fischer and Gleim, *Ann.,* **521,** 157 (1935).
[23] Rothemund, *J. Am. Chem. Soc.,* **58,** 625 (1936).

Hemoglobin, the red coloring material in blood, consists of a protein fragment, *globin,* and a colored portion called *hemochromogen.* Hemoglobin easily forms a compound with oxygen, *oxyhemoglobin,* which readily gives up this oxygen to the tissues and regenerates hemoglobin. In this manner hemoglobin acts in the biological transportation of oxygen.

The hemochromogen portion of hemoglobin is a porphin derivative in which an atom of iron is complexed in the ferrous state. Through the residual valences of the iron, it is capable of entering into loose combination with various bases or the amino acid nitrogen of proteins.

Once hemoglobin leaves the organism, it is converted to *methemoglobin* in which the iron is in the ferric state and which now contains firmly bound oxygen. Methemoglobin then can no longer act as an oxygen transport medium. Removal of the globin portion of this molecule leaves *hematin,* again an iron-complexed porphin derivative in which the ferric iron holds a hydroxyl group. In *hemin,* this hydroxyl group is replaced by chlorine; *heme* is merely reduced hematin; the hydroxyl of the latter is removed leaving the iron in the ferrous state.

Protoporphyrin   Hemin

Hemochromogen and hematin are easily interrelated since both yield the same porphyrins upon removal of the iron. Both form protoporphyrin and hematoporphyrin. These compounds have been obtained synthetically, and protoporphyrin has been reconverted into hemin that is identical with the natural product. The relationship between protoporphyrin and hemin is indicated.

Chlorophyll, the green coloring matter of plants, is a porphin derivative complexed with magnesium and containing a molecule of phytol. The role of chlorophyll in photosynthesis has not yet been defined, although it is likely that it bears a relationship to the vegetable similar to hemoglobin in the animal.

Natural chlorophyll has been resolved into two fractions, A and B, the latter containing one more oxygen and two less hydrogens than the former. Chlorophyll A is bluish green and makes up about three-fourths of natural chlorophyll. Chlorophyll B is yellowish green and makes up about one-fourth of natural chlorophyll. The relationship between chlorophyll A and chlorophyll B is indicated by the equations. Willstätter in 1913 determined the empirical formula

$$C_{32}H_{30}ON_4Mg \overset{COOCH_3}{\underset{COOC_{20}H_{39}}{<}} \xrightarrow{\text{alkali}} C_{32}H_{30}ON_4Mg \overset{COOH}{\underset{COOH}{<}} + C_{20}H_{40}O + CH_3OH$$

Chlorophyll A   Chlorophyllin A   Phytol   Methanol

$$C_{32}H_{28}O_2N_4Mg \overset{COOCH_3}{\underset{COOC_{20}H_{39}}{<}} \xrightarrow{\text{alkali}} C_{32}H_{28}O_2N_4Mg \overset{COOH}{\underset{COOH}{<}} + C_{20}H_{40}O + CH_3OH$$

Chlorophyll B   Chlorophyllin B   Phytol   Methanol

of chlorophyll, $C_{55}H_{72}N_4O_5Mg$, and this formula was confirmed later by Fischer and by Stoll. Structural studies have not proved beyond question the constitution of chlorophyll, but the formulas shown are generally accepted for chlorophylls A and B.

Chlorophyll A, R = CH$_3$
Chlorophyll B, R = CHO

Removal of the magnesium in the chlorophylls leaves the porphyrin structures which are called *pheophytins A and B*. These porphyrins complex readily with a variety of metals and the products have been used in medicine. Iron pheophytin is reported to be of value in anemias, and mercury pheophytin has antiseptic properties.

The chlorophyllins as salts are water-soluble products. Thus sodium magnesium chlorophyllin and sodium copper chlorophyllin (chloresium) have been used in foods and pharmaceutical products for some time.

Sodium magnesium chlorophyllin has been reported to be an effective bacterial inhibitor, harmless and soothing to the tissues. It is particularly effective against anaerobic organisms, a fact that has led to the suggestion that it acts by liberating oxygen from carbon dioxide. Applied in the forms of solution, ointments, and wet dressings, it has been reported to be valuable in the treatment of skin diseases and internal infections such as peritonitis, brain ulcers, bone ulcers, pyorrhea and trench mouth, sinus infections, and head colds.

There has been a tremendous increase in the use of chlorophyll derivatives for their reputed deodorant properties. Although their value in this connection is controversial, many such products are being marketed.

Bilirubin is the red-brown pigment of bile. It may be regarded as an open-chain derivative of porphin with the currently accepted formula as shown.

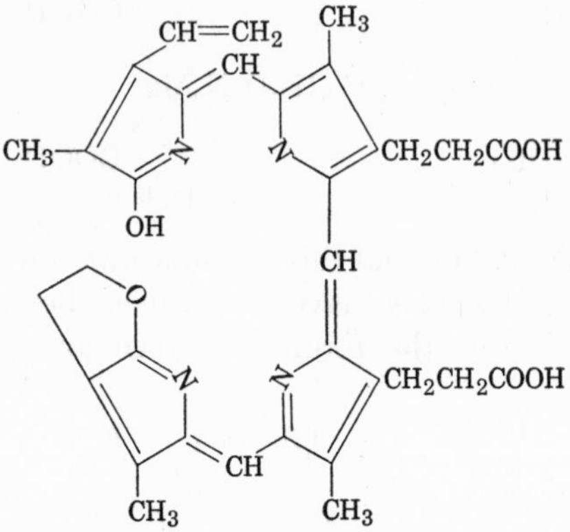

Bilirubin

Benzopyrroles

Benzopyrrole may be considered as pyrrole with the benzene nucleus fused at the 2,3 positions or at the 3,4 positions, as shown.

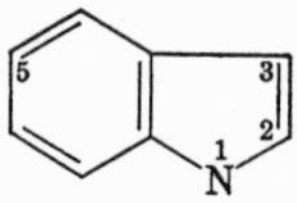

2,3-Benzopyrrole,
indole

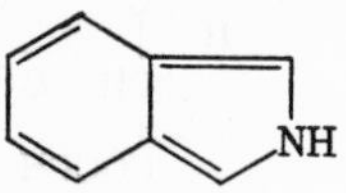

3,4-Benzopyrrole,
isoindole

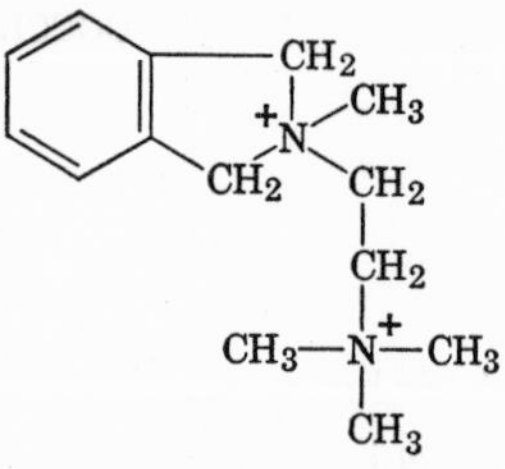

Ecolid

Ecolid, a 3,4-benzoindoline derivative of the structure shown, is reported to be a ganglionic blocking agent and useful for the treatment of hypertension.[24]

Indole and **β-Methylindole** are present in fecal matter and in protein decomposition products. They are present also in many natural perfumes, e.g., in jasmine and in orange blossom. They are probably formed from tryptophan. They impart an intense fecal odor when concentrated.

3-Indoleacetic Acid (Heteroauxin) has been identified as a plant-growth hormone; also its higher homologs act as plant-growth hormones, producing effects analogous to those of the auxins. It is estimated that the amount of auxin is 2.68×10^{-5} gram per kernel of immature corn; 9 per cent of this was

[24] *Chem. Eng. News,* **33,** 4799 (1955).

characterized as 3-indoleacetic acid.[25]   The synthetic plant hormones, such as
indoleacetic and indolebutyric acids, also stimulate the development of the plant
pathogens.[26]

3-Indoleacetic acid   Gramine

Gramine (Donaxine), $C_{11}H_{14}N_2$, has been detected in barley mutants, and
in *Arundo donax* L.   In its pharmacological behavior gramine resembles $(+)$-ψ-
ephedrine; in the dog small doses raise the blood pressure, large doses lower it;
changes in venal volume parallel the blood pressure.

Tryptophan, a β-indolyl derivative of alanine, is an essential amino acid.
Tryptophan deficiency in rats results in vascularization of the cornea, alopecia,
malformation of incisor teeth, atrophy of the testes, and aspermiogenesis.[27]

The normal metabolism of tryptophan is initiated by hydroxylation at position 5,[28] then decarboxylation to serotonin,[29] followed by oxidative deamination

Tryptophan   5-Hydroxytryptophan

Tryptamine, produces   Serotonin
catalepsy in the cat

Bufotenine   5-Hydroxyindoleacetic acid

to 5-hydroxyindoleacetic acid, and finally to ring rupture.   Abnormal metabolism, it is suggested, may give rise to hallucinogenic products which may plaus-

---

[25] Haagen-Smit, Dandliker, Witwer, and Murneek, *Am. J. Botany*, **33,** 118 (1946); *C.A.*, **40,**
2503 (1946).
[26] Stuart and McClellan, *Science*, **97,** 15 (1943).
[27] Albanese and Buschke, *Science*, **95,** 584 (1942).
[28] Ek and Witkop, *J. Am. Chem. Soc.*, **76,** 5579 (1954).
[29] Udenfried, Clark, and Titus, *J. Am. Chem. Soc.*, **75,** 501 (1953).

ibly account for some psychotic conditions in human beings.[30]   (See also adreno-chrome, below.)

Serotonin (5-Hydroxytryptamine, Enteramine) is the vasoconstrictor principle originally isolated from the serum of clotted mammalian blood by Page and his co-workers [31] and since found [32] widely distributed in a variety of animal tissues in the form of its creatinine sulfate complex salt.   The β-indolylethylamine structure of serotonin was proved by its synthesis [33] which made available sufficient material for extensive biological investigations of its function in the body.   There is insufficient evidence to establish the functional significance of

$$C_6H_5CH_2O \quad \text{---CH}_2N \begin{matrix} CH_3 \\ \\ CH_3 \end{matrix} \xrightarrow[\text{3. debenzylation}]{\substack{\text{1. NaCN} \\ \text{2. LiAlH}_4}} HO \quad \text{---CH}_2CH_2NH_2$$

5-Benzyloxygramine   Serotonin

serotonin.   Among other possibilities, its occurrence in brain tissue together with the finding that lysergic acid diethylamide (a serotonin antagonist) produces mental aberrations in man suggests that it may be concerned with nerve metabolism.   In addition, Brodie and his co-workers [34] have indicated that serotonin is implicated in the mode of action of reserpine on brain centers.

Bufotenine (N,N-Dimethylserotonin) is a 5-hydroxytryptamine derivative isolated from toads as well as a variety of natural sources.   It antagonizes the action of serotonin and may be involved in its metabolism.   In the monkey, bufotenine produces behavior disturbances paralleling those of lysergic acid diethylamide.[35]

Hypophorine has been isolated from various species of *Erythrina*.   It is a betaine derived from tryptophan.   It increases reflex irritability and tetanic convulsions in the frog.

$$\text{C---CH}_2\text{---CH---CO}_2{}^- $$

Hypophorine

Adrenochrome is one of the products of the enzymatic oxidation of epinephrine.   In 1937, Green and Richter [36] observed that epinephrine taking part in an oxidation-transport enzyme for lactic and malic acids assumed a red color.   This

[30] Fabing, *Neurology,* **5,** 603 (1955).
[31] Rapport, Green, and Page, *J. Biol. Chem.,* **176,** 1243 (1948).
[32] Erspamer, *Naturwissenschaften,* **11,** 318 (1953).
[33] Hamlin and Fischer, *J. Am. Chem. Soc.,* **73,** 5007 (1951).
[34] Shore, Silver, and Brodie, *Science,* **122,** 284, 374 (1955).
[35] Evarts, *Abstracts Medicinal Chemistry Symposium,* Syracuse, N. Y., 1954.
[36] *Biochem. J.,* **31,** 596 (1937).

color is due to the formation of adrenochrome.[37]   Reduced coenzyme converts the pigment into colorless leucoadrenochrone.

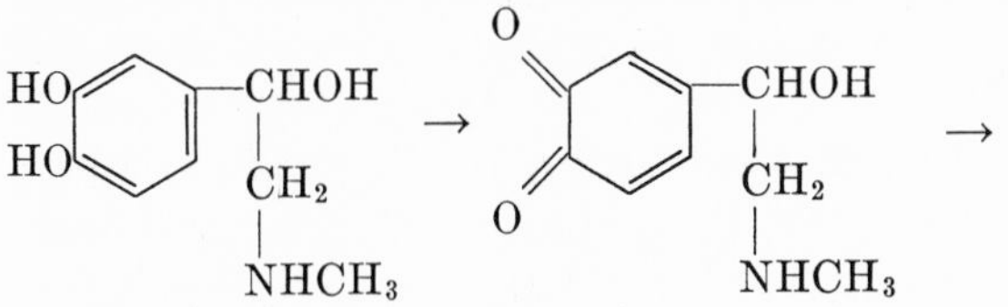

Epinephrine

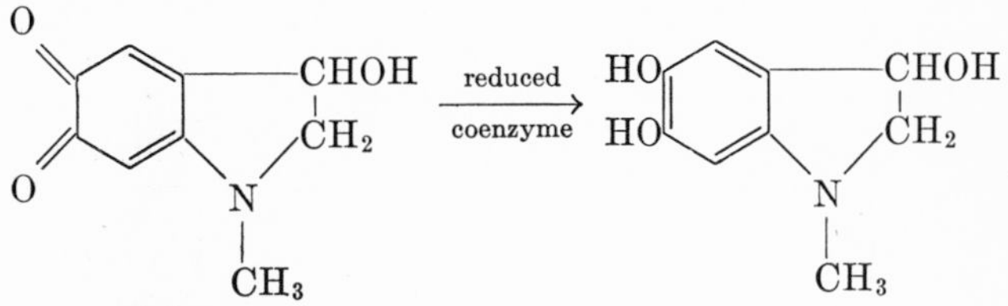

$\rightarrow$

$\rightarrow$

Adrenochrome,
1-Methyl-3-hydroxy-
2,3-dihydroindole-
5,6-quinone

reduced coenzyme $\longrightarrow$

Leucoadrenochrome

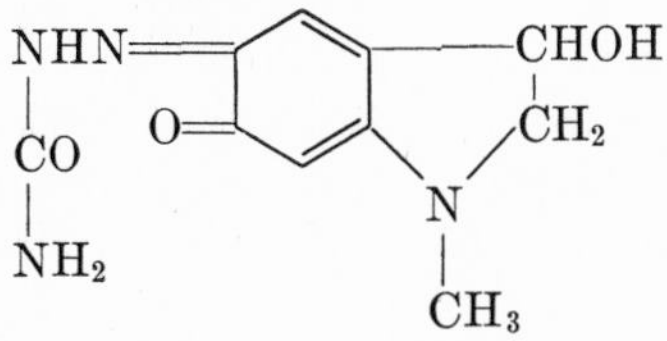

Adrenochrome semicarbazone

It is suggested that epinephrine, whose biological functions are not well understood, may be a precursor for products whose biochemistry is even less well known.   For example, the biological need for adrenochrome is not established, yet it exhibits intriguing pharmacodynamic properties.   It lowers blood pressure in experimentally hypertensive rats but has no effect on normal animals.[38]   It possesses hemostatic properties.[39]   Administration of 0.5 mg. adrenochrome to guinea pigs produced marked capillary resistance, and the effect persisted for several days.[40]

Bacq and Heirman [41] are of the opinion that adrenoxine, obtained by the further oxidation of adrenochrome and as yet unidentified, plays an important biochemical role. It possesses cardioinhibitor properties, and its mydriatic activity is about 10,000 times that for epinephrine.

Carbazochrome Salicylate, N.N.R., a complex of adrenochrome monosemicarbazone with sodium salicylate, is suggested as a systemic hemostat.

It has been reported that adrenochrome may be classified as a "phantastica" or hallucinogen.   And it is postulated that adrenochrome, or some other faulty metabolic product from epinephrine, may be responsible for some psychotic states in humans.[42, 43]

[37] Richter and Blaschko, *J. Chem. Soc.*, **1937**, 610.
[38] Oster and Sabotka, *J. Pharmacol.*, **78**, 100 (1943).
[39] Derouaux, *Arch. internat. Pharmacodynamie*, **69**, 142 and 348 (1943).
[40] Parrot and Cotereau, *Compt. rend. soc. biol.*, **139**, 907 (1945); *C.A.*, **40**, 6654 (1946).
[41] Bacq and Heirman, *Arch. internat. Physiol.*, **50**, 129 (1940).
[42] Rinkel, *Diseases of Nervous System*, **16**, 229 (1955).
[43] Fabing, *Neurology*, **5**, 605 (1955).

Further oxidation of adrenochrome via adrenoxine results in dark pigments, called *melanins*, which contribute to skin coloration.

Adrenochrome monosemicarbazone possesses hemostatic properties.[44]

Erythrina Alkaloids

Because of their curarelike activity and the possibility that they may be useful muscle-relaxing agents, the alkaloids found in numerous species of *Erythrina* are of considerable interest. Of the many alkaloids isolated in the crystalline state, β-erythroidine is the most important; its structural formula is indicated.[45]

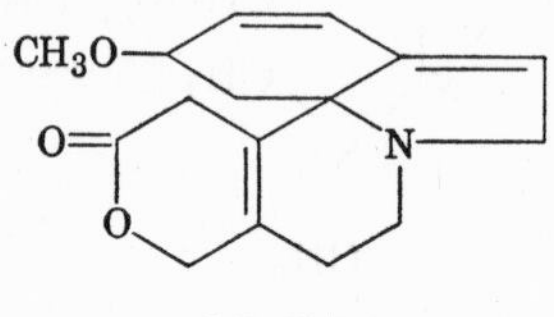

β-Erythroidine

Physostigma Alkaloids

Physostigma venosum (Leguminosae), also known as the ordeal bean, eserenut, and calabar bean, contains several alkaloids of which the most important is **Physostigmine.**   The structure of this alkaloid has been established by the synthesis that is summarized.[46]

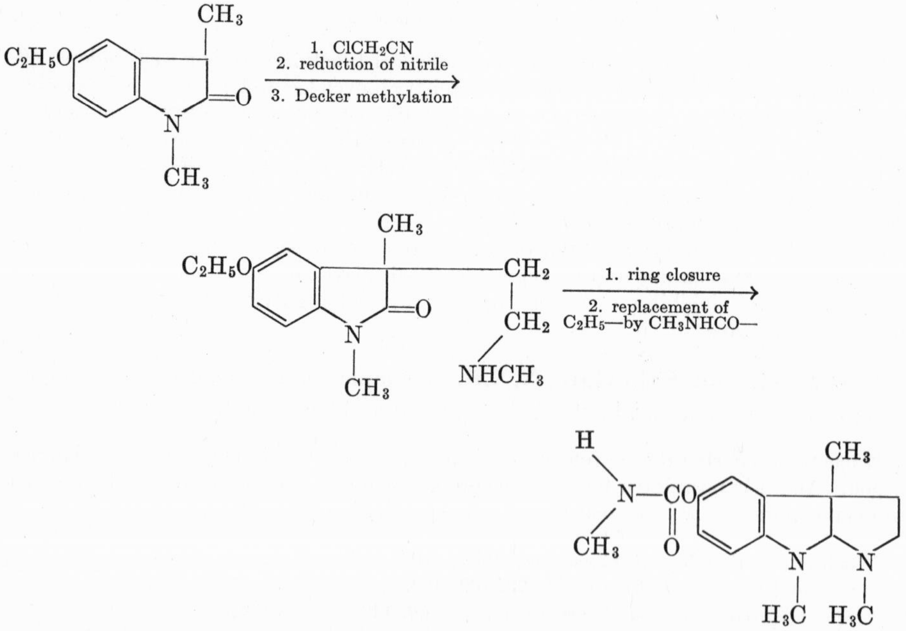

Physostigmine

[44] Beaudet, Trabert, and Heneaux, *Arch. intern. physiol.*, **57,** 343 (1950).
[45] Boekelheide *et al.*, *J. Am. Chem. Soc.*, **75,** 2550 (1953).
[46] Julian and Pikl, *J. Am. Chem. Soc.*, **57,** 563, 755 (1935).

Benzpyrinium bromide

Physostigmine Salicylate, U.S.P. (Eserine Salicylate), is the salt usually used in therapeutics. It consists of slightly yellow crystals, soluble about 1:75 in water. The salt and its aqueous solutions change color on exposure to air and light, first to pink and then to a brownish red, owing to oxidation with the formation of rubreserine. The alkaloid acts physiologically by inhibiting the enzyme cholinesterase in the body fluids and tissues. Thus it prevents the rapid and continuous destruction of acetylcholine. In this way it acts as a powerful parasympathetic stimulant. The chief use of physostigmine is to reduce intraocular pressure in glaucoma. It is usually instilled into the eye in 0.1 to 1 per cent solutions, or it is administered in gelatin discs for this purpose. Internally, it is used to some extent to increase the tone and motility of the intestines and to treat muscular weakness (myasthenia gravis), often being injected intramuscularly.

Benzpyrinium Bromide, N.N.R. (Stigmonene Bromide), is 1-benzyl-3-(dimethylcarbamyloxy) pyridinium bromide and is a cholinergic agent similar to neostigmine, useful in the treatment of atony of the intestinal and bladder musculature.

Yohimbe and Rauwolfia Alkaloids

Yohimbine is the most important of the alkaloids of *Corynanthe johimbe* bark. Although it has little value in modern medicine, it has many physiological effects, most famous of which is its aphrodisiac action.

As a result of considerable effort, the structure of yohimbine has been established from a knowledge of its degradation products.[47]

Alloyohimbine, X = —OH, Y = —H, Z = —COOCH₃.
Yohimbine or Rauwolscine, X = —H, Y = —OH, Z = —COOCH₃.

Reserpine, R = —OCH₃, X = 3,4,5-trimethoxybenzoyloxy-.
Deserpidine, R = —H, X = 3,4,5-trimethoxybenzoyloxy-.

[47] Barger and Scholz, *Helv. Chim. Acta*, **16**, 1343 (1933); **18**, 923 (1935). Wibaut and van Gastel, *Rec. trav. chim.*, **54**, 85 (1935). Clemo and Swan, *J. Chem. Soc.*, **1946**, 617; **1949**, 487.

The structural relationships between the yohimbe and the Rauwolfia alkaloids, as shown, have been established by the efforts of many workers.[48]

Recognition of the hypotensive action of extracts of *Rauwolfia serpentina* [49,50] has resulted in extensive researches into the chemistry, pharmacology, and medical aspects of the Rauwolfia alkaloids. This species of the Rauwolfia family is a climbing shrub widely distributed in India, Burma, and Southeast Asia in general. **Rauwolfia** is considered to be the dried roots of *Rauwolfia serpentina* containing not less than 0.8 per cent of total alkaloids. Extracts of the root on pharmacological examination were shown to be relatively potent hypotensive agents with sedative effects and with quite low toxicity.

Chemical investigations to isolate the alkaloid in which the physiological effect was greatest have indicated that at least fifteen alkaloids are present in this plant. These have been obtained in crystalline form and may be divided broadly into the strongly basic yellow alkaloids such as *serpentine* and *serpentinine* and the weakly basic colorless compounds, *ajuvaline, rauwolscine,* and *reserpine.*

Reserpine is the most important alkaloid from *Rauwolfia serpentina;* it has also been isolated from *R. heterophylla* which is indigenous to Central and South America. The structure of the pure alkaloid was established by Schlittler [51] and his co-workers.

Early efforts [52] to alter the chemical structure of reserpine to improve its pharmacological properties have not been fruitful. Derivatives in which the indole nitrogen is alkylated are devoid of sedative and hypotensive properties.

Pharmacological and clinical investigators have found that the crystalline alkaloid has most of the therapeutically desirable effects of Rauwolfia. Reserpine is one thousand times as potent as the crude drug. It is a useful adjuvant to other hypotensive agents and has found an important place in the treatment of hypertension.

Perhaps more important is the sedative action which is found in reserpine. This drug brings about a "tranquillizing" effect in animals and humans. It provides a state of quiescence which has value in the treatment of mental illness,[53] and it has assumed an important role in the treatment of schizophrenia and chronic psychoses. In contrast to barbiturates, reserpine in effective sedative doses brings about sleep without loss of muscular coordination.

First isolated in 1952,[54] reserpine yielded the secret of its structure in three years,[55] and by 1956 its total synthesis was announced.[56] This synthesis is summarized schematically.

[48] Chatterjee et al., *Chemistry & Industry,* **1954,** 491. Van Tamelen and Hance, *J. Am. Chem. Soc.,* 77, 4692 (1955). Schlittler et al., *ibid.,* 4335 (1955).

[49] Lesser, *Drug & Cosmetic Ind.,* 74, 500 (1954).

[50] Phillips and Chadha, *J. Am. Pharm. Assoc.,* 44, 553 (1955).

[51] Schlittler et al., *Helv. Chim. Acta,* 37, 59 (1954).

[52] Huebner, *J. Am. Chem. Soc.,* 76, 5792 (1954).

[53] Noce, Williams, and Rappoport, *J. Am. Med. Assoc.,* 156, 821 (1954).

[54] Müller, Schlittler, and Bein, *Experientia,* 8, 338 (1952).

[55] Weisenborn et al., *J. Am. Chem. Soc.,* 78, 2021, 2022 (1956).

[56] Woodward, Bader, Bickel, Frey, and Kierstead, *J. Am. Chem. Soc.,* 78, 2023, 2657 (1956).

Racemic methyl O–acetyl*iso*reserpate
Resolved through di–*p*-toluyl-L-tartaric acid

(1) deacetylation
(2) $(CH_3O)_3C_6H_2COCl$

Reserpine

Deserpidine (Canescine, Recanescine), an alkaloid isolated from *Rauwolfia canescens*, is 11-desmoethoxyreserpine. Evidence by Slater and his co-workers [57] indicates that it has substantially the same pharmacological activity as reserpine.

Strychnos Alkaloids

The most important alkaloids of *Strychnos nux vomica* and *S. ignatii* are strychnine and brucine. Intensive studies of the structures of these compounds of high molecular weight and great complexity have resulted in the acceptance of the indicated formulas.

Strychnine, N.F., is a white, crystalline powder, practically insoluble in water (1:6420), soluble in chloroform 1:5. It is a potent stimulant of the central

(−)Isomer used

Strychnine, R = H
Brucine, R = OCH₃

nervous system and in toxic doses causes contraction of many muscles, leading to tonic or spinal convulsions. Because it is intensely bitter, it is employed as a bitter tonic; the bitter taste can be detected in dilutions of 1:1,000,000 to 1:500,000. Elixir of iron, quinine, and strychnine and similar preparations are used as tonics. It is prescribed often for failing circulation and low blood pressure but is of little value in these conditions. It is a valuable respiratory stimulant especially for use in treating the effects of overdosage with depressants of the central nervous system such as the barbiturates. The low solubility of the free base in water has led to the use of salts which are generally administered in the form of tablets. The official salts include: *Strychnine Sulfate, N.F., Strychnine Nitrate, N.F.,* and *Strychnine Phosphate, N.F.* Liquid nux, a mixture of strychnine and brucine salts (*Solution of Nux Vomica Alkaloids, N.F.*), is extensively used in veterinary practice.

The total synthesis of strychnine has been achieved in a brilliant sequence of reactions.[58] The starting point was the phenylhydrazone of 3,4-dimethoxy-

[57] Slater *et al.*, *Proc. Soc. Exptl. Biol. Med.*, **88**, 293 (1955).
[58] Woodward *et al.*, *J. Am. Chem. Soc.*, **76**, 4749 (1954).

acetophenone; the magnitude and character of the result may be appreciated from the very abbreviated summary shown.

Strychnine is readily absorbed and, except for the about 20 per cent which is eliminated through the kidneys, readily destroyed. The rate of destruction is sufficiently rapid so that over a period of 24 hr. two lethal doses may be taken without appreciable toxic or cumulative symptoms.

PYRIDINE AND PIPERIDINE DERIVATIVES

The heterocycle composed of five carbon atoms and one nitrogen atom is found very widely distributed in nature, and among these compounds are some of the most useful and important medicines and drugs. Among these are many antihistamine products (page 211), including Doxylamine, Prophenpyridamine, Pyrilamine, Tripelennamine, and Carbinoxamine.

Pyridine Compounds

Pyridine occurs up to 2.4 per cent dry weight in rayless goldenrod, *Aplopappus hartwegi* Blake. 3-Methoxypyridine has been found to a small extent in *Equisetum arvense* L. and in *Thermopsis rhombifolia*.

Pyridine is isosteric with benzene and pyran. It has a resonance energy of 43 kg.-cal. per mole, higher than that for benzene. First isolated from bone oil (Anderson, 1849), it is now obtained in commercial quantities from coal distillation. When pure, it is a colorless liquid, b.p. 115°, with a very characteristic odor, miscible with water in all proportions. It shows definite aromatic characteristics; it may be sulfonated, halogenated, and to a limited extent it may even be nitrated. Coupled with these aromatic properties are those of a tertiary amine. Thus, with an alkyl halide, it will form a quaternary ammonium salt, known as an alkylpyridinium salt.

Pyridine

N-Methylpyridinium Hydroxide is a strongly alkaline, nonvolatile liquid, capable of producing curarelike action. It has been isolated from crab extract; it appears in human urine after smoking; it appears in the urine after the ingestion of coffee, probably being formed by the decarboxylation of trigonelline. The

N-methylpyridinium hydroxide   R = CH₃, X = OH⁻
Ceepryn   R = N—C₁₆H₃₃, X = C/

higher alkylpyridinium salts like the quaternary salts of the "zephiran" type are excellent germicides. Thus cetylpyridinium chloride is being promoted as an antiseptic.

Cetylpyridinium Chloride (Ceepryn), m.p. 80°, is a white, crystalline powder which occurs as the monohydrate. It is relatively nontoxic. In the absence of serum it is active at a dilution 1:65,000 toward *S. aureus*, and in the presence of 10 per cent serum it is active at 1:11,500 dilution.[59] Concentrations as low as 0.003 per cent of cetylpyridinium chloride are effective in preserving solutions of gelatin and of sucrose.[60]

The higher homologs of pyridine are analogous to the higher homologs of benzene. If pyridine has a —CH_2— group substituted in the α- or the γ-position,

α-Picoline   β-Picoline   γ-Picoline   2,4-Lutidine

the methylene group is active, reacting, for example, with aldehydes and nitroso compounds:

$$C_5H_4N—CH_3 + OCH—R \rightarrow C_5H_4N—CH{=}CHR + HOH$$

$$C_5H_4N—CH_3 + ON—C_6H_4NMe_2 \rightarrow C_5H_4N—CH{=}N—C_6H_4NMe_2 + HOH$$

On hydrogenation pyridine takes up three molecules of hydrogen, forming hexahydropyridine or piperidine. Conversely, the dehydrogenation of piperidine

Pyridine   Piperidine

forms pyridine. Piperidine possesses all the characteristics of a secondary amine. It has an aminelike odor, and it forms a nitrosamine with nitrous acid, etc.

Nicotinic Acid, U.S.P. (Niacin, 3-Pyridinecarboxylic Acid, Picolinic Acid, β-Pyridinecarboxylic Acid), occurs as white, nonhygroscopic needles or powder, m.p. 235°, soluble in water about 1:60, in alcohol about 1:80, and insoluble in ether. It is stable in air and may be autoclaved without appreciable destruction. It is reported that no more than 20 per cent is lost during the canning of foods.

[59] Warren, Becker, Marsh, and Shelton, *J. Pharmacol.*, **74**, 401 (1942).
[60] Tice and Moore, *J. Am. Pharm. Assoc.*, **36**, 48 (1947).

Good sources include dried or concentrated yeast, liver, lean meat, buttermilk, cabbage, spinach, and wheat germ.

Nicotinic acid

Nicotinic acid, first obtained by the oxidation of nicotine, was isolated as its amide from liver extract in 1912. It is now prepared technically by the oxidation of 5-ethyl-2-methylpyridine by nitric acid. In 1937, Elvehjem and his co-workers discovered its specific curative value in canine black tongue and that it possessed antipellagric properties.[61]

Nicotinic acid, nicotinamide, and the sodium salt of nicotinic acid have proved to be effective agents in the treatment of pellagra. They are also used as a prophylactic against this disease. Numerous symptoms caused by or related to pellagra are cleared up by the administration of nicotinic acid or its derivatives, e.g., profuse vomiting over long periods leading to undernourishment, Vincent's angina, sickness resulting from sulfanilamide therapy, and x-ray irradiation, delirium tremens, etc. The administration of nicotinic acid and its derivatives is usually by mouth in the form of tablets.

The daily normal requirements of this vitamin have been estimated as follows:

Infancy and childhood	5 to 25 mg.
Adolescence and maturity	25 to 50 mg.
Pregnancy and lactation	50 to 100 mg.
Acute deficiency	100 to 1500 mg.

3-Acetylpyridine (Methyl β-Pyridyl Ketone) is an antagonist to nicotinic acid and nicotinamide. When fed to mice in doses of 2 mg. per day or greater, symptoms of nicotinamide deficiency developed.

It is suspected that the high incidence of pellagra in people living on a corn diet may result not so much from a deficiency of nicotinic acid as from the presence in the corn of an antivitamin factor.

The same compound is also suggested as a precursor of niacin.[62]

Nicotinamide, U.S.P. (Nicotinic Acid Amide, Pyridine-3-carboxylic acid Amide), is a white, slightly deliquescent, crystalline powder, m.p. 128–131°, soluble in water 1:1, in alcohol 1:1.5, in glycerol 1:10, and slightly soluble in ether or benzene. As already mentioned, it has been isolated from highly active liver extracts; and it has been isolated also from beef hearts, 147 mg. of pure amide from 15 kg. of hearts.[63] It is probably the amide rather than the acid which is the natural active fraction. It is reported that the amide does not produce the alarming but harmless side effects of flushing and tingling of the face,

[61] Elvehjem et al., J. Am. Chem. Soc., **59**, 1767 (1937).
[62] Beher and Anthony, J. Biol. Chem., **203**, 895 (1953); McDaniel, Federation Proc., **12**, 472 (1953.)
[63] Kühn and Vetter, Ber., **68**, 2374 (1935).

neck, and extremities associated with a transient lowering of blood pressure shown by nicotinic acid. The amide is sometimes used by parenteral administration.

The physiological activity of the amide or of the acid is considerably modified by any change in structure. Thus, in the cultivation of the dysentery bacillus, nicotinamide was active at 1×10^{-7} molar concentration; trigonelline amide required ten times that concentration. Other compounds, such as α-pyridinesulfonic acid, trigonelline, 6-methylnicotinic acid, γ-picolinic acid, β-acetylpyridine, and β-picoline were devoid of any growth-promoting activity.[64]

Cozymase (Coenzyme I, Codehydrogenase I), the coenzyme of alcoholic fermentation, was discovered by Harden and Young in 1905. It appears to be an indispensable constituent of nearly every living cell, playing an important role along with coenzyme II in biological oxidations and reductions. The coenzymes I and II act as hydrogen transport systems in the metabolism of fats, carbohydrates, and amino acids. The mechanism of this action is explained by the quaternary nitrogen atom of the nicotinamide portion of the molecule which acts as a hydrogen acceptor or donor. The accepted structures of the enzymes are shown.

$n = 2$ for coenzyme I
$n = 3$ for coenzyme II

6-Aminonicotinamide is a potent antagonist to nicotinamide and is quite toxic in experimental animals. Simultaneous administration of nicotinamide with 6-aminonicotinamide protects mice against eight times the LD_{50} for the latter. It probably forms an inactive diphosphonucleotide analog which is biologically inactive.[65]

Nikethamide, N.N.R. (Coramine, β-Pyridine carboxylic acid Diethylamide), C_5H_4N—CO—NEt_2, is a slightly yellow, viscid, bitter liquid, consisting of a 25 per cent solution in water, with added lactic acid to make the product more palatable. It is used as a respiratory stimulant in excessive depression of the central nervous system as in accidents, poisoning, anesthetic accidents, and collapse. It is usually administered orally or by injection subcutaneously, intramuscularly, or intravenously.

Isoniazid, U.S.P. (Isonicotinyl Hydrazide), is an antitubercular drug. Despite early exaggerated claims made for it following its release in 1952, it is now widely accepted together with streptomycin and p-aminosalicylic acid for the treatment of tuberculosis. It is thought to be of particular value against the

[64] Dorfman et al., J. Am. Chem. Soc., **60**, 2004 (1938).
[65] Johnson and McColl, Science, **122**, 834 (1955).

miliary form of the disease and against tuberculous meningitis. It is converted *in vitro* by tissue enzymes into isonicotinc acid and ammonia.[66] A product consisting of molecular proportions of streptomycin and isoniazid is marketed as *Streptohydrazid* for the treatment of tuberculosis.[67]

Isoniazid is synthesized as shown.

Iproniazid (N-Isopropyl isonicotinyl Hydrazide) and **Aldinamide** (Pyrazineamide) are also being examined for their antitubercular properties.

Trigonelline, a betaine of N-methyl nicotinic acid, is perhaps the most widely distributed of the natural pyridine derivatives, the coffee bean being especially rich in this compound. It seems to be pharmacologically inert, and it probably is formed as a detoxification product in the organism from nicotinic acid.

Trigonelline

Pyridium (3-Phenylazo-2,6-diaminopyridine Monohydrochloride) is a dark red, microcrystalline powder, slowly soluble in cold water, readily soluble in hot water, alcohol, and glycerol. It is used as a genitourinary antiseptic for such conditions as cystitis, pyelitis, and prostatitis. It is administered orally in the form of tablets. Solutions of about 0.1 per cent are used for irrigations and instillations, and a 1 per cent jelly is used for topical application on tampons or swabs.

[66] Porcellati and Preziosi, *Enzymologia*, **17**, 47 (1954); *C.A.*, **49**, 11122 (1955).
[67] *Drug Trade News*, **29**, 47 (1954); *Antibiotic Med.*, **1**, 446 (1955).

The synthesis of pyridium from pyridine may be represented as shown.

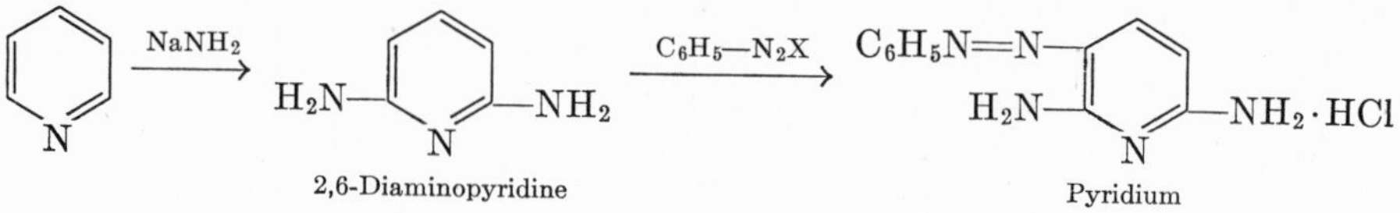

2,6-Diaminopyridine   Pyridium

Vitamin B$_6$

Pyridoxine, U.S.P. [Vitamin B$_6$, Factor I, 4,5-*bis*(Hydroxymethyl)-3-hydroxy-2-methylpyridine], is usually prepared as the hydrochloride, which consists of white platelets, m.p. 206–208° with decomposition, soluble in water about 1:4.5, in alcohol about 1:90, and insoluble in acetone. Aqueous solutions have a pH of about 3.2. It is stable in hydrochloric acid solutions at high temperatures, and it is not affected by heating with alkalies.

Good sources include dried yeast, liver, rice polishings, meat, fish, whole wheat, and corn. The usual dose is 5 mg. of the pure vitamin.

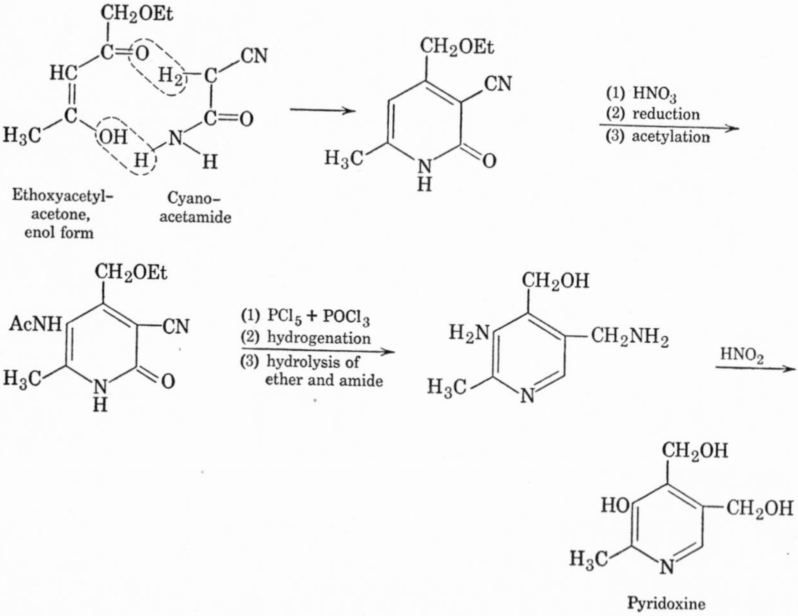

Ethoxyacetyl-   Cyano-
acetone,   acetamide
enol form

Pyridoxine

Many of the therapeutic claims for pyridoxine still remain to be cleared up, for its role in the body is not fully understood. Deficiency states in man involve the skin, mucous membranes, and the central and peripheral nervous systems.[68] Pyridoxine has been used in the treatment of nausea and vomiting in pregnancy. It is considered useful in treating radiation sickness.

Pyridoxine deficiency in monkeys leads to vascular lesions similar to those found in human atherosclerosis. The vitamin plays a role in the formation and

[68] Vilter, *J. Am. Med. Assoc.*, **159**, 1210 (1955).

utilization of unsaturated fatty acids; hence a deficiency might result in the formation of an excess of the less soluble saturated fatty acid esters of cholesterol.[69]

It can be made synthetically as indicated according to the accompanying equations.[70]

Evidence indicates that vitamin B_6 is perhaps not a single entity and that there are at least three components, viz., pyridoxine, pyridoxal, and pyridoxamine.[71] Perhaps in many organisms there is a biochemical interconversion, as shown.[72]

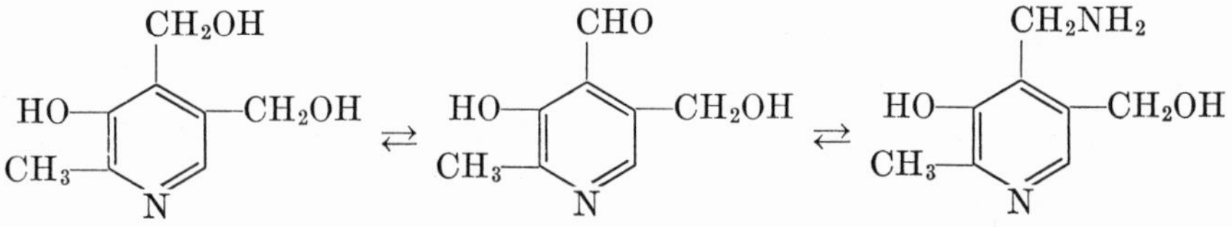

$$CH_2OH \qquad CHO \qquad CH_2NH_2$$

$$HO \!-\!\!\!\!<\!\!\!\!\!\!>\!-\!CH_2OH \rightleftharpoons HO\!-\!\!\!\!<\!\!\!\!\!\!>\!-\!CH_2OH \rightleftharpoons HO\!-\!\!\!\!<\!\!\!\!\!\!>\!-\!CH_2OH$$

Pyridoxine   Pyridoxal   Pyridoxamine

Phosphorylated pyridoxal, the monophosphoric ester of the 5-hydroxymethyl group, has now been identified as *codecarboxylase*, the coenzyme of amino acid decarboxylases and transaminases.[73, 74]

That the 5-hydroxymethyl group is essential to the metabolically active form of vitamin B_6 is shown by the inactivity of the synthetic 5-desoxy analogs, which, indeed, are inhibitors.[75]

2-Pyridine Aldoxime Methiodide, PAM, is a promising antagonist to diisopropyl fluorophosphate and other anticholinesterases of the phosphoric ester type; hence it is being considered as an antidote in "nerve gas" poisoning.[76]

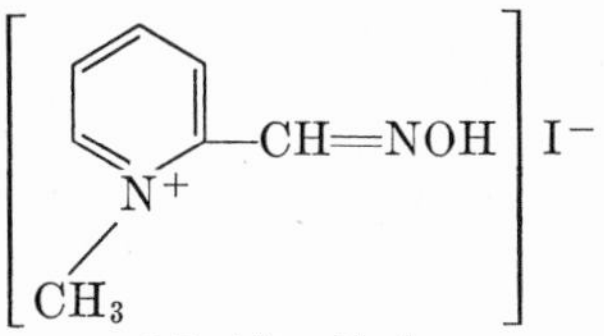

2-Pyridine aldoxime methiodide

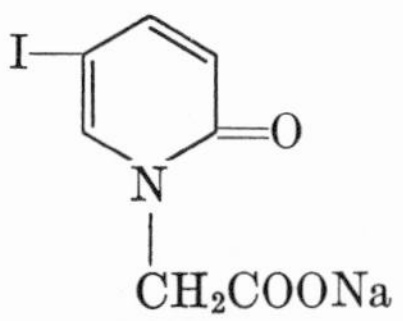

Uroselectan

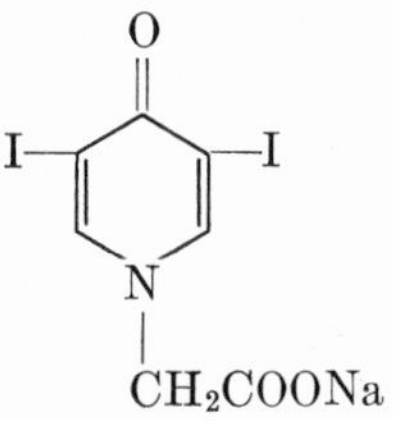

Diodrast

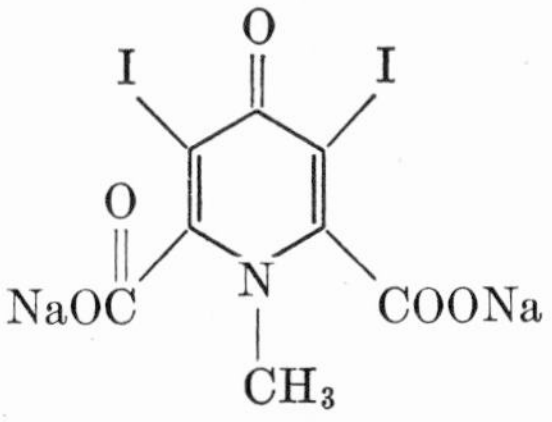

Neo-iopax

[69] Schroeder, *J. Chron. Diseases*, **2**, 28 (1955).
[70] Harris and Folkers, *J. Am. Chem. Soc.*, **61**, 1245 (1939).
[71] Harris, Heyl, and Folkers, *J. Am. Chem. Soc.*, **66**, 2088 (1944).
[72] Dutcher and Guerrant, *Ann. Rev. Biochem.*, **15**, 278 (1946); Snell, *ibid.*, 384.
[73] Gunsalus, Umbreit, Bellamy, and Faust, *J. Biol. Chem.*, **161**, 743 (1945).
[74] Heyl, Luz, Harris, and Folkers, *J. Am. Chem. Soc.*, **73**, 3430, 3434, 3436, 3437 (1951).
[75] Rabinowitz and Snell, *Arch. Biochem. and Biophys.*, **43**, 399 (1953).
[76] *Chem. Eng. News*, **34**, 1446 (1956).

Iodinated Pyridine Derivatives

Uroselectan, the sodium salt of 5-iodo-2-keto-1-pyridineacetic acid, is used as a contrast medium in urography, that is, in x-raying the urinary tract. It is reported to have weakly antiseptic action in urine and to be relatively non-toxic.

Iodopyracet Injection, U.S.P., is a sterile solution of 3,5-diiodo-4-pyridon-N-acetic acid with diethanolamine. It is used as a radiopaque medium in urography and retrograde pyelography. The sodium salt of the acid is known as *diodrast.*

Neo-Iopax, N.N.R. (Disodium N-methyl-3,5-diiodo-4-keto-pyridino-2,6-di-carboxylate), is a white, crystalline powder, readily soluble in water. It is used as a contrast medium in pyelography, being injected intravenously in solution; the rate of excretions serves as an indication of kidney function.

Areca Nut Alkaloids

Several simple alkaloids have been isolated from the areca nut. All of them are partially hydrogenated derivatives of nicotinic acid. Guvacine is 1,2,5,6-tetrahydronicotinic acid; its methyl ester is guvacoline; arecaidine is N-methyl-guvacine, and its methyl ester is arecoline.

| Guvacine | Guvacoline | Arecaidine | Arecoline |

Arecoline Hydrobromide, N.F., is a white, crystalline, water-soluble powder, having typical parasympathetic muscarinic effects. It is used chiefly in veterinary medicine as an anthelmintic. Its action as a cholinergic drug serves to stimulate intestinal peristalsis in the host while paralyzing the parasitic cestodes, thus removing the worms.

Piperidine Compounds

Hemlock Alkaloids. Of the naturally occurring bases in hemlock the most important is coniine, a colorless liquid, b.p. 166–167°, $[\alpha]_D^{19} + 15.7°$, strongly alkaline, with an odor resembling that of a foul pipe. Coniine was the first of the natural bases whose synthesis was duplicated in the laboratory.[77] This synthesis was carried out by the steps indicated. The synthetic DL-2-*n*-propylpiperidine was resolved with tartaric acid, and the dextroisomer was identical with the natural base.

[77] Ladenburg, *Ber.*, **19,** 2578 (1886).

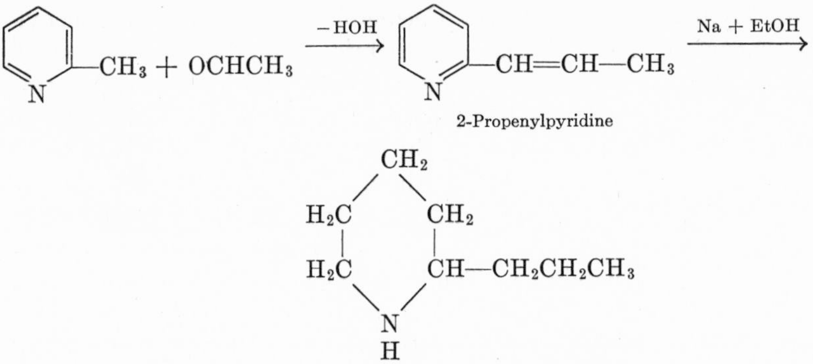

2-Propenylpyridine

2-n-Propylpiperidine, DL-coniine

The poisonous properties of hemlock have been known from the earliest times, the classic example being the drinking of oil of hemlock by Socrates when he was condemned to death.

Coniine produces paralysis of the motor nerve endings and stimulation followed by depression of the central nervous system. Death results from respiratory failure.

It was found that the toxicities of the homologs of DL-coniine increase in the ratio $-H:CH_3-:C_2H_5-:C_3H_7-::1:2:4:8$.[78]

Pomegranate Alkaloids. The root bark of the pomegranate tree, used as an anthelmintic, contains several alkaloids closely related in structure to coniine. Of these, pelletierine is believed to be the active constituent; it is said to be highly toxic to tapeworms and not very toxic to man. Its close relationship to coniine is indicated by the following observations:

(*a*) It forms an oxime; the oxime may be dehydrated to a nitrile; the nitrile may be hydrolyzed to an acid which contains all the carbon atoms originally present in pelletierine. This series of reactions can be accounted for if the carbonyl group was present only as an aldehyde.

$$C_7H_{14}N-CHO \rightarrow C_7H_{14}N-CH\!=\!NOH \xrightarrow{PCl_5} C_7H_{14}N-CN \xrightarrow{HOH} C_7H_{14}N-COOH$$

(*b*) Reduction of the hydrazone of pelletierine with sodium and alcohol forms DL-coniine

The structures of some pomegranate alkaloids are given; it will be observed how closely they are related.

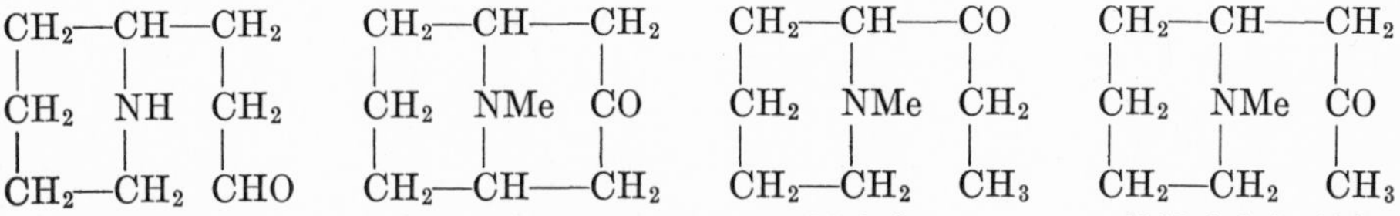

| Pelletierine | pseudo-Pelletierine | Methyliso-pelletierine | α-N-Methyl-piperidyl-2-propanone |

Pelletierine Tannate is a mixture of the tannates of the alkaloids obtained from *Punica grannatum*. It is a light yellow, amorphous powder, soluble in water about 1:250. It is an effective anthelmintic and teniafuge. It is usually administered in capsules followed by a cathartic within about 30 min.

[78] Mameli, *Boll. chim. farm.*, **68**, 949 (1929).

Meperidine Hydrochloride, U.S.P. (Demerol, Ethyl 1-methyl-4-phenyl-piperidine-4-carboxylate Hydrochloride), is a white, crystalline powder, which dissolves in water to form neutral stable solutions which withstand sterilization by boiling for a short period. It is reported to combine the antispasmodic properties of atropine and papaverine with the analgesic action of papaverine.[79] It has a neurospasmolytic action on smooth muscle and a central analgesic action like morphine.[80] It has value in alleviating the withdrawal symptoms in morphine addiction because of its analgesic and spasmolytic properties; however, it is not without addiction liability.[81] The hydrochloride produces pronounced corneal anesthesia when applied directly to the eye.[82] One of the greatest values of this drug is in decreasing the intensity of labor pains in childbirth; it is used together with barbiturates in this connection.

Demerol can be synthesized by several methods, one of which is illustrated.[83]

$$\begin{array}{c}
\text{Cl} \quad \text{Cl} \\
| \quad\quad | \\
CH_2 \quad CH_2 \\
| \quad\quad | \quad \xrightarrow[\text{NaNH}_2]{C_6H_5CH_2CN} \\
CH_2 \quad CH_2 \\
\diagdown \diagup \\
O
\end{array}
\quad
\begin{array}{c}
C_6H_5 \quad CN \\
\diagup \\
\text{(ring)} \\
O
\end{array}
\quad \xrightarrow{\text{HCl}} \quad
\begin{array}{c}
C_6H_5 \quad CN \\
\diagup \\
ClH_2C \quad CH_2Cl
\end{array}$$

$$\downarrow CH_3NH_2$$

$$\begin{array}{c}
C_6H_5 \quad COOC_2H_5 \\
\diagup \\
\text{N} \\
| \\
CH_3 \\
\text{Meperidine}
\end{array}
\quad \xleftarrow[\text{H}_2\text{SO}_4]{C_2H_5OH} \quad
\begin{array}{c}
C_6H_5 \quad CN \\
\diagup \\
\text{N} \\
| \\
CH_3
\end{array}$$

Meperidine is rapidly demethylated and hydrolyzed, chiefly in the liver; only about 10 per cent is excreted unchanged in the urine.

Replacement of the N-methyl group of meperidine by p-aminophenethyl affords a product that is severalfold more active and approaches morphine as an analgesic. It exhibits antitussive properties against experimental cough in animals.[84]

$$NH_2-\text{(ring)}-CH_2CH_2N-\text{(ring)}\diagdown\genfrac{}{}{0pt}{}{C_6H_5}{COOC_2H_5}$$

1-(p-Aminophenethyl)-4-phenyl-
4-carbethoxypiperidine

The success of meperidine as a potent analgesic drug stimulated the synthesis of many analogs of this compound.

[79] Eisleb and Schaumann, *Deut. med. Wochschr.*, **65**, 967 (1939); *C.A.*, **33**, 9442 (1939).
[80] Schaumann, *Arch. exptl. Path. Pharmakol.*, **196**, 109 (1940); *C.A.*, **35**, 2976 (1941).
[81] Himmelsbach, *J. Pharmacol.*, **75**, 64 (1942).
[82] Way, *Science*, **101**, 566 (1945).
[83] Bergel, Morrison, and Rinderknecht, *J. Chem. Soc.*, **1944**, 265.
[84] Weijlard *et al.*, *J. Am. Chem. Soc.*, **78**, 2342 (1956).

Ketobemidone, 4-(*m*-hydroxyphenyl)-1-methyl-4-piperidyl ethyl ketone, is a synthetic compound similar to meperidine in which the carbethoxy group is replaced by a propionyl group. Ketobemidone is significantly more effective as an analgesic agent but is severely addictive.

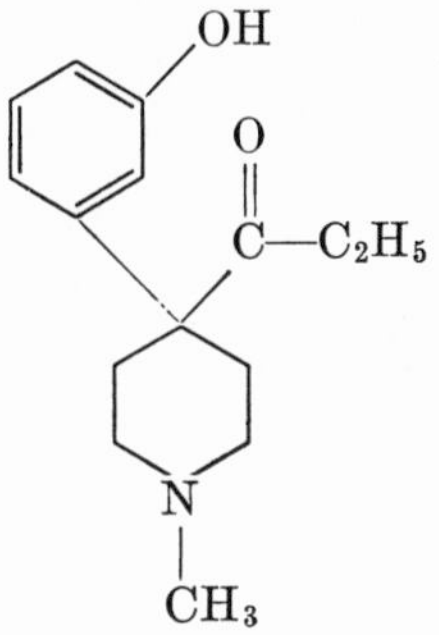

Ketobemidone

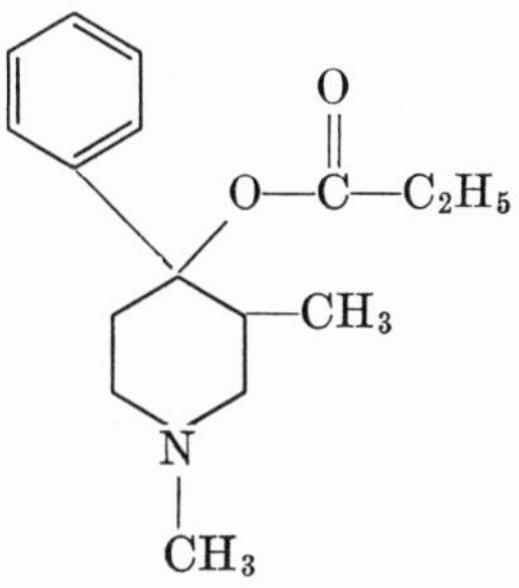

Prisilidene

Prisilidene (Nisentil) is the *cis* form of DL-1,3-dimethyl-4-phenyl-4-pro-pionoxypiperidine. It too causes addiction but is considered to be a valuable analgesic in obstetrics.

Diphemanil Methylsulfate, N.N.R. (Prantal Methylsulfate, 4-Diphenyl-methylene-1,1-dimethylpiperidinium Methylsulfate), is an agent that selectively blocks through parasympathetic ganglia, inhibits gastric secretion and motility, and relieves pylorospasm. It is used for the treatment of peptic ulcer, hyper-acidity, and chronic hypertrophic gastritis.

Cycrimine Hydrochloride, N.N.R. [Pagitane Hydrochloride, 1-Cyclopentyl-1-phenyl-3-(1-piperidino)propan-1-ol], finds use for the treatment of paralysis agitans; it exhibits about half the spasmolytic activity of atropine and a tenth the sialogogue effect.

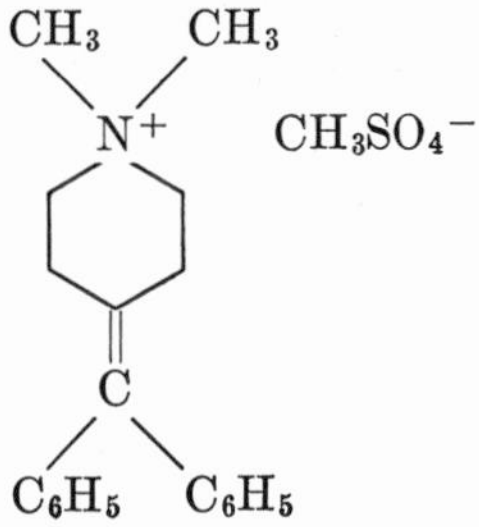

Diphemanil
methylsulfate

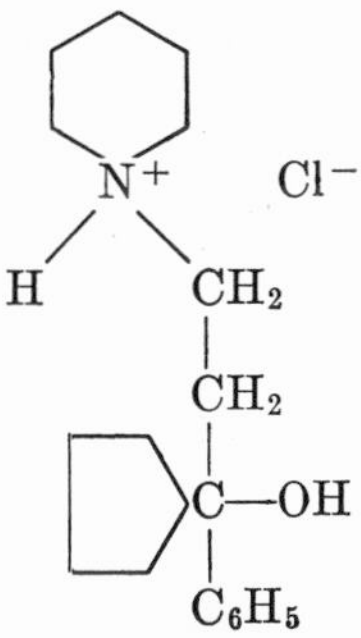

Cycrimine
hydrochloride

Trihexyphenidyl [Artane, 1-Cyclohexyl-1-phenyl-3-(1-piperidino)propan-1-ol Hydrochloride] resembles atropine in its peripheral action on autonomic effector cells; it is being used for the treatment of parkinsonism with considerable en-couragement.[85]

[85] Schwab and Prichard, *Arch. Neurol. Psychiat.*, **65,** 489 (1951).

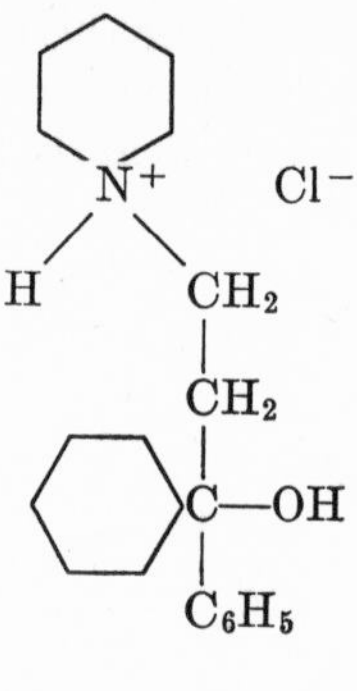

Trihexyphenidyl
hydrochloride

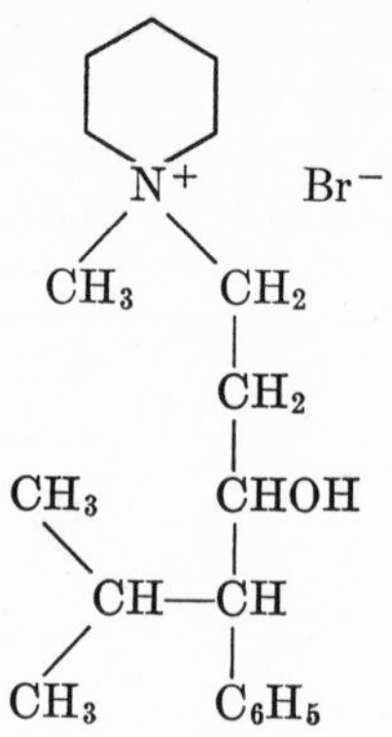

Darstine

Darstine is an antispasmodic of the anticholinergic type and antigastric secretory structure and is being tried for the relief of peptic ulcer.

Two piperidyl diphenylcarbinols are finding use and arousing interest because of their unusual reaction on the nervous system. 2-Piperidyl diphenyl carbinol, **Pipradrol, N.N.R.,** or **Meratran,** used as its hydrochloride, is a central nervous stimulant, acting on the higher centers; it is reported to relieve depression whether mental or emotional, to elevate the mood, and to relieve psychogenic fatigue.[86, 87]

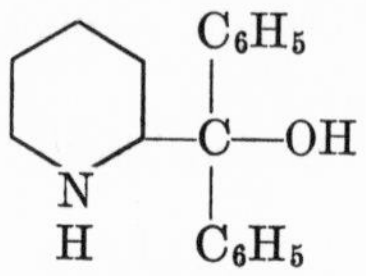

Meratran

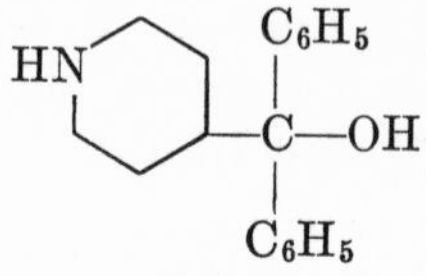

Frenquel

4-Piperidyl diphenyl carbinol, *Azacyclonol* or *Frenquel*, used as the hydrochloride, is an antihallucinatory and anticonfusion agent; it is stimulating interest because of its reported beneficial effects for the treatment of schizophrenic psychoses. It is effective in blocking psychoses produced by LSD 25 [88] and has been used with promise in the treatment of mentally disturbed patients with psychoses that have persisted for longer periods of time.[89]

Pepper Alkaloids

Piperine, $C_{17}H_{19}NO_3$, may be isolated from several species of Piperaceae, varying from 1 to 2 per cent in the long pepper to 5 to 9 per cent in black and white pepper. As a solid it is tasteless, but somewhat pungent in ethanolic solution. *Chavicine,* isomeric with piperine, may be isolated from the resins of

[86] Fabing, *Diseases of Nervous System*, **16**, January 1955; Oettinger, *ibid.*, October 1955.
[87] Schutt and Himwich, *Am. J. Psychiat.*, **111**, 837 (1955).
[88] Fabing, *Science*, **121**, Feburary 11, 1955.
[89] Rinaldi, Rudy, and Himwich, *Am. J. Psychiat.*, **112**, 343 (1955).

pepper. Both substances on hydrolysis form piperidine as one of the products; from piperine is isolated piperic acid, and chavicine forms chavicinic acid. Both acids take up two molecules of hydrogen to form 5-(3,4-methylenedioxyphenyl)-valeric acid, i.e., each acid contains two ethylenic bonds, giving rise to *cis-trans* isomers. Piperic acid is the *trans-trans* and chavicinic acid the *cis-cis* dienic acid. The natural products are amides of the respective acids as indicated.

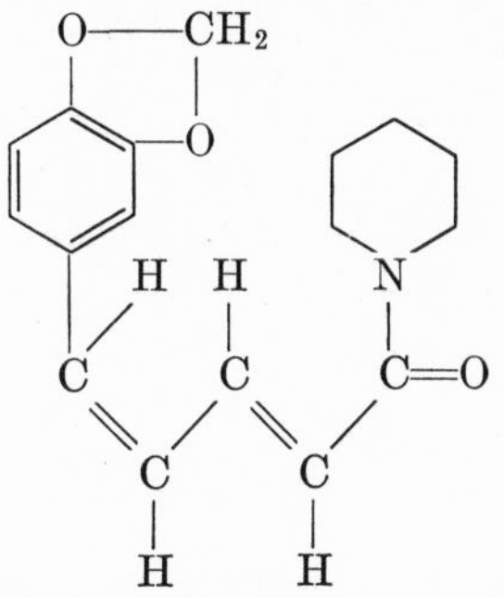

Piperine

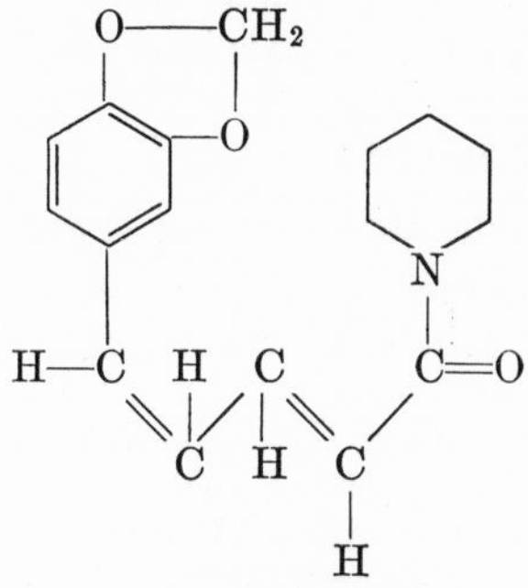

Chavicine

Leucenol appears in the seeds and leaves of *Leucaena*, which are valuable as fodder for cattle, but which are irritating to horses. It possesses a unique structure, a γ-pyridone derivative of alanine.

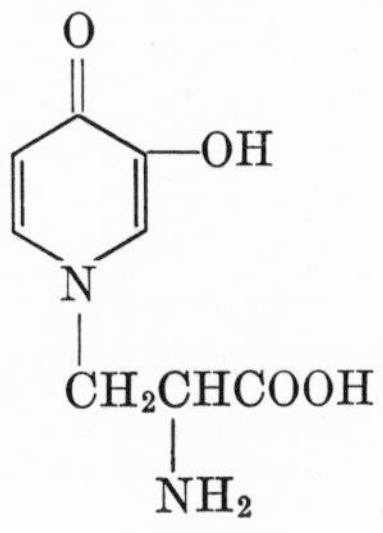

Leucenol

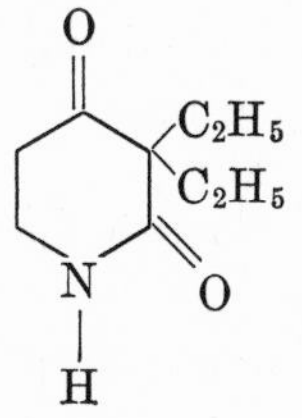

Piperidione

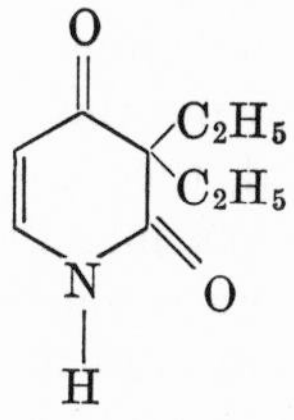

Presidon

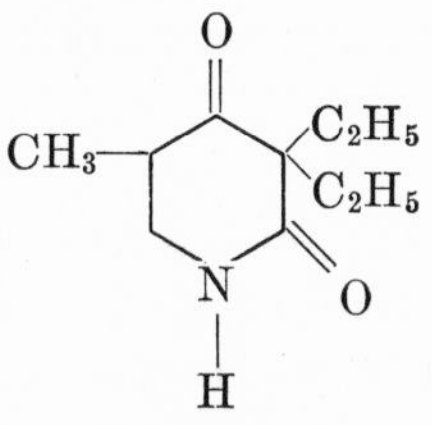

Methyprylon

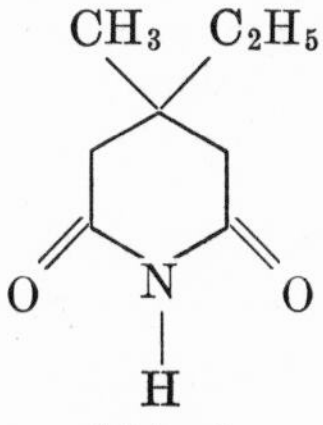

Malysol

Piperidione (Sedulon, 3,3-Diethyl-2,4-dioxopiperidine), having sedative properties, is an antitussive agent recommended for use as a cough depressant. It is considered together with its dehydro-derivative **Presidon** (3,3-diethyl-2,4-dioxotetrahydropyridine), which, though having good sedative properties, was withdrawn from use owing to its untoward toxic effects. Sedulon is thought to be metabolized in the body to Presidon.

Methyprylon (Noludar, 3,3-Diethyl-5-methyl-2,4-piperidinedione) is used in the treatment of insomnia. It is reported to be free of "hangover" effects and is also recommended for use as a daytime sedative.

Malysol (4-Methyl-4-ethyl-2,6-dioxypiperidine) in animal and preliminary clinical trials has afforded dramatic recoveries, without apparent untoward side effects, in opium and barbiturate poisoning.[90,91]

Tobacco Alkaloids

Tobacco, the dried leaf of *Nicotianum tabacum* or, in the case of the East Indian and Turkish tobaccos, of *N. rustica*, owes its use in part to the volatile alkaloids, of which the following have been identified:

> Nicotine, $C_{10}H_{14}N_2$, Posselt and Reiman (1828)
> Nicotimine or anabasine, $C_{10}H_{14}N_2$, Pictet and Rotschy (1901)
> Nornicotine, $C_9H_{12}N_2$, Ehrenstein (1931)
> Anatabine, $C_{10}H_{12}N_2$, Späth and Kesztler (1937)
> Nicotyrine, $C_{10}H_{10}N_2$, Späth and Kesztler (1937)
> N-Methylanatabine, $C_{11}H_{14}N_2$, Späth and Kesztler (1937)
> N-Methylanabasine, $C_{11}H_{16}N_2$, Späth and Kesztler (1937)
> 2,3'-Dipyridyl, $C_{10}H_8N_2$, Späth and Kesztler (1937)

In addition to these pyrrolidine, N-methyldihydropyrrole, N-methylpyrrolidine and trimethylamine have been isolated and identified.

Although nicotine is one of the most violent poisons known and tobacco is widely used, there are few mortality cases from it on record. A toxic dose of tobacco taken into the stomach causes mental confusion, paleness of countenance, severe vomiting and retching, etc. Although during smoking the greater part of the nicotine is converted into nontoxic pyrogenic decomposition products, it is well established that one-seventh to one-third of the nicotine passes unchanged in the smoke.

The probable role of tobacco as a causative agent in lung cancer is receiving serious study. In cigarette tar produced by mechanical smokers there is a neutral fraction that produces cancerous lesions when applied to the skin of mice.[92] There is, however, no evidence that implicates the alkaloids of tobacco.

Nicotine is the most abundant and best known of the tobacco alkaloids. In certain tobaccos, however, for example, in certain German tobaccos and in *N. sylvestris* (grown on an experimental plot in Maryland) nornicotine predominates. The other bases occur to a very limited extent. It is interesting to compare the structures of these various bases and to note many points of similarity.

[90] Canbäck, Diding, Ohlson, and Werkö, *Svensk. Farm. Tidskr.*, **29**, 685 (1955); *C.A.*, **50**, 2870 (1956).
[91] McCallum, *J. Pharm. Pharmacol.*, **7**, 276 (1955).
[92] Wynder, *Chem. Eng. News*, **34**, 2242 (1956).

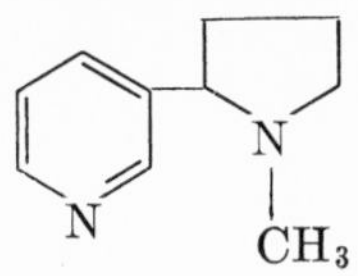

Nicotine

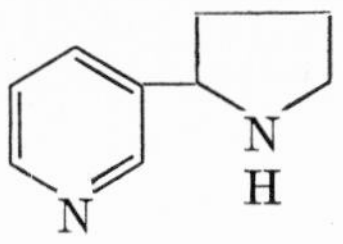

Nornicotine

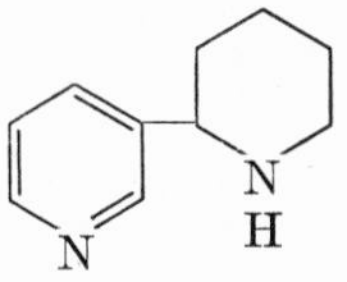

Anabasine
(nicotimine)

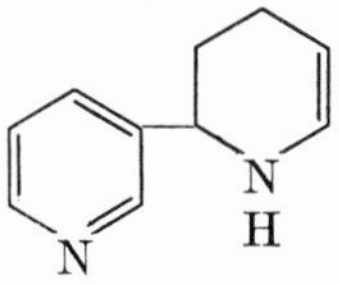

Anatabine

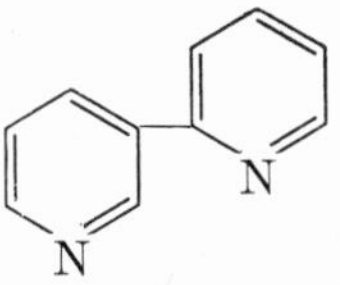

α,β'-Dipyridyl

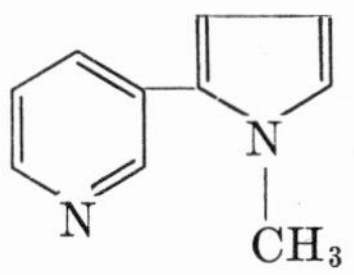

β-Nicotyrine

It is postulated that the biogenesis of nornicotine and nicotine proceeds from ornithine and lysine somewhat as shown.[93, 94]

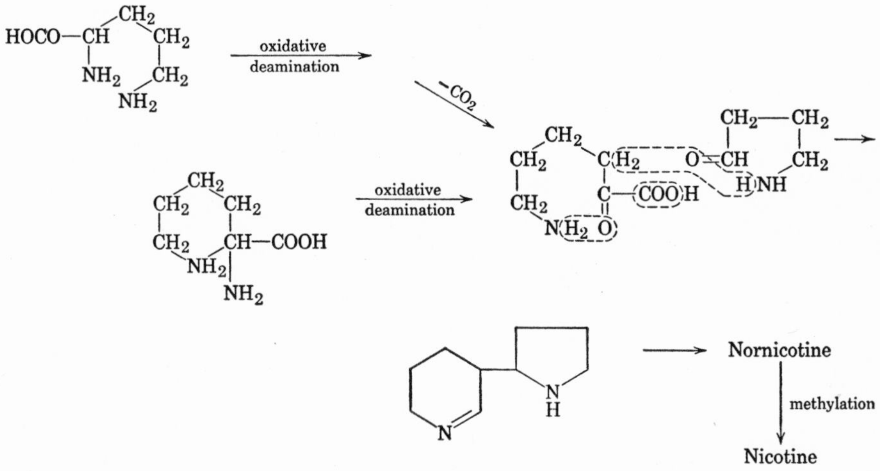

$$\text{HOCO—CH} \begin{smallmatrix} CH_2 \\ \\ CH_2 \end{smallmatrix} \quad \xrightarrow{\text{oxidative deamination}}$$

NH_2 CH_2
NH_2

$-CO_2$

oxidative deamination

Nornicotine

methylation

Nicotine

Concentrated extracts of tobacco containing mixtures of the total alkaloids as sulfates are used extensively as insecticides and fungicides, especially in plant sprays.

[93] Leete, *Chemistry & Industry*, **1955**, 537.
[94] Dewey, Byerrum, and Ball, *Biochim. et Biophys. Acta*, **18**, 141 (1955); *C.A.*, **49**, 16089 (1955).

Lobelia Alkaloids

The drug *Lobelia inflata, N.F.*, contains several alkaloids. Only one of these is of interest, namely, lobeline.

Lobeline (α-Lobeline) is used as the sulfate and hydrochloride. These are white, crystalline salts readily soluble in water. Lobeline is a respiratory stimulant used to treat asphyxia in the newborn, accidents during anesthesia, poisoning, etc. The alkaloid has been largely replaced by more effective agents since the early claims for its effectiveness have not been substantiated. It is usually administered parenterally. Lobeline has also been used in breaking the tobacco habit. A cross tolerance between this alkaloid and nicotine makes possible control of the withdrawal symptoms. It is usually administered orally in capsules for this purpose.

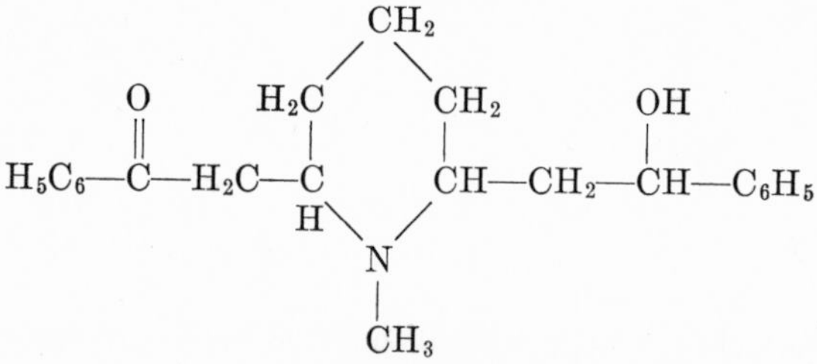

Lobeline

QUINOLINE DERIVATIVES

Benzopyridine may exist in two forms, known as quinoline and isoquinoline. Both are important as basic structures appearing in natural and medicinally important compounds.

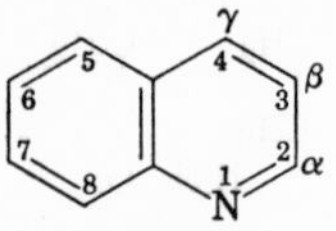

2,3-Benzopyridine, quinoline

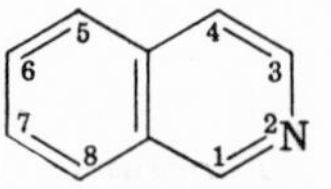

3,4-Benzopyridine, isoquinoline

Quinoline is found in some of the coal-tar distillates. Its properties are those that might logically be expected of a compound containing both a pyridine and an aromatic nucleus.

Among the derivatives of quinoline that possess medicinal interest are those illustrated.

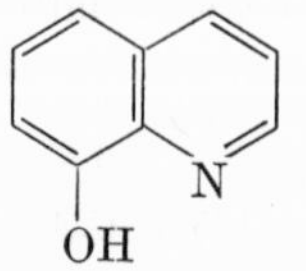

8-Hydroxyquinoline

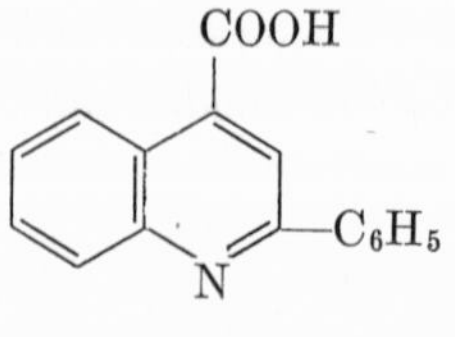

Cinchophen

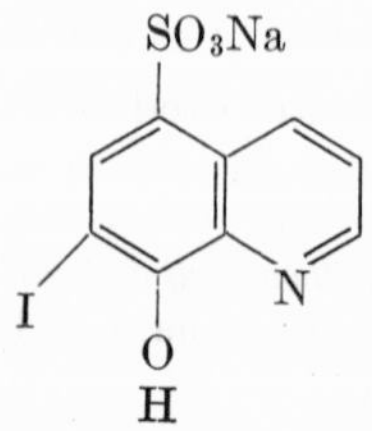

Yatren

8-Hydroxyquinoline, also called chinosol, is used as an antiseptic and also as an analytical reagent.

Cinchophen, N.F. (2-Phenylquinoline-4-carboxylic Acid, 2-Phenylcinchoninic Acid), is a slightly yellow, bitter powder, insoluble in water, soluble in alcohol about 1:120, m.p. 213° to 216°. It has antipyretic and analgesic activities similar to that of the salicylates. It is used in the treatment of rheumatic fever and gout. Numerous cases of liver damage by cinchophen have been reported. It is usually administered as tablets or in capsules along with agents such as sodium bicarbonate, sodium acetate, or sodium citrate to alkalinize the urine. Cinchophen is absorbed from the intestinal tract, and it is almost completely destroyed *in vivo* by metabolism.[95]

Neocinchophen, N.F. (Novatophan, the ethyl ester of 6-methylcinchophen), is a slightly yellow, crystalline powder with properties similar to those of cinchophen. It has the advantage that it does not cause severe gastric irritation as does cinchophen. It is reported also to cause less liver damage.

Yatren (the sodium salt of 7-iodo-8-hydroxyquinoline-5-sulfonic acid) is a yellow, crystalline powder, soluble in water about 1:25. It is used like chiniofon to treat amebiasis.

Chiniofon, U.S.P., is a mixture of 7-iodo-8-hydroxyquinoline-5-sulfonic acid in the form of its sodium salt with sodium bicarbonate. It has properties similar to those of yatren. Products of this type were introduced as wound antiseptics, but they are now used chiefly in the treatment of amebic dysentery. It is administered in cachets, pills, solution, and preferably as enteric coated tablets. Solutions of 0.5 to 2.5 per cent are sometimes administered rectally.

Vioform, N.N.R. (7-Iodo-8-hydroxy-5-chloroquinoline), is a slightly yellow powder, insoluble in water but soluble in alcohol, used as an antiseptic substitute for iodoform, being applied as a dusting powder. It has practically no odor. It is also used to treat amebic infections, being administered as the powder in capsules.

Vioform   Diodoquin   Chloroquinaldol

Diiodohydroxyquinoline, U.S.P. (Diodoquin, 5,7-Diiodo-8-quinolinol), is an amebicidal drug similar in action to Yatren and Vioform. It is orally active and is considered the drug of choice against *Endameba histolytica*. It is also recommended for use in vaginitis caused by *Trichomonas vaginalis*.

Chloroquinaldol, N.N.R. (5,7-Dichloro-8-hydroxyquinaldine), is a mild antibacterial and antifungal agent, and it is used for external application.

[95] Axelrod and Chenkin, *Proc. Soc. Exptl. Biol. Med.*, **86,** 401 (1954).

Acaprin, 6,6′-ureylene-*bis*-(1,1′-dimethylquinolinium)sulfate, is employed for the control of tick fever by the cattle industry of Queensland, Australia.

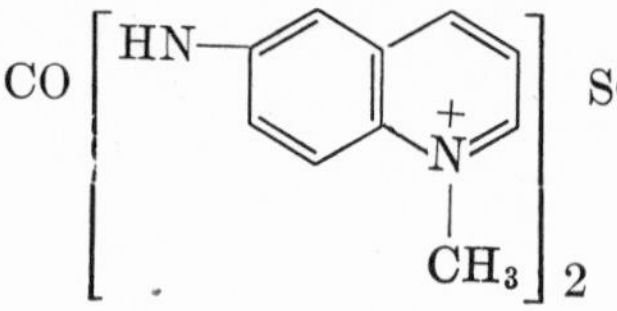

Acaprin

Angostura Alkaloids

From the angostura bark of the West Indies and South America are obtained products once used as a febrifuge in the form of bitters. The alkaloids consist of cusparine, nearly 75 per cent, galipine, nearly 25 per cent, smaller amounts of galipoline and 2-*n*-amyl-4-methoxyquinoline. During the nineteenth century the bark was used as an adulterant in nux vomica and thus fell into disrepute. Cusparine and galipine have spasmolytic activity resembling that of papaverine but to a much lower degree.[96]

Schöpf and Lehman [97] advance the opinion that these alkaloids are synthesized in the plant from methyl anthranilate (galipoline from anthranilic acid) and a β-keto-acid. Thus the biosynthesis of cusparine would involve methyl anthranilate and the acid, a condensation with a simultaneous decarboxylation in the manner shown. An interesting synthe-

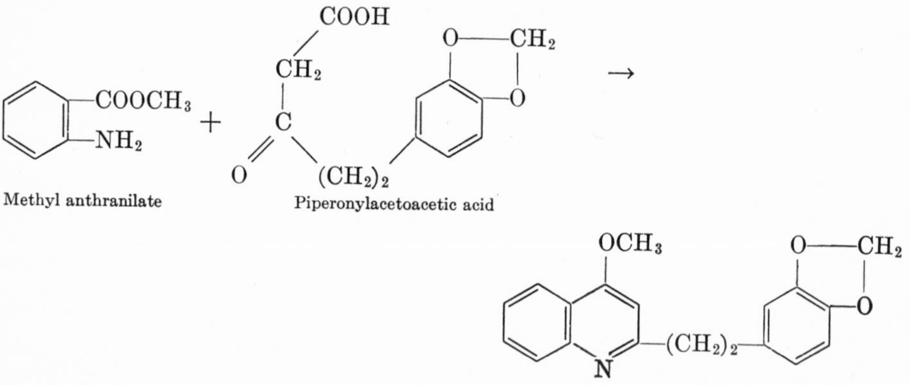

Methyl anthranilate   Piperonylacetoacetic acid

Cusparine

sis of these compounds involves the use of a 2-methylquinoline derivative as an intermediate. (Cf. the synthesis of coniine, page 345.)

[96] Krakau, *Kgl. Fysiograph. Sällskap. Lund. Förh.*, **15**, 289 (1945); *C.A.*, **43**, 3527 (1949).
[97] *Ann.*, **497, 7** (1932).

4-Methoxy-2-methylquinoline

Veratral

$-H_2O$ H_2

Galipine

Cinchona Alkaloids

The most important of the quinoline derivatives are the cinchona alkaloids and related compounds.

When the Jesuits first arrived in Peru they learned from the native medicine men that malarial fever could be effectively treated with the bark from a certain tree. The bark was admitted into the London pharmacopoeia in 1677 under the name of "Cortex Peruanus," and the "compound tincture of cinchona" was adopted in 1788. In 1827 Pelletier and Caventou received the 10,000-franc prize from the French Institute of Science for isolating the active principles. Following this, the world seems to have become quinine conscious, for Pelletier even manufactured a dentifrice containing it. The demand for the material increased so that for a time it sold for a dollar a grain.

It was conditions such as these that led to the offer of prizes for methods which would relieve the stringency and induced organic chemists to hope that the bases might be obtained synthetically. The hope of winning one of the prizes prompted eighteen-year-old William Henry Perkin, then an apprentice to the celebrated A. W. von Hofmann, to try the oxidation of aniline, thinking that he might obtain quinine. It was this mistake which led to the production of the first synthetic dye and the subsequent phenomenal growth of the dye industry.

Although originally cinchona was obtained from South America, trees were planted in other parts of the world to assure a continuous and adequate supply of this valuable drug. Peruvian resources have now become practically depleted, and Java has almost a complete monopoly in its cultivation and production. The hardier *Cinchona succiruba* is planted but, since it is low in alkaloidal content, on it is grafted the young stock of *C. ledgeriana*, which is much richer in quinine, up to 18.5 per cent.

The cinchona alkaloids are composed of two heterocycles, one of which is quinoline or a substituted quinoline, and the other is 3-vinylquinuclidine; these are joined by means of a hydroxymethylene bridge as indicated.

Quinoline heterocycle

Quinuclidine heterocycle

In cinchonidine and cinchonine R' = H, R = —CH:CH₂.
In quinine and quinidine R' = —OCH₃, R = —CH:CH₂.
In cupreine R' = —OH, R = —CH:CH₂.

It will be noted that positions 3,4,8, and 9 are centers of optical asymmetry, theoretically giving rise to 16 possible stereoisomers. Fortunately positions 3 and 4 remain constant in all the natural alkaloids. The stereoconfiguration of the various alkaloids has been elucidated and is summarized in the accompanying formulas (in which Qu represents the quinoline or substituted quinoline heterocycle).[98]

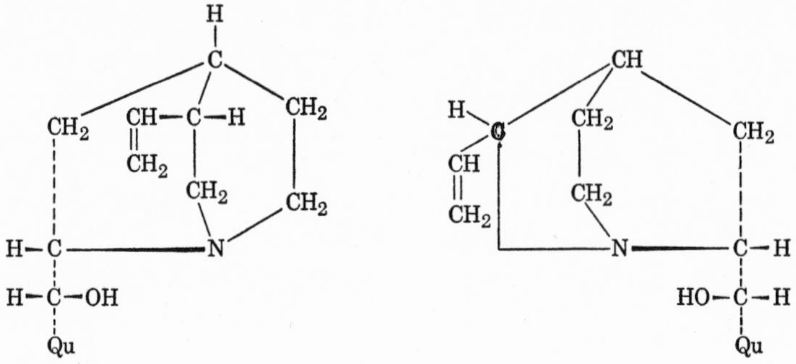

Quinine
Cinchonidine
Cupreine

Qu = quinoline heterocycle

Quinidine
Cinchonine

The structural relationships of some of the more common cinchona compounds may be seen from the general formula and Table XXII.

TABLE XXII

CINCHONA BASES

(−)-Isomer	(+)-Isomer	R′	R
Quinine	Quinidine	CH_3O-	$CH_2:CH-$
Cinchonidine	Cinchonine	$H-$	$CH_2:CH-$
Hydroquinine	Hydroquinidine	CH_3O-	CH_3CH_2-
Hydrocinchonidine	Hydrocinchonine	$H-$	CH_3CH_2-
Quininal	Quinidinal	CH_3O-	$-CHO$
Quitenine	Quitenidine	CH_3O-	$-COOH$
Ethylquitenine	Ethylquitenidine	CH_3O-	$-COOEt$
Cupreine	—	$HO-$	$CH_2:CH-$
Ethylcupreine	—	$EtO-$	$CH_2:CH-$
Hydrocupreine	Hydrocupreidine	$HO-.$	CH_3CH_2-
Ethylhydrocupreine (Optochin)	Ethylhydrocupreidine	$EtO-$	CH_3CH_2-
Apocupreine	—	$HO-$	$CH_3CH:(C)$
Hydroxyethylapocupreine	—	$HOCH_2CH_2-$	$CH_3CH:(C)$
Ethylapocupreine	—	$EtO-$	$CH_3CH:(C)$
Isoamylhydrocupreine (Eucupin)	—	$i\text{-}C_5H_{11}O-$	CH_3CH_2-
Isoöctylhydrocupreine	—	$i\text{-}C_8H_{17}O-$	CH_3CH_2-

[98] An excellent discussion of these sterochemical relationships is given by Turner and Woodward in Manske and Holmes, *The Alkaloids*, The Academic Press, New York, Vol. III, 1953, p. 27 *et seq.*

Quinine, quinidine, cinchonine, and cinchonidine are the predominant alkaloids in cinchona bark. Cupreine is obtained from the bark of *Remijia pedunculata*, a plant closely related though distinct from the cinchonas.

All the compounds are generally active provided that the phenolic hydroxyl in position 6' is etherified by means of an alkyl group, and provided that the vinyl group attached to position 3 is not oxidized to a carboxyl group; if the latter is a carboxyl, activity may be partially restored when it is esterified.

The metabolic detoxication of the cinchona alkaloids appears to attack first the 2 position of the quinuclidine nucleus; the 2-hydroxy alkaloids are eliminated in the urine.[99]

Isoöctylhydrocupreine (Vuzin) is said to possess powerful antiseptic properties; it was used during World War I by the Germans for the treatment of septic wounds. Ethylhydrocupreine, its higher homologs, and the corresponding alkylapocupreines have been examined for their pneumococcicidal properties. Although they are effective, they may cause visual disturbances, sometimes even blindness. Hydroxyethylcupreine, however, is much less toxic (detoxifying property of the alcoholic hydroxyl), and it retains its antipneumococcic activity.

Ethylhydrocupreine (Optochin) occurs in the bark of *Remijia pedunculata*. It has a specific action against pneumococci, and it is employed as the hydrochloride to treat pneumococcic infections of the eye, usually being instilled in 1 to 2 per cent solution.

Quinine, N.F., is one of the most useful drugs. The free base is a white powder, crystallizing with three molecules of water; the crystals are efflorescent in dry air. It is soluble about 1:1560 in water, 1:0.8 in alcohol, 1:1.1 in chloroform, and 1:1.9 in ether at 25°. It has an intense and persistent bitter taste. It forms soluble salts readily with many acids. The insoluble salts serve to mask the bitter taste of the alkaloid. The soluble salts dissolve with the formation of solutions having a characteristic blue fluorescence. The commonly used salts and their approximate solubilities in water at 25° are:

Quinine Bisulfate, N.F.	1:9
Quinine Ethylcarbonate	1:110
Quinine Hydrobromide, N.F.	1:40
Quinine Hydrochloride, U.S.P.	1:16
Quinine Phosphate, N.F.	1:600
Quinine Salicylate	Insol.
Quinine Sulfate, U.S.P.	1:810
Quinine and Urea Hydrochloride, N.F.	1:0.9

The most important use of quinine and its salts is in the treatment of malaria. The manner in which quinine acts in malaria is not completely known. It is known that the alkaloid when properly administered cures the acute symptoms of the disease by decreasing the multiplication of the plasmodia in the body. Quinine and its salts are usually administered by mouth in the form of tablets or capsules. Cures in 90 to 95 per cent of cases with acute malaria have been re-

[99] Brodie, Baer, and Craig, *J. Biol. Chem.*, **188,** 567 (1951).

ported. The soluble bisulfate is commonly employed for oral use. When intravenous administration is necessary, the more soluble dihydrochloride is generally employed.

Quinine is also used for a large number of other conditions. Briefly, these may be indicated as follows:

1. As an analgesic and antipyretic for the relief of colds, neuralgia, etc. It has the same type action as the salicylates and is somewhat less effective.

2. As a sclerosing agent in the treatment of varicose veins. *Quinine Hydrochloride and Ethyl Carbamate Injection* is used for this purpose. *Quinine and Urea Hydrochloride, N.F.,* is used as a sclerosing agent for the treatment of hemorrhoids.

3. As a local anesthetic. The quinine salts act as anesthetics by toxic action on the protoplasm. *Quinine and Urea Hydrochloride, N.F.,* is used in the form of an ointment in treating painful hemorrhoids. Other anesthetics are superior to the quinine salts for most purposes.

4. As an oxytocic. It is used to initiate labor at term; quinine combined with castor oil is sometimes used with success.

5. Other uses include: bitter tonic, contraceptive in jellies and douches, fluorescent coloring matter in hair tonics.

The other alkaloids of cinchona have activity similar to that of quinine, but they differ quantitatively.

Quinidine Sulfate, U.S.P., and **Quinidine Gluconate, N.F.,** have been found to be effective for the treatment of auricular fibrillation by restoring normal rhythm. The salt is usually administered orally in capsules or in tablets. The major clinical value of quinidine is in the prevention and abolition of certain cardiac arrhythmias.

Cinchonidine Sulfate and **Cinchonine Sulfate** are employed to secure the antimalarial effects of the cinchona alkaloids. They are usually administered in forms such as *Elixir of Cinchona Alkaloids.*

Totaquine, N.F., is a combination of the total alkaloids of cinchona. It is extensively used in the orient and in the tropics as a remedy for malaria.

Quinamine, $C_{19}H_{24}O_2N_2$, m.p. 185–186°, $[\alpha]_D + 116°$, is a minor alkaloid from cinchona bark. First isolated by Hesse in 1872, its structure has been established by Kirby [100] and by Witkop [101] as an indole analog of the cinchona bases.

Quinamine

[100] Kirby, *J. Chem. Soc.*, **1945**, 528.
[101] B. Witkop, *J. Am. Chem. Soc.*, **72**, 2311 (1950).

Quaternary ammonium compounds prepared by the reaction of quinine with alkyl halides, e.g., hexyl chloride, produce curarelike paralysis on frogs and neuromuscular paralysis in dogs.[102]

Synthesis of Quinine. The synthesis of quinine has been achieved. Woodward and Doering[103] started with aminoacetal, m-hydroxybenzaldehyde, and quinic acid and prepared quinatoxine. This compound was identical with the quinatoxine obtained by degradation of the natural alkaloid, and from which Rabe and Kindler[104] had previously resynthesized quinine. The essential steps are summarized as shown.

$$\text{HO}\!-\!\!\bigcirc\!\!-\text{CHO} \; + \; \text{H}_2\text{NCH}_2\text{CH}(\text{OC}_2\text{H}_5)_2 \xrightarrow{(80\% \; \text{H}_2\text{SO}_4)} \text{HO}\!-\!\!\bigcirc\!\!\bigcirc\!\!-\text{N}$$

$\xrightarrow{\text{2 steps}}$ (HO, isoquinoline with CH₃) $\xrightarrow{\text{3 steps}}$ (decalin-type structure)

$\text{CH}_2 \quad \text{CH}_2$ / $\text{H}_2\text{C} \quad \text{CH} \quad \text{CH}_2$ / $\text{HOHC} \quad \text{CH} \quad \text{NCOCH}_3$ / $\text{CH} \quad \text{CH}_2$ / CH_3

$\xrightarrow[\text{7-keto derivative}]{\text{CrO}_3}$

$\xrightarrow[\text{in EtOH}]{\text{Na + EtONO}}$

$\text{CH}_2 \quad \text{CH}_2$ / $\text{H}_2\text{C} \quad \text{CH} \quad \text{CH}_2$ / $\text{COOEt} \quad \text{CH} \quad \text{N}\!-\!\text{COCH}_3$ / $\text{HON}\!=\!\text{C} \quad \text{CH}_2$ / CH_3

$\xrightarrow[\substack{\text{then Hofmann}\\\text{exhaustive methyl-}\\\text{ation, with hydrolysis}}]{\text{reduction of oxime}}$

$\text{CH}_2\text{CH}_2\text{COOH}$ / CH / $\text{CH}_2\!=\!\text{CH}\!-\!\text{HC} \quad \text{CH}_2$ / $\text{H}_2\text{C} \quad \text{CH}_2$ / N / H

cis-isomer used

$\xrightarrow{\text{5 steps}}$

$\text{CH}_2\text{CH}_2\text{COOC}_2\text{H}_5$ / CH / $\text{CH}_2\!=\!\text{CH}\!-\!\text{HC} \quad \text{CH}_2$ / $\text{H}_2\text{C} \quad \text{CH}_2$ / NH

$\xrightarrow[\substack{\text{with ethyl quinate,}\\\text{"ketone" synthesis}}]{\text{Claisen condensation}}$

[102] Chase, Lehman, and Rickards, *J. Pharmacol. Exptl. Therap.*, **82**, 266 (1944).
[103] Woodward and Doering, *J. Am. Chem. Soc.*, **67**, 860 (1945).
[104] Rabe and Kindler, *Ber.*, **51**, 466 and 1360 (1918).

Quinatoxine,
(+)-isomer identical with
that obtained from quinine

Quininone

Synthetic Antimalarial Agents

After the attack on Pearl Harbor and the loss to the United States of the major portion of the world's supply of quinine, and with a war raging in some of the earth's worst malaria regions, an intensive campaign was instituted by the Allied Powers to increase the effectiveness of available antimalarial drugs and, if possible, to provide new ones with greater efficacy. Hope that better synthetic antimalarial compounds might be found was encouraged by the pre-war discoveries of pamaquine and quinacrine. Under the guidance of the Committee of Medical Research of the Office of Scientific Research and Development a program was set up in the United States by which all types of substances might be tested in experimental malaria; on the basis of results obtained, the activity was correlated with chemical structure, and the synthesis of likely new compounds was projected. Academic, governmental, and industrial laboratories co-operated in an extensive program.

The survey sponsored the screening of 12,400 compounds. Of these 103, including for comparison some that were previously known, were tested in man for suppressive, prophylactic, or curative activity. Only the most important are mentioned here.[105, 106]

Chloroquine [SN 7,618, 7-Chloro-4-(4-diethylamino-1-methylbutylamino)-quinoline] is three times as effective against avian malaria and twice as effective against human malaria as quinacrine. Doses of 1.0 to 1.4 grams given over one or two days are highly effective in terminating acute attacks of vivax malaria. Suppression of relapses has been accomplished with doses of 0.3 gram weekly. It does not cause discoloration of the skin. It is used as *Chloroquin Phosphate, U.S.P.* It is obtained by coupling 4,7-dichloroquinoline with 5-diethylamino-2-aminopentane.

[105] For more extended discussions of the program and of results see Elderfield, *Chem. and Eng. News*, **24**, 2598–2602 (1946).

[106] For a complete report see *Survey of Antimalarial Drugs 1941–1945*, F. Y. Wiselogle, editor; J. W. Edwards, Ann Arbor, 1946.

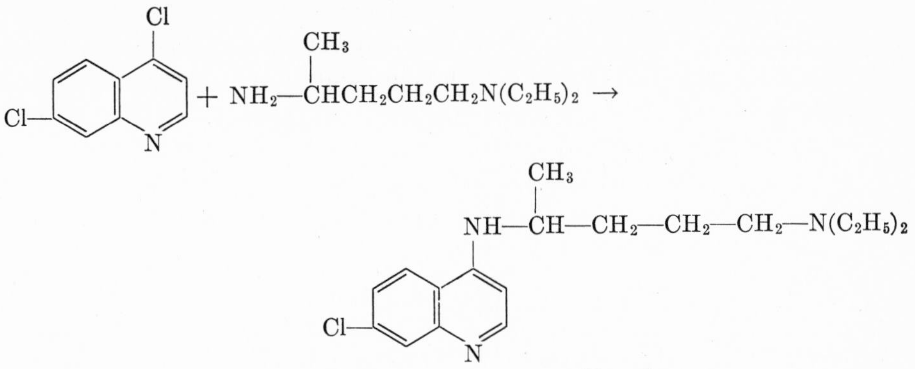

$$\text{Cl-quinoline} + NH_2\text{—CHCH}_2CH_2CH_2N(C_2H_5)_2 \rightarrow$$

Chloroquine

Introduction of a methyl group into the 3 position of the chloroquine molecule, as in SN 6,911, reduces the effectiveness. Chloroquine is used as the diphosphate in the form of tablets for the routine suppression and treatment of malaria. It does not give prophylactic protection against vivax infection in endemic areas.

Camoquin [SN 10,751, 4-(7-Chloro-4-quinolylamino)-α-diethylamino-o-cresol] is an antimalarial of low toxicity and is three to four times as active as quinine as a suppressive drug against vivax and falciparum malarias. It has no value as a curative or prophylactic in malaria since relapses occur after a few months of treatment. It is prepared by the reaction of 4,7-dichloroquinoline with 4-amino-α-diethylamino-o-cresol.

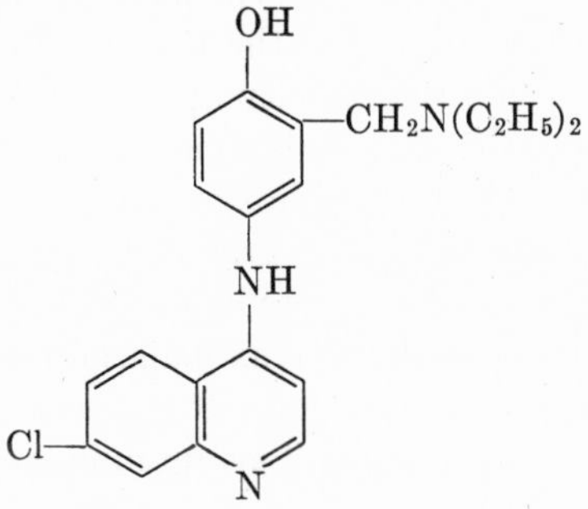

Camoquin

Pamaquine Naphthoate (Aminoquin Naphthoate, Plasmochin, SN 971, Naphthoate of 6-Methoxy-8-(1-methyl-4-diethylamino)-butylaminoquinoline) was introduced as an antimalarial in 1926. It has a specific toxicity for the gametocytes of all forms of plasmodia. In bird malaria it has been reported to be about sixty times as effective as quinine. It has the advantage over quinine that it destroys the sexual forms of the parasites. It does not cause cinchonism, and it has little if any oxytocic activity. Tablets are the usual mode of administration, but it is also given in capsules and in the form of a combination with quinine.

Plasmochin is prepared by condensing 6-methoxy-8-aminoquinoline, obtained by a Skraup synthesis on 3-nitro-4-aminoanisole, followed by reduction with 1-diethylamino-4-bromopentane. It is purified by distillation in a high vacuum after the removal of unreacted methoxyaminoquinoline by steam distillation. The 1-diethylamino-4-bromopentane is prepared from the same ketone obtained as an intermediate in atabrine manufacture, by catalytic reduction to the alcohol, followed by bromination.

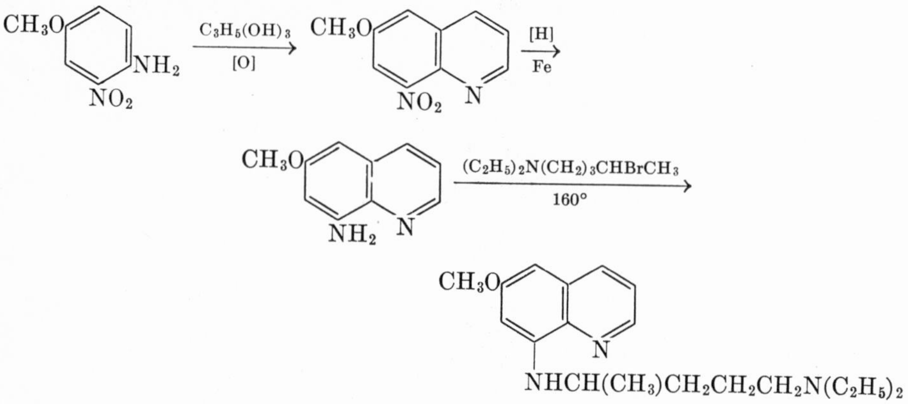

Pamaquine may be of some value in selected cases of resistant malaria. It cannot be used alone for suppressive treatment or to control malarial seizures. It is toxic and has a narrow margin of safety. Its use has declined as more effective drugs have been discovered.

Studies of the relationships between chemical constitution and antimalarial activity in compounds of the pamaquin type indicate that: (1) branching of the diethylaminoalkyl side chain decreases the therapeutic index except for the α-methyl group which decreases the toxicity and causes an increase in the index; (2) the diethylamino and the dipropylamino terminal basic groups yield the highest therapeutic index; (3) the methoxy group in position 6 is essential for appreciable activity. With larger ether groups, the activity tends to disappear.

Pentaquine [SN 13,276, 8-(5-Isopropylaminopentylamino)-6-methoxyquinoline] is probably prophylactic against vivax malaria if given for at least six days in doses of 120 mg. per day after infection. It is curative against the same strain if given 60 mg. daily for 14 days with 2 gr. quinine, and it may prove curative when given alone.

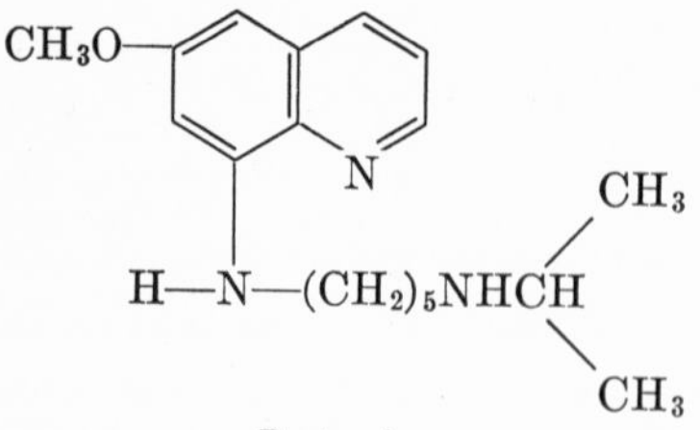

Pentaquine

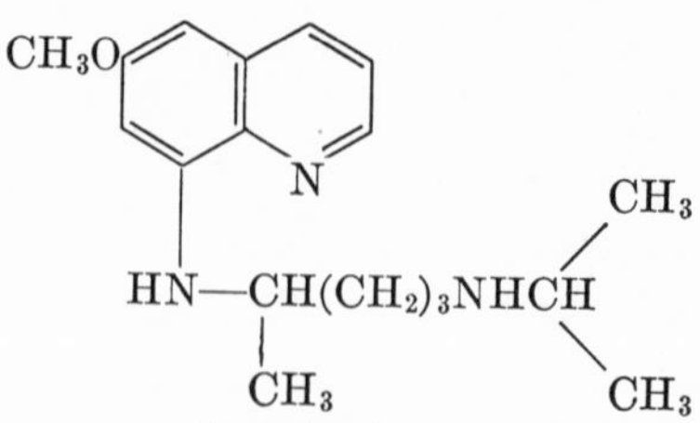

Isopentaquine

Isopentaquine [SN 13,274, 8-(4-Isopropylamino-1-methylbutylamino)-6-methoxyquinoline], when used in conjunction with quinine, is reported to effect cures of 95 per cent of all malaria relapse cases.

Primaquine, U.S.P. [8-(4-Amino-1-methylbutylamino)-6-methoxyquinoline], is considered a superior synthetic antimalarial in its curative properties. It also has shown excellent results in preventing relapses and has a good therapeutic index. It received very favorable reports in field trials on soldiers returning from the Korean war. Primaquine is synthesized [107] by coupling the appropriate side chain to 8-chloro-6-methoxyquinoline.

$$CH_3O-$$

$$NHCH-(CH_2)_3-NH_2$$
$$|$$
$$CH_3$$

Primaquine

Quinacrine [Mepacrine, Atabrine, SN 390, 6-Chloro-9-(4-diethylamino-1-methylbutylamino)-2-methoxyacridine] is used as the dihydrochloride in *Quinacrine hydrochloride, U.S.P.* It is a yellow powder with a bitter taste, soluble in water about 1:30, forming neutral fluorescent solutions. It will be noted that quinacrine has the same side chain as pamaquin. It was introduced as an antimalarial in 1930 after Mauss and Mietzch had synthesized it and many other closely related compounds. It appears that quinacrine is about as effective as quinine in the treatment of malaria. It has the advantages that it has no oxytocic action and so can be used during pregnancy when quinine is contraindicated; it is well tolerated, and the margin of safety between the effective and the toxic dose is relatively large; it does not cause cinchonism; and it does not have the intense bitter taste of quinine. It may be administered alone, or in combination with pamaquin. It is administered orally in capsules or as tablets. Parenterally, it is administered as a 1 per cent solution intravenously or as a 2 per cent solution intramuscularly. It is active against the erythrocytic phase of all forms of malaria.

The procedure used in the large-scale production of atabrine consists in condensing 2,4-dichlorobenzoic acid, obtained from the 2,4-chloroaminotoluenes by the Sandmeyer reaction followed by oxidation, with *p*-anisidine, closing the ring with phosphorus oxychloride, and heating the resulting 2-methoxy-6,9-dichloroacridine with 1-diethylamine-4-aminopentane in anhydrous phenol.

The aminoalkylamino side chain has a marked effect on the activity of compounds of the quinacrine type. Maximum activity is attained in a homologous series with a C_4 side chain. Lower members are more active but also more toxic. The activity diminishes in the C_5 and C_6 compounds. The presence of an α-methyl group more than doubles the therapeutic index of the amyl side chain. Straight- and branched-chain hexyl derivatives have about the same therapeutic index.

It checks the progress of the disease because it is active against the asexual forms (Trophozoites) of the organisms causing malaria. Quinacrine is absorbed

[107] Elderfield *et al., J. Am. Chem. Soc.*, **68**, 1525 (1946).

readily from the intestines and is excreted chiefly in the urine and feces. It colors the urine an intense yellow and may cause yellow coloration of the skin, which disappears a week or two after withdrawal of the drug. Its metabolic fate is still undetermined.

The guiding principle in the early work in synthetic antimalarials was appreciation of the requirement of a basic fragment linked to a heterocycle, such as quinoline, acridine, and benzoxazine. Schönhöfer suggested that activity in these compounds is associated with tautomerism; for quinacrine this may occur as shown.

With the hope of breaking away from the conventional heterocycles Curd, Davey, and Rose turned to pyrimidine, thinking in terms of sulfadiazine without the —SO₂— bridge. 2-Aminopyrimidine derivatives were found to be active;

these also may exhibit tautomerism. Next the guanidino group was tried in con-

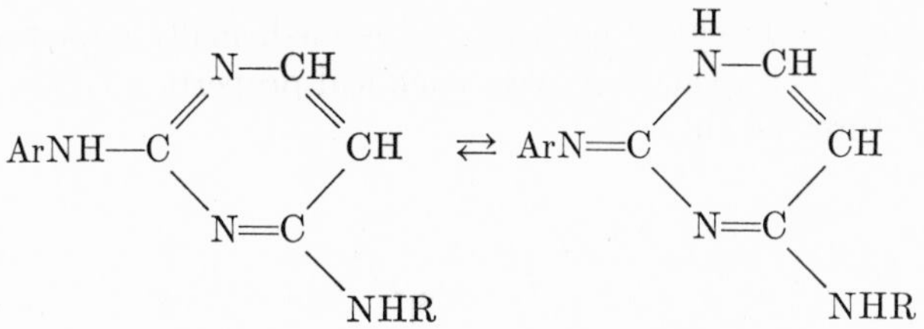

junction with the pyrimidine heterocycle; p-chlorophenyl-2-(4-methyl-6-diethyl-aminoethylaminopyrimidyl)guanidine, number 3349, proved superior and was

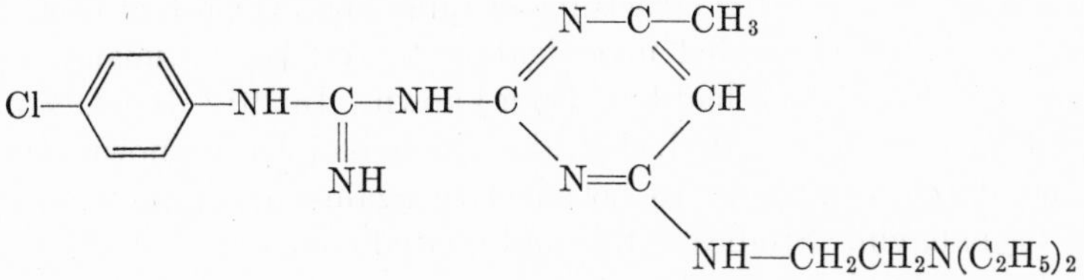

effective against *Plasmodium vivax*. This was in harmony with the original hypothesis, suggesting that antimalarial activity may be associated with interplay of tautomerism. The next step was to examine compounds which, in effect, have the pyrimidine cycle opened, that is, the biguanides; this line of investigation culminated in the discovery of Chlorguanide, **Paludrine**, "4888" (page 530), a com-

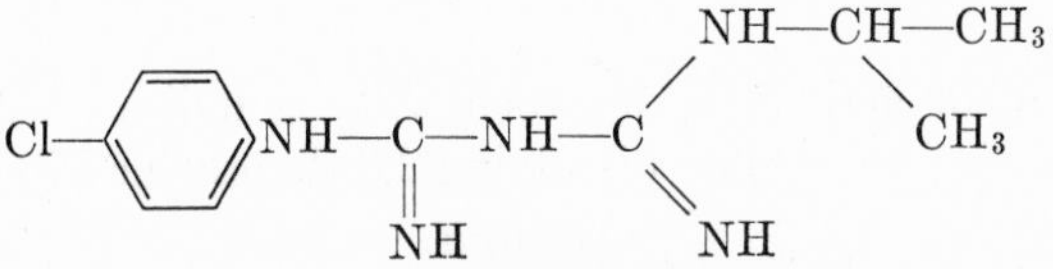

Paludrine

pound that stands out particularly for its intensity and range of activity.[108]

Daraprim [(5-p-Chlorophenyl)-2,4-diamino-6-ethylpyrimidine, Pyrimethamine] is a direct result of research to find superior antimalarial activity among the 2,4-diaminopyrimidines. Daraprim offers great promise of proving a valuable drug for combating malaria and is under clinical investigation.[109]

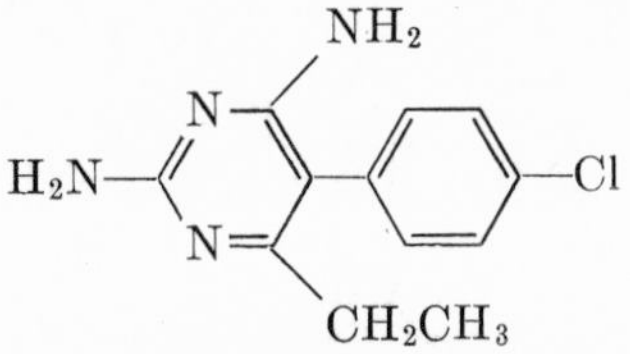

Daraprim

[108] Curd, Davey, and Rose, *Ann. Trop. Med. Parasitol.*, **39**, 208 (1945).
[109] Russell and Hitchings, *J. Am. Chem. Soc.*, **73**, 3763 (1951).

Acridines

Acridine is a constituent of coal tar and is medicinally important chiefly for its derivatives. It is a weak base with chemical properties similar to quinoline; it has the structure shown.

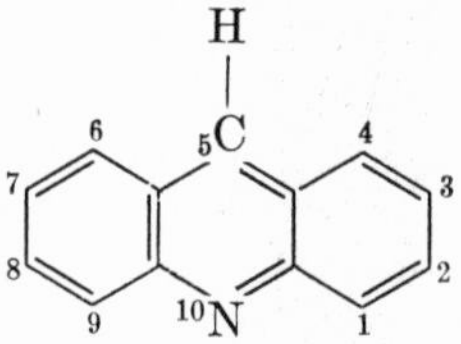

Acridine

The similarity between the structures of quinoline, which had been obtained from quinine, and acridine led investigators to test for antimalarial activity various acridine dyes which had long been known. In 1912, Benda synthesized pure diaminoacridinium methyl chloride which had been known since 1890. Ehrlich found this compound to be effective against trypanosomes and later named it Trypaflavin. Studies of this and related compounds by Browning and his co-workers in England in 1913 led to the introduction of acriflavine (Ehrlich's Trypaflavin), acriflavine hydrochloride, and proflavine as wound antiseptics, which were used extensively by the Allies during World War I. Later work (1921–1923) by Morgenroth and his co-workers on the bactericidal action of the alkoxy derivatives of the diaminoacridines resulted in the discovery of Rivanol. Chemotherapeutic studies of antimalarial synthetic products in the dye industry at Elberfeld in Germany brought about the introduction of Quinacrine (page 363).

The preparation of acriflavine hydrochloride is indicated by the equations shown. Proflavine is prepared by dissolving 2,8-diaminoacridine in sulfuric acid.

$$C_6H_5NH_2 + CH_2O \rightarrow C_6H_5N{=}CH_2 \xrightarrow[\text{HCl}]{C_6H_5NH_2}$$

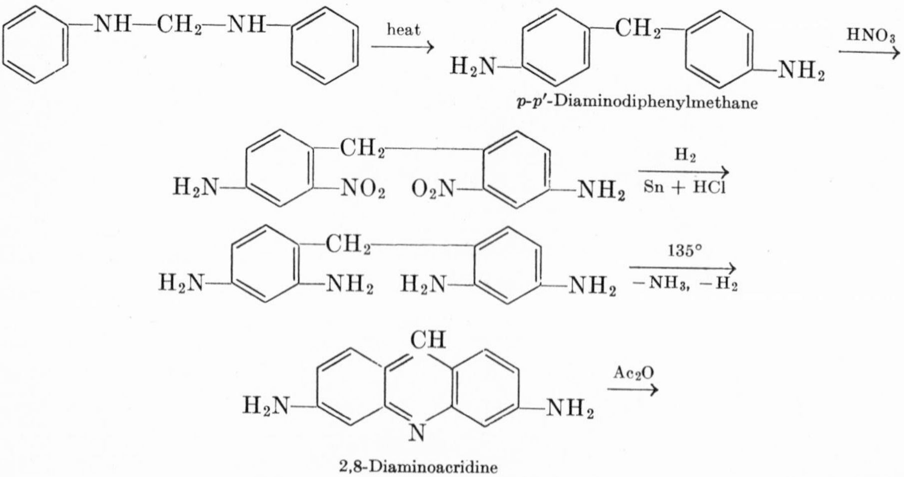

p-p'-Diaminodiphenylmethane

2,8-Diaminoacridine

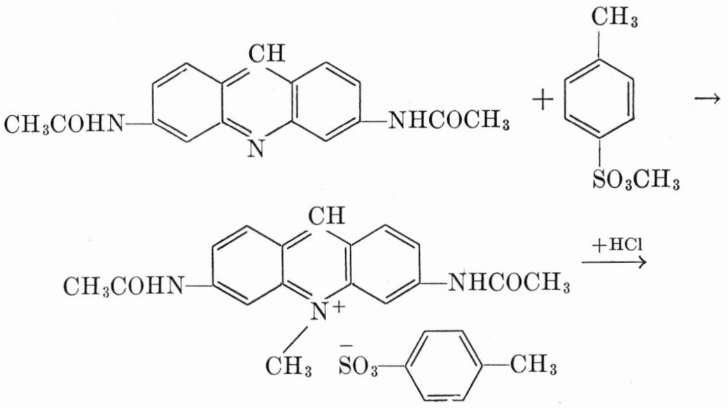

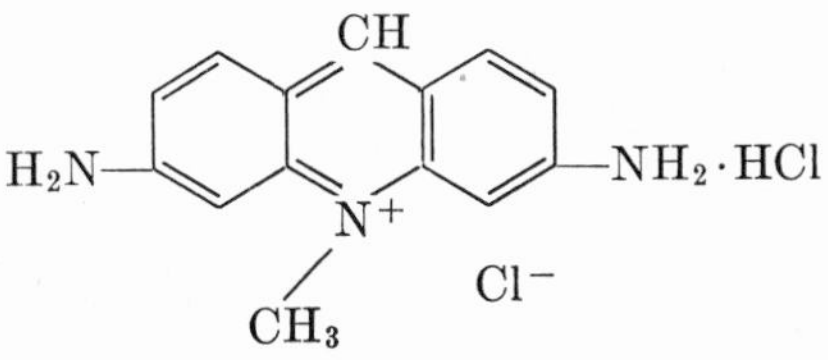

Acriflavine hydrochloride

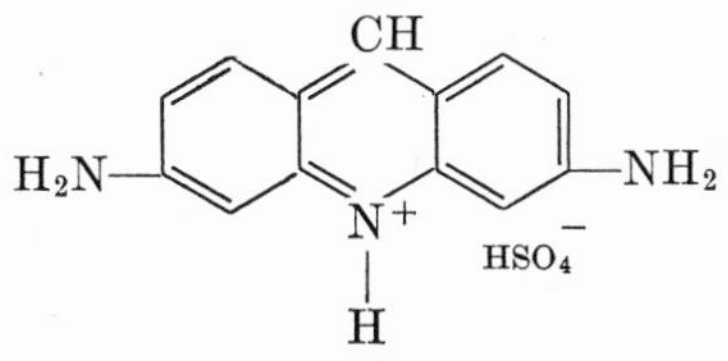

Proflavine sulfate

Acriflavine, N.F., Acriflavine Hydrochloride, N.F., Proflavine Dihydro-chloride, and **Proflavine Sulfate, N.N.R.,** are brownish-red, odorless, crystalline or granular powders of bitter taste which dissolve readily in water, forming fluorescent solutions. They are slightly soluble in organic solvents. Aqueous solutions are stable on boiling but are sensitive to light.

Acriflavine, proflavine, and their salts are actively antiseptic and bacteriostatic. Acriflavine is more toxic and more antiseptic than proflavine, and it acts more slowly. The free bases are often preferred to the salts for use on sensitive mucous surfaces, owing to the irritation of the latter. The antiseptic value of these compounds is well maintained in the presence of wound secretions. They are claimed to be very slightly toxic to phagoctyes and epithelium and to interfere very little with the healing process. They have been used in the treatment of wounds, eczema, urethritis, gonorrhea, and other conditions which require the use of an antiseptic. Intravenous administration in the treatment of influenza, pneumonia, rheumatism, etc., has been found to be ineffective (Ruhnou, 1920). When taken by mouth these compounds are of value as urinary antiseptics provided that the urine is alkaline.

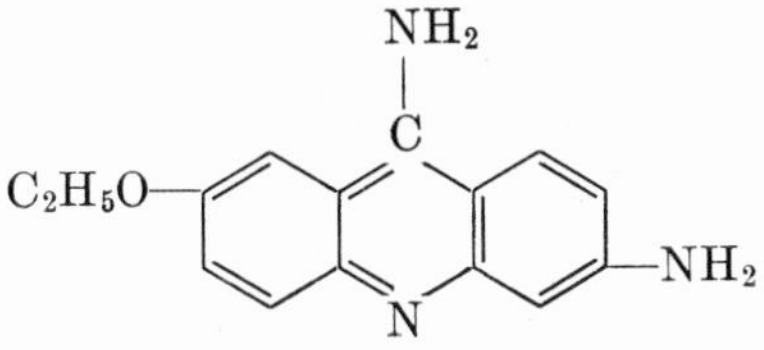

Rivanol is an acridine derivative of the structure shown. It was found by Morgenroth (1921) to be the most effective compound in a homologous series extending from the methoxy to the isoamyloxy derivatives. It is a yellow dye, soluble 1:15 in water. Rivanol is used to some extent in the treatment of amebic dysentery.

Quinacrine, an acridine derivative, is discussed under synthetic antimalarials, page 363.

Cyanine Dyes

Antifilarial agents are found among the **cyanine dyes.** One compound, (1-amyl-2,5-dimethyl-3-pyrrole) (1,6-dimethyl-2-quinoline)dimethinecyanine chloride, is completely curative at maximally tolerated doses. These dyes inhibit oxygen consumption by adult filariae at effective concentrations from 1:25 million to 1:6 million. As study with these compounds progressed, it appeared that activity is associated with the grouping $=\overset{+}{N}=C-(C=C)_n-$ $N= \leftrightarrow =N-C=(C-C)_n=\overset{+}{N}=$. One or both nitrogen atoms may be part of a heterocyclic system. One dye was particularly effective, 1'-ethyl-3,6-dimethyl-2-phenyl-4-pyrimido-2'-cyanine chloride.

Infested rats receiving this compound intravenously in doses of 1 mg. per kg., repeated 3 to 6 times at 1, 3, or 7 days, were invariably cured. During administration of the drug there was a transient hypotensive effect with compensatory tachycardia.[110]

Ergot Alkaloids

Ergot, a species of *Claviceps purpurea*, is a fungus growth on rye. It was undoubtedly known to the early Teutons, and it was responsible for the outbreaks of ergotism which are now known to have resulted from eating contaminated rye bread. It was also known to the early midwives of France and Germany, who employed it with effectiveness, especially in prolonged labor. The modern use of ergot in medicine dates to 1808, when Stearns, of Saratoga County, New York, published his paper on the "Account of Pulvis Parturiens, a Remedy for Quickening Childbirth."

Ergot, belonging to one of the lowest botanical orders, was regarded as a unique substance because of the complexity of its products. Since the advent of antibiotics, however, the scientist has come to expect from fungi not only unusually complex but widely diversified substances.

[110] Welch, Peters, Bueding, Valk, and Higashi, *Science*, **105**, 486 (1947).

The alkaloids have been separated into six diastereoisomeric pairs, which are given in Table XXIII.

Lysergic acid is common to all the alkaloids and obviously holds the key to their fundamental structure. It is a monobasic acid, $C_{16}H_{16}O_2N_2$, containing condensed quinoline and indole heterocycles. Although the synthesis of dihydrolysergic acid [111] clearly established the arrangement of the groupings and heterocyclic rings, the first synthesis of lysergic acid itself is shown.[112]

Lysergic acid

The simplest of the ergot alkaloids is the ergonovine-ergometrinine pair. Each on hydrolysis yields lysergic acid and 2-amino-1-propanol. Indeed, the recon-

$$C_{19}H_{23}O_2N_3 + HOH \rightarrow C_{16}H_{16}O_2N_2 + CH_3-\overset{\overset{\displaystyle NH_2}{|}}{CH}-CH_2OH$$

version of lysergic acid to ergonovine was accomplished by Stoll.[113] Thus, the synthesis of lysergic acid illustrated also constitutes the complete synthesis of ergonovine.

[111] Uhle and Jacobs, *J. Org. Chem.*, **10**, 76 (1945).

[112] Kornfeld, Fornefeld, Kline, Mann, Jones, and Woodward, *J. Am. Chem. Soc.*, **76**, 5256 (1954).

[113] Stoll and Hofmann, *Helv. Chim. Acta*, **26**, 922, 944 (1943).

TABLE XXIII

ERGOT ALKALOIDS

Molecular formula	Alkaloid	Melting Point (dec.)	$[\alpha]_D$ in Chloroform	Discovered by	Year
$C_{35}H_{39}O_5N_5$	Ergocristine*	165–70	−183	Stoll and Hofmann	1943
	Ergocristinine	226	+336	Stoll and Hofmann	1943
$C_{32}H_{41}O_5N_5$	Ergocryptine*	212–4	−187	Stoll and Hofmann	1943
	Ergocryptinine	240–2	+408	Stoll and Hofmann	1943
$C_{31}H_{39}O_5N_5$	Ergocornine*	182–4	−188	Stoll and Hofmann	1943
	Ergocorninine	228	+409	Stoll and Hofmann	1943
$C_{33}H_{35}O_5N_5$	Ergotamine	213	−155	Stoll	1918
	Ergotaminine	252	+385	Stoll	1918
$C_{30}H_{35}O_5N_5$	Ergosine	—	−194	Smith and Timmis†	1936
	Ergosinine	228	+522	Smith and Timmis	1936
$C_{19}H_{23}O_2N_3$	Ergonovine (ergometrine)	160	− 44	Thompson	1935
	Ergometrinine	195	−520	Dudley and Moir	1936

* Ergocristine, ergocryptine and ergocornine were separated in about equal amounts from ergotoxine. [Stoll and Hofmann, *Helv. Chim. Acta*, **26**, 1570 (1943).] Ergotoxine was originally characterized as a pure compound, $C_{35}H_{39}O_5N_5$, by Barger and Carr in 1907. Hence, there is no doubt that ergotinine, isolated by Tanret in 1875 and considered as the (+)-di-astereoisomer of ergotoxine, is also a mixture.

† Smith and Timmins, *J. Chem. Soc.*, **1937**, 396.

The other alkaloids, appearing in Table XXIII, are composed of lysergic acid, two amino acids, one of which is L-proline, an α-keto acid, and ammonia. By employing reductive fission of the alkaloids with hydrazine and with lithium aluminum hydride, Stoll and his co-workers [114] were able to show that the structures of the alkaloids follow a general pattern, as indicated.

A = Lysergic acid fragment
B = Ammonia fragment
C = -Keto acid fragment
D = -Amino acid fragment
E = L-Proline fragment. On alkaline hydrolysis of the ergot alkaloids the proline component isomerizes and D-proline may then be isolated.

[114] Stoll *et al.*, *Helv. Chim. Acta*, **33**, 57 (1950); **34**, 1544 (1951).

The individual alkaloids are further identified in the general structure as follows:

ergocristine-ergocristinine	R = isopropyl,	R′ = benzyl
ergocryptine-ergocryptinine	isopropyl,	isobutyl
ergocornine-ergocorninine	isopropyl,	isopropyl
ergotamine-ergotaminine	methyl,	benzyl
ergosine-ergosinine	methyl,	isobutyl

It is postulated that in the levorotatory alkaloids the double bond of lysergic acid is found in the 5,10 position which for the dextrorotatory isomers shifts to the 9,10 position.

The physiologically active alkaloids include the levorotatory isomers. Of these, ergotoxine, ergotamine, and ergonovine are used medicinally. The ergot alkaloids are used for their action on the uterus and blood vessels. Numerous preparations combine the activities of the total alkaloids of the drug. They vary from simple extractives such as the fluid extract to water-clear products. The chief use of all the products is to stimulate contraction of the uterine musculature, to check postpartum hemorrhage, and to stimulate uterine involution.

Ergotamine Tartrate, U.S.P. (Gynergen), consists of colorless crystals, soluble in water about 1:500 and in alcohol about 1:500. It is more effective when given subcutaneously than when administered orally.

Ergotoxine Ethanesulfonate is a white, crystalline powder, insoluble in water, and decomposed by light and air. It is used as the standard of activity for the ergot alkaloids.

Ergonovine (Ergotrate, Ergometrine) is available as two different salts, namely, *Ergonovine Maleate, U.S.P.*, and ergonovine hydracrylate (Ergotrate-H) in tablets for oral use and in sterile ampuled solution for intravenous or intramuscular injection. The free base, ergonovine, is readily soluble in water. It is active on the uterus in smaller doses than ergotamine or ergotoxine, and it is less toxic than the latter alkaloids.

Methylergonovine, N.N.R. (Methergine), is the α-hydroxymethylpropyl-amide of lysergic acid and possesses the same oxytocic properties as ergonovine. It was first prepared by Stoll [115] from (+)-2-amino-1-butanol in a manner similar to that for ergonovine.

D-Lysergic Acid Diethylamide (L.S.D., L.S.D. 25) is the diethylamide of lysergic acid. It produces hallucinations and "depersonalizing" effects resembling schizophrenia [116] and is a serotonin antagonist. The value of L.S.D. as a drug for use in experimental psychiatry is being explored.

The dihydro alkaloids do not possess the characteristic physiological properties of ergot.[117] They are, however, being examined for other therapeutic uses. Dihydroergotamine (DHE 45) is sympatholytic [118] and has been used for the treatment of migraine.[119] Dihydroergocornine, dihydroergocryptine, and to a lesser

[115] Stoll and Hofmann, U. S. pat. 2,265,207 (1941).
[116] Hoch, Cattell, and Penner, *Am. J. Psychiat.*, **108**, 579 (1952).
[117] Stoll, Hofmann, and Petrzilka, *Helv. Chim. Acta*, **29**, 635 (1946).
[118] Hazard *et al.*, *Compt. rend. soc. biol.*, **140**, 407 (1946); *C.A.*, **41**, 807 (1947).
[119] Yonkman, *Medicinal Chemistry Symposium*, Ann Arbor, 1948.

extent dihydroergocristine are known to have favorable effect in hypertensive patients,[120, 121] and to normalize the resting load of the heart in angina pectoris.[122]

ISOQUINOLINE COMPOUNDS

About 4 per cent of the quinoline fraction obtained from coal tar is isoquinoline. The two isomers are separated by fractional crystallization of their sulfates, isoquinoline sulfate being less soluble. Isoquinoline possesses an odor resembling that of benzaldehyde. As a base it is somewhat stronger than quinoline. Like quinoline the hetero ring is more susceptible to reduction but extremely stable toward oxidation. Tetrahydroisoquinoline possesses all the properties

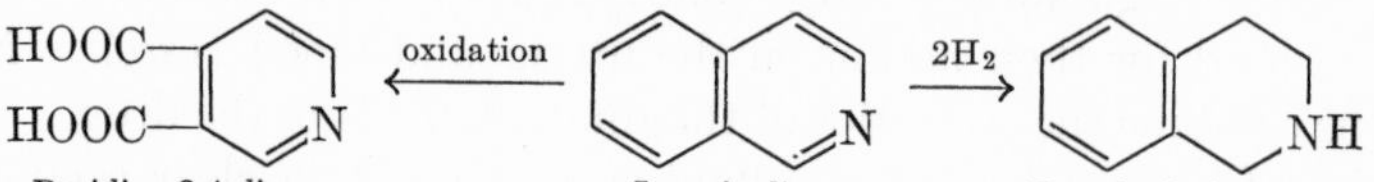

Pyridine-3,4-dicar-
boxylic acid,
Cinchomeronic acid

Isoquinoline

Tetrahydroisoquinoline

characteristic of a secondary benzylamine; it is sufficiently basic to react with the carbon dioxide of the air to form a carbonate. The isoquinoline nucleus is present in many natural and medicinally important bases.

The manner of the biogenesis of the isoquinoline alkaloids has not been determined, but speculations in this respect are not lacking. A general mechanism would involve a condensation somewhat as shown, to give closure of the heterocycle; this followed by bio-

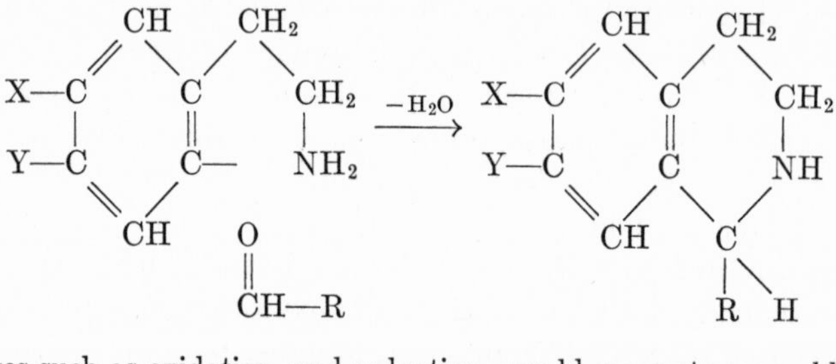

logical processes such as oxidation, and reduction, would account reasonably for the formation of the bases such as the mescaline compounds or the benzylisoquinoline derivatives. Aldehydes are known natural products and hence are readily explained. The necessary phenylethylamine intermediate may very well be derived, by biological degradation, oxidation, etc., from a substituted phenylalanine, as shown. Evidence for such a mech-

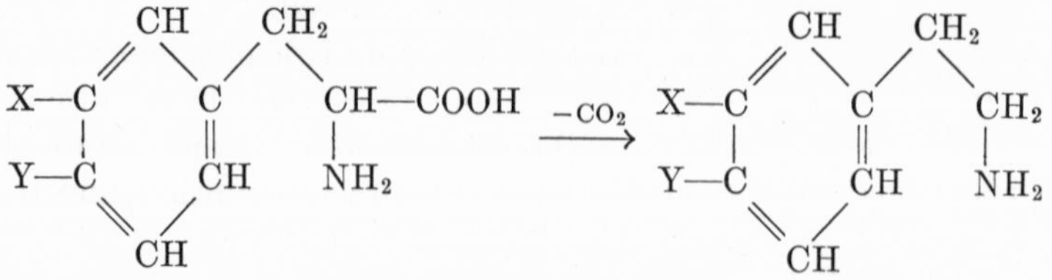

[120] Hates et al., J. Clin. Invest., 28, 615 (1949); C.A., 44, 10168 (1950).
[121] Freis et al., Am. J. Med. Sci., 216, 163 (1948); C.A., 44, 750 (1950).
[122] Schimeert and Zockgraf, Klin. Wochschr., 27, 59 (1949); C.A., 44, 10175 (1950).

anism in nature may be presumed in the Bischler-Napieralski reaction. Here, however, the conditions are so drastic that biological conditions cannot duplicate them. Therefore, to check the hypothesis under conditions approximating nature with respect to pH range and temperature, Schöpf and Bayerle [123] allowed a solution of $M/25$ 3,4-dihydroxyphenyl-ethylamine and $M/12.5$ acetaldehyde to stand for 3 days at $25°$ at pH 5; at the end of that time they reported excellent yields of 6,7-dihydroxy-1-methyltetrahydroisoquinoline. This reaction took place spontaneously and without the aid of enzymes or catalysts. It is not impossible that many natural products are prepared in an analogous manner.

Dimethisoquin Hydrochloride, N.N.R. (Quotane Hydrochloride, 1-Di-methylaminoethoxy-3-n-butylisoquinoline Hydrochloride), is useful for surface application for the relief of itching, irritation, burning, and a wide variety of other dermatoses.

Dimethisoquin

Cactus Alkaloids

A group of closely related isoquinoline bases has been isolated from the mescal button, *Anhalonium lewinii*. A comparison of the structural formulas of some of them will show how all of them may be considered as having a common precursor with mescaline, the most abundant of the entire group.

Mescaline   N-Methylmescaline   Anhalinine, 6,7,8-trimethoxy-tetrahydroisoquinoline

Mescal (Peyoté) has no usage in therapy, but it is employed by certain Indian tribes in the southwestern part of the United States in religious ceremonies for the hallucinations and psychic effects which it produces.

[123] *Ann.*, **513**, 190 (1930).

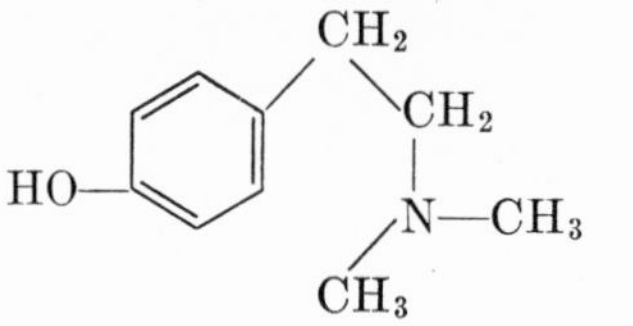

Anhaline
(identical with hordenine)

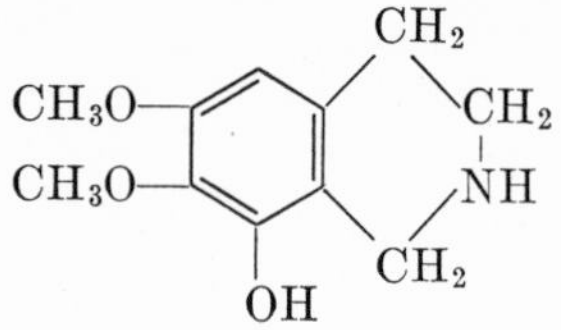

Anhalamine,
6,7-dimethoxy-8-
hydroxy-tetrahydro-
isoquinoline

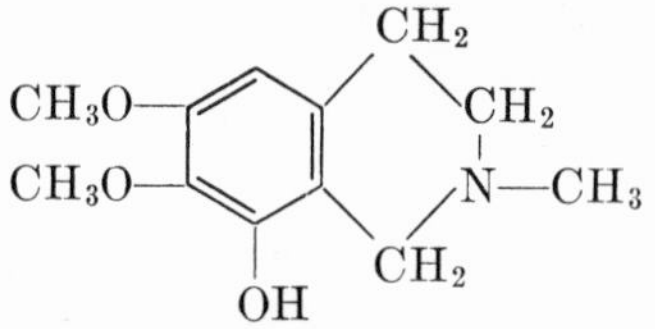

Anhalidine,
6,7-dimethoxy-8-
hydroxy-2-methyltetrahydro-
isoquinoline

From the *Carnegia gigantea*, another cactus species, has been isolated carnegine, 1,2-dimethyl-6,7-dimethoxy-tetrahydroisoquinoline, a compound closely related to the mescal alkaloids. From the *Salsola richteri karel*, a desert plant belonging to Chenopodiaceae, has been obtained salsoline, 6-hydroxy-7-methoxy-1-methyl-tetrahydroisoquinoline. Salsoline is reported to relieve hypertension without interfering with cardiac activity.[124]

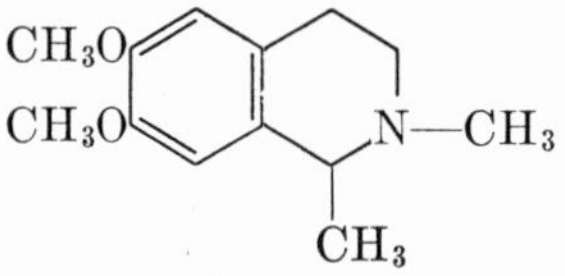

Carnegine

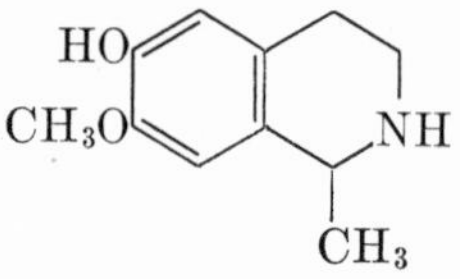

Salsoline

These closely related cactus alkaloids serve as an excellent illustration of the principle that the products of biosynthesis in a plant are structurally very similar. This holds true often not only for a single species but also for closely related or allied species.

Opium Alkaloids

Opium (from Greek meaning juice) is the sun-dried latex from the unripe fruit of *Papaver somniferum*. About 20 per cent of the crude material consists of natural bases. Because of the great medicinal importance of the opium alkaloids the world's production in normal times is very large. It is estimated that the illegitimate annual production of opium is many times that produced legitimately. The opium poppy is cultivated in Egypt, India, China, Persia, and other countries, but the chief source of medicinal opium is Asia Minor. The gummy exudate from the incised capsules is dried and molded to form gum opium. This may be dried, powdered, deodorized, and processed to make the official powdered opium or granular opium.

[124] Wastl, *Hahnemannian Monthly*, **81**, 243 (1946); *C.A.*, **40**, 5147 (1946).

Opium contains about 20 to 25 per cent total alkaloids, the remainder consisting of true gums, sugars, resins, organic acids, fixed oils, and proteins. In Table XXIV is given a list of the chief alkaloids that have been isolated from opium.

TABLE XXIV

ALKALOIDS FROM OPIUM

Formula	Alkaloid	Amount in Opium, Per Cent	Discovered by	Year
$C_{17}H_{19}O_3N$	Morphine	9	Sertürner	1805
$C_{22}H_{23}O_7N$	Narcotine	5	Robiquet	1817
$C_{20}H_{21}O_4N$	Papaverine	0.8	Merck	1848
$C_{19}H_{21}O_3N$	Thebaine	0.4	Pelletier and Thibouméry	1835
$C_{18}H_{21}O_8N$	Codeine	0.3	Robiquet	1832
$C_{23}H_{27}O_8N$	Narceine	0.2	Pelletier	1832
$C_{21}H_{23}O_5N$	Cryptopin	0.08	Smiles	1857
$(C_{17}H_{18}O_3N)_2$	Pseudomorphine	0.02	Pelletier and Thibouméry	1835
$C_{20}H_{25}O_4N$	Laudanine	0.01	Hesse	1870
$C_{23}H_{25}O_4N$	Lanthopine	0.006	Hesse	1870
$C_{20}H_{19}O_5N$	Protopine	0.003	Hesse	1870
$C_{20}H_{25}O_4N$	Codamine	0.002	Hesse	1870
$(C_{21}H_{27}O_3N)_2$	Tritopine	0.0015	Kauder	1890
$C_{21}H_{27}O_4N$	Laudanosine	0.0008	Hesse	1871

The alkaloids of opium may be divided into two distinct groups on the basis of their chemical constitution and their physiological activity, e.g.:

1. Derivatives of benzylisoquinoline include papaverine, narcotine, and narceine. They have little action on the nervous system and a marked antispasmodic action on smooth muscle.

2. Derivatives of phenanthrene include morphine, codeine, and thebaine. These act primarily on the central nervous system to produce a combination of stimulant and depressant effects, and they stimulate the contraction of smooth muscle.

Papaverine Hydrochloride, U.S.P., is the only official salt representative of the benzylisoquinoline derivatives. It is a white, crystalline powder, soluble in water about 1:40. Its chief action is as an antispasmodic causing relaxation of smooth muscle. It is not analgesic or hypnotic in therapeutic doses. The chief use is in the treatment of pulmonary arterial embolism when it is administered in solution by intravenous injection. It is also used to relax the spasms in renal and biliary colic, etc., when it is administered orally or by injection. Preparations of papaverine with codeine have been recommended for the treatment of colds.

The oral ingestion of papaverine in quantities ten times the therapeutic dose produced no untoward results. The intravenous administration of the alkaloid should be conducted cautiously, however, since it may produce cardiac arrhythmias.[125]

[125] Sagall and Dorfman, *New England J. Med.*, **233,** 590 (1945).

Papaverine is soluble in acid solutions but insoluble in water and alkalies. It is optically inactive. It was the first of the naturally occurring bases to be identified as being derived from isoquinoline.

The structure for papaverine was confirmed by its synthesis (Pictet and Gams, 1909) according to the steps shown.

Papaverine, R = —CH$_3$
Perperine, R = —CH$_2$CH$_3$

Laudanosine, R = —CH$_3$

Perperine, synthesized from appropriate intermediates as indicated for papaverine, and the tetraethyl ether analog, possesses papaverinelike properties.

Laudanosine, N-methyltetrahydropapaverine, may be synthesized as indicated.

In a further search for synthetic modifications of papaverine that might have superior physiological effects, other useful drugs were prepared. Variations in the alkoxy substituents resulted in **Paveril, Eupaverine,** and **Octaverine,** all active antispasmodics.

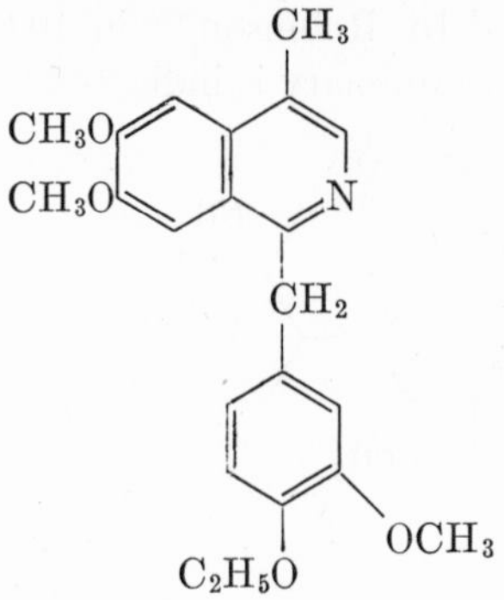

Paveril

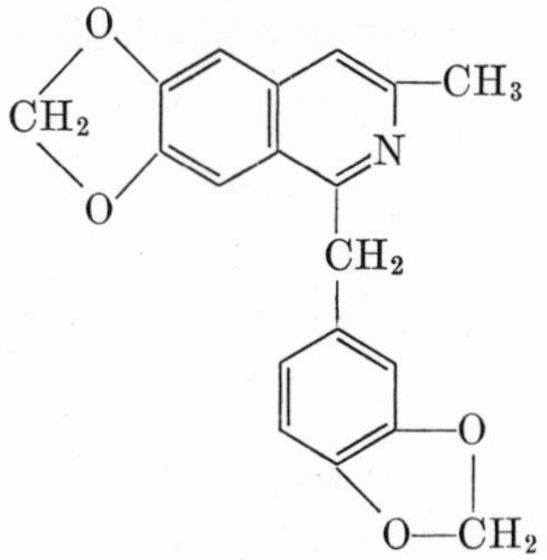

Eupaverine

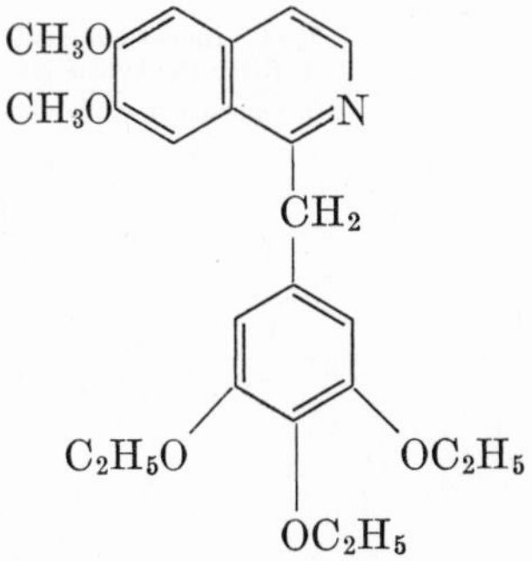

Octaverine

Cotarnine Chloride (Stypticine) is a pale yellow, crystalline powder, very soluble in water with the formation of neutral solutions.

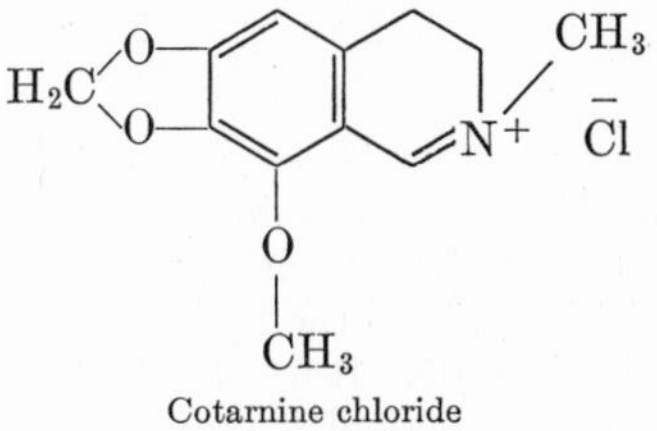

Cotarnine chloride

It is used in arresting hemorrhage, e.g., in profuse menstruation, climacteric hemorrhage, and nosebleed. It may be administered in the form of tablets or by subcutaneous injection. Externally, it may be applied topically as a 30 per cent solution on gauze or cotton.

Morphine and the compounds related to it are the most important alkaloids derived from opium. Morphine is usually employed in the form of its salts, namely, *Morphine Sulfate, U.S.P.*, and *Morphine Hydrochloride, N.F.*, which are more soluble than the free base. These are white, crystalline salts. The sulfate is soluble about 1:15.5, and the hydrochloride about 1:17 in water at room temperature.

The structure of morphine, first proposed by Robinson [126] in 1923, has now been fully confirmed by synthesis, of which a summary is indicated.[127, 128]

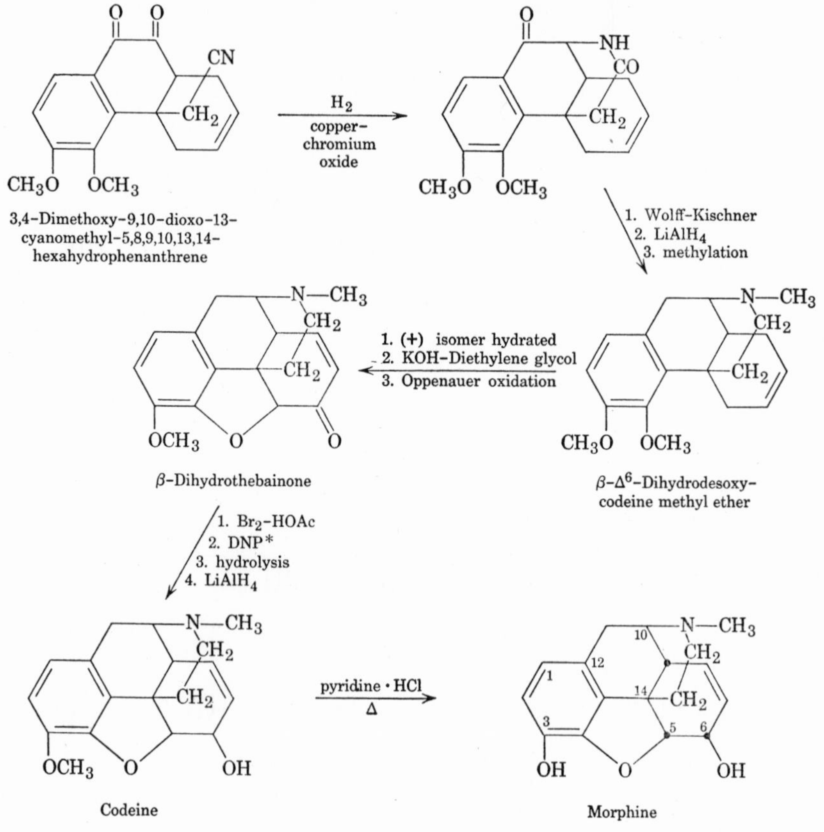

3,4-Dimethoxy-9,10-dioxo-13-
cyanomethyl-5,8,9,10,13,14-
hexahydrophenanthrene

H₂
copper–
chromium
oxide

1. Wolff–Kischner
2. LiAlH₄
3. methylation

β-Dihydrothebainone

1. (+) isomer hydrated
2. KOH–Diethylene glycol
3. Oppenauer oxidation

β-Δ⁶-Dihydrodesoxy-
codeine methyl ether

1. Br₂-HOAc
2. DNP*
3. hydrolysis
4. LiAlH₄

Codeine

pyridine · HCl
Δ

Morphine

* 2,4-Dinitrophenylhydrazine

In the formula given for morphine the heavy dots at positions 5, 6, and 9 are intended to indicate that the hydrogen atoms at these positions occupy *cis* orientation with respect to each other and are *trans* with respect to the hydrogen atoms at positions 14 and 10.[129]

Sertürner [130] isolated morphine in 1805. It was the first of the organic compounds to be identified as having alkalilike, hence alkaloidal, properties. It is appropriate that on the sesquicentennial of this discovery the mysteries of morphine's structure should be completely solved.

Morphine and some of its related compounds are the best-known agents for the relief of pain. Morphine in therapeutic doses exerts a strong narcotic action evidenced by marked analgesia and sleep, but pain may be relieved without causing hypnosis. It exhibits other effects, such as depression of mental facul-

[126] Robinson, *J. Chem. Soc.*, **123**, 980 (1923).

[127] Gates and Tschudi, *J. Am. Chem. Soc.*, **72**, 4839 (1950); **74**, 1109 (1952); **78**, 1380 (1956).

[128] Rapoport, Lovell, and Tolbert, *J. Am. Chem. Soc.*, **73**, 5900 (1951).

[129] Rapoport *et al.*, *J. Org. Chem.*, **15**, 1093 (1950); *J. Am. Chem. Soc.*, **74**, 2630 (1952); **75**, 5329 (1953).

[130] Sertürner, *Trommsdorf's Journal der Pharmazie*, **13**, 1, 234 (1805).

ties, respiration, dulling or abolition of the cough reflex, and constriction of the pupils, and increases the tone of the musculature of the intestines with decrease in peristaltic activity. Morphine is usually administered in the form of tablets, e.g., *Tablets of Morphine Sulfate, U.S.P.*, or by injection of a solution of its salts. Other preparations, such as *Syrup of White Pine with Morphine*, have been used as cough sedatives. Morphine when used continuously develops addiction.

The administration of therapeutic doses of morphine in which the methyl on the nitrogen atom contains C^{14} disclosed that the major portion of the radio-activity is excreted in 24 hours, mostly in the urine, 7 to 10 per cent in the feces, and 3.5 to 6 per cent through the lungs as $C^{14}O_2$.[131]

Codeine, N.F., is a white, crystalline powder, soluble about 1:120 in water at room temperature. It is often used as the salts, *Codeine Phosphate, U.S.P.*, soluble about 1:25 in water, and *Codeine Sulfate, N.F.*, soluble about 1:30 in in water. The alkylation of the phenolic hydroxyl of morphine decreases the analgesic, depressant, intestinal spasmodic, and respiratory activity. Thus, larger doses of codeine are required, but it causes less mental depression and is much less likely to lead to addiction. The most extensive use for codeine is for the relief of dry, irritating cough. For this purpose it is often incorporated with agents which stimulate secretion of mucous, e.g., *Elixir of Terpin Hydrate and Codeine, N.F.*, and *Compound White Pine Syrup with Codeine, N.F.* Codeine phosphate or sulfate may be administered by injection in solution or orally as tablets.

In man, codeine is partly metabolized to morphine and to N-desmethylcodeine. With tagged drug, in which the N-methyl is $C^{14}H_3$, administered to rats, about 13 per cent of the radioactivity is accounted for in the exhaled air.[132]

Heroin, Diacetylmorphine, the morphine molecule in which both the phenolic and alcoholic hydroxyl groups are acetylated, is a very potent drug. However, because of its strong addiction liability it is no longer used.

Pantopon is a purified mixture of the natural alkaloids of opium suitable for injection.

The relative analgesic activity for morphine and related compounds in the cat is given in Table XXV.

TABLE XXV

ANALGESIC ACTIVITY OF MORPHINE AND DERIVATIVES *

Hydrochloride of	Minimum Analgesic Dose mg./kg.	Relative Analgesia	Relative Toxicity
Morphine	0.75	1.00	1.00
Codeine	8.04	0.093	3.72
Allopseudocodeine	13.36	0.056	2.058
Isocodeine (acid tartrate)	13.08	0.057	1.176
Pseudocodeine	17.82	0.042	0.502

* For a detailed discussion of the relationship between chemical structure and analgesic potency in the morphine series see Forneau, *Chimie & industrie*, **39**, 1043 (1938).

[131] Elliott, Tolbert, Adler, and Andersons, *Proc. Soc. Exptl. Biol. Med.* **85**, 77 (1954).
[132] Adler, *J. Pharmacol. Exptl. Therap.*, **106**, 371 (1952).

It may at first seem inconsistent with the general principle of similarity in constitution of alkaloids in the same plant or species of plants to find what has been spoken of as the benzylisoquinoline alkaloids (papaverine, etc.) and the phenanthrene alkaloids (morphine). However, models will show that morphine also is a derivative of benzylisoquinoline.

A number of synthetic derivatives related to morphine have been studied. Some of these offer promise. For details, see the reference to the monograph by Small et al.[133]

Ethylmorphine Hydrochloride (Dionin) is intermediate between morphine and codeine in activity. It is a white, crystalline powder soluble about 1:8 in water. It is used for its local irritant action in eye diseases in concentrations of 5 to 10 per cent. Other uses and forms of administration are similar to those of codeine.

Dihydromorphinone Hydrochloride, U.S.P. (Dilaudid Hydrochloride), differs from morphine in that the alcoholic hydroxyl is oxidized to a keto group and a double bond is hydrogenated. As in the acylated compounds, the narcotic and respiratory depressant properties are increased. The dose is about one-fourth that of morphine. In equal amounts, it is about ten times more analgesic than morphine and about four times as hypnotic. Thus, it is a desirable agent for the relief of pain. It is administered orally as tablets, by injection in solution, and in the form of suppositories. It is reported to be somewhat less habit forming and to cause less constipation than morphine.

Metopon, N.N.R. (Methyldihydromorphinone), is obtained by an involved chemical modification of thebaine, one of the rarer alkaloids of opium. It was prepared under the sponsorship of the Committee on Drug Addiction of the National Research Council. Metopon is not devoid of addiction properties, and tolerance toward its use develops slowly: hence, it is subject to narcotic control.

In comparison with morphine, metopon is a more powerful analgesic, is less depressing on the mental functions, is free from emetic effect, is effective after oral administration, and its use is not accompanied by nausea or drowsiness.

Metopon   Dihydrocodeinone   Levorphan

Dihydrocodeinone, N.N.R. (Hycodan), is an antitussive agent of the codeine type. It is more active but more addicting than codeine, having no particular advantages.

Levorphan, N.N.R. (Dromoran), is (-)-3-hydroxy-N-methylmorphinan, a synthetic analgesic having physiological effects similar to morphine. Although it is

[133] Small, Eddy, Mosettig, and Himmelsbach, "Studies on Drug Addiction," *Pub. Health Rpts.*, Supplement 138, U. S. Gov't. Printing Office, Washington, 1938.

active in much smaller doses, its therapeutic index is about equivalent to morphine, and it also produces addiction. The *levo* isomer is considered much more effective than the racemic mixture, **Racemorphan.** The formula for this compound is indicated.

Methylation of the phenolic hydroxyl affords a codeine analog both chemically and pharmacologically. The methyl ether has antitussive activity about equal to that of codeine but devoid of undesirable side effects.[134]

Dihydrocodeinone Enol Acetate (Acedicon) and **Dihydrohydroxycodeinone** (Eucodal) are synthetic morphine derivatives which have useful analgesic properties. Acedicon has found greatest use as an antitussive agent; they both possess addictive properties.

| Acedicon | Eucodal | N–Allylnormorphine |

N-Allylnormorphine, N.N.R. (Nalline), as the hydrochloride, antagonizes the action of morphine, demerol, methadone, etc.; it reverses the circulatory disturbances of these narcotics, and in patients intoxicated with morphine it reverses the electroencephalogram pattern from that of deep sleep to that of a waking state.[135]

N-Allylnormorphine is prepared by refluxing equimolar portions of normorphine and allyl halide in an organic solvent in the presence of sodium bicarbonate.[136] Nalline is a useful antidote to combat the symptoms of excessive doses of narcotic agents as well as to overcome the respiratory depressant action of such drugs when necessary. It, however, has no value in relieving narcotic addiction.

Very little is known about the effect produced by stereochemical changes on physiological activity. There is an alkaloid, *sinomenine*, isolated from the roots and stems of *Sinomenium acutum* and *S. diversifolius*, climbing plants indigenous to Southern Japan; in this alkaloid the asymmetric centers, where they occur, are of opposite configuration to the corresponding positions in morphine.

Sinomenine is active against avian malaria, is a uterine stimulant, and in large doses is capable of terminating pregnancy, and it has been used for treating rheumatism.

[134] Cass, Frederick, and Andosca, *Am. J. Med. Sci.*, **227**, 291 (1954).
[135] Eckenhoff *et al.*, *Am. J. Med. Sci.*, **222**, 115 (1951); **223**, 191 (1952).
Huggins, Glass, and Bryan, *Proc. Soc. Exptl. Biol. Med.*, **75**, 740 (1950).
Smith, Lehman, and Gilfillan, *Federation Proc.*, **10**, 335 (1951).
[136] Brit. pat. **722,571**, January 26, 1955; *C.A.*, **50**, 2689 (1956).

This alkaloid opens an interesting route to the possible synthesis of some of the enantiomorphs of the opium alkaloids.

Sinomenine   Hydrastine

Dextrorphan, (+)-3-Hydroxy-N-methylmorphinan, is the enantiomorph of Levorphan (page 380). This isomer is reported to have very good antitussive qualities with diminished or absent analgesic properties.[137]

The plant *Hydrastis canadensis* (Ranunculaceae) contains three alkaloids, namely, hydrastine, berberine, and canadine, that are obtained chiefly from the roots and rhizomes.

Hydrastine Hydrochloride is the only alkaloid from hydrastis used to any extent in medicine. It is a white, slightly hygroscopic powder, very soluble in water. It was used extensively at one time as a uterine hemostat through its stimulation of the uterine musculature. It has been largely replaced by more effective agents. A close relationship exists between the structure of hydrastine and the narcotine of opium as may be seen from a comparison of their structures. Hydrastine has the formula shown.

Ipecac Alkaloids

The drug, ipecac, derived from the roots and rhizomes of *Cephaelis ipecacuanha* and *Cephaelis acuminata* (Rubiaceae) contains several alkaloids. The most important alkaloid is emetine although cephaeline has some activity.

Ipecac was known to the natives of South America who used the drug to treat diarrhea. It was introduced into Europe from Brazil in 1658, but it was not until about 1840 that the drug was used to treat dysentery. The drug is cultivated in India, the Federated Malay States, and other countries. The alkaloid, emetine, was first isolated from ipecac and described by the French pharmacist Pelletier, in 1817.

Emetine Hydrochloride, U.S.P., is a white, or slightly yellow, crystalline powder, readily soluble in water and in alcohol. It is lethal to the motile forms of *Endameba histolytica*, the pathogenic organism causing amebiasis, but not so effective against the cyst form. It is usually administered by intramuscular injection. Emetine bismuth iodide proposed by DuMez in 1915 for the treatment

[137] Ralph, *Am. J. Med. Sci.*, **227**, 297 (1954).

of amebiasis has the advantage that it can be administered by mouth; usually it is administered in capsules. The presently accepted structure [138] is shown.

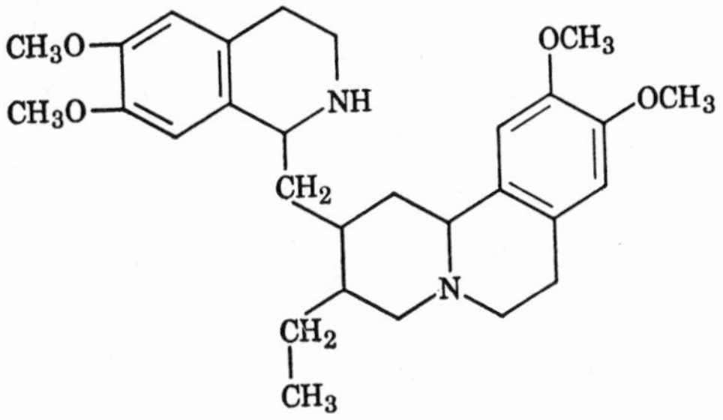

Emetine

Emetine is an emetic and expectorant, but the galenical preparations of ipecac are more suitable for this purpose.

Aporphine Alkaloids

Apomorphine Hydrochloride, U.S.P., is the salt of an alkaloid obtained by synthesis from morphine by heating the latter in a sealed tube at 140° to 150°. The elements of one molecule of water are removed in the process with a partial molecular rearrangement to yield the formula given. It consists of white or gray-colored crystals which become slightly green on exposure to air and light. It is soluble about 1:50 in water. The change in structure from morphine to apomorphine greatly decreases the narcotic and increases the excitant effects on the central nervous system. The stimulation is particularly pronounced on the "chemoreceptor trigger zone" for emesis.[139] It therefore finds use as an emetic in poisoning. In small doses it is used as an expectorant. It is usually administered hypodermically to ensure prompt and efficient absorption. The use of a stomach tube is considered safer and better when available than apomorphine or other drugs that cause emesis.

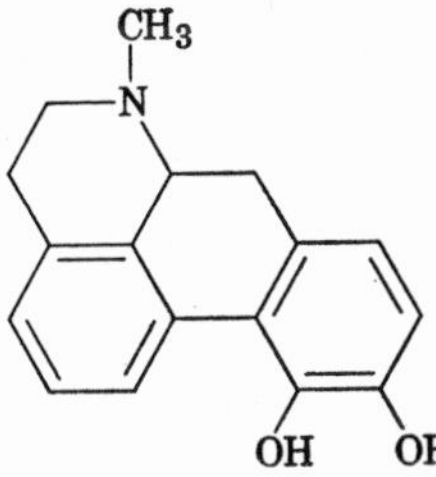

Apomorphine

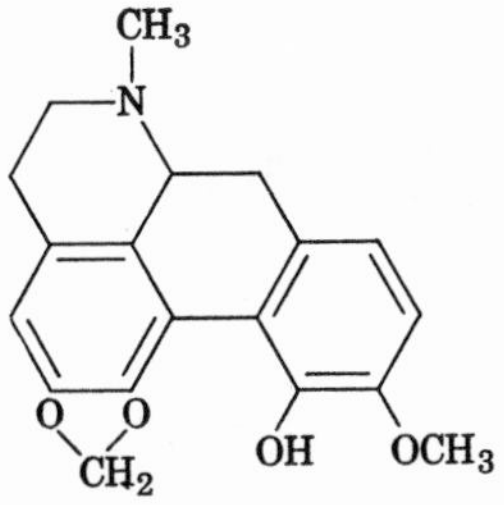

Bulbocapnine

Bulbocapnine is an alkaloid obtained from *Bulbocapnus cava (Corydalis cava)*. It is a colorless, crystalline compound, m.p. 199°, dextrorotatory, insoluble in

[138] Manske and Holmes, *The Alkaloids*, Vol. III, p. 365, Academic Press, New York, 1953.
[139] Borison and Wang, *J. Neurophysiol.*, **12**, 305 (1949).

water, and soluble in organic solvents. It is used in the form of its salts, chiefly the phosphate, administered as tablets for the control of tremors, paralysis agitans, etc.

Curare

Curare, a dark-colored resinoid mass, used by South American Indians as an arrow poison, possesses a lissive action, suggesting its use in spastic and other hyperkinetic neuromuscular disorders, possibly even in the acute stage of poliomyelitis.[140]

Curare has been difficult to analyze since uniform material has not been available and the components not only are numerous but they vary from sample to sample. Three kinds of curare are known; the name indicates the container rather than the source. Tubocurare was filled into bamboo tubes. Calabash curare was packed in gourds. Pot curare was found in native earthen pots. It is now established that tubocurare originated with the Indian tribes of the upper Amazon River and is of menispermaceous origin, the chief alkaloid coming from *Chondrodendron tomentosum*.[141] Calabash curare is obtained from the upper Orinoco region and is prepared from *Strychnos* species. Pot curare comes from the Amazon.

Tube curare has been studied most. From it have been isolated several alkaloids, of which (+)-tubocurarine, a quaternary ammonium compound, is the most active constituent. (−)-Curine and (+)-chondocurine are other alkaloids, which are tertiary bases and physiologically inactive. Elucidation of their structure shows that they have a double benzylisoquinoline structure.[142, 143]

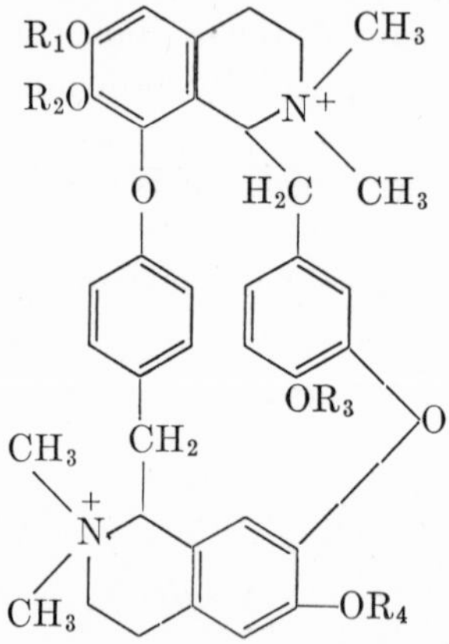

(+)-Tubocurarine chloride
R_1 is CH_3 and R_2 is H
or
R_1 is H and R_2 is CH_3
R_3 is H
R_4 is CH_3

(+)-Chondocurine dimethochloride
R_1 is H and R_2 is CH_3
or
R_1 is CH_3 and R_2 is H
(reverse of tubocurarine)
R_3 is H
R_4 is CH_3

(−)-Curine is a ditertiary base of similar structure.

Pot curare contains many alkaloids, quite phenolic in character. Of these, neoprotocuridine, $C_{36}H_{38}O_6N_2 \cdot 8H_2O$, possessing weak curare activity, probably is built up of a double benzylisoquinoline structure. Isomeric with it but prob-

[140] Ransohoff, *J. Am. Med. Assoc.*, **129**, 129 (1945).
[141] Wintersteiner and Dutcher, *Science*, **97**, 467 (1943).
[142] King, *J. Chem. Soc.*, **1935**, 1381; **1939**, 1157.
[143] Dutcher, *J. Am. Chem. Soc.*, **68**, 419 (1946).

ably of quite different structure is protocuridine, an active alkaloid. A third component which is the most active physiologically is a quaternary ammonium compound whose iodide has the formula $C_{20}H_{25}O_8NI_2$.[144]

From calabash curare several alkaloids have been isolated. C-Curine I hydrochloride, $C_{20}H_{21}N_2Cl$, and C-dihydrotoxiferine hydrochloride, $C_{20}H_{23}N_2Cl$, have been obtained in pure form. These alkaloids are not related chemically to those obtained from tube or pot curare. On the basis of their botanical origin they may be expected to show some structural similarity to the strychnos alkaloids.

Tubocurarine Chloride, U.S.P. (Intocostrin), is used as an adjunct to general anesthesia. Under proper methods of administration it has been found to have a wide field of usefulness, for example, to produce muscular relaxation during the reduction of fractures and in prolonged surgical operations where light, general anesthesia is desirable, to ameliorate the traumatic effects of shock therapy in neuropsychiatry, and as a direct agent for the control of diseases characterized by convulsive states. It is usually administered by injection in aqueous solution.

TROPANE ALKALOIDS

Alkaloids derived from the tropane skeleton occur widely distributed in nature. The solanaceous alkaloids include atropine and hyoscyamine from *Atropa belladonna, Hyoscyamus niger,* and *Datura stramonium.* Scopolamine occurs in many plants of the *Solanaceae* family but especially in *Datura metel* and *Scopolia carniolica.* Numerous other closely related alkaloids that are not used in therapy occur in the solanaceous plants, e.g., apoatropine, belladonnine, noratropine, meteloidine, etc.

The chief structural characteristic of the tropine bases is that they are diheterocyclic, one cycle five-membered and the other six-membered, with the nitrogen atom and its two adjacent carbon atoms common to the two cycles.

$$
\begin{array}{ccc}
\overset{7}{CH_2}-\overset{1}{CH}&\!\!\!\!-\!\!\!\!&\overset{2}{CH_2} \\
| & & | \\
& \overset{8}{N}CH_3 & \overset{3}{C}H_2 \\
| & & | \\
\underset{6}{CH_2}-\underset{5}{CH}&\!\!\!\!-\!\!\!\!&\underset{4}{CH_2}
\end{array}
$$

Tropane

They may be looked upon as being derived from a system in which pyrrolidine and piperidine cycles are condensed. Tropane may be considered the parent compound.

3-Hydroxytropane or 3-tropanol is also known as tropine, and the corresponding ketone is known as tropanone. The structure of these two compounds follows from a simple synthesis worked out by Robinson. The esters of tropine are sometimes called tropeines, of which an extensive series has been synthesized and investigated for physiological merit.

[144] King, *J. Chem. Soc.,* **1937,** 1472.

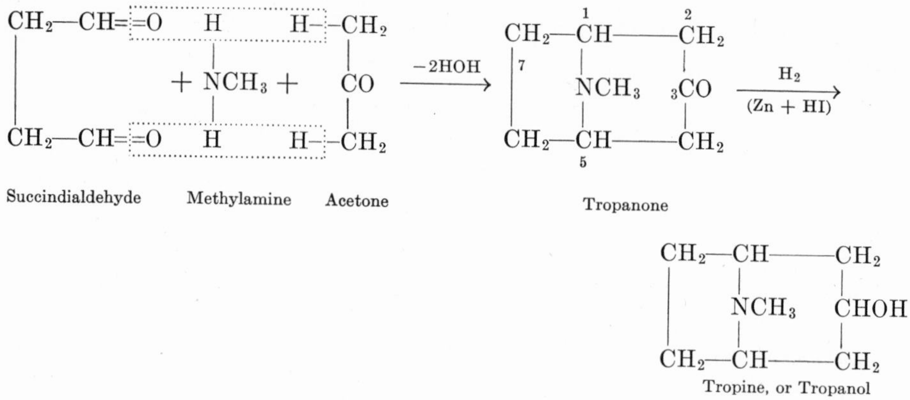

$$CH_2-CH=\!\!=\!\!O \quad H \qquad H-\!\!-CH_2$$
$$| \qquad\qquad +\; NCH_3\; + \qquad CO \qquad \xrightarrow{-2HOH}$$
$$CH_2-CH=\!\!=\!\!O \quad H \qquad H-\!\!-CH_2$$

$$\overset{1}{CH_2}-\overset{}{CH}\!\!-\!\!-\!\!-\overset{2}{CH_2}$$
$$\overset{7}{|} \qquad | \qquad |$$
$$NCH_3 \quad _3CO \qquad \xrightarrow[(Zn\; +\; HI)]{H_2}$$
$$CH_2-\underset{5}{CH}\!\!-\!\!-\!\!-CH_2$$

Succindialdehyde   Methylamine   Acetone   Tropanone

$$CH_2-CH\!\!-\!\!-\!\!-CH_2$$
$$| \qquad | \qquad |$$
$$\qquad NCH_3 \quad CHOH$$
$$| \qquad | \qquad |$$
$$CH_2-CH\!\!-\!\!-\!\!-CH_2$$

Tropine, or Tropanol

Hyoscyamine, the most abundant of the tropane alkaloids, very closely resembles atropine, the chief physical difference being its optical activity, $[\alpha]_D^{20} = -20.75$; it melts at 108.5° and is slightly more soluble in water. The center of optical asymmetry is in the tropic acid portion; hence, hyoscyamine is (−)-tropyltropeine. Hyoscyamine racemizes so readily that there is little doubt that it is the configuration which occurs naturally and that during isolation it racemizes into atropine.

Hyoscyamine Hydrobromide, N.F., and **Hyoscyamine Sulfate, N.F.,** are employed for their sympatholytic properties.

Atropine, which is racemic tropyltropeine, was isolated almost simultaneously by Mein and by Geiger and Hesse (1831) from belladonna roots, where it is found to occur with an isomer, hyoscyamine. The structure of atropine is indicated by the fact that it is hydrolyzed to tropanol and tropic acid, and by its resynthesis from these two fragments. It is optically inactive, melts at 114–116° and, by virtue of its amino group, this alkaloid forms salts that are soluble in water.

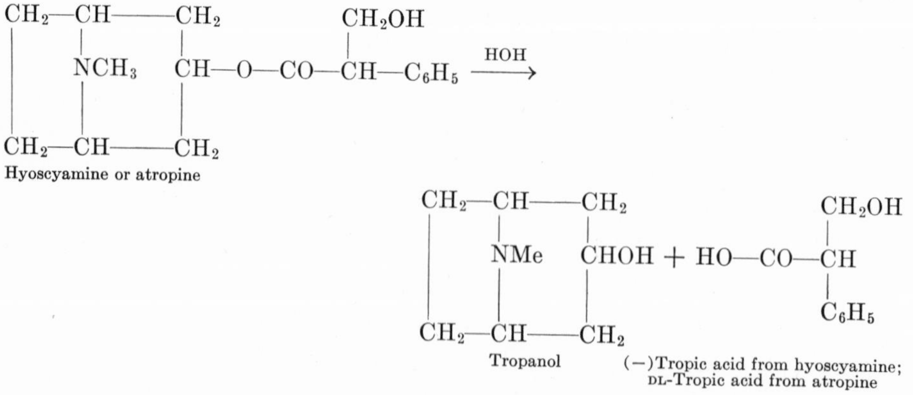

$$CH_2-CH\!\!-\!\!-\!\!-CH_2 \qquad CH_2OH$$
$$| \qquad | \qquad | \qquad\qquad |$$
$$\quad NCH_3 \quad CH-O-CO-CH-C_6H_5 \xrightarrow{HOH}$$
$$| \qquad | \qquad |$$
$$CH_2-CH\!\!-\!\!-\!\!-CH_2$$

Hyoscyamine or atropine

$$CH_2-CH\!\!-\!\!-\!\!-CH_2 \qquad\qquad CH_2OH$$
$$| \qquad | \qquad | \qquad\qquad\qquad |$$
$$\quad NMe \quad CHOH + HO-CO-CH$$
$$| \qquad | \qquad | \qquad\qquad\qquad |$$
$$CH_2-CH\!\!-\!\!-\!\!-CH_2 \qquad\qquad C_6H_5$$

Tropanol   (−)Tropic acid from hyoscyamine;
                  DL-Tropic acid from atropine

DL-Tropic acid may be synthesized in yields up to 80 per cent from phenylacetic acid via the Ivanov reagent according to the accompanying scheme.[145]

[145] Blicke, Raffelson, and Barna, *J. Am. Chem. Soc.,* **74,** 253 (1952).

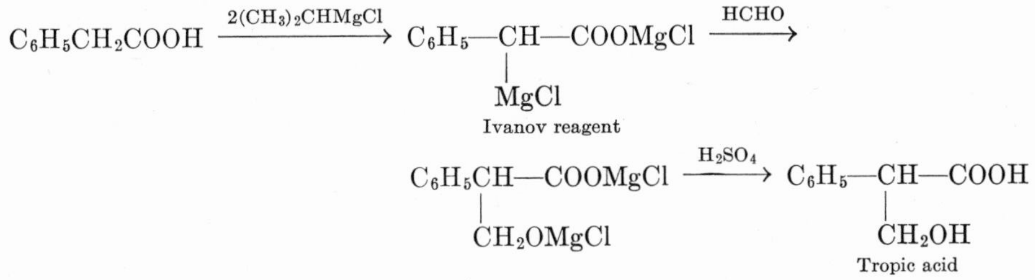

$$C_6H_5CH_2COOH \xrightarrow{2(CH_3)_2CHMgCl} C_6H_5-CH-COOMgCl \xrightarrow{HCHO}$$
$$\underset{\text{Ivanov reagent}}{\overset{|}{MgCl}}$$

$$C_6H_5CH-COOMgCl \xrightarrow{H_2SO_4} C_6H_5-CH-COOH$$
$$\underset{CH_2OMgCl}{|} \qquad\qquad \underset{\underset{\text{Tropic acid}}{CH_2OH}}{|}$$

Atropine exhibits a complex physiological action when administered in toxic doses; it first stimulates and eventually depresses the central nervous system, giving rise to hallucinations, a feeling of exaltation, inconsequent speech, delirium, and convulsions, followed by stupor and coma. It paralyzes the peripheral nerve endings and in this way affects the secretory glands, the heart, and organs containing unstriped muscle; it paralyzes the vagus and slows respiration. In medicine it is used principally as a mydriatic. The dilation of the pupil is produced by a paralysis of the motor nerve terminations in the circular muscle of the iris, and it paralyzes the accommodation by acting on the nerve endings of the ciliary muscle. Internally, atropine and closely related compounds are used to alter the cardiac rate; to inhibit the gland secretions of the nose, throat, and larynx in coryza, colds, and bronchitis and of the sweat glands in tuberculosis; to stimulate the respiration; and to secure symptomatic relief in paralysis agitans, etc.

Atropine, N.F., consists of colorless crystals, soluble in water about 1:450 and readily soluble in most organic solvents and fixed oils. The free base is used chiefly as a mydriatic in ophthalmological practice in 0.5 to 1 per cent solution in a fatty oil or in gelatin discs.

Atropine Sulfate, U.S.P., consists of colorless crystals which effloresce in dry air. It is soluble about 1:0.4 in water and slightly soluble in organic solvents. It is used in the form of the powder in capsules, as tablets, or in aqueous solutions which may be injected subcutaneously or intravenously. Solution of 0.5 to 1 per cent are used in ophthalmology. Such solutions should be freshly prepared as they are unstable owing to gradual hydrolysis of the ester. The sulfate alone or combined with morphine sulfate is often used prior to anesthesia to decrease secretions of the respiratory tract during inhalation anesthesia.

A number of synthetic substitutes for atropine have been developed, such as:

Homatropine Hydrobromide, U.S.P. (Mandelyltropeine), consists of a white, crystalline powder, soluble in water about 1:6, m.p. about 212° with decomposition. It is less active and less toxic than atropine. It is used primarily as a substitute for atropine as a mydriatic; the effects wear off in 1 to 2 days, whereas with atropine mydriasis may continue for 5 to 12 days. Solutions of 1 to 2 per cent are usually dropped in the eye, or gelatin discs may be employed.

Homatropine Methylbromide, U.S.P. (Novatrin), m.p. 191–192°, is soluble in water and alcohol. It is administered usually as tablets for the treatment of hyperchlorhydria and gastrointestinal spasm.

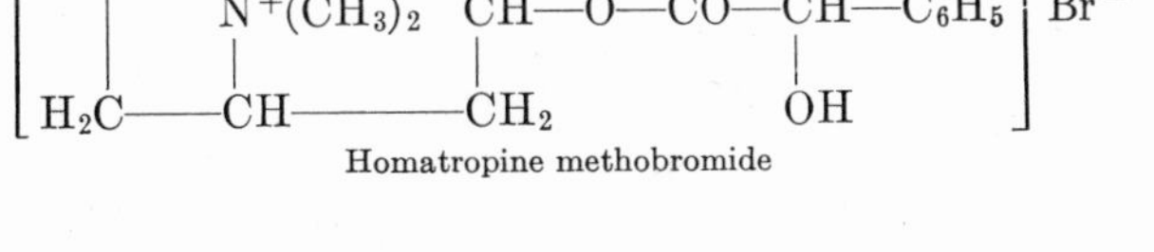

$$\left[\begin{array}{l} H_2C-CH-CH_2 \\ \qquad | \qquad | \\ \qquad N^+(CH_3)_2 \quad CH-O-CO-CH-C_6H_5 \\ \qquad | \qquad | \qquad\qquad\qquad | \\ H_2C-CH-CH_2 \qquad\qquad OH \end{array}\right] Br^-$$

Homatropine methobromide

Eumydrine (N-Methyl-Atropine Nitrate) is used as a substitute for atropine in ophthalmology. It is usually employed in a 0.5 per cent solution. It is less potent and less persistent than atropine, the effects wearing off in 12 to 24 hr.

Eucatropine Hydrochloride, U.S.P. [Euthalmine Hydrochloride, 4(1,2,2,6-Tetramethylpiperidyl) mandelate], is a white, granular powder, stable in air and very soluble in water. It is used as a mydriatic in solutions of 5 to 10 per cent concentration as drops instilled into the eye. The mydriatic effects wear off in about 12 hr.

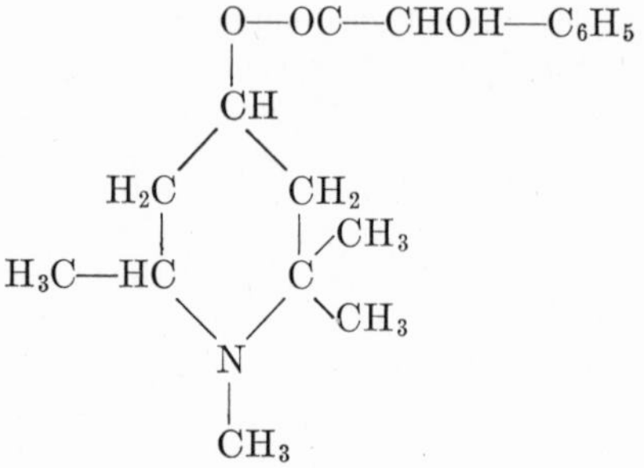

$$O-OC-CHOH-C_6H_5$$

Eucatropine

Tropacocaine has been isolated from both the Javanese and Peruvian coca leaves. It has been used in lumbar anesthesia and is reported to be more potent than cocaine; however, it unfortunately produces hyperemia. On hydrolysis tropacocaine yields benzoic acid and pseudo-tropanol, which is epimeric with tropanol.

From molecular models it may be seen that two isomeric tropanols may exist, which on oxidation form identical ketones. The ketone, tropanone, may be reduced by catalytic means to tropanol, identical with the moiety obtained from atropine, and by means of sodium and ethanol to pseudo-tropanol, identical with the fragment obtained by the hydrolysis of tropacocaine. Pseudo-nor-tropanol undergoes acyl migration with much greater facility; that is, the hydroxyl and amino functions are in closer proximity, and hence it is assigned the structure indicated.[146, 147]

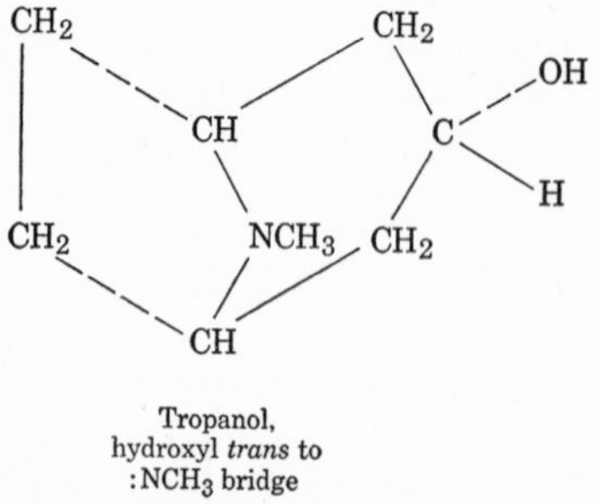

Tropanol,
hydroxyl *trans* to
:NCH3 bridge

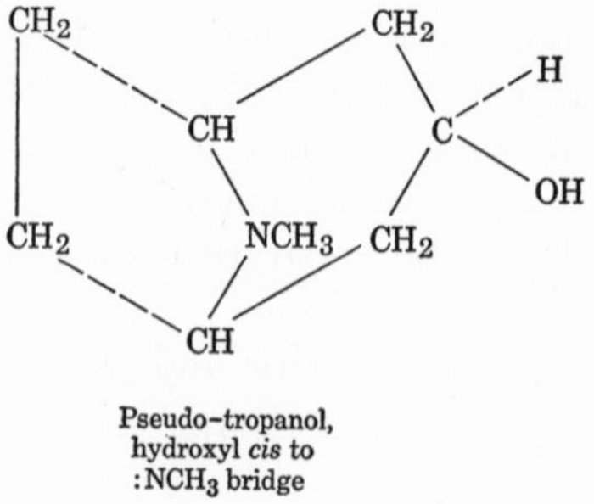

Pseudo–tropanol,
hydroxyl *cis* to
:NCH3 bridge

[146] Fodor and Nador, *Nature*, **169**, 462 (1952).
[147] Nickon and Fieser, *J. Am. Chem. Soc.*, **74**, 5566 (1952).

Robinson originally postulated that ornithine might be a precursor for the required succindialdehyde in the proposed biosynthetic mechanism. Support for this idea is obtained from finding that the stramonium grown in a nutrient medium containing ornithine-2-C^{14} forms radioactive alkaloid with the radiocarbon incorporated into the tropanol moiety.[148]

Willstätter suggested that tropanone is probably the first intermediate in the biological synthesis of the tropane alkaloids. The probable starting materials for the plant are indicated in Robinson's elegant synthesis from acetone, methylamine, and succindialdehyde. This synthesis, however simple it may appear, requires strongly alkaline conditions, quite beyond the biological pH range. Accordingly Schöpf [149] suggested that in this synthesis the acetone may be replaced by acetone dicarboxylic acid, and that the ring system, once formed, could easily be decarboxylated. In order to test this hypothesis he set up experimental conditions in which the succindialdehyde was $M/45$, methylamine was $M/25$, and acetonedicarboxylic acid $M/20$; these reagents were allowed to stand together for 3 days at 25° at varying pH ranges, with yields of tropanone for the various ranges as indicated below:

pH 3	47 per cent tropanone
pH 5	54
pH 7	65
pH 9	66
pH 11	86
pH 13	3

Thus it is seen that the reaction can take place under pH conditions that do

Succindialde-   Methyl-   Acetone-   Tropanone
hyde   amine   dicarboxylic
                            acid

actually exist in the plant. Biohydrogenation of the ketone would then produce tropanol. If, for example, in this biosynthesis, only one carboxyl group is removed and the ketone is reduced, the formation of ecgonine will readily be understood. In nature succindialdehyde arises by oxidative deamination of putrescine.[150] If succindialdehyde, a primary amine, and acetonedicarboxylic acid are allowed to react spontaneously, the N-homologs of tropanone may be obtained.[151]

Scopolamine, known also as hyoscine, is the chief constituent of *Datura metel*. The free base is a syrup, $[\alpha]_D^{25} = -24°$ to $-26°$, capable of forming well-

[148] Leete, Marion, and Spenser, *Can. J. Chem.*, **32**, 1116 (1954); *C.A.*, **49**, 6394 (1955).
[149] *Ann.*, **518**, 1 (1935).
[150] Cromwell, *Biochem. J.*, **37**, 722 (1944).
[151] Keagle and Hartung, *J. Am. Chem. Soc.*, **68**, 1608 (1946).

defined salts. Its structure is closely related to that of hyoscyamine. On hydrolysis it forms tropic acid and scopine. In scopine the hydroxyl group at the 3

$$\begin{array}{c} \text{HC—CH——CH}_2 \\ \diagup \;\mid\quad\;\mid\quad\quad\mid \\ \text{O}\quad\mid\;\;\;\text{N—CH}_3\;\;\text{CH—O—CO—CH—C}_6\text{H}_5 \xrightarrow{\text{HOH}} \\ \diagdown\;\mid\quad\;\mid\quad\quad\mid\qquad\qquad\mid \\ \text{HC—CH——CH}_2\qquad\qquad\text{CH}_2\text{OH} \end{array}$$
$$\text{Scopolamine}$$

$$\begin{array}{c} \text{CH—CH——CH}_2\qquad\qquad\qquad\qquad\text{COOH} \\ \diagup\;\mid\quad\;\mid\quad\quad\mid\qquad\qquad\qquad\quad\mid \\ \text{O}\quad\mid\;\;\;\text{NCH}_3\;\;\text{CHOH} + \text{HOCH}_2\text{—CH—C}_6\text{H}_5 \\ \diagdown\;\mid\quad\;\mid\quad\quad\mid \\ \text{CH—CH——CH}_2 \end{array}$$
$$\text{Scopine}\qquad\qquad\qquad\qquad\text{Tropic acid}$$

position is *trans* to the N-methyl bridge, as in tropanol; this is indicated by the
ease with which it rearranges into the isomeric scopoline.[152] The epoxide bridge
is *cis* to the N-bridge.[153]

Scopine   Scopoline

Scopolamine Hydrobromide, U.S.P. (Hyoscine Hydrobromide), consists
of colorless crystals soluble about 1:1.5 in water and slightly soluble in most
organic solvents, m.p. 190–192°. The activities of scopolamine and atropine are
quite similar in their peripheral effects, but the action of atropine is more pronounced and prolonged on the heart, intestinal, and bronchiolar muscle, whereas
scopolamine is the stronger blocking agent for the iris and salivary, bronchial,
and sweat glands. Scopolamine is used occasionally in ophthalmology, but it is
used primarily for its central effects. Its systemic action is primarily that of a
depressant, and therapeutic doses are used to cause dreamless sleep in motor
excitement, delirium, and mania. It is administered orally as *Tablets of Scopolamine Hydrobromide, N.F.*, or in aqueous solution by injection.

Methscopolamine Nitrate, N.N.R., and **Methscopolamine Bromide,
N.N.R.,** salts of N-methylated scopolamine, are sympatholytic agents, and as
anticholinergic compounds are antisecretory and antispasmodic.

Meteloidine is an alkaloid found in *Datura meteloides*. On hydrolysis it yields
tiglic acid and 3,6,7-trihydroxytropane, commonly known as teloidine. Hence,

[152] Smith and Hartung, *J. Am. Chem. Soc.*, **75**, 3856 (1953).
[153] Heusner, *Chem. Ber.*, **87**, 1063 (1954).

it is an ester of teloidine with tiglic acid, presumably the ester being attached at position 3.

HOCH
        \
         CH₂
       CH
            \
HOCH   CH – OCO – C = CH– CH₃
      NCH₃ |
         CH₂   CH₃
       CH

Meteloidine

CH₂
    \
     CH₂
   CH
        \
         CHOCH₂C₆H₅
CH₂   N – CH₃
         CH₂
       CH

Benzotropine

Benzotropine Methanesulfonate, N.N.R., a salt of the benzyl ether of tropanol, combines the structural elements of atropine and of Benadryl. It was hoped that it might combine in a single molecule antihistamine activity with antiparkinson effects. It may be useful for the latter.[154] It is a parasympatholytic, somewhat anesthetic, has anticholinergic power about equal to that of atropine, and is suggested for the treatment of paralysis agitans.

Coca Alkaloids

Another series of related tropane derivatives is found in the leaves of *Erythroxylon coca* and other species of Erythroxylon. The alkaloids on hydrolysis yield ecgonine, an organic acid, and methanol.

Explorers of South America as early as 1532 reported that the natives ascribed a peculiar action to the coca leaves, that the chewing of them banished uncomfortable feelings and even pangs of thirst and hunger. The aborigines believed that if they had enough of the leaves to eat they might perform all manner of feats and heavy work without eating. Although Wöhler in 1860 had observed the local action of cocaine it was not used until Koller, a Viennese eye specialist, in 1884, reported favorable clinical results from its use.

The structure of ecgonine can be shown to a carboxylic acid derivative of tropanol, and the carboxyl group has been located by various procedures, e.g., by Willstätter's synthesis from tropanone.

$$CH_2—CH——CH$$
$$\quad | \qquad || \qquad \xrightarrow{CO_2}$$
$$\quad NCH_3 \quad C—ONa$$
$$\quad | \qquad |$$
$$CH_2—CH——CH_2$$

Sodium enol derivative
of tropanone

$$CH_2—CH——CH—COOH$$
$$\quad | \qquad | \qquad \xrightarrow{H_2}$$
$$\quad NCH_3 \quad C{=}O$$
$$\quad | \qquad |$$
$$CH_2—CH——CH_2$$

$$CH_2—CH——CH—COOH$$
$$\quad | \qquad |$$
$$\quad NCH_3 \quad CHOH$$
$$\quad | \qquad |$$
$$CH_2—CH——CH_2$$

Ecgonine

[154] Doshay, Constable, and Fromer, *Neurology,* **2,** 233 (1952).

Cocaine, on hydrolysis, yields ecgonine, methanol, and benzoic acid. It can be shown that these component fragments are linked in the manner indicated.

$$
\begin{array}{l}
\text{CH}_2\text{—CH——CH—COOCH}_3 \\
\quad\quad\;|\quad\quad\; | \\
\quad\quad\text{NCH}_3 \;\; \text{CH—O—CO—C}_6\text{H}_5 \\
\quad\quad\;|\quad\quad\; | \\
\text{CH}_2\text{—CH——CH}_2
\end{array}
$$

Cocaine

Cocaine may be synthesized by the benzoylation of the alcoholic hydroxyl group and methylation of the carboxyl group in ecgonine. Most of the cocaine used for drug purposes is obtained synthetically in this manner, the ecgonine being provided from the other naturally occurring cocaine bases. Cocaine, crystallized from alcohol, forms monoclinic prisms which melt at 98°. Its specific rotation is $[\alpha]_D^{20} = -15.8°$. It forms well-defined salts, of which the hydrochloride is most widely used.

Cocaine, N.F., is a white, crystalline powder, m.p. 96–98°, soluble about 1:600 in water, about 1:100 in mineral oil, and about 1:12 in olive oil. It is used in oil solutions and ointments for the same purposes as cocaine hydrochloride. *Cocaine Hydrochloride, U.S.P.*, consists of colorless crystals, soluble about 1:0.5 in water. It is usually employed in aqueous solutions in concentrations of 0.1 to 4 per cent for surface anesthesia in ophthalmology to 10 or 20 per cent for nose and throat work. Epinephrine is commonly added to the solutions to decrease the rate of absorption of the cocaine. Disadvantages of cocaine are that it is strongly narcotic and may lead to drug addiction and that the ester linkages are hydrolyzed when solutions are boiled for sterilization. Consequently, cocaine has been displaced to a considerable extent by other local anesthetics.

Related to cocaine are cinnamyl cocaine and the truxillines. These, on hydrolysis, form ecgonine, methanol, and cinnamic or truxillic acid. Truxillic acids are naturally occurring derivatives of cyclobutane which may be looked upon as dimerized cinnamic acid, as shown. The structures for these alkaloids are shown.

$$
\begin{array}{ccc}
\text{C}_6\text{H}_5\text{—CH=CH—COOH} & & \begin{array}{c} \text{H}\;\;\text{H} \\ |\;\;\; | \\ \text{C}_6\text{H}_5\text{—C—C—COOH} \end{array} \\
+ & \rightarrow & \\
\text{HOCO—CH=CH—C}_6\text{H}_5 & & \begin{array}{c} \text{HOCO—C—C—C}_6\text{H}_5 \\ |\;\;\; | \\ \text{H}\;\;\text{H} \end{array}
\end{array}
$$

α-Truxillic acid

$$
\downarrow
$$

$$
\begin{array}{c}
\text{H}\;\;\text{H} \\
|\;\;\; | \\
\text{C}_6\text{H}_5\text{—C—C—COOH} \\
\\
\text{C}_6\text{H}_5\text{—C—C—COOH} \\
|\;\;\; | \\
\text{H}\;\;\text{H}
\end{array}
$$

Truxinic acid

$$C_8H_{13}N\begin{cases} COOCH_3 \\ \\ OCO-CH-CHC_6H_5 \end{cases}$$

$$\underset{\text{Truxilline}}{C_6H_5CH-CHCOOC_8H_{13}NCOOCH_3}$$

$$\underset{\text{Cinnamyl cocaine}}{C_6H_5CH=CHCOOC_8H_{13}NCOOCH_3}$$

Although the coca tree is indigenous to Bolivia, it is now cultivated in India, Java, and Ceylon. South America (Peru) in 1906 produced 2,800,000 kg. of the leaves and in 1920 only 450,000 kg. Java, on the other hand, exported 800,000 kg. of the leaves in 1912 and 1,280,000 kg. in 1922. The alkaloidal content of the South American plant consists of about 75 to 90 per cent cocaine; the Javanese product consists mainly of cinnamyl cocaine. However, this is not objectionable since all these bases supply the essential ecgonine, which may be converted into cocaine.

Although the custom of chewing coca leaves originated with the South American Indians, cocaine habituation as a white man's affliction started in Europe. It is estimated that the illegitimate production of cocaine in the world amounts to 15,000 to 20,000 kg. annually.

The relationship between the chemical structure and physiological activity of the tropane alkaloids presents many interesting problems. Cocaine, although predominantly anesthetic, behaves also as a mydriatic. Tropacocaine shows no mydriatic activity and does not lead to drug addiction. Ecgonine or the ecgonine alkyl esters possess no anesthetic activity; ecgonine has no anesthetic activity upon benzoylating the hydroxyl group. If the carboxyl group is esterified and the hydroxyl group is benzoylated, ecognine becomes highly active. Acylation of the hydroxyl group of methylecgonine with a fatty acid radical produces no activity, and of the aromatic acids, benzoic is the most effective.

Lupin Alkaloids

Also belonging to the diheterocyclic alkaloids in which a single nitrogen atom is common to the two cycles are the members of the lupinan group; these are found in the Papilionaceae. Since lupine seeds are used extensively for animal feed, considerable attention has been given to the removal of the more toxic alkaloids or to "debittering." The parent structure of the lupinan bases is that of two piperidine cycles with the N atom common.

Lupinine, one of the simpler natural derivatives, has the structure indicated.

β-Lupinan

Lupinine

Sparteine, $C_{15}H_{24}N_2$, is the chief alkaloid of the common broom. The synthesis has been accomplished from ethyl 2-pyridylacetate as shown.[155]

Sparteine

Sparteine Sulfate, N.F., is a salt derived from the alkaloid which occurs in *Scoparius* (Broom top). It is a hygroscopic crystalline compound that has been used to a limited extent to decrease the pulse rate in cardiac disturbances. Its effects are uncertain, and its value is questionable.

[155] Leonard and Beyler, *J. Am. Chem. Soc.*, **72**, 1316 (1950).

Cycles with
Two or More Heteroatoms

The five-membered heterocycle composed of two nitrogen and three carbon atoms may exist in two isomeric forms, known as pyrazole and imidazole respectively.

$$
\begin{array}{ccc}
\text{CH}\!\!-\!\!-\!\!\text{CH} & & \text{N}\!\!-\!\!-\!\!\text{CH} \\
\| \quad\quad \| & & \| \quad\quad \| \\
\text{CH} \quad\ \text{N} & & \text{CH} \quad\ \text{CH} \\
\diagdown \quad \diagup & & \diagdown \quad \diagup \\
\text{NH} & & \text{NH}
\end{array}
$$

Pyrazole   Imidazole

Pyrazole compounds are synthesized from hydrazine and 1,3-dicarbonyl derivatives. No member of the pyrazole series is known to be formed in nature.

PYRAZOLE DERIVATIVES

The only effective agent for the reduction of temperature in fevers for many years was quinine. After Pelletier and Caventou had isolated quinine in 1820, it was many years before the constitution of this alkaloid was determined. It was known quite early, however, that quinine yielded quinoline upon decomposition. Since quinoline was found to have antipyretic activity, although too toxic for use in therapy, efforts were made to prepare nontoxic compounds to replace the then expensive quinine. The formula attributed to quinine at that time was incorrect. Nevertheless, several compounds having antipyretic activity but lacking the antimalarial action of quinine were prepared.

Ludwig Knorr in 1887, seeking to make a tetrahydroquinoline derivative from phenylhydrazine and acetoacetic ester, prepared a compound which he at first believed was similar to quinine in structure.[1] Later Knorr showed that the compound which he had made was a pyrazole derivative.[2] The product which Knorr obtained was almost completely insoluble in water and seemed worthless for use in therapy. Upon methylation, he obtained a compound readily soluble in water (an unusual effect on solubility). This soluble product was introduced into therapy under the name antipyrine.

Antipyrine, N.F. (Phenazone, Phenyldimethylpyrazolone, Analgesin), may be prepared in several ways of which one is shown.

$$CH_3-C=O \quad + \quad H_2N-NH-C_6H_5$$
$$|$$
$$O$$
$$||$$
$$CH_2-C-O-C_2H_5$$

Acetoacetic ester + Phenylhydrazine

$$\xrightarrow[-H_2O]{Cold}$$

$$CH_3-C=N-N-C_6H_5$$
$$| \qquad \qquad H$$
$$O$$
$$||$$
$$CH_2-C-O-C_2H_5$$

Acetoacetic ester Phenylhydrazone

$$\xrightarrow[-C_2H_5OH]{Hot}$$

$$CH_3-C=N$$
$$| \qquad \qquad N-C_6H_5$$
$$CH_2-C=O$$

Phenyl-methyl-pyrazolone

$$\xrightarrow{CH_3I}$$

$$CH_3-C-N^{CH_3}$$
$$|| \qquad \qquad N-C_6H_5$$
$$CH-C=O$$

Phenyl-dimethyl-pyrazolone, antipyrine

Antipyrine is a white, odorless, crystalline solid, m.p. 111–113°, having a somewhat bitter taste. It is slightly hygroscopic; 1 g. dissolves in less than 1 ml. water. It is very soluble in alcohol and chloroform.

Although originally introduced as an antipyretic, it is used more as an analgesic. It is employed to reduce temperatures in fevers and to allay pain in headache, gout, neuralgia, rheumatism, and other conditions. It is included in many preparations sold publicly for the relief of pain.

In vivo up to 40 per cent of antipyrine is converted to 4-hydroxyantipyrine, which is then conjugated with either glucuronic or sulfuric acid and excreted in the urine. The metabolic fate of the other 60 per cent is not established.[3]

Aminopyrine, N.F. (Pyramidon, Amidopyrine, 4-Dimethylaminoantipyrine), was first prepared by Stolz in 1893. It is a white, crystalline solid, m.p. 107–109°, soluble in water 1:18 and readily soluble in alcohol, benzene, and chloroform.

Aminopyrine is an effective antipyretic and anodyne. Its action is similar to that of antipyrine, but it is slower in action, the effects last longer, and smaller doses

[1] *Ber.*, **16**, 2597 (1883); **17**, 2037 (1884).
[2] *Ann.*, **238**, 137, 160, 203 (1887).
[3] Brodie and Axelrod, *J. Pharmacol. Exptl. Therap.*, **99**, 171 (1950).

are required. The drug has been reported to produce serious and sometimes fatal agranulocytopenia, especially in susceptible individuals. It should be used with caution.

Aminopyrine undergoes demethylation in the liver to 4-aminoantipyrine, which is then acetylated and excreted by way of the kidneys.[4]

Aminopyrine   Isopropylantipyrine   Tolypyrine

Isopropylantipyrine, isosteric with aminopyrine, also shows antipyretic activity. The higher homolog, **isobutylantipyrine,** possesses about equal antipyretic activity but, as measured on tadpoles, has greater narcotic activity.[5]

Tolypyrine (*p*-Tolyldimethyl Pyrazolone, Tolylantipyrine) is a stronger analgesic and antipyretic than antipyrine, but it is also more toxic.

Melubrin (Sodium Antipyrine Aminomethanesulfonate) is prepared by warming aminoantipyrine with a solution of formaldehyde and sodium bisulfite. It is a white, crystalline powder, sinters with decomposition at 231–233°, soluble in water 1:1 to form unstable solutions, and insoluble in organic solvents, except alcohol.

It is claimed that melubrin is a powerful antipyretic, that it is analgesic, and that it is nontoxic in ordinary or even large doses. It is employed as an analgesic in painful affections, such as neuralgias, as an antipyretic in febrile conditions, and is reported to be of value in acute rheumatism. **Novalgin** is N-methyl-melubrin.

Melubrin, R = H
Novalgin, R = CH₃

Salipyrine

[4] Brodie and Axelrod, *J. Pharmacol. Exptl. Therap.*, **99**, 171 (1950).
[5] Orestano, *Arch. ital. sci. farmacol.*, **8**, 353 (1939); *C.A.*, **39**, 1926 (1945).

Salipyrine (Antipyrine Salicylate) is a simple salt formed with equimolar quantities of the weakly basic antipyrine and salicylic acid. This salt is a white, crystalline solid, m.p. 91–92°, soluble in water 1:200, and readily soluble in alcohol.

Salipyrine combines the antipyretic and analgesic activity of antipyrine with the antirheumatic action of salicylic acid. It has been used in the treatment of sciatica, rheumatic fever, pleurisy, influenza, and related affections.

Iodopyrine (Iodoantipyrine, Antipyrine Iodide) is an analgesic and antipyretic containing 40 per cent iodine. It is recommended as a substitute for metal iodides in rheumatism and syphilis.

Phenylbutazone (Butazolidine, 4-Butyl-1,2-diphenyl-3,5-pyrazolidinedione), also an analgesic and antipyretic, has been introduced for the treatment of rheumatoid arthritis.

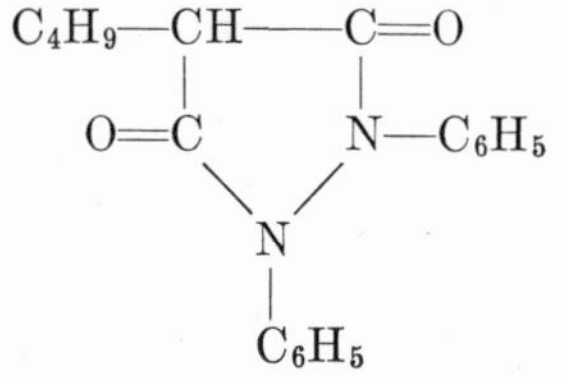

Phenylbutazone

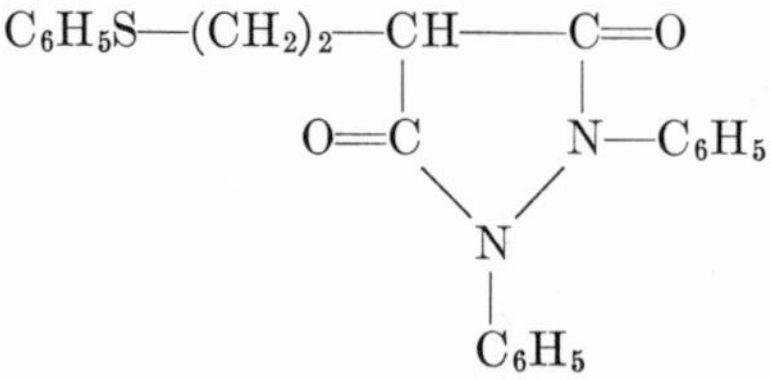

4-(Phenothioethyl)-1,2-diphenyl-
3,5-pyrazolidinedione

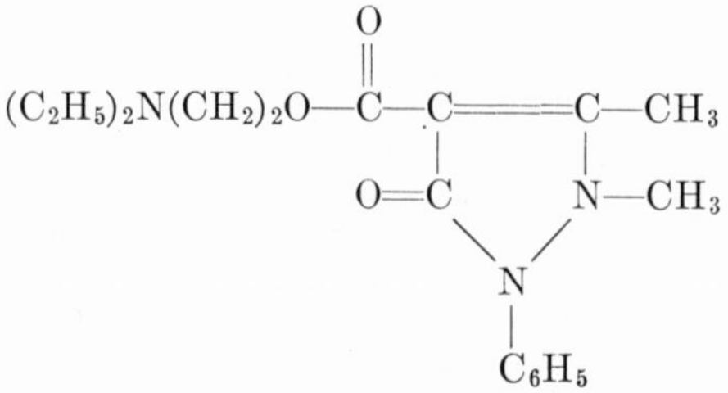

Polinal

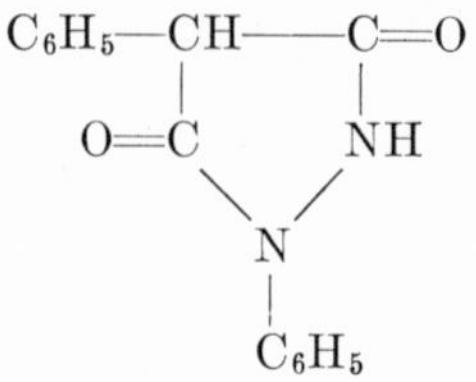

Osadrin

4-(Phenothioethyl)-1,2-diphenyl-3,5-pyrazolidinedione has been reported [6] to have antirheumatic effects in gouty and rheumatoid arthritis without causing retention of sodium ion and water.

Polinal (2,3-Dimethyl-1-phenyl-5-pyrazolone-4-carboxylic Acid β-Diethylaminoethyl Ester) and **Osadrin** (1,4-Diphenyl-3,5-pyrazolidinedione) are on trial in European countries as antiarthritic and analgesic agents.

Histalog (3-Pyrazolylethylamine) is the pyrazole analog of histamine (page 399) and is used to test the gastric secretory capabilities of an individual. Since it has only $\frac{1}{25}$ the side effects and is equivalent in activity as a gastric secretory stimulant, histalog is suggested as a substitute for histamine for this purpose.

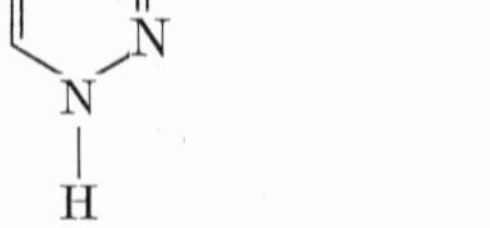

Histalog

[6] *Chem. Eng. News*, **32**, 3986 (1954).

IMIDAZOLE DERIVATIVES

Imidazole or glyoxaline may be synthesized from glyoxal, ammonia, and formaldehyde.

$$HC{=}O \quad H_2N{-}H$$
$$+ \qquad + \ O{=}CH_2 \xrightarrow{-3HOH}$$
$$HC{=}O \quad H_2N{-}H$$

$$\left[\begin{array}{c} H{-}C{=\!=}N \\ | \qquad\qquad \diagdown \\ \qquad\qquad\quad CH_2 \\ | \qquad\qquad \diagup \\ H{-}C{=\!=}N \end{array}\right]$$

$$\downarrow$$

$$\begin{array}{c} H{-}C^5{-\!-}NH \\ \| \qquad\qquad 1\diagdown \\ \qquad\qquad\qquad {}_2CH \\ \|4 \qquad 3 \diagup \\ H{-}C{-\!-}N \end{array}$$

Imidazole

Imidazole derivatives of particular interest include histidine, hercynine, histamine, ergothionine, and pilocarpine.

$$\begin{array}{c} H{-}C{=\!=}C{-}CH_2{-}CH{-}COOH \\ | \qquad\quad | \qquad\qquad | \\ H{-}N \qquad N \qquad\quad NH_2 \\ \diagdown \ \diagup \\ C \\ H \end{array}$$

Histidine

$$\begin{array}{c} H{-}C{=\!=}C{-}CH_2CH{-}COO^- \\ | \qquad\quad | \\ H{-}N \qquad N \qquad N(CH_3)_3{}^+ \\ \diagdown \ \diagup \\ C \\ H \end{array}$$

Hercynine

$$\begin{array}{c} H{-}C{=\!=}C{-}CH_2{-}CH{-}COO^- \\ | \qquad\quad | \qquad\qquad | \\ H{-}N \qquad N \qquad\quad N(CH_3)_3{}^+ \\ \diagdown \ \diagup \\ C{-}SH \end{array}$$

Ergothionine

$$\begin{array}{c} H{-}C{=\!=}C{-}CH_2{-}CH_2 \\ | \qquad\quad | \qquad\qquad | \\ H{-}N \qquad N \qquad\quad NH_2 \\ \diagdown \ \diagup \\ CH \end{array}$$

Histamine

Histidine [β-(4-Imidazolyl)alanine], an essential amino acid, was discovered by Kossel in 1896. It is present in all proteins, blood containing up to 10 per cent of it. Plant proteins contain 2 to 3 per cent histidine. The L-form melts 287–288°, and its specific rotation is $-39.7°$. It is thought to be necessary for maintaining gastric mucosa in normal condition.

Rats receiving a histidine-deficient diet showed regressive changes in the pituitary, testes, thymus, adrenal cortex, and bone.[7]

Histidine Hydrochloride, N.F., is a white, crystalline compound, readily soluble in water. It is used in the therapy of peptic ulcers, etc., to give relief from distress. It is usually injected intramuscularly in the form of a sterile solution.

Hercynine, a betaine of histidine, has been isolated from various molds.

[7] Scott, *Arch. Pathol.*, **58**, 129 (1954).

Ergothionine, which is closely related to histidine, is present in ergot to the extent of 0.1 per cent. Its structure is that of a thiol derivative of histidine betaine.

Histamine is the decarboxylation product of histidine. It was first known from synthetic sources [8] and later was found in ergot.

The structural relationship between this compound and the pressor amines is of interest. The cycle here is separated from the amino group by a chain of two carbon atoms. The physiological effect, however, is quite different; histamine produces a lowering of blood pressure by capillary dilatation. In a manner analogous to the phenylethylamine series, if the imidazolyl group and the amino group are separated by three carbon atoms, the depressor activity is appreciably diminished.

Histamine Phosphate, U.S.P., consists of colorless crystals, stable in air, soluble in water about 1:4, m.p. about 130°. It possesses a wide variety of actions, such as dilation of capillaries and arterioles, causing a sharp lowering of blood pressure, constriction of bronchioles, stimulation of the glands of external secretion, especially the gastric glands, and stimulation of the uterus at term. The complexity of its activities decreases its usefulness. It is used chiefly as a diagnostic agent to determine the capacity of the stomach to secrete hydrochloric acid, e.g., in pernicious anemia. It is usually administered in solution by subcutaneous or intramuscular injection. Evidence indicates that histamine may be the causative agent in certain cold allergies. Successful treatment of allergy due to cold has been reported by desensitization with histamine. It is of interest that the enzyme, histaminase, has been used for similar purposes.

The necessary structural requirements for histaminlike activity are postulated as shown, where $(a) = 1.36 \pm 0.01$ A, $(b) = 1.38 \pm 0.02$ A, and $(c) = 1.40 \pm$

$$-CH-(a)-N-(b)-CH-(c)-CH_2CH_2NH$$

0.01 A, and when chelation between the nitrogen atoms occurs in the cation.[9]

Jaborandi Alkaloids

Alkaloids belonging to the imidazole series occur in certain plants of the family Rutaceae. The most important of these is pilocarpine found in the leaves of *Pilocarpus Jaborandi* Holmes and *Pilocarpus microphyllus* Stapf. Its constitution is shown. Pilocarpine, in addition to the imidazole heterocycle, has a γ-lactone structure.

$$H_5C_2-CH\underline{\quad\quad}CH-CH_2-C\underline{\quad\quad}N-CH_3$$

$$OC \qquad CH_2 \qquad HC \qquad CH$$

$$\diagdown \diagup \qquad\qquad \diagdown \diagup$$

$$O \qquad\qquad\qquad N$$

Pilocarpine

Pilocarpine Nitrate, U.S.P., is a crystalline salt, m.p. 170–173°, soluble in water 1:4. Pilocarpine base is a viscid oil. It is a parasympathetic stimulant.

[8] Windaus and Vogt, *Ber.*, **40**, 3691 (1907).
[9] Niemann and Hays, *J. Am. Chem. Soc.*, **64**, 2288 (1942).

It stimulates involuntary smooth muscle and the sweat and salivary glands. Applied to the eye, it causes myosis which may last from 8 to 24 hr. It is employed in solutions of 0.5 to 3 per cent to cause myosis, usually to overcome the mydriasis caused by atropine. It may also be applied in gelatin discs or in the form of an ointment. It has also been used as a diaphoretic and to stimulate salivation. Minor uses include its employment as an expectorant to stimulate the bronchial glands. Its use in hair restorers as a stimulant of the sebaceous glands is not considered sound. **Pilocarpine Hydrochloride, U.S.P.,** has properties and uses similar to those of the nitrate, but it is incompatible with silver nitrate. Atropine counteracts all the autonomic responses caused by pilocarpine.

Imidazolines

2-Alkylimidazolines (2-Alkyl-4,5-dihydroimidazoles) are conveniently prepared by heating the diamide of ethylenediamine.[10] Many compounds of this

$$
\begin{array}{c}
\text{CH}_2\text{NHCOR} \\
| \\
| \\
\text{CH}_2\text{NHCOR}
\end{array}
\xrightarrow{270°}
\begin{array}{c}
\text{CH}_2\text{—N} \\
| \quad\quad\; \diagdown \\
| \quad\quad\quad \text{C—R + RCOOH} \\
\text{CH}_2\text{—NH} \diagup
\end{array}
$$

type are of considerable pharmacological interest.[11] 2-Methylimidazoline, as reported by Ladenburg in 1895, cured a patient of chronic gout; perhaps this may be associated with the observation that this compound is the only one of a homologous series to increase the acidity of the urine.

Tolazoline Hydrochloride, U.S.P. (2-Benzylimidazoline, Priscoline), has been used as a vasodilator in the treatment of various circulatory diseases. It is histaminic in nature, sympatholytic, and in general produces vasodilatation and increased venous return.[12] Introduction of a methoxyl group in the para position of 2-benzylimidazole modifies the physiological properties very little; a free phenolic hydroxyl group in the same position, on the other hand, converts the compound into a potent pressor.[11]

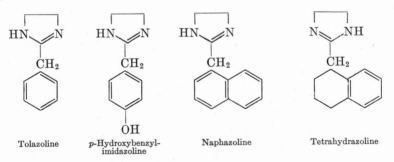

| Tolazoline | p-Hydroxybenzyl-imidazoline | Naphazoline | Tetrahydrazoline |

[10] Chitwood and Reid, *J. Am. Chem. Soc.*, **57**, 2424 (1935).
[11] Scholz, *Ind. Eng. Chem.*, **37**, 120 (1945).
[12] Ahlquist, Huggins, and Woodbury, *J. Pharmacol.*, **89**, 271 (1947).

Naphazoline Hydrochloride, U.S.P. [Privine, 2-(1-Naphthylmethyl)-imidazoline], is a potent vasoconstrictor, similar to ephedrine in its pharmacodynamic properties,[13] and less active than epinephrine.[14]   Prolonged use for nasal decongestion beyond the period of immediate need may aggravate the congestion and develop dependence.[15]   Its use may also be attended by drowsiness.[16]

Tetrahydrazoline Hydrochloride, N.N.R. (Tyzine Hydrochloride), possesses properties similar to those of Naphazoline.

The high degree of pharmacologic action found in compounds of the imidazoline structure has led to the synthesis of many other analogs of the type. It is interesting that, although the useful compounds arising from this work may be considered broadly as cardiovascular drugs, there is little correlation of structure to resultant activity.   One compound is adrenergic whereas its close relative is adrenolytic.

Phedrazine [2-(3,4,5-Trimethoxybenzyl)-imidazoline], in contrast to Priscoline, is recommended as a vasoconstrictor.   **Otrivine** (2-Anilinomethylimidazoline) is also a vasoconstrictor having a particularly long duration of action.

Phedrazine   Otrivine   Phentolamine

Phentolamine Methanesulfonate, U.S.P. [Regitine, 2-(N'-p-tolyl-N'-m-hydroxyphenylaminomethyl)imidazoline], is an orally effective hypotensive agent having potent adrenolytic action.   It is useful in the diagnosis of pheochromocytoma.

Antazoline Hydrochloride, U.S.P., see page 220.

Hydantoins

Hydantoin may be looked upon as a condensation product of urea and glycolic acid.   The unsubstituted compound has been isolated from molasses.   Hydantoins are formed according to the equation shown.   This reaction is used in characterizing carbonyl compounds.

[13] Yonkman, Rennick, and Schwerma, *J. Pharmacol. Exptl. Therap.*, **84**, 197 (1945).

[14] Cravor, *Proc. Soc. Exptl. Biol. Med.*, **58**, 128 (1945).

[15] Herwick, *J. Am. Med. Assoc.*, **130**, 702 (1946).

[16] Waring, *ibid.*, **129**, 129 (1945).

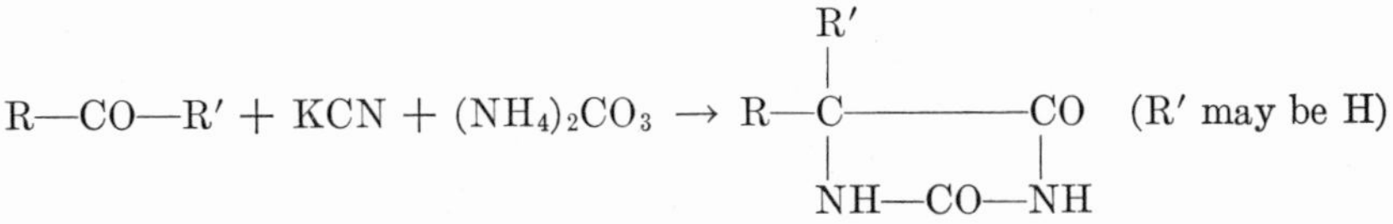

$$R—CO—R' + KCN + (NH_4)_2CO_3 \rightarrow R—\overset{\overset{\displaystyle R'}{|}}{\underset{\underset{\displaystyle NH—CO—NH}{|}}{C}}————CO \quad (R' \text{ may be H})$$

5,5-Disubstituted hydantoins are important in medicine as anticonvulsant agents. They act to depress the motor cortex in the brain without completely depressing the central nervous system. In general, they have had their greatest value in controlling the grand mal and psychomotor seizures of epilepsy.

Nirvanol (5-Ethyl-5-phenylhydantoin) was introduced into medicine as a hypnotic with properties resembling those of phenobarbital. It was used for a time in the treatment of chorea in children. Toxic reactions caused by the drug have resulted in its replacement by more effective agents.

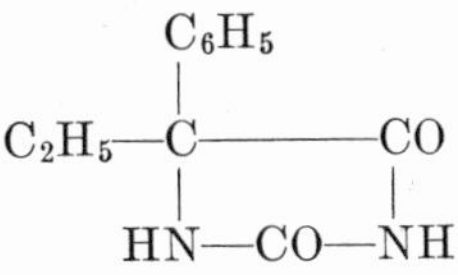

Nirvanol

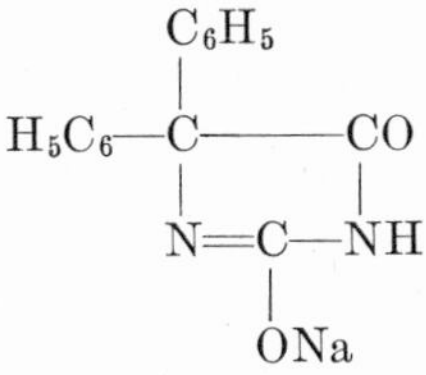

Diphenylhydantoin sodium

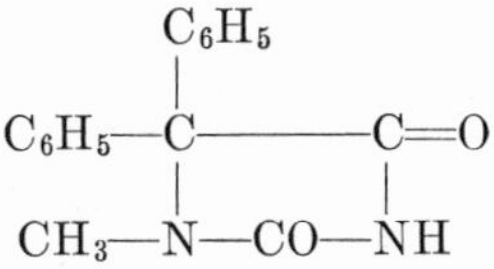

Phenantoin

Diphenylhydantoin Sodium, U.S.P. (Dilantin Sodium, Sodium-5,5-diphenylhydantoinate), was found to be the least hypnotic and most strongly anticonvulsant of the compounds in a series of similar structure.[17] It is a white, crystalline powder, readily soluble in water to form alkaline solution. It is used in the treatment of epilepsy for which it has proved effective in a large percentage of cases. It is usually administered in the form of sealed gelatin capsules.

Phenantoin (Mesantoin, 3-Methyl-5-ethyl-5-phenylhydantoin) was reported to be superior to diphenylhydantoin sodium in the treatment of epilepsy, particularly in combating grand mal seizures. It is also said to be less toxic.[18]

Phethenylate Sodium (Thiantoin Sodium) is sodium 5-phenyl-5-(2-thienyl)-hydantoinate. It is an antiepileptic drug having much the same properties as Dilantin Sodium. However, because of its severely toxic side effects, it has been withdrawn from the market.

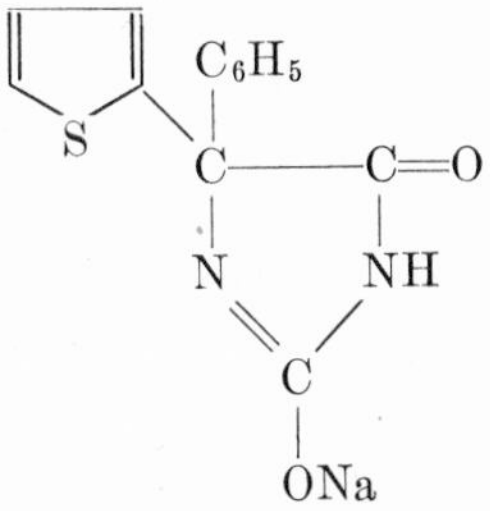

Phethenylate sodium

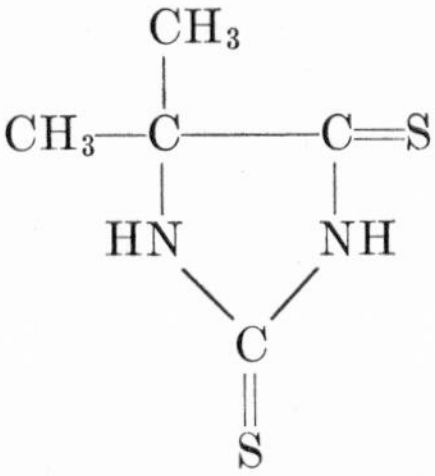

Dimethyldithiohydantoin

[17] Merritt and Putnam, *Arch. Neurol. Psychiat.*, **39**, 1003–1015 (1938).
[18] *Chem. Eng. News*, **25**, 1888 (1947).

$$
\begin{array}{c}
\text{CH}_3 \\
| \\
\text{C}_6\text{H}_5\text{—CH—CH—C}\text{——}\text{C}=\text{O} \\
| \quad\quad | \quad | \quad\quad\quad | \\
\text{Br} \quad \text{Br} \quad \text{HN} \quad\quad \text{NH} \\
\backslash \quad / \\
\text{C} \\
\| \\
\text{O}
\end{array}
\qquad
\begin{array}{c}
(\text{C}_6\text{H}_5)_2\text{C}\text{——}\text{C}=\text{O} \\
| \quad\quad\quad\quad | \\
\text{HN} \quad\quad\quad \text{NH} \\
\backslash \quad\quad / \\
\text{CH}_2
\end{array}
$$

Pesomin

5,5-Diphenyltetrahydro-
imidazole-4-one

Dimethyldithiohydantoin has been on trial in several European countries as an anticonvulsant agent. Its acceptance as a useful medicinal product must await further evaluation.

Pesomin [5-Methyl-5-(α,β-dibromophenethyl)-hydantoin] has been introduced in Europe as an appetite depressant.[19]

5,5-Diphenyltetrahydroimidazole-4-one (SKF 2599) has been used with promise in patients afflicted with grand mal or psychomotor seizures that could not be controlled with Dilantin or phenobarbital.[20]

Allantoin (Glyoxyldiureide) is related to hydantoin. Interest in this compound was stimulated by the discovery that allantoin was released and presumably was the effective agent in the maggot therapy of ulcers, etc. It may be synthesized from ethyl glyoxalate and urea at 100°. It is possible that allantoin exists in dynamic equilibrium in the three forms indicated. Allantoin is a white,

$$
\begin{array}{c}
\text{OH} \\
| \\
\text{HN—C——NH} \\
| \quad\quad\quad | \\
\text{OC} \quad\quad \text{CO} \\
| \quad\quad\quad | \\
\text{HN—CH—NH}
\end{array}
\;\leftrightarrows\;
\begin{array}{c}
\\
\text{H}_2\text{N} \; \text{OC——NH} \\
| \quad\quad\quad | \\
\text{CO} \quad\quad \text{CO} \\
| \quad\quad\quad | \\
\text{H—N——CH—NH}
\end{array}
\;\leftrightarrows\;
\begin{array}{c}
\text{OH} \\
| \\
\text{H}_2\text{N} \; \text{C—NH} \\
| \quad\quad \| \quad\quad | \\
\text{OC} \quad\quad \text{CO} \\
| \quad\quad\quad | \\
\text{HN—C—NH}
\end{array}
$$

crystalline powder, stable in air, slightly soluble in cold water, and readily soluble in hot water. It is used to stimulate cell proliferation and tissue growth in indolent ulcers and wounds and in the healing of septic infections. It may be applied as a wet dressing in solution, or in the form of an ointment, e.g., allantoin urea compound ointment. It is also used internally in the form of a colloidal solution or suspension to treat gastric or duodenal ulcers. Solutions should be freshly prepared.

Creatinine is another physiologically important imidazole derivative, which is probably formed from creatine during metabolism somewhat in the manner shown. It is a white, crystalline powder, slightly soluble in cold water and readily soluble in hot water. It is used to stimulate cell proliferation and tissue growth and induce granulation of indolent ulcers. It is employed as a wet dressing

[19] Kunz, *Arch. Pharm.*, **287**, 412 (1954).
[20] Milichap, Goodman, and Madsen, *Neurology*, **5**, 700 (1955).

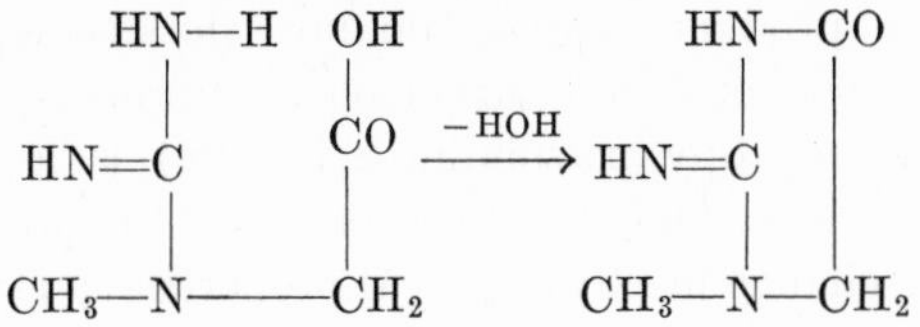

Creatine   Creatinine

or pack in about 0.4 per cent solutions and in compound ointments or jellies with urea and other agents.

Biotin can be regarded as an imidazole derivative. It is an important member of the vitamin B group and for purposes of convenience is discussed on page 429 with other members of this complex.

Arfonad (RO-2-2222), d-3,4(1′,3′-Dibenzyl-2′-ketoimidazolido)-1,2-trimethyl-enethiophanium (+)camphorsulfonate, has an unusual structure similar to that of biotin. It is on trial as a hypotensive agent in surgery. Its hypotensive effect is said to be independent of its ganglionic blocking action.[21, 22]

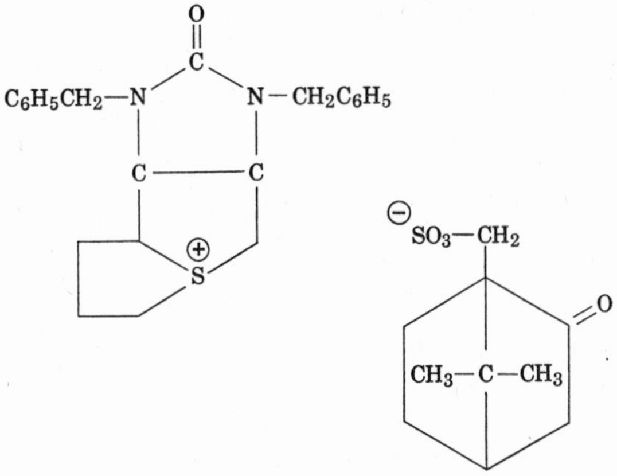

Arfonad

OXAZOLE DERIVATIVES

Stoughton [23] observed that the esters of the dialkylglycolic acids condense with urea to give good yields of 5,5-dialkyloxazolidine-2,4-diones. The close structural

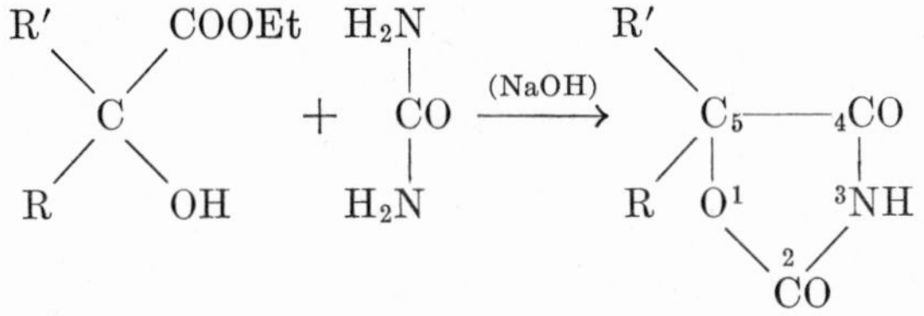

[21] McCubbin *et al.*, *J. Pharmacol. Exptl. Therap.*, **105**, 437 (1952).
[22] Nicholson, Sarnoff, and Crehan, *Anesthesiology*, **14**, 215 (1953).
[23] *J. Am. Chem. Soc.*, **63**, 2376 (1941).

relationship of these products to compounds possessing hypnotic activity prompted an investigation of their pharmacological properties.

Propazone (5,5-Di-n-propyloxazolidine-2,4-dione) is a potent, long-acting hypnotic and anticonvulsant agent.[24] Alkylation of the nitrogen atom produces a marked qualitative change in physiological properties; a strong analgesic effect appears.[25]

Trimethadione, U.S.P. (Tridione, 3,5,5-Trimethyloxazolidine-2,4-dione), white crystals, m.p. 45–46.5°, with camphorlike odor, is the best compound of the series. It is an anticonvulsant and is effective in relieving epileptic seizures of the petit mal type.[26] It is usually administered in capsules.

Trimethadione acts primarily on the central nervous system, and is specific for petit mal. It is absorbed from the gastrointestinal tract and completely destroyed, probably in the liver. In humans it undergoes demethylation at the 3 position, and the product formed is devoid of any antiepileptic action.[27]

$$
\begin{array}{ccc}
\text{C}_3\text{H}_7 & \text{CH}_3 & \text{CH}_3 \\
| & | & | \\
\text{C}_3\text{H}_7-\text{C}-\text{C}=\text{O} & \text{CH}_3-\text{C}-\text{C}=\text{O} & \text{C}_2\text{H}_5-\text{C}-\text{C}=\text{O} \\
| \quad \quad | & | \quad \quad | & | \quad \quad | \\
\text{O} \quad \text{NH} & \text{O} \quad \text{N}-\text{CH}_3 & \text{O} \quad \text{N}-\text{CH}_3 \\
\diagdown \diagup & \diagdown \diagup & \diagdown \diagup \\
\text{C} & \text{C} & \text{C} \\
\| & \| & \| \\
\text{O} & \text{O} & \text{O} \\
\text{Propazone} & \text{Trimethadione} & \text{Paramethadione}
\end{array}
$$

$$
\begin{array}{ccc}
\text{CH}_3 & \text{C}_6\text{H}_5 & \text{CH}_3 \\
| & | & | \\
\text{CH}-\text{C}=\text{O} & \text{C}_6\text{H}_5-\text{C}-\text{C}=\text{O} & \text{CH}_3-\text{C}-\text{C}=\text{O} \\
| \quad \quad | & | \quad \quad | & | \quad \quad | \\
\text{O} \quad \text{N}-\text{CH}_2\text{CH}=\text{CH}_2 & \text{O} \quad \text{NH} & \text{O} \quad \text{N}-\text{C}_2\text{H}_5 \\
\diagdown \diagup & \diagdown \diagup & \diagdown \diagup \\
\text{C} & \text{C} & \text{C} \\
\| & \| & \| \\
\text{O} & \text{O} & \text{O} \\
\text{Malazol} & \text{Epidone} & \text{Dimedione}
\end{array}
$$

Paramethadione (Paradione, 3,5-Dimethyl-5-ethyloxazolidine-2,4-dione) is effective in petit mal epilepsy. Although it is considered less active than trimethadione, it is used in cases unaffected by the latter.

Other oxazolidinediones which have been introduced as agents against epilepsy are **Malazol** (Malidone, 3-Allyl-5-methyloxazolidine-2,4-dione), **Epidone** (5,5-Diphenyloxazolidine-2,4-dione), and **Dimedione** (5,5-Dimethyl-3-ethyloxazolidine-2,4-dione).

Gantrisin is an isoxazole derivative of the "sulfa" group. It together with its acetyl derivative is considered on page 286.

[24] Tainter, *J. Pharmacol.*, **79**, 42 (1943).
[25] Spielman, *J. Am. Chem. Soc.*, **66**, 1244 (1944).
[26] Lennox, *J. Am. Med. Assoc.*, **129**, 1069 (1945).
[27] Butler, *J. Pharmacol. Exptl. Therap.*, **108**, 11 (1953).

THIAZOLES

The thiazole heterocycle, a five-membered ring incorporating both sulfur and nitrogen, is not found widespread in nature. The natural products in which it is found are, however, extremely important. One of these, penicillin, a hydrogenated thiazole derivative, is discussed on page 484. Thiamine, a thiazole- and pyrimidine-containing structure, is considered later along with other members of the vitamin B complex.

Synthetic derivatives of thiazole have been found useful.

2-Aminothiazole, prepared according to the equation shown, is an inter-

$$XCH_2CHX-O-CHX-CH_2X + NH_2CSNH_2 \rightarrow$$

2-Aminothiazole

mediate in the synthesis of sulfathiazole, see page 283. As a derivative of thiourea it also exhibits antithyroid activity.

2-(4-Thiazolyl)ethylamine has biological properties similar to those of histamine.

Thiazolylethylamine   Enheptin   Fenamizol

Enheptin (2-Amino-5-nitrothiazole) is used in veterinary medicine for the control of blackhead in turkeys.

Fenamizol (2,4-Diamino-5-phenylthiazole) shows promise of becoming a useful reagent for the treatment of poisoning by barbiturates and opium.[28]

Thiazolesulfone, N.N.R. (2-Amino-5-sulfanilylthiazole), possesses properties analogous to those of glucosulfone but is less toxic; it may be administered by mouth.

Thiazolsulfone   Asterol

Derivatives of 6-aminobenzothiazole exhibit antitubercular properties *in vitro* and in animals. More important, many of these derivatives exhibit fungicidal properties. **Asterol** [6-(β-Diethylaminoethoxy)-2-dimethylaminobenzothiazole] is the best of the group and is used as a 5 per cent solution against fungus infections including Trichophyton and Microsporon. It is also considered particularly useful against monilial infections.

[28] Canbäck, Ohlson, and Werkö, *Svensk Farm. Tidskr.*, **29**, 685 (1955); *C.A.*, **50**, 2870 (1956).

DIAZINES

Six-membered cycles of four carbon and two nitrogen atoms are known as diazines. Three isomeric diazines are possible and all are known. Of these the

$$
\begin{array}{ccc}
\text{CH} & \text{CH} & \text{N} \\
\text{H—C} \quad \text{C—H} & \text{H—C} \quad \text{N} & \text{H—C} \quad \text{C—H} \\
\text{H—C} \quad \text{N} & \text{H—C} \quad \text{C—H} & \text{H—C} \quad \text{C—H} \\
\text{N} & \text{N} & \text{N}
\end{array}
$$

| Pyridazine, 1,2-diazine | Pyrimidine, 1,3-diazine | Pyrazine, 1,4-diazine |

pyrimidines are of special interest to the pharmaceutical chemist. Derivatives of this group include the accompanying compounds which are present in biological products, taking part in the structure of the nucleic acids.

$$
\begin{array}{cccc}
\text{CO} & \text{CO} & \text{NH}_2 & \text{NH}_2 \\
 & & \text{C} & \text{C} \\
\text{CH}_3\text{—C} \quad \text{N—H} & \text{H—C} \quad \text{N—H} & \text{H—C} \quad \text{N} & \text{CH}_3\text{—C} \quad \text{N} \\
\text{H—C} \quad \text{CO} & \text{H—C} \quad \text{CO} & \text{H—C} \quad \text{CO} & \text{H—C} \quad \text{CO} \\
\text{NH} & \text{NH} & \text{NH} & \text{NH}
\end{array}
$$

| Thymine, 5-methyl-2,4-pyrimidinedione | Uracil, 2,4-pyrimidinedione | Cytosine, 4-amino-2-pyrimidone | Methylcytosine, 4-amino-5-methyl-2-pyrimidone |

The sulfanilyl derivatives of certain of these diazines are very important drugs (see page 283).

Barbituric Acids

The most numerous and perhaps the best-known derivatives of the pyrimidines are the compounds commonly known as barbituric acids. The parent compound may be synthesized from malonic acid, preferably the diethyl ester of malonic acid, and urea. The barbituric acids may exist in tautomeric form, as indicated,

$$
\begin{array}{ccc}
\text{CO—OEt} & \text{H—NH} & \text{H} \quad \text{CO}_6\text{—}_1\text{NH} \\
\text{CH}_2 & \text{CO} \xrightarrow[-2\text{EtOH}]{(\text{NaOEt})} & \text{C}^5 \quad {}^2\text{CO} \\
\text{CO—OEt} & \text{H—NH} & \text{H} \quad \text{CO}^4\text{—}^3\text{NH}
\end{array}
$$

Barbituric acid

$$
\begin{array}{ccc}
\text{R} \quad \text{CO—NH} & \text{R} \quad \text{CO—NH} & \text{R} \quad \text{CO—NH} \\
\text{C} \quad \text{CO} \rightleftarrows & \text{C} \quad \text{C—OH} & \text{C} \quad \text{C—ONa} \\
\text{R}' \quad \text{CO—NH} & \text{R}' \quad \text{CO—N} & \text{R}' \quad \text{CO—N}
\end{array}
$$

of which the latter form is capable of forming stable salts. Derivatives in which the two hydrogen atoms at the 5 position are substituted with groups of varying complexity are hypnotic, sedative, and even anesthetic in their action. All 5,5-dialkylbarbituric acids are prepared by the condensation of the appropriately substituted malonic ester with urea or with thiourea for the thiobarbituric acid derivatives. For 5-arylbarbituric acids, such as phenobarbital, the intermediate malonic esters are available through indirect synthetic methods.

The variations in the number of barbiturates that have been synthesized are very great. Over 2000 derivatives of barbituric acid are recorded in *Chemical Abstracts*. The most important and medicinally useful of these compounds are included in Table XXVI; they are given by popular name in ascending order of molecular weight.

The barbiturates form a considerable item in the production of drugs. In 1946, the production was more than 806,000 pounds, valued at more than $3 million.

The barbiturates have become established as important therapeutic agents. They are extensively used for a number of purposes, namely:

1. For hypnotic effect: When administered orally, the barbiturates induce sleep. The promptness with which they act and the duration of activity vary. Thus barbital and phenobarbital act in for $\frac{1}{2}$ to 1 hr., and their effect may last from 4 to 12 hr. with some lassitude on awakening; amytal and pentobarbital act in from 15 to 30 min., and their effect may last for about 2 to 8 hr.; and the barbiturates of short duration of action act promptly often in less than 15 min., and their effect may be dissipated in 2 to 4 hr.

2. As sedatives: The barbiturates act promptly and have proved valuable where immediate activity is needed as in insomnia, nausea, delirium tremens, nervous excitability, maniacal states, etc.

3. As anticonvulsants: The barbiturates have proved effective in the control of convulsions such as occur in eclampsia, epilepsy, tetany, and poisoning by strychnine. Among the barbiturates particularly useful in epilepsy are phenobarbital and Gemonil.

4. For the potentiation of analgesics: The analgesic action of drugs such as acetylsalicylic acid is increased by the barbiturates.

5. For anesthesia and premedication in anesthesia: Certain of the barbiturates, especially those with a short duration of action, have proved of value as anesthetics. Given prior to inhalation anesthesia, either alone or in combination with atropine or scopolamine, they serve as sedatives and hypnotics and in part as anesthetics to make general anesthesia easier and to decrease the amount of the general anesthetic required. The short-acting barbituric acids given intravenously induce anesthesia rapidly, and recovery is prompt. The absence of explosion hazards makes this type of anesthesia of increasing importance, especially for short operations and under war conditions.

The thiobarbiturates are especially short-acting and are very valuable as general anesthetics. Pentothal received particular use during field operations in World War II. N-Methylbarbiturates such as Evipal are also considered as ultra rapid in duration of action.

TABLE XXVI

THE BARBITURATES

$$\begin{array}{c} O \\ \| \\ R_2\ C{-}NH \\ \diagdown \quad | \\ C \quad C{=}X \\ \diagup \ | \quad | \\ R_3\ C{-}N{-}R_1 \\ \| \\ O \end{array}$$

Name	R_1	R_2	R_3	X	Molecular Formula
Barbital	H	C_2H_5	C_2H_5	O	$C_8H_{12}N_2O_3$
Ipral	H	C_2H_5	$(CH_3)_2CH$	O	$C_9H_{14}N_2O_3$
Gemonil	CH_3	C_2H_5	C_2H_5	O	$C_9H_{14}N_2O_3$
Dial	H	$CH_2{=}CH{-}CH_2$	$CH_2{=}CH{-}CH_2$	O	$C_{10}H_{12}N_2O_3$
Nostal	H	$(CH_3)_2CH$	$CH_2{=}CBr{-}CH_2$	O	$C_{10}H_{13}BrN_2O_3$
Mosidal	H	C_2H_5	$CH_2{=}C(CH_3){-}CH_2$	S	$C_{10}H_{14}N_2O_2S$
Alurate	H	$(CH_3)_2CH$	$CH_2{=}CHCH_2$	O	$C_{10}H_{14}N_2O_3$
* Kalypnon	H	C_2H_5	$CH_3CH{=}CHCH_2$	O	$C_{10}H_{14}N_2O_3$
* Inactin	H	C_2H_5	$CH_3CH_2CH(CH_3)$	S	$C_{10}H_{16}N_2O_2S$
Neonal	H	C_2H_5	$n{-}C_4H_9$	O	$C_{10}H_{16}N_2O_3$
Butisol	H	C_2H_5	$CH_3CH_2CH(CH_3)$	O	$C_{10}H_{16}N_2O_3$
Rutonal	H	CH_3	C_6H_5	O	$C_{11}H_{10}N_2O_3$
Dormovit	H	$(CH_3)_2CH$	2-furyl	O	$C_{11}H_{12}N_2O_4$
Pernoston	H	$CH_3CH_2CH(CH_3)$	$CH_2{=}CBrCH_2$	O	$C_{11}H_{15}BrN_2O_3$
Eunarcon	CH_3	$(CH_3)_2CH$	$CH_2{=}CBrCH_2$	O	$C_{11}H_{15}BrN_2O_3$
* Baytinal	H	$CH_2{=}CHCH_2$	$(CH_3)_2CHCH_2$	S	$C_{11}H_{16}N_2O_2S$
Vinbarbital	H	C_2H_5	$CH_3CH_2CH{=}C(CH_3)$	O	$C_{11}H_{16}N_2O_3$
Sandoptal	H	$CH_2{=}CH{-}CH_2$	$(CH_3)_2CHCH_2$	O	$C_{11}H_{16}N_2O_3$
Pentothal	H	C_2H_5	$CH_3(CH_2)_2CH(CH_3)$	S	$C_{11}H_{18}N_2O_2S$
Thioethamyl	H	C_2H_5	$(CH_3)_2CH(CH_2)_2$	S	$C_{11}H_{18}N_2O_2S$
Nembutal	H	C_2H_5	$CH_3(CH_2)_2CH(CH_3)$	O	$C_{11}H_{18}N_2O_3$
Amytal	H	C_2H_5	$(CH_3)_2CH(CH_2)_2$	O	$C_{11}H_{18}N_2O_3$
Phenobarbital	H	C_2H_5	C_6H_5	O	$C_{12}H_{12}N_2O_3$
Cyclopal	H	$CH_2{=}CH{-}CH_2$	Δ^2-cyclopentenyl	O	$C_{12}H_{14}N_2O_3$
Phanodorn	H	C_2H_5	Δ^1-cyclohexenyl	O	$C_{12}H_{16}N_2O_3$
Evipal	CH_3	CH_3	Δ^1-cyclohexenyl	O	$C_{12}H_{16}N_2O_3$
Sigmodal	H	$CH_2{=}CBrCH_2$	$CH_3(CH_2)_2CH(CH_3)$	O	$C_{12}H_{17}BrN_2O_3$
Surital	H	$CH_2{=}CHCH_2$	$CH_3(CH_2)_2CH(CH_3)$	S	$C_{12}H_{18}N_2O_2S$
Seconal	H	$CH_2{=}CHCH_2$	$CH_3(CH_2)_2CH(CH_3)$	O	$C_{12}H_{18}N_2O_3$
* Thiogenal	H	$CH_3S{-}CH_2CH_2$	$CH_3(CH_2)_2CH(CH_3)$	S	$C_{12}H_{20}N_2O_2S_2$
* Thionarcex	H	C_2H_5	$CH_3(CH_2)_3CH(CH_3)$	S	$C_{12}H_{20}N_2O_2S_2$
Ortal	H	C_2H_5	$CH_3(CH_2)_4CH_2$	O	$C_{12}H_{20}N_2O_3$
* Butylsedal	H	C_2H_5	$CH_3(CH_2)_3CH(CH_3)$	O	$C_{12}H_{20}N_2O_3$
Alphenate	H	$CH_2{=}CHCH_2$	C_6H_5	O	$C_{13}H_{12}N_2O_3$
Mebaral	CH_3	C_2H_5	C_6H_5	O	$C_{13}H_{14}N_2O_3$
Kemithal	H	$CH_2{=}CHCH_2$	Δ^2-cyclohexenyl	S	$C_{13}H_{16}N_2O_2S$
Heptabarbital	H	C_2H_5	Δ^1-cycloheptenyl	O	$C_{13}H_{18}N_2O_3$

* On clinical trial in European countries.

The metabolism of the barbiturates and thiobarbiturates is of importance. Since the metabolic rate of destruction of these compounds determines the rapidity as well as the duration of their action, this subject has been given considerable attention.[29] The 5,5-dialkylbarbituric acids undergo oxidation of the side chain, whereas N-methylbarbituric acids are probably demethylated. Most of the metabolism takes place in the liver of the patient.

The many valuable medicinal properties of this class of compounds are not without danger. They are central nervous depressants, and overdosage can result in death by respiratory failure. The high rate of suicide from large doses of barbiturates has necessitated their close control by law. In addition, it should be noted that both stimulant and depressive components of activity have been noted in the same barbituric acid.[30]

All the barbituric acid derivatives are slightly soluble compounds. They form water-soluble salts with alkalies; e.g., sodium, calcium, and magnesium salts are employed in therapy. The chief action of the barbiturates is depression of the central nervous system, particularly the brain. The intensity and duration of depression depend upon the structure of the barbiturate, the route of administration, and the dose, If the dose is small, the depression is slight and the effect is sedative; larger doses cause the onset of natural sleep and the effect is hypnotic; very large doses or a high concentration in the blood cause unconsciousness, and the effect is anesthetic.

The barbiturates are usually administered as tablets or in capsules for their sedative and hypnotic effects. Liquid preparations such as *Elixir of Phenobarbital, U.S.P.*, are used to some extent. Ampuled solutions of practically all products are available for parenteral administration.

The analgesic action of drugs such as acetylsalicylic acid is increased by the barbiturates. Combinations, e.g., Lumalgin (phenobarbital + acetylsalicylic acid), Evicyl (evipal + acetylsalicylic acid), Allonal (allurate + aminopyrine), Pyraminol (phenobarbital + aminopyrine), Cibalgen (dial + aminopyrine), offer little advantage since the proportions of the ingredients are fixed. Each drug may be given separately to advantage so that the quantity and effect of each component may be more properly regulated.

$$NH—CO$$

Alloxan (Mesoxalylurea), CO$\diagup$ $\diagdown$CO, is obtained from uric acid by

$$NH—CO$$

oxidation with nitric acid. Because of the pink color it imparts to the skin it was once used as a cosmetic like rouge. Administered orally or intravenously to cats it produces diabetes. It has a destructive effect on the beta cells of the pancreas, injures the adrenal cortex, pituitary, liver, and kidneys.[31] The toxic

---

[29] Maynert and Van Dyke, *J. Pharmacol. Exptl. Therap.*, **96**, 217 (1949); Butler *et al.*, *J. Pharmacol. Exptl. Therap.*, **111**, 425 (1954).

[30] Domino, Fox, and Brody, *J. Pharmacol. Exptl. Therap.*, **114**, 473 (1955).

[31] Ruben and Yardumian, *Science*, **103**, 220 (1946).

and diabetogenic activity is increased in animals receiving low-protein and high-fat diet. This property is counteracted by methionine and thiouracil.[32] Alloxan is useful as an intermediate in the synthesis of riboflavin.

Thiouracils

The observations of Astwood [33,34] and the Mackenzies [35] showed that certain compounds including thiouracil, propylthiouracil, thiourea, and derivatives such as phenylthiourea and thiobarbituric acid, sulfonamides, o-, m-, and p-benzoic acids, and the thiocyanates inhibit the production of thyroid hormone. Propylthiouracil was the most active of more than 300 compounds tested by Astwood. Drugs of this type have been tested for use in thyrotoxicosis as an alternative to thyroidectomy or as a means of preparing patients for surgery. These tests have shown that propylthiouracil has an activity about five times that of thiouracil in man and that it is less toxic. Propylthiouracil may replace surgery largely in the treament of thyrotoxicosis since its use gives rise to sustained remissions in a large proportion of cases.

Astwood and his co-workers have shown that antithyroid activity is found in compounds having the structure —N—C—R where R is —N—, —S—, or —O—. In substituted 2-thiouracils, activity has been shown to vary with the position and nature of the substituent. Substitution in position 6 gives greater antithyroid effect than substitution at position 5; maximum activity is attained when the alkyl group contains 3 to 4 carbon atoms. The presence of the double bonds is essential. Substitution of methyl or ethyl groups on an N atom decreases activity. Replacement of the hydrogen atom at position 5 or 6 by a group other than a hydrocarbon group causes complete loss of activity, suggesting that the activity is associated with the polar nature of substituents.

The thiouracils may be synthesized from a β-ketonic ester and thiourea, in yields varying from 4 to 78 per cent, depending on the intermediate, according to the equation shown.[36]

$$
\begin{array}{ccc}
NH_2 & COOR & HN_3\text{—}_4CO \\
| & | & | \quad | \\
C\!=\!S + CHR' \rightarrow & S\!=\!C_2 \quad {}^5C\text{—}R' \\
| & | & | \quad \| \\
NH_2 & COR'' & HN^1\text{—}{}^6C\text{—}R''
\end{array}
$$

2-Thiouracil,
R' and R'' = H

It has been suggested that the thiouracils owe their antithyroid activity to the ease with which iodine oxidizes them.[37]

[32] Houssay and Martinez, *Science*, **105**, 548 (1947).

[33] *J. Pharmacol. Exptl. Therap.*, **78**, 79 (1943).

[34] *Endocrinology*, **37**, 456 (1945).

[35] *Endocrinology*, **37**, 185 (1943).

[36] Anderson, Halverstadt, Miller, and Roblin, *J. Am. Chem. Soc.*, **67**, 2197 (1945).

[37] Miller, Roblin, and Astwood, *J. Am. Chem. Soc.*, **67**, 2201 (1945).

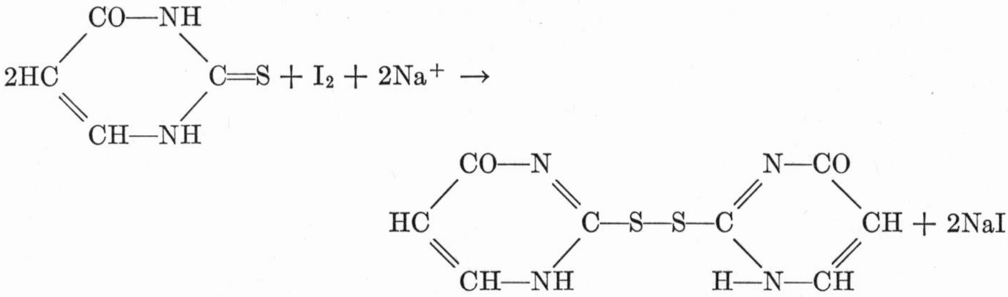

$$2HC \underset{CH-NH}{\overset{CO-NH}{\diagup}} C{=}S + I_2 + 2Na^+ \rightarrow$$

$$HC \underset{CH-NH}{\overset{CO-N}{\diagup}} C-S-S-C \underset{H-N-CH}{\overset{N-CO}{\diagup}} CH + 2NaI$$

Propylthiouracil is a white, crystalline, stable powder, practically insoluble in water, alcohol, acetone, and fixed oils but readily soluble in alkaline solutions. Solutions in alkali adjusted to a pH of 9.5 can be sterilized by heating for 30 min. at 15 lb. pressure. It is usually administered in the form of tablets, capsules, or a suspension of the microcrystalline powder.

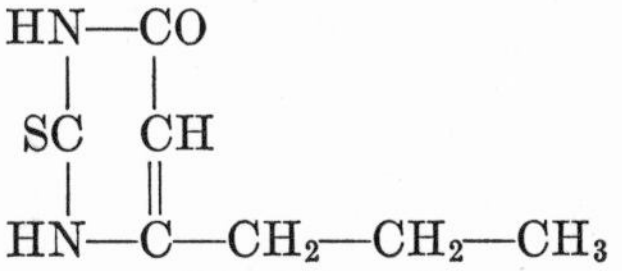

$$\begin{array}{ccc} HN & - & CO \\ | & & | \\ SC & & CH \\ | & & \| \\ HN & - & C-CH_2-CH_2-CH_3 \end{array}$$

Propylthiouracil

Antrycide [4-Amino-6-(2-amino-6-methyl-4-pyrimidylamino)quinaldine-1,1'-dimetho Salts] was introduced by Curd and Davey [38] as a trypanocidal drug particularly useful in the African cattle form of infection. It is reported effective both as a prophylactic and curative. Its structure is shown.

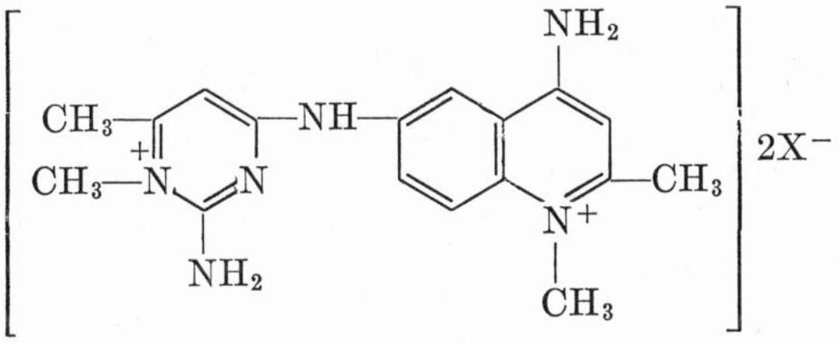

Antrycide 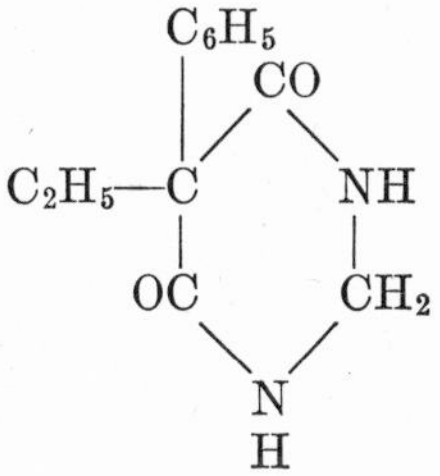   Primidone

Primidone, N.N.R. (Mysoline, 5-Ethyl-5-phenylhexahydropyrimidine-4,6-dione), a structural analog of phenobarbital, is suggested as an anticonvulsant, effective for the control of grand mal and psychomotor seizures. It is less potent and less toxic than phenobarbital.

Piperazines

Piperazine or hexahydropyrazine is a saturated 1,4-diazine. It is a strong base, behaving chemically and physically much like ethylenediamine. It is synthesized commercially by the deamination of diethylenetriamine and ethylenediamine. Although piperazine may be obtained in anhydrous form, it forms a

[38] Curd and Davey, *Nature*, **163**, 89 (1949).

stable hexahydrate which is commonly available. Piperazine itself has had use in medicine as an agent for the treatment of gout and as a diuretic. It is now marketed as an anthelmintic for the treatment of pinworm infections and ascariasis.

Piperazine Estrone Sulfate (Sulestrex Piperazine) is the stable oral form of the hormone estrone.

As a basic moiety, piperazine has found its way into a number of synthetic drugs including antihistaminic agents such as Chlorcyclizine (see page 220). Other similar agents, probably originally intended as antihistamine drugs, are recommended for combating motion sickness. These are **Cyclizine** (Marezine, N-Benzhydryl-N'-methylpiperazine), **Meclizine** (Bonamine, N-p-Chlorobenzhydryl-N'-m-methylbenzylpiperazine), and **Buclizine** (Vibazine, N-p-Chlorobenzhydryl-N'-p-t-butylbenzylpiperazine).

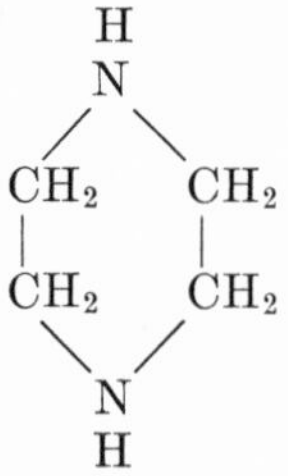

Piperazine

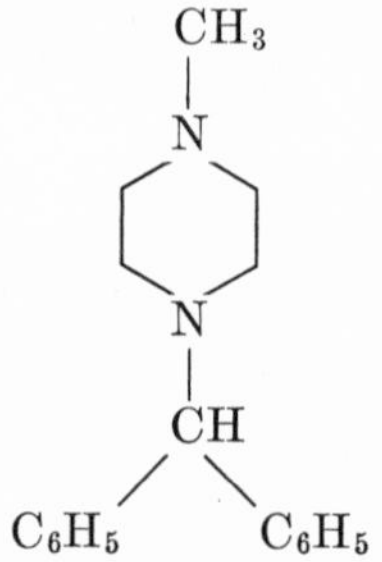

Cyclizine

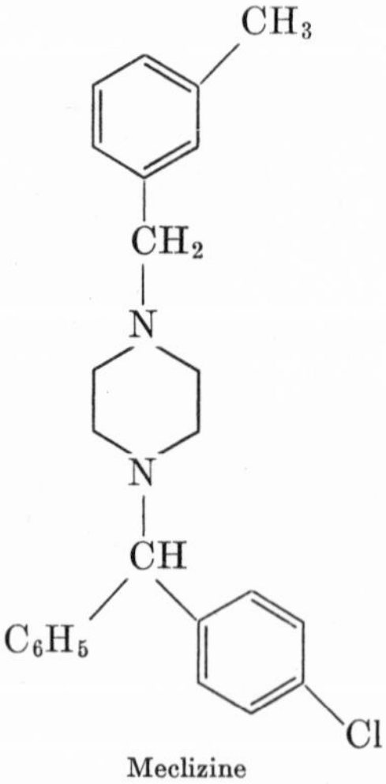

Meclizine

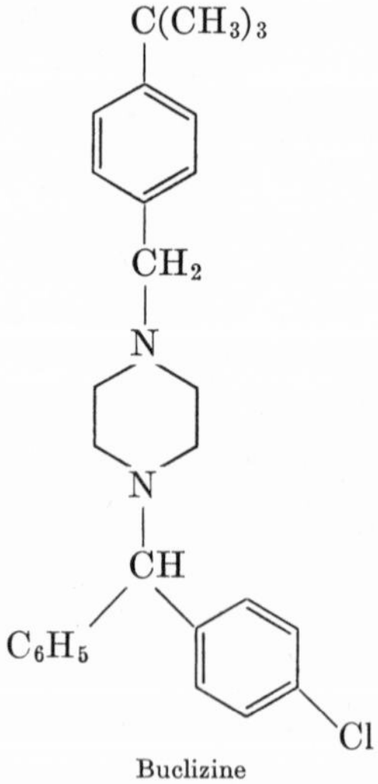

Buclizine

Piperazine derivatives have proved useful in chemotherapy as filaricides or agents that will kill the microfilariae in the blood stream or the adult worms in the lymphatic vessels causing the disease *filariasis*.[39] Most useful of these derivatives

[39] Hawking, *Trans. Roy. Soc. Trop. Med. Hyg.*, **44**, 153 (1950).

is **Diethylcarbamazine, U.S.P.,** or Hetrazan.   This drug is 1-diethylcarbamyl-4-methylpiperazine and is recommended for loaiasis and onchocerciasis in addition to filariasis.   Its synthesis is of interest.   Since both nitrogen atoms in

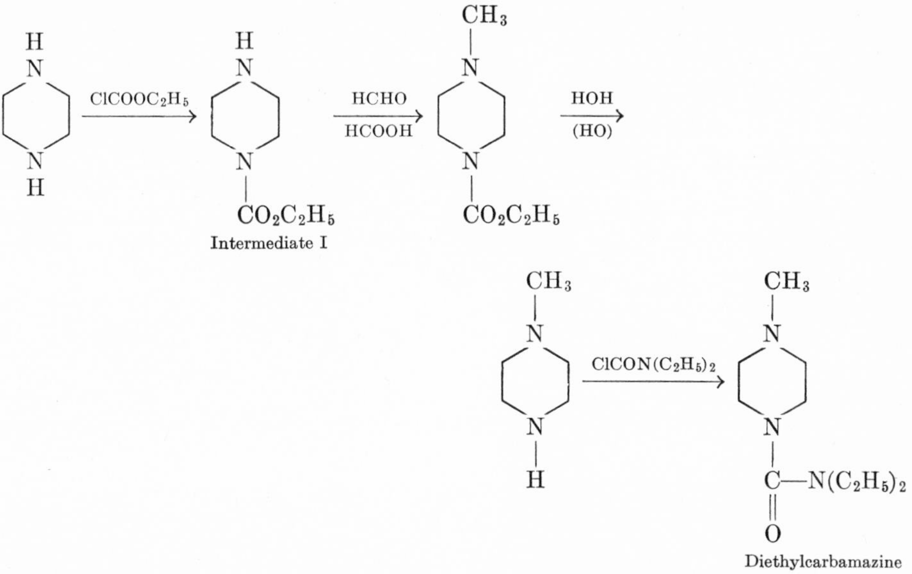

Intermediate I

Diethylcarbamazine

piperazine are equally basic, it is difficult to obtain a monosubstituted derivative. Under carefully buffered conditions, Intermediate I can be found in good yield. This serves as a useful step in the synthesis of many unsymmetrically disubstituted piperazines.

Piperazine salts such as **Piperazine Citrate, N.N.R.** (Antepar Citrate), and **Piperazine Tartrate, N.N.R.,** are effective anthelmintics against pinworms, *Enterobius vermicularis* and *Oxyuris vermicularis,* and for the treatment of ascariasis.[40]

Hydroxyzine, {Atarax, 1-(p-Chlorobenzhydryl)-4-[2-(hydroxyethoxy)ethyl] piperazine},

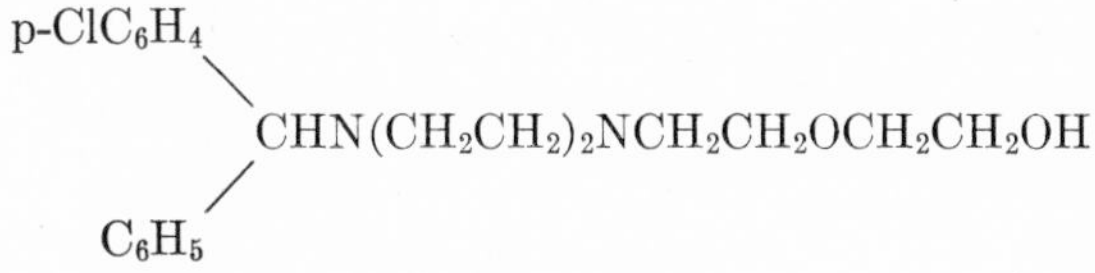

$$p\text{-}ClC_6H_4$$
$$CHN(CH_2CH_2)_2NCH_2CH_2OCH_2CH_2OH$$
$$C_6H_5$$

used as its hydrochloride, is reported to be effective for relieving mental depression, especially senile anxiety states,[40a] and for dermatoses affected by psychogenic stimuli.[40b]

---

[40] Swartzwelder, Miller, and Sappenfield, *Pediatrics,* **16,** 115 (1955).
[40a] Shalowitz, *Geriatrics,* **11,** 312 (1956).
[40b] Robinson, Robinson, and Strahan, *J. Am. Med. Assoc.,* **161,** 604 (1956).

PURINES

Derivatives of purine are widely scattered throughout the plant and animal kingdom. Historically the chemistry of the purines begins with Scheele's discovery of uric acid (1776).

Uric Acid (2,6,8-Trioxypurine) was the first of purine compounds to be discovered. Its relationship to urea is evident from its various methods of synthesis, one of which is indicated.

Purine

Isobarbituric acid   Urea   Uric acid

Xanthine (2,6-Dihydroxypurine), $C_5H_4O_2N_4$, was first isolated from a urinary stone. It has since been isolated from muscle, liver, and tea leaves, and it is a natural component of human urine. It probably exists as an equilibrium mixture as indicated.

Xanthine, keto form   Xanthine, enol form

Other purine derivatives of biochemical interest include those shown.

Guanine   Hypoxanthine   Adenine

Guanine (2-Amino-6-ketopurine) occurs widely in the plant kingdom, and it has been isolated also from various animal tissues and from excreta. **Hypoxanthine** (6-Ketopurine) appears in various animal organs and body fluids and in a variety of plants, such as the lupines, barley, pepper, and beet. **Adenine** (6-Aminopurine) is widely distributed in both the plant and the animal kingdom; it occurs as a constituent fragment of the nucleic acids.

A number of closely related compounds may be regarded as simple methylated derivatives of xanthine, or they may be regarded as derivatives of purine. They occur in a number of vegetable products used throughout the world in beverages such as tea, coffee, cocoa, guarana, and maté. Tea and coffee contain 1 to 1.5 per cent caffeine, cocoa contains from 1 to 3 per cent theobromine, and tea also contains xanthine and theophylline. It is of interest to note that these stimulant xanthine beverages were used widely in various parts of the world long before means of intercommunication were established. Thus, tea and coffee were used by the ancient tribes of Asia, kola nuts were used by the natives of West Africa, guarana by the natives of the Argentine, and maté by the Indians of Brazil since early times. All these beverages cause stimulation of the central nervous system, but there is no evidence that they are harmful when used in moderation except to individuals who are particularly susceptible and those suffering from certain disorders such as gout (uric acid formed from the xanthines), hypertension, and cardiac irregularities.

The xanthines of importance are caffeine, theophylline, and theobromine. They are similar in their physiological activity, but there is a considerable difference in the intensity of action on various structures. The nature and the relative order of their activities are indicated in Table XXVII.

TABLE XXVII

RELATIVE ACTIVITIES OF THE XANTHINE ALKALOIDS

Alkaloid	Stimulation				Diuretic Activity
	Central Nervous System	Respiration	Heart and Circulation	Skeletal Muscle	
Caffeine	1	1	3	2	3
Theobromine	3	3	2	1	2
Theophylline	2	2	1	3	1

Order of decreasing activity is 1, 2, 3.

The close relationship between the structures of these compounds is indicated by their formulas.

Theophylline   Theobromine   Caffeine

The variation in activity is utilized in therapy. Thus caffeine is preferred for its action on the central nervous system, especially in the treatment of poisoning by central depressants, e.g., morphine. Theobromine and theophylline are used for their action on the coronary circulation and as diuretics. The free xanthine bases are rather irritant to the gastric mucosa. The salts are less irritant, and the discomfort and nausea following their use can be largely eliminated by administering them after a meal.

The xanthines are very weak bases which do not form stable salts with acids. They form crystalline, soluble, double salts with compounds such as sodium acetate and sodium salicylate.

Theophylline, U.S.P. (Theocin), is a white, crystalline powder, soluble in water about 1:120, m.p. about 272°. The more soluble derivatives, **Theophylline Ethylenediamine** (Aminophylline) and **Theophylline** and **Sodium Acetate, N.F.,** are double salts readily soluble in water. **Oxtriphylline, N.N.R.** (Choledyl, Choline Theophyllinate), is employed as a mild diuretic, as a myocardial stimulant and vasodilator.

Much of the compound used medicinally is obtained from 4,5-diamino-1,3-dimethyl-2,6-dioxyprimidine, by heating the formyl derivative with alkali.

Theophylline

Theobromine, N.F. (3,7-Dimethylxanthine), is a white, crystalline powder, slightly soluble in water and organic solvents. It is soluble in alkalies and forms soluble double salts with a number of substances. It is generally employed in the form of its double salts such as, *Theobromine Sodium Salicylate, N.F.* (diuretin), *Theobromine Sodium Acetate, U.S.P.*, and *Theobromine Calcium Salicylate, N.F.* (a mixture of calcium theobromine and calcium salicylate). The theobromine compounds are usually administered orally as tablets or as a powder in capsules.

Although most of the theobromine is obtained by extraction of the hulls of cacao beans, it can be synthesized from 3-methyluric acid.

Caffeine, U.S.P. (Theine, 1,3,7-Trimethylxanthine), consists of white crystals, slightly efflorescent in air, soluble in water about 1:46, and less soluble in organic solvents; m.p. when anhydrous about 236°. It is used as such in powder contained in capsules or in the form of tablets for oral administration. The more soluble double salts, *Citrated Caffeine, U.S.P.*, *Caffeine and Sodium Benzoate, U.S.P.*, and *Caffeine and Sodium Salicylate, N.F.*, are commonly used.

Caffeine is readily obtained by the extraction of tea dust, as a by-product in the manufacture of decaffeinated coffee or by the methylation of theobromine.

Mercaptopurine, N.N.R. (6-Purinethiol), an antagonist to purine metabolism, has been found active against cancer in experimental animals. It has been shown to inhibit certain sarcomas,[41] and together with aminopterin (see page 429) it is effective against mouse-induced leukemia. This compound is reported to be useful for the treatment of acute leukemia.

6-Purinethiol   Hyphylline

Hyphylline, N.N.R. [7-(2,3-Dihydroxypropyl)theophylline], is a neutral product that exhibits peripheral vasodilator and bronchodilator properties of other theophylline compounds.

Dimenhydrinate, N.N.R. [Dramamine, 2-(Benzohydryloxy)-N,N-dimethyl-

Dimenhydrinate

ethylamine 8-chlorotheophyllinate], a salt of diphenhydramine and 8-chlorotheophylline, is a white, odorless, crystalline product which couples mild sedation with antihistamine activity. It is used to control nausea and vomiting in motion sickness and for the management of vestibular dysfunction.

THE VITAMIN B COMPLEX

For the sake of clarity, the members of the vitamin B complex having in their structures heterocycles containing two or more heteroatoms are considered as a group at this point in the text.

The large amount of research carried out in different laboratories on vitamin B has resulted in a confusing multiplicity of names for various factors and groups of factors. These may be summarized as follows:

Vitamin B: The entire vitamin B complex.
Vitamin B$_1$: Thiamine hydrochloride, thiamine chloride, aneurin, antineuritic factor, antiberiberi factor.
Vitamin B$_2$: Riboflavin, vitamin G, lactoflavin, ovoflavin, flavin.

[41] Skipper *et al.*, *Cancer Research*, **14**, 294 (1954).

Vitamin B_3: A growth factor for the pigeon. A factor capable of curing specific paralytic symptoms in the rat. May be pantothenic acid.

Vitamin B_4: A factor associated with specific paralytic symptoms in rats and chicks. May be a mixture of arginine and glycine.

Vitamin B_5: A weight-maintenance factor for pigeons.

Vitamin B_6: Pyridoxine, pyridoxine hydrochloride, adermin. An antidermatitis factor for rats. Has properties common to, but not necessarily identical with, vitamin H, factor I. (See page 342.)

Vitamin B_{12}: The true antianemic factor.

Vitamin B_c: Nutrition factor for the chick. Folic acid.

Vitamin G: See Vitamin B_2.

Vitamin H: Biotin, coenzyme R.

Vitamin L: Lactation vitamin. Probably two separate factors, one present in liver filtrate, the other in yeast filtrate; necessary for the growth of the rat.

Choline: Prevents fatty liver in the depancreatized dog.

Factor W: A growth factor essential to rats. Contains pantothenic acid, and an unidentified growth substance; lacks vitamin B_6; may be biotin.

Factor X: Necessary to prevent graying of black hair in rats.

Nicotinic Acid: Prevents or cures certain characteristic aspects of pellagra.

Nicotinic Acid Amide: Probably Goldberger's P–P factor. An essential constituent of cozymase molecule. Same therapeutic actions as nicotinic acid.

p-Aminobenzoic Acid: A hair-color factor for the rat and a growth-promoting factor for the chick.

Pantothenic Acid: "The universal vitamin." Chick antidermatitis factor, contained in the filtrate factor.

Following or concurrent with the discovery of the vitamins and factors of this vitamin group, their participation in enzyme systems has been clearly demonstrated. The organic chemistry of most of these compounds is well established, but their role in biochemical systems is just emerging. For the fully expanded pattern of these interrelated enzymatic reactions, one must await the complex results of research in progress in many laboratories.

Thiamine

The determination of the structure and the synthesis of vitamin B_1, thiamine, is one of the most romantic detective stories of modern chemistry. Rice bran and yeast were found, by biological tests, to be the richest sources of the vitamin. The vitamin could be adsorbed on clay, from which it was most effectively displaced by means of quinine sulfate. In 1933, Williams and his co-workers were able to isolate about 5 g. of pure vitamin from a ton of rice polishings.

In 1929 Professor Eijkmann, of Utrecht, received the Nobel Prize for having made the discovery in 1898 that polyneuritis in fowls was identical with human beriberi. It was subsequently discovered that both afflictions may be cured by the ingestion of rice bran. It remained for R. R. Williams, who became "inoculated in 1910 with a curiosity about the beriberi-preventing substance in rice bran," to solve the mystery in the early thirties of the present century.

"In this operation we used as vessels a 1300 gallon tank at the first stage and a 20 cc. test tube in the twentieth and last stage."

Donath had isolated an impure product with high activity, but he was unable to determine the elementary analysis of the vitamin. Windaus isolated sufficient of the active material to establish the presence of sulfur in the molecule.

Thanks to microchemical procedures, smaller amounts sufficed in 1933 to permit a thorough investigation of the pure vitamin. Its composition was determined to be $C_{12}H_{18}N_4OSCl_2$. Sulfur dioxide was found to split the molecule according to the equation

$$C_{12}H_{18}N_4SOCl_2 + H_2SO_3 \rightarrow \underset{1}{C_6H_9N_3SO_3} + \underset{2}{C_6H_9NSO} + 2HCl$$

Fragment 1 was shown to be a 6-aminopyrimidine derivative of the structure I. The other fragment was shown to be a thiazole derivative of the structure II.

From various considerations, it was postulated that in the vitamin the two fragments were united in such manner as to form the quaternary ammonium salt, 2-methyl-5(4-methyl-5-β-hydroxyethyl-thiazolium chloride)-methyl-6-aminopyrimidine.

To establish this structure, there are three possibilities of synthesis. The pyrimidine and thiazole rings may be formed separately and then connected by quaternization to the thiazolium derivative. The appropriate pyrimidine with an

Vitamin B₁ bromide hydrobromide

aminomethyl group in the 5 position can be synthesized followed by formulation of the thiazole ring around the primary amino group. The thiazole ring can be prepared, a suitable side chain added in the form of a thiazolium salt, followed by ring closure of the pyrimidine ring. All three methods are reported in the literature, and it is probable that the first two are commercially feasible. The first is summarized as shown.

Thiamine plays an important role in biochemical transformations. In a long series of experiments, Peters and his co-workers [42] demonstrated that thiamine has an important function in carbohydrate as well as pyruvic acid metabolism. The oxidative effect of thiamine is not due to the vitamin itself but to a coenzyme, **Cocarboxylase,** which with *carboxylase,* an enzyme found in yeast and other microorganisms, catalyzes the metabolism of α-oxycarboxylic acids. Cocarboxylase has been chemically synthesized from thiamine and pyrophosphoric acid.[43]

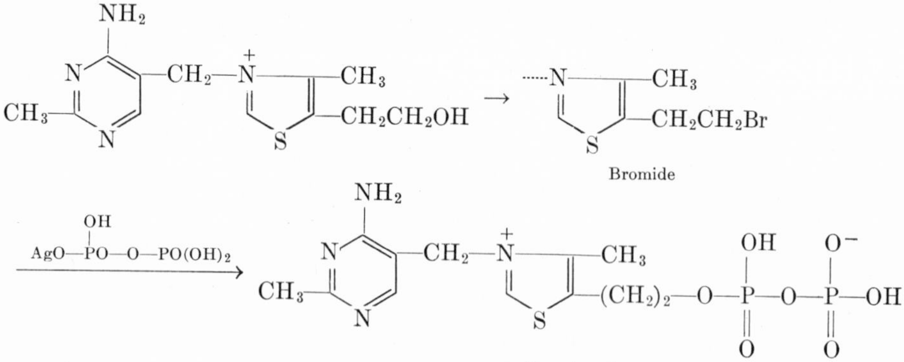

Bromide

Cocarboxylase

Thiamine triphosphate and thiamine polyphosphates have also been prepared and are active coenzymes.[44] Carboxylase is considered a complex involving a protein of high molecular weight, a molecule of cocarboxylase and five atoms of magnesium.

On the theory of metabolite antagonists, several structural analogs of thiamine have been synthesized. Thiamine is a bacterial growth promoter. Antagonists to thiamine, such as **Neopyrithiamine,** 1-[(2-Methyl-4-amino-) 5-pyrimidyl-methyl]-2-methyl-3-(β-hydroxyethyl) pyridinium bromide, have been shown to have inhibitory effects on pathogenic organisms. Such compounds have been disappointing as therapeutic agents.

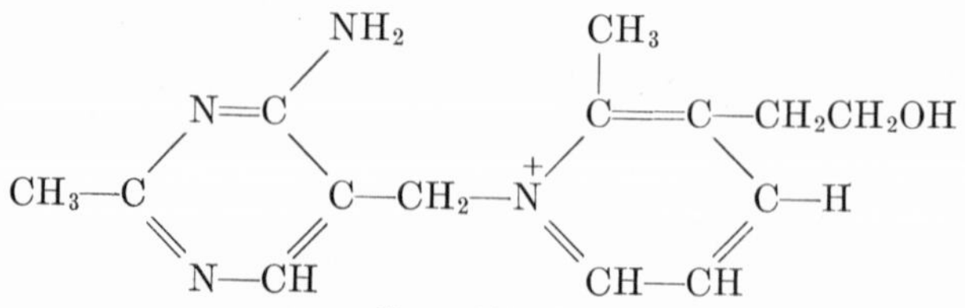

Neopyrithiamine

[42] Peters, *Biochem. J.,* **30,** 2206 (1936).

[43] Weil-Malherbe, *Biochem. J.,* **34,** 980 (1940).

[44] Roux, Feysseire, and Duchesne, *Bull. soc. chim. biol.,* **30,** 592 (1948).

Thiamine Hydrochloride, U.S.P. (Vitamin B_1 Hydrochloride, Thiamine Chloride), is a white, crystalline product, readily soluble in water to form an acid solution. The crystals absorb water on exposure to air. It is slightly soluble in alcohol and insoluble in oils. It is relatively stable to heat; solutions may be sterilized by boiling for 1 hr. or at 120° for 20 min. without appreciable loss of potency. Cooking of acid foods is said to destroy from 5 to 15 per cent of the vitamin, and in alkaline products 80 per cent may be lost.

Good sources include yeast, rice polishings, lean pork, liver, oysters, wheat germ, egg yolk, whole-grain cereals, peanuts, dried beans, and milk.

The unit of potency is the antineuritic activity of 3 γ (0.003 mg.) of pure synthetic thiamine hydrochloride.

Deficiency of the vitamin may be caused by inadequate intake due to improper food habits or by destruction of the vitamin in cooking. Inadequate absorption as in the vomiting of pregnancy, chronic diarrhea, etc., may cause deficiency. Increased requirements as in lactation, hyperthyroidism, fever, alcoholism, and violent exercise also may lead to deficiency.

The normal daily requirements have been estimated as follows:

Infancy and childhood	0.6 to 1.5 mg. (200 to 500 units)
Adolescence and maturity	1.5 to 2 mg. (500 to 666 units)
Pregnancy and lactation	2 to 5 mg. (666 to 1665 units)
Acute deficiency	10 to 50 mg. (3330 to 16650 units)

The vitamin is used to treat conditions that arise from deficiency such as neuritis of alcoholism, pregnancy, wasting diseases, etc., and in cardiovascular disease of dietary origin, gastrointestinal disorder such as poor appetite and constipation, ulcerative colitis, and numerous other conditions. It is administered orally as tablets, or intramuscularly in solution by injection.

Thiamine Mononitrate, U.S.P., being nonhygroscopic, is more stable than thiamine hydrochloride. It is used especially in the food industry and is also preferred in certain pharmaceutical applications.

Riboflavin

Riboflavin, U.S.P. (Vitamin B_2, Lactoflavin, Ovoflavin, Dimethylribityl-isoalloxazine), is an orange-yellow, crystalline powder, slightly soluble in water with the formation of yellow-green fluorescent solutions, m.p. about 280° with decomposition. It is destroyed by alkalies and slowly by light, but it is heat stable. Canning is reported to destroy from 5 to 20 per cent of the vitamin. Cooking by stewing does not cause much decomposition but roasting and frying do.

Riboflavin was known as early as 1879 as the water-soluble, yellow-green, fluorescent pigment from milk, lactochrome. It was not until 1925 that Kallman isolated appreciable amounts of the pigment. In 1932, Warburg and Christian observed that this pigment is present in the "yellow enzyme," which acts as a transporter of molecular oxygen to the substrate.

It was shown by Kuhn and his co-workers in 1933 that the oxygen-containing side chain of riboflavin can be removed by irradiation in alkaline solution to form an isoalloxazine called *lumiflavin*. If the irradiation is carried out in neutral or acid solution, **Lumichrome,** 6,7-dimethylalloxazine, is the product. From these and other considerations, a structure for riboflavin was proposed which was confirmed by synthesis.[45]

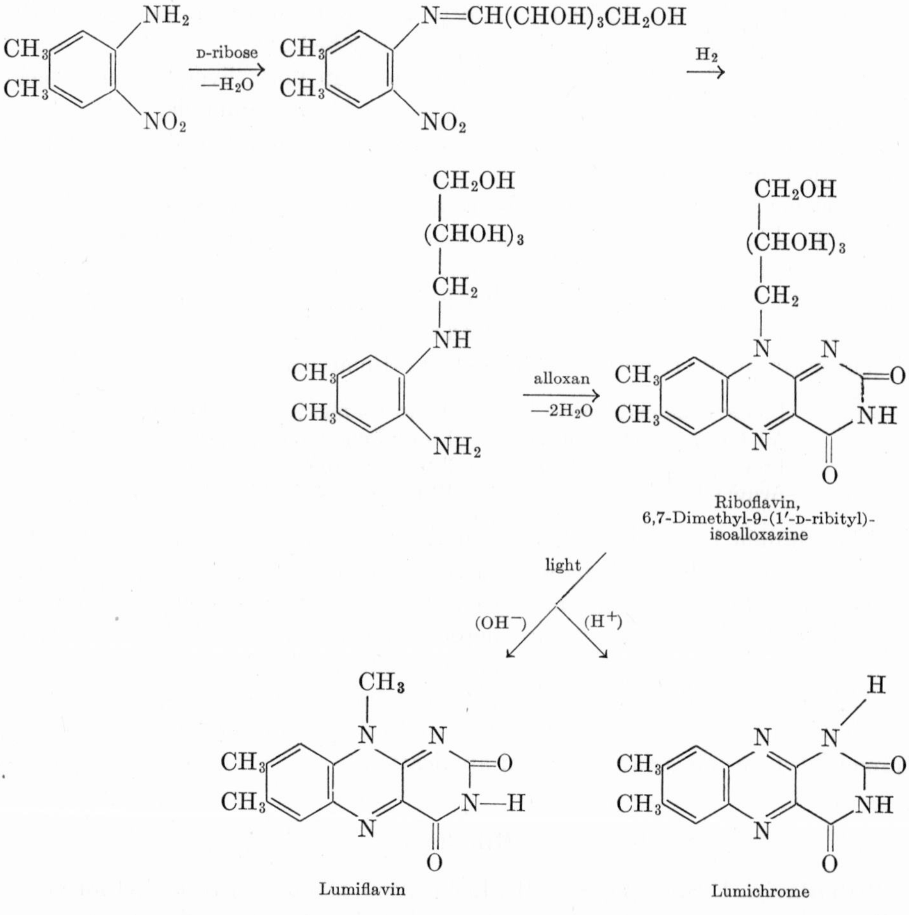

Riboflavin,
6,7-Dimethyl-9-(1'-D-ribityl)-
isoalloxazine

Lumiflavin

Lumichrome

Newer methods of synthesis substitute barbituric acid or a substituted barbituric acid for the more expensive alloxan.

Riboflavin in the form of riboflavin-5-phosphate or riboflavin mononucleotide acts as a coenzyme in many oxidation-reduction biochemical reactions. Together with riboflavin adenine dinucleotide, these coenzymes can readily be hydrogenated and in turn will give up this hydrogen in biochemical systems, functioning as hydrogen transfer agents. When bound to certain specific proteins called *apoenzymes,* the coenzymes form enzymes such as Warburg's "yellow enzyme of respiration."

[45] Karrer *et al., Helv. Chim. Acta,* **18,** 69, 1435 (1935).

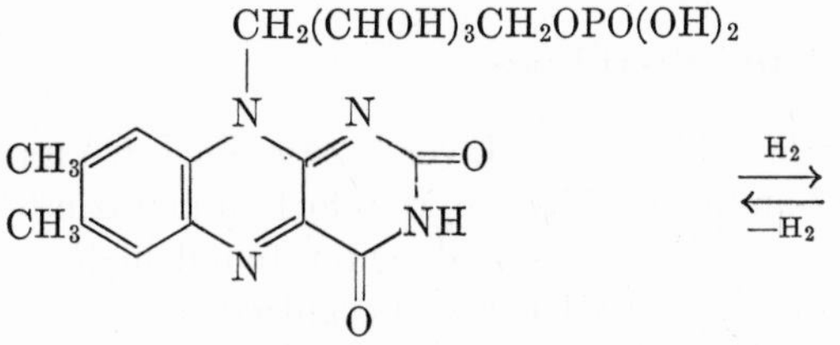

$CH_2(CHOH)_3CH_2OPO(OH)_2$

Riboflavin phosphate

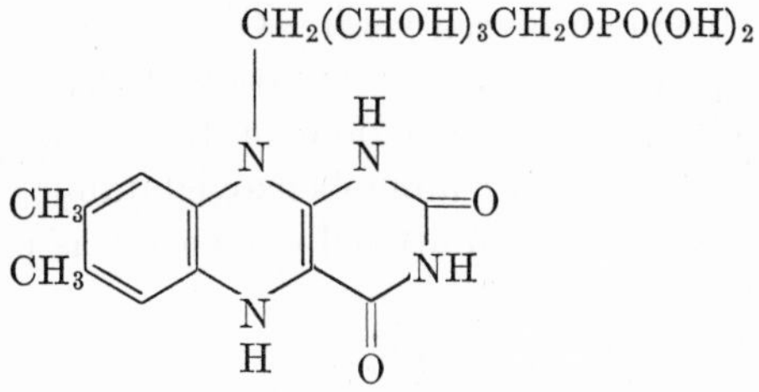

$\xrightleftharpoons[-H_2]{H_2}$

$CH_2(CHOH)_3CH_2OPO(OH)_2$

Leucoflavin form

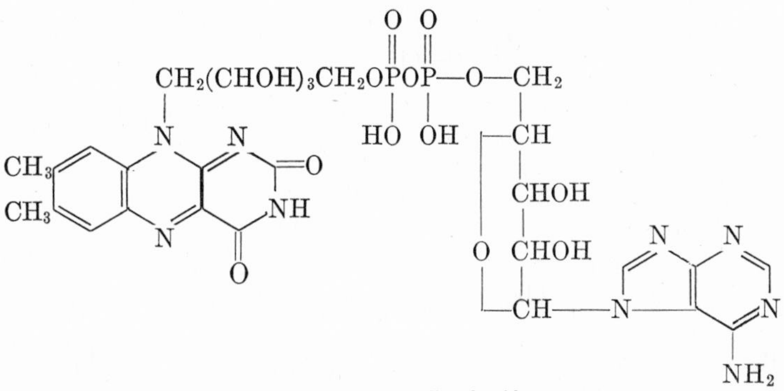

Riboflavin adenine dinucleotide

Good sources of this vitamin include dried yeast, liver, kidney, eggs, meat, wheat germ, milk, cheese, spinach, turnip greens, and carrots.

The daily requirements of this vitamin have been estimated at 1.5 to 2 mg. for children, to 2 or 3 mg. for adults, and 3 to 5 mg. during pregnancy and lactation. Deficiency leads to ocular disturbances such as photophobia and blurred vision, to skin disturbances such as dermatitis and loss of hair, and to lowered general tone of the health. The vitamin is employed to counteract such symptoms. It is administered in the form of tablets or capsules by mouth, and in sterile solution for intramuscular or subcutaneous injection.

Among the antagonists to riboflavin are D-araboflavin, 2,4-diamino-7,8-di-methyl-10-ribityl-5,10-dihydrophenazine, 6,7-dichloro-9-ribitylisoalloxazine, and 5,6-dimethyl-9-ribitylisoalloxazine.[46]

[46] Woolley, *Advances in Enzymol.*, **6,** 131 (1946); v. Euler and Karrer, *Helv. Chim. Acta,* **29,** 353 (1946).

Folic Acid and Pteridines

Folic Acid, U.S.P. (Pteroylglutamic Acid, P.G.A., Liver *L. casei* Factor, Vitamin B_c, Vitamin M), is N-{*p*-{[(2-amino-4-hydroxypyrimido[4,5,b]pyrazin-6-yl)-methyl]-amino}-benzoyl}-glutamic acid, an essential factor found in liver, green leaves, yeast, and grasses. As early as 1931 it was recognized that a particular form of pernicious anemia was caused by the deficiency of a factor available in autolyzed yeast. Other workers reported similar findings until some ten years later when the isolation of this factor was accomplished.

Degradation reactions on the vitamin indicated the presence of a substituted pteridine and *p*-aminobenzoylglutamic acid. The structure derived from this and considerable additional evidence was proved by four syntheses, one of which is indicated.[47]

Folic acid,
pteroylglutamic acid

Pteroic Acid was synthesized by the same method in which *p*-aminobenzoic acid was substituted for *p*-aminobenzoylglutamic acid. This compound is essential for *S. faecalis* and other Enterococci.

Since folic acid is involved with many nutritional phenomena in a variety of animals including man and since the research on these phenomena has been carried out in many laboratories, there has been much confusion as to nomenclature.

[47] Angier *et al., Science,* **103,** 667 (1946).

Other preparations having biological activity due to pteroylglutamic acid have been isolated. Subsequently these have been shown to be identical with or conjugates of the vitamin with varying numbers of glutamic acid residues. Thus, factors identical with folic acid are indicated above as synonyms. In addition, the "fermentation *Lactobacillus casei* factor" has been identified as pteroyl-γ-glutamyl-γ-glutamylglutamic acid, and "vitamin B_c conjugate" is pteroylheptaglutamic acid.

The primary biochemical role of folic acid appears to be the synthesis of compounds such as purines, pyrimidines, and certain amino acids which involve the incorporation of a single carbon fragment probably by way of *Citrovorum Factor* (see page 428). It has been shown [48] to be essential for the synthesis of serine from glycine and formate by *S. faecalis* R and is involved in the synthesis of serine, the conversion of serine to glycine, the synthesis of methionine, and the synthesis of purines in the rat.

The pathology of folic acid deficiency in man is expressed in a number of clinical manifestations but particularly in altered hematopoiesis. The vitamin is effective in producing blood regeneration in Addisonian pernicious anemia, nutritional macrocytic anemia, and the macrocytic anemia of sprue. Only rarely is decreased dietary intake of folic acid the sole cause of clinical deficiencies. These deficiencies more likely result from metabolic defects present which impair the liberation of the vitamin from its conjugated form.

The daily requirement of folic acid in normal nutrition is unknown. It is likely that only a fraction of a milligram is necessary. In deficiency states, 5 to 10 mg. of the vitamin is prescribed daily. Folic acid is available for oral administration in tablets or in an aqueous solution of the sodium salt for injection.

The presence of *p*-aminobenzoic acid in the folic acid molecule points the way to an appreciation of the mode of action of the sulfa drugs. If it is assumed that *p*-aminobenzoic acid is an essential substrate from which pteroylglutamic acid is biologically synthesized, then the isosteric sulfa compounds would be expected to compete with it. It has been experimentally proved that sulfonamides markedly inhibit the formation of folic acid by bacteria.[49] Bacteria that require folic acid but are incapable of synthesizing it are not inhibited by the sulfa drugs; presumably there is no synthesizing enzyme to inhibit.[50, 51]

A large number of folic acid analogs have been made, most of which are antagonists to the vitamin. Others have been found naturally and have an important place in the biochemical picture.

Xanthopterin (2-Amino-4,6-dihydroxypteridine) is one of the pigments originally found in the wings of butterflies. Its synthesis [52] from a 4,5-diaminopyrimidine and glyoxalic acid proved it to be a pteridine. Derivatives are xanthopterin, a yellow pigment; leucopterin, colorless crystals; ichthyopterin, $C_8H_8O_8N_4$, a blue

[48] Lascelles, Cross, and Woods, *Biochem. J.*, **49**, lxvi (1951).

[49] Miller, *Proc. Soc. Exptl. Biol. Med.*, **57**, 151 (1944).

[50] Lampen and Jones, *J. Biol. Chem.*, **164**, 485 (1946).

[51] Woolley, *Ann. Rev. Biochem.*, **16**, 375 (1947).

[52] Purrmann, *Ann.*, **548**, 284 (1941).

fluorescent substance found in fish.[53] Xanthopterin has been separated chromatographically from urine and from the crab.

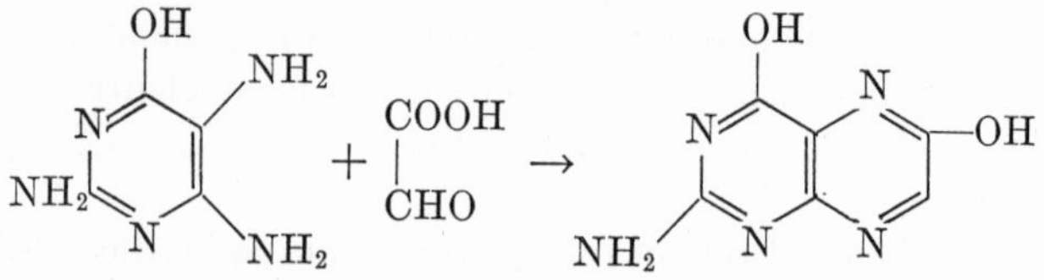

2,4,5-Triamino-4-hy-
droxypyrimidine   Glyoxalic
acid   Xanthopterin

Medical interest was aroused in these compounds when it was found that xanthopterin could be converted by yeast into folic acid,[54] that it exerted beneficial effects in anemia,[55] and was a possible biological precursor of folic acid.[56]

The true role of xanthopterin in nutrition is still unknown. Welch and Heinle [57] suggest that it may inhibit the inactivation of a precursor of folic acid.

Rhizopterin (Formylpteroic Acid) is a folic acid factor having high growth-promoting activity for *S. faecalis* R. It was shown by Wolf and his co-workers [58] to be pteroic acid formylated in the N^{10} position. Rhizopterin was synthesized by treatment of pteroic acid with formic acid.

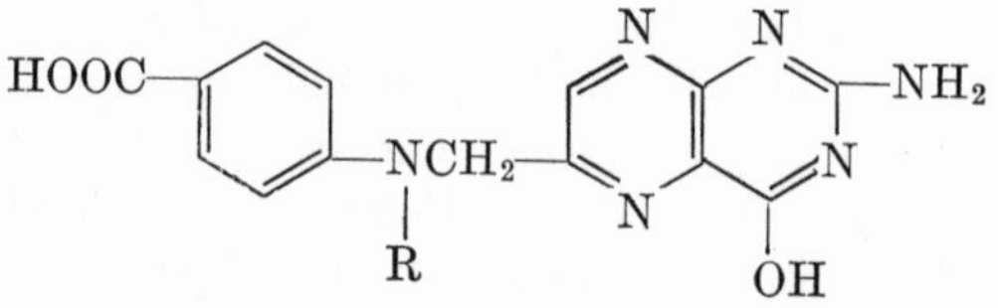

Pteroic acid, R = H.
Rhizopterin, R = —CHO. The formyl group may be introduced at position 10 by heating pteroic acid with formic acid at 100°.

Citrovorum Factor (Leucovorin, Folinic Acid) is a folic acid factor first shown to be essential to the organism *Leuconostoc citrovorum*. It was soon shown to be closely related to folic acid in chemical structure. Chemical transformation indicated that it was 5-formyl-5,6,7,8-tetrahydropteroylglutamic acid. This was proved by synthesis. Reduction of 10-formylpteroylglutamic acid to the 5,6,7,8-tetrahydro derivative and migration of the formyl group results in leucovorin.

It appears likely that folic acid is a precursor of leucovorin in an enzymatic transformation. Leucovorin in turn possibly acts as a coenzyme in single-carbon transfer in animals, as discussed under folic acid.

[53] Hüttel and Sprengling, *Ann.*, **554**, 69 (1943).
[54] Trotter, Mims, and Day, *Science*, **100**, 223 (1944).
[55] Simmons and Norris, *J. Biol. Chem.*, **140**, 679 (1941).
[56] Wright and Welch, *Science*, **98**, 179 (1943).
[57] Welch and Heinle, *Pharmacol. Revs.*, **3**, 345 (1951).
[58] Wolf *et al.*, *J. Am. Chem. Soc.*, **69**, 2753 (1947).

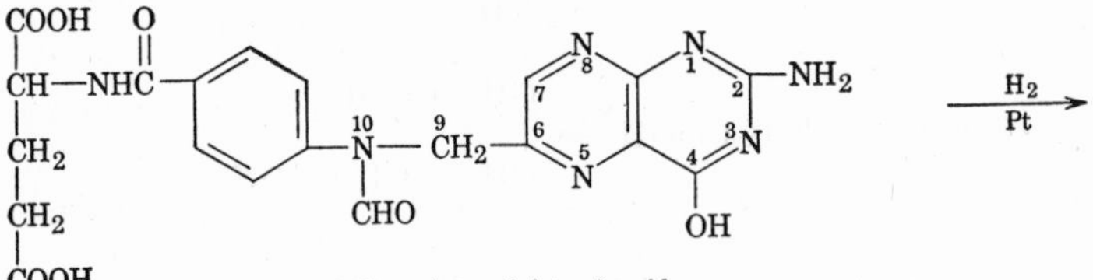

10-Formylpteroylglutamic acid

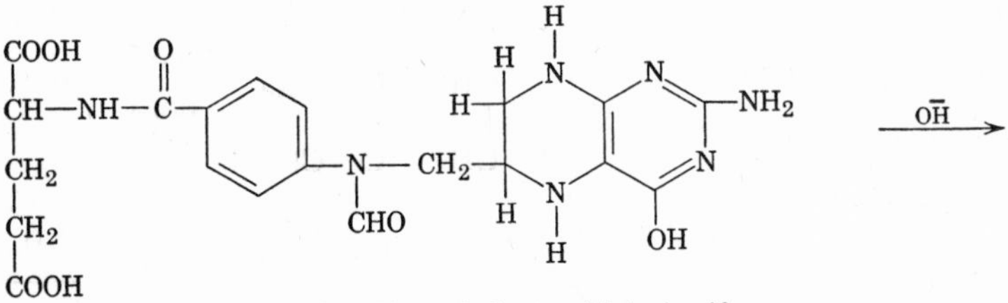

10-Formyl-5,6,7,8-tetrahydropteroylglutamic acid

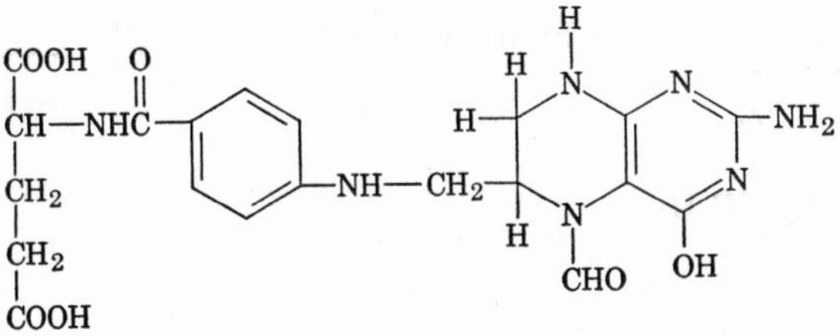

Leucovorin

Aminopterin Sodium, N.N.R. (Sodium 4-Aminopteroylglutamate, Ametho-pterin, Sodium N-{p-[(2,4-diamino-6-pteridyl)-methylamino benzoyl]glutamate}, a folic acid analog is a useful antagonist to the vitamin. It probably blocks the conversion of folic acid to the citrovorum factor, and thus it acts to depress hematopoiesis. It is indicated for the treatment of acute leukemia in children.[59]

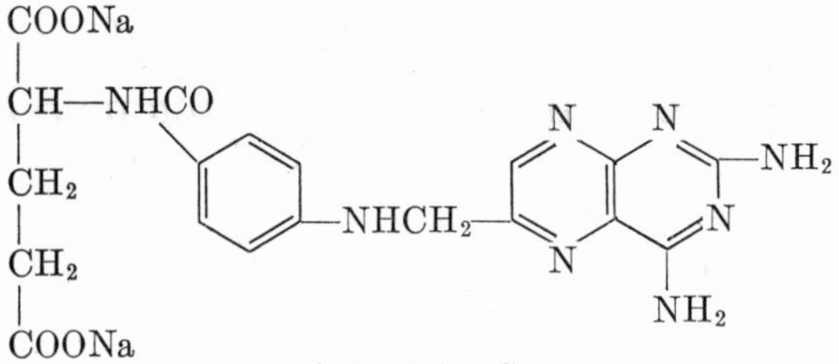

Aminopterin sodium

Biotin

Biotin (Vitamin H, Coenzyme R) was first called vitamin H and recognized as the curative factor for "egg white injury" as early as 1916. It was shown that

[59] *J. Am. Med. Assoc.*, **159**, 680 (1955).

$$\text{HSCH}_2\text{CH}-\text{COOH} + \text{ClCH}_2\text{COOH} \rightarrow$$

$$\underset{\text{NH}_2}{|}$$

$$\begin{array}{c} \text{NH}_2 \\ | \\ \text{CH}-\text{COOH} \\ | \\ \text{CH}_2 \quad \text{CH}_2\text{COOH} \\ \diagdown\;\text{S}\;\diagup \end{array} \xrightarrow[\substack{2.\ \text{ROH}-\overset{+}{\text{H}} \\ 3.\ \text{NaOR}}]{1.\ \text{C}_6\text{H}_5\text{COCl}}$$

$$\begin{array}{c} \overset{\text{O}}{\overset{\|}{}} \\ \text{NH}-\text{C}-\text{C}_6\text{H}_5 \\ | \\ \text{CH}-\text{C}-\text{ONa} \\ | \qquad \| \\ \text{CH}_2 \quad \text{C}-\text{COOR} \\ \diagdown\;\text{S}\;\diagup \end{array} \xrightarrow[\text{HOAc}]{\text{HCl}} \begin{array}{c} \overset{\text{O}}{\overset{\|}{}} \\ \text{NH}-\text{C}-\text{C}_6\text{H}_5 \\ | \\ \text{CH}-\text{C}=\text{O} \\ | \qquad | \\ \text{CH}_2 \quad \text{CH}_2 \\ \diagdown\;\text{S}\;\diagup \end{array}$$

Intermediate A

$$\overset{\displaystyle \ulcorner\text{O}\urcorner}{\text{O}=\text{C}(\text{CH}_2)_3\text{C}=\text{O}} \xrightarrow{\text{CH}_3\text{OH}} \text{HOOC}-(\text{CH}_2)_3\text{COOCH}_3 \xrightarrow{\text{SOCl}_2}$$

$$\text{ClOC}(\text{CH}_2)_3\text{COOCH}_3 \xrightarrow[\text{H}_2]{\text{Pd}} \text{OCH}-(\text{CH}_2)_3\text{COOCH}_3$$

Intermediate B

Intermediate A
+
Intermediate B

$$\rightarrow \begin{array}{c} \overset{\text{O}}{\overset{\|}{}} \\ \text{NH}-\text{C}\text{C}_6\text{H}_5 \\ | \\ \text{CH}-\text{C}=\text{O} \\ | \qquad | \\ \text{CH}_2 \quad \text{C}=\text{CH}(\text{CH}_2)_3\text{COOCH}_3 \\ \diagdown\;\text{S}\;\diagup \end{array} \xrightarrow[\substack{2.\ \text{Zn}-\text{HOAc} \\ 3.\ \text{Pd}-\text{H}_2}]{1.\ \text{oxime}}$$

$$\begin{array}{c} \overset{\text{O}}{\overset{\|}{}} \\ \text{NH}\text{C}-\text{C}_6\text{H}_5 \\ | \qquad\qquad \overset{\text{O}}{\overset{\|}{}} \\ \text{C}-\!\!-\text{C}-\text{NH}\text{C}-\text{CH}_3 \\ | \qquad | \\ \text{CH}_2 \quad \text{CH}-(\text{CH}_2)_4\text{COOCH}_3 \\ \diagdown\;\text{S}\;\diagup \end{array} \xrightarrow{\text{Ba(OH)}_2} \begin{array}{c} \text{NH}_2 \\ | \\ \text{CH}-\!\!-\text{CHNH}_2 \\ | \qquad | \\ \text{CH}_2 \quad \text{CH}(\text{CH}_2)_4\text{COOH} \\ \diagdown\;\text{S}\;\diagup \end{array} \xrightarrow{\text{COCl}_2}$$

$$\begin{array}{c} \overset{\text{O}}{\overset{\|}{}} \\ \text{C} \\ \diagup_{2'}\diagdown \\ \text{HN}_{1'} \qquad {}_{3'}\text{NH} \\ | \qquad\quad | \\ \text{HC}_4\!\!-\!\!-{}_3\text{CH} \\ | \qquad\quad | \\ \text{H}_2\text{C}_5 \quad {}_2\text{CH}(\text{CH}_2)_4\text{COOH} \\ \diagdown_{1}\diagup \\ \text{S} \end{array}$$

Biotin

an organic protective substance was able to neutralize the toxic effects of excessive amounts of egg white in the diet of rats. Following attempts by many biochemists to isolate this substance, the identity of vitamin H and biotin, a growth factor for yeast, was established. This same substance is also believed to be identical with coenzyme R, a growth and respiration factor for many strains of legume nodule bacteria.

After considerable study of the degradation of biotin, du Vigneaud and his co-workers [60] formulated its structure which was then established by synthesis.[61] One synthesis has been summarized.

Biotin contains three asymmetric carbon atoms making possible four racemic modifications. All these isomers, DL-biotin, DL-epibiotin, DL-allobiotin, and DL-epiallobiotin, have been synthesized. Natural biotin is the dextrorotatory form; the levo isomer is essentially inactive.

It is likely that biotin by analogy to other members of the B vitamin group acts in biochemical systems as part of a coenzyme bound on a protein. The isolation and identification of such a system has not yet been achieved. Evidence has been obtained, however, that biotin is involved in various enzymatic reactions such as the decarboxylation of oxalacetate and succinate, the deamination of aspartic acid, serine, and threonine, and the dehydrogenation of succinic acid possibly by way of intra- or intermolecular hydrogen transport.[62]

Since biotin can be synthesized in the intestinal tract and is so readily available in the diet, there is some question as to its deficiency symptoms in man. There is evidence that it relieves skin lesions involving the sebaceous glands. Synthetic racemic biotin is used as a reference standard; it has one-half the activity of the natural form.

Biotin is widely distributed in both the plant and the animal kingdoms but the best sources are yeast, liver, fruits, and vegetables. In such states, it occurs mainly in the bound form which upon hydrolysis yields free biotin. One such bound compound is *biocytin* which is the biotin compound occurring in many soluble natural products, especially during the controlled autolysis of actively metabolizing yeast.

$$
\begin{array}{c}
\text{O} \\
\parallel \\
\text{C} \\
\diagup\;\diagdown \\
\text{NH}\qquad\text{NH} \\
\mid\qquad\quad\mid \\
\text{CH}\!-\!\!-\!\text{CH} \\
\mid\qquad\quad\mid \\
\text{CH}_2\quad\text{CH(CH}_2)_4\text{CONH(CH}_2)_4\text{CHCOOH} \\
\diagdown\;\diagup\qquad\qquad\qquad\qquad\mid \\
\text{S}\qquad\qquad\qquad\qquad\text{NH}_2
\end{array}
$$

Biocytin

[60] Melville, Moyer, Hofmann, and du Vigneaud, *J. Biol. Chem.*, **146**, 487 (1942).

[61] Harris *et al.*, *Science*, **97**, 447 (1943); *J. Am. Chem. Soc.*, **66**, 1756, 1757, 1806 (1944); *ibid.*, **67**, 2096 (1945).

[62] Lichtstein, *Vitamins and Hormones*, **9**, 27 (1951).

Another bound form of biotin is the combination of biotin and the protein constituent of egg white called *avidin*, the toxic component of raw egg white.

Biotin analogs have been synthesized. **Desthiobiotin** and **Oxybiotin,** as shown, have variable activities compared to biotin, depending upon the organism involved.

$$
\begin{array}{cc}
\text{O} & \text{O} \\
\| & \| \\
\text{C} & \text{C} \\
\diagup \diagdown & \diagup \diagdown \\
\text{NH} \quad \text{NH} & \text{NH} \quad \text{NH} \\
| \quad | & | \quad | \\
\text{CH}\!-\!\!-\!\text{CH} & \text{C}\!-\!\!-\!\text{C} \\
| \quad | & | \quad | \\
\text{CH}_3 \quad \text{CH}_2(\text{CH}_2)_4\text{COOH} & \text{H} \quad \text{H} \\
& \text{CH}_2 \quad \text{CH}\!-\!(\text{CH}_2)_4\text{COOH} \\
& \diagdown \quad \diagup \\
& \text{O}
\end{array}
$$

Desthiobiotin   Oxybiotin

Cyanocobalamin

Cyanocobalamin, U.S.P., Vitamin B_{12}, is a dark red, crystalline compound isolated from liver extracts or from the fermentation broths of several *Streptomyces* species. After the discovery in 1926 that pernicious anemia could be controlled therapeutically with whole liver, considerable effort went into the isolation of the responsible factor. The isolation of crystalline vitamin B_{12} was announced by Rickes and his co-workers [63] in 1948.

Chemically, vitamin B_{12} is a highly complex molecule containing one atom of cobalt and one atom of phosphorus and having a molecular formula of $C_{63}H_{90}N_{14}O_{14}PCo$.

Early degradation studies revealed the presence of the 1-α-D-ribofuranosido-5,6-dimethylbenzimidazole structure. In addition, alkali fusion produced pyrroles suggesting that vitamin B_{12} was a cobalt complexed porphyrin. This and other data established its structure as shown. This formulation was confirmed and supported by x-ray analysis.[64]

After the isolation of crystalline vitamin B_{12}, three other crystalline substances were isolated from the fermentation broths of *Streptomyces* species. These were originally named vitamins B_{12b} (B_{12a}), B_{12c}, and B_{12d}. Since that time it has been shown that the cyano group in vitamin B_{12} is co-ordinately bound to the cobalt and can readily be replaced by other anions. Thus, it is now established that vitamin B_{12} is cyanocobalamin, vitamin B_{12a} (also B_{12b} and B_{12d}) is hydroxocobalamin, and vitamin B_{12c} is nitritocobalamin. Other similar analogs have been described.

[63] Rickes, Brink, Koniuszy, Wood, and Folkers, *Science*, **107**, 396 (1948).
[64] *Chem. Eng. News*, **33**, 3487 (1955).

Vitamin B_{12}

Although its precise biochemical function in the body has yet to be established, it seems likely that, as a member of the B vitamins, vitamin B_{12} will be shown to have an important role in enzyme systems. It is known to influence nitrogen metabolism in animals, and it may act as a catalyst in the conversion of p-aminobenzoic acid into the coenzyme, citrovorum factor (see page 428).

Vitamin B_{12} is also known as the "extrinsic factor" in pernicious anemia and together with the yet unknown "intrinsic factor" is considered to be a complete treatment for this disease. Vitamin B_{12} is used as a hemopoietic agent in the treatment of tropical and nontropical sprue and nutritional macrocytic anemia. Insufficient data are available to estimate the optimum dosage schedules, although the minimum is believed to be $1\mu g$. per day. It is most effective by parenteral administration.

PHTHALAZINES

Useful among the phthalazines as a medicinal is **Hydralazine Hydrochloride, N.N.R.** (Apresoline Hydrochloride, 1-Hydrazinophthalazine Hydrochloride). This drug is classified as a sympatholytic agent, being antagonistic to angiotonin, serotonin, epinephrine, and arterenol. It is useful in controlling essential and early malignant hypertension and possibly certain kidney malfunctions.

Nepresol (1,4-Bishydrazinophthalazine) has been introduced in Europe as a drug having activity similar to Hydralazine.

Hydralazine   Nepresol   Preludin

MORPHOLINES

Morpholine (Tetrahydro-1,4,2H-oxazine) is the most important of the six-membered heterocyclic rings having a nitrogen and an oxygen atom. It is a strong base and is found in the side chains of several medicinal agents. Only a few valuable compounds are built around the morpholine ring itself. One such compound is **Preludin** (3-Methyl-2-phenylmorpholine). This drug is on trial in European countries as an appetite depressant, possessing few central nervous stimulant effects.

NON-NITROGEN HETEROCYCLES

Dioxolanes

The five-membered heterocycle composed of two oxygen and three carbon atoms is encountered infrequently in medicinal chemistry. It is seen most frequently as a fused ring system with benzene and is usually referred to in such cases as a methylenedioxy bridge. Examples of this structure are common among a large group of essential oils such as safrole, apiol, and myristicin (see page 83).

In addition to the above, 1,2-glycols react with aldehydes and ketones to form cyclic acetals and ketals. These compounds known as **1,3-dioxolanes** are easily hydrolyzed to the parent carbonyl compounds. For this reason, they are often used in synthetic procedures for "blocking" active carbonyl groups during certain reaction sequences.

Glyketal (2-Methyl-2-*n*-amyl-4-hydroxymethyl-1,3-dioxolane) is prepared from glycerol and 2-heptanone as shown. Glyketal is reported [65] as an anticonvulsant and muscle relaxant.

Glyketal

[65] Berger, *Federation Proc.*, **8**, 274 (1949).

Dioxanes

Dioxane or 1,4-diethylene dioxide is the most important member of the group of six-membered heterocyclic rings containing two oxygen atoms. It is prepared by distilling ethylene glycol with dilute sulfuric acid and has wide use as a very versatile solvent.

Derivatives of 1,4-benzodioxan have received attention as medicinal agents. **Piperoxan, N.N.R.** (Benodaine), is 2-(1-piperidylmethyl)-1,4-benzodioxane. It is used chiefly as an agent for the diagnosis of pheochromocytoma, a form of hypertension resulting from hypersecretion of norepinephrine. Piperoxan, acting as an adrenolytic agent on administration to patients suffering from this disease, results in a lowering of blood pressure. This compound, considered as an early lead in the field of antihistaminic agents, is synthesized as shown.

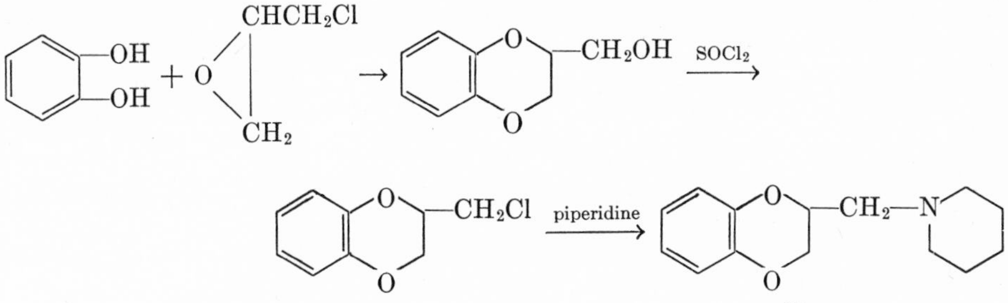

Piperoxan

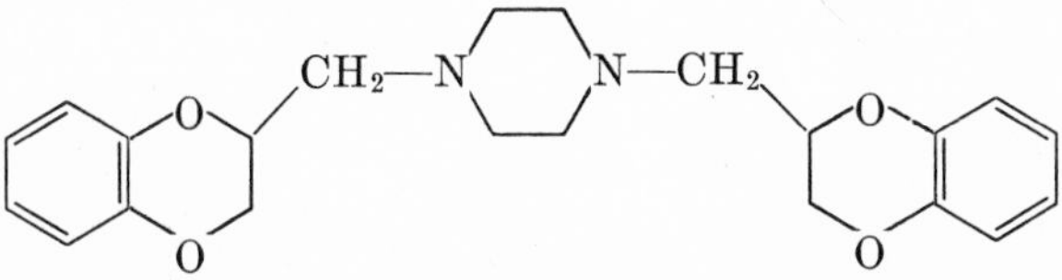

Dibozane

Dibozane(N,N'-*bis*-2-(1,4-Benzodioxanyl)methylpiperazine) has been suggested [66] as a hypotensive agent.

Dithianes

Mesulphen (Mitigal) is 2,6-dimethyldiphenylene disulfide and is an example of a medicinally useful product having a heterocycle containing two sulfur atoms. It is used in the treatment of various skin diseases. Its synthesis is indicated.

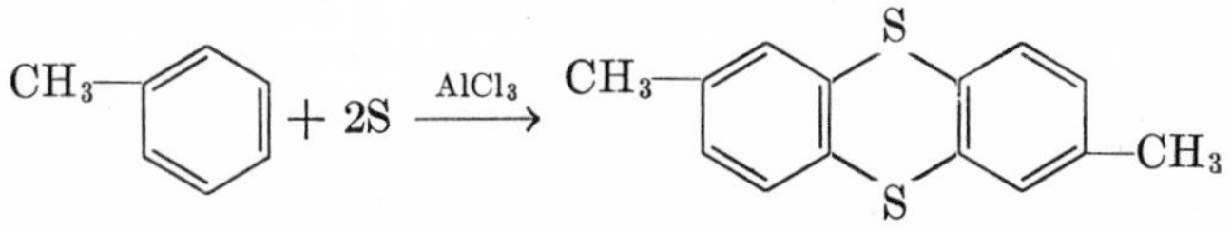

Mesulphen

[66] Swain and Nagel, *J. Am. Chem. Soc.*, **76**, 5091 (1954).

PHENOTHIAZINES

Fusion of the benzene ring with that of thiamorpholine results in the pheno-thiazine heterocycle.   There are a number of important medicinal agents which. contain this structure.

Phenothiazine, N.F. (Thiodiphenylamine), is a greenish-yellow compound. It is slightly soluble in water and in organic solvents, m.p., 180°.   It has been found to be highly effective against certain insects, e.g., the tent caterpillar, culicine mosquito, and the codling moth larvae.   It appears to be a specific poison for certain insects and to be nontoxic to plants and warm-blooded animals.

It is extensively used in veterinary therapy to remove internal parasites from animals and poultry.   In human therapy, it is employed in the form of lotions and ointments as a parasiticide.   It is recommended for *Oxyuris* infestation, but with sensitive patients close observation is necessary.[67]   10-Ethylphenothiazine and 10-methylphenothiazine are also effective.[68]

Addition of a dialkylaminoalkyl side chain to the 10 position of phenothiazine has resulted in useful drugs of several applications.

Phenothiazine

Promethazine X = H,
$$R = -CH_2CH\begin{matrix}CH_3\\N(CH_3)_2\end{matrix}$$
Chlorpromazine X = Cl,
$R = -CH_2CH_2CH_2N(CH_3)_2$
Promazine X = H,
$R = -CH_2CH_2CH_2N(CH_3)_2$

$CH_2CH_2N(C_2H_5)_2$

Diparcol

Pyrathiazine [Pyrrolazote, 10-(2-Pyrrolidylethyl)-phenothiazine] is an anti-histaminic agent (page 220) recommended for symptomatic relief in allergic dis-orders.

Diparcol [Diethazine, 10-(Diethylaminoethyl)-phenothiazine] exhibits para-sympatholytic activity and has been employed in the treatment of Parkinson's disease.   It is prepared by reacting diethylaminoethyl chloride with the sodio derivative of phenothiazine.

Chlorpromazine [Thorazine, 2-Chloro-10-(3-dimethylaminopropyl)-phenothi-azine] was synthesized originally as an antihistaminic agent and then found to have use in the prevention of motion sickness.   Once on clinical trial, chlorpro-mazine has been found to have unusual tranquillizing properties in various mental

[67] Deschiens, *Presse méd.*, **54,** 53 (1946); *C.A.*, **41,** 529 (1947).

[68] Deschiens and Lamy, *Compt. rend. soc. biol.*, **139,** 447 (1945); *C.A.*, **40,** 4434 (1946).

disorders. It is thought to be a useful tool in the management of certain schizo-phrenic states. Chlorpromazine is also being investigated in the induction of artificial hibernation in major surgical operations.[69]

Thionine Dyes

Methylene Blue, N.F. (Methylthionine Chloride), was prepared first by Caro (1876) by oxidizing dimethyl-*p*-phenylenediamine in the presence of hydro-gen sulfide. Later Bernthsen (1889) used sodium thiosulfate as a means of intro-ducing the sulfur, and this method is extensively used at the present time. Di-methyl-*p*-phenylenediamine in the presence of sodium thiosulfate forms the thiosulfonic acid of the base. The latter, when mixed with dimethylaniline and subjected to further oxidation, yields an indamine thiosulfonic acid which parts with sulfuric acid to form methylene blue upon boiling with dilute hydrochloric acid. Methylene blue is a dark green, crystalline solid, soluble in water 1:25 and

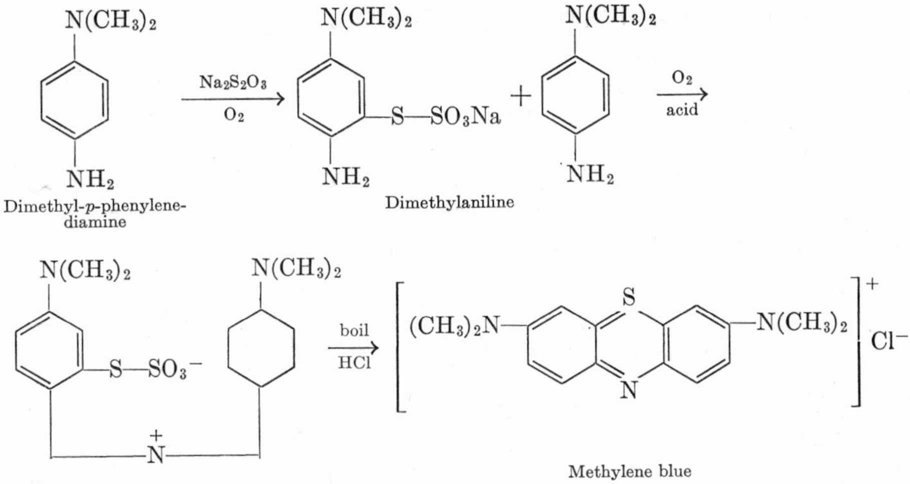

Dimethyl-*p*-phenylene-
diamine

Dimethylaniline

Methylene blue

in alcohol 1:70 with the formation of solutions having a deep blue color. The commercial dye which comes on the market as its zinc chloride double salt is not suitable for medicinal use.

After Ehrlich had studied the use of this dye in vital nerve staining, Ehrlich and Guttmann (1891) discovered that it has a specific action in malaria. Since then, numerous other workers have shown that, although methylene blue is less effective than the cinchona alkaloids, especially quinine, on the plasmodia, it has some value in tertian and quartan malaria. It is an analgesic of doubtful value, used to some extent in neuralgia, neuritis, and sciatica. It is a slow and weak antiseptic used externally in skin diseases and as a urinary antiseptic. It has also been used to test the functional activity of the kidney, but it has been re-placed largely by phenolsulfonphthalein.

[69] Dundee, Mesham, and Scott, *Anesthesia*, **9**, 296 (1954).

Tolonium Chloride (Blutene Chloride) is 3-amino-7-dimethylamino-2-methylphenazothionium chloride, a purified form of Toluidine Blue O. It is recommended as a coagulant for hemorrhagic conditions caused by an excess of heparin. Tolonium chloride is administered orally for the treatment of hypermenorrhea and menometrorrhagia (excessive menstruation). Toluidine Blue is also used as a diagnostic agent to detect corneal lesions.

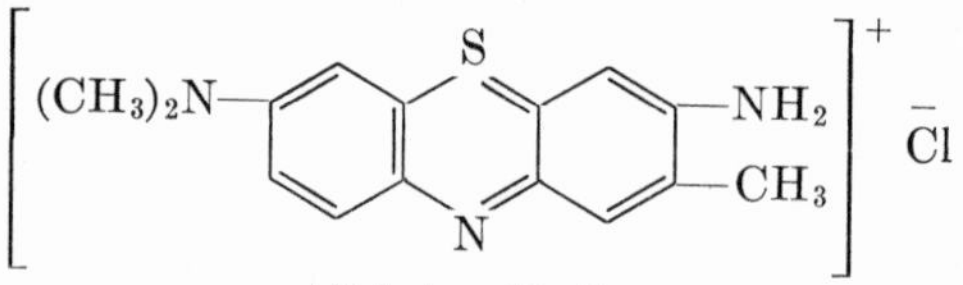

Tolonium chloride

Dolitrone (5-Ethyl-6-phenyl-*m*-thiazane-2,4-dione) has been introduced as an analgesic and central nervous depressant of considerable interest. Early trials have indicated that it may be valuable as an intravenous anesthetic but further work must establish its proper place in medicine. Its synthesis [70] is indicated.

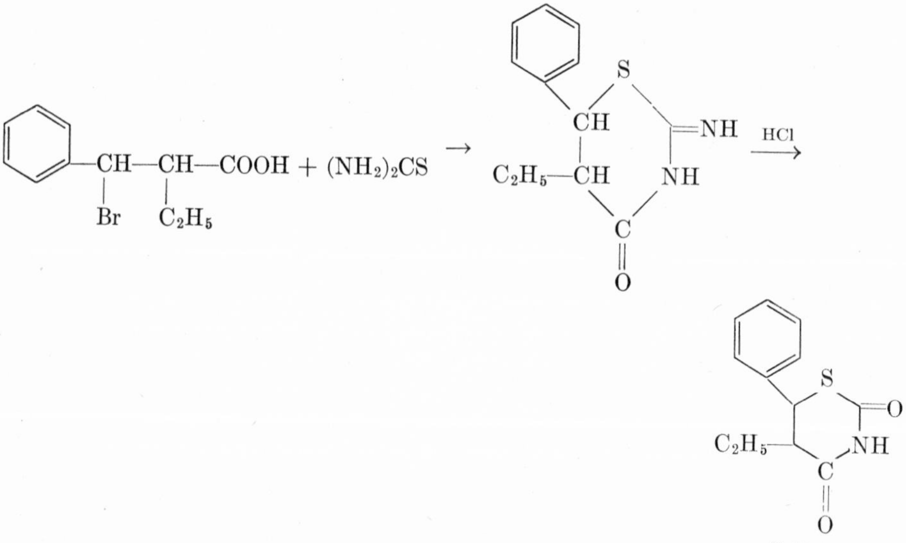

Dolitrone

THREE HETEROATOMS

Acetazoleamide, N.N.R. (Diamox, 2-Acetylamino-1,3,4-thiadiazole-5-sulfonamide), is useful as an oral diuretic in patients with congestive heart failure.[71] Its diuretic effect is brought about by an inhibition of carbonic anhydrase, altering the salt balance in body tissues and increasing the secretion of potassium ion accompanied by diuresis. Diamox is also considered of possible value in epi-

---

[70] Wheeler and Gash, U. S. pat. 2,585,064, 1952.

[71] Friedberg, Taymor, Minor, and Halpern, *New Eng. J. Med.*, **248**, 883 (1953); *C.A.*, **47**, 12612 (1953).

lepsy,[72, 73] since the function of carbonic anhydrase in hastening the removal of carbon dioxide may be interfered with. This may decelerate the return of nerve sensitivity.

Acetazoleamide   Triethylenemelamine   Pentylenetetrazole

Triethylene Melamine, N.N.R. [T.E.M., 2,4,6-*Tris*-(aziridine)-*s*-triazine], is an alkylating agent with properties similar to the nitrogen mustards (see methchlorethamine, page 192). It is suggested for the treatment of lymphomas and various forms of leukemia, being selected as the most promising of a large group of cytotoxic compounds with tumor inhibitory activity.[74]

Pentylenetetrazole, U.S.P. (Metrazole, Cardiazol), is an analeptic drug acting by way of central nervous stimulation. This action has several applications in medical practice. Metrazole is useful in shock therapy in several forms of mental aberrations, principally schizophrenia and depressive psychoses. It is used to combat the depressive effects of overdoses of barbiturates and is also a pharmacological tool in the screening of anticonvulsive drugs.

[72] Merlis, *Neurology*, 4, 863 (1954).
[73] Millichap et al., *J. Pharmacol. Exptl. Therap.*, **115**, 251 (1955).
[74] Rose, Hendry, and Walpole, *Nature*, **165**, 993 (1950).

CHAPTER

13

Stereoisomerism

In 1815, Biot observed that certain organic compounds, either as crystals or in solution, have the ability to rotate plane polarized light. The study of this phenomenon since then has served to shed considerable light on the kinetics and mechanisms of reactions, not only *in vitro* but also as they proceed *in vivo*. The effect of these substances on polarized light is but a manifestation of a more fundamental character of the compounds, namely a tridimensional arrangement of the atoms composing the molecule, which permits in may cases an asymmetry that gives rise to left-handed or to right-handed structures, related to each other as are the left hand to the right hand, or as is the image in a mirror to the original. Such isomerism in space is called stereoisomerism. Knowledge of such structures is important not only for theoretical reasons but for a better appreciation of the biochemical pathways of metabolism, for understanding the action of drugs, and for clarifying theories of biogenesis.

Molecular asymmetry may be observed in various types, e.g., in certain clathrate compounds, in biphenyl derivatives with restricted rotation, and in spiro- and allene-types of structures, but it is best known in molecules constructed from elements whose valence angles form a tetrahedron. Of these the compounds of carbon have received the preponderance of study and provide almost exclusively the substances that make stereoisomerism so important to the medicinal and biological chemist.

The tridimensional, tetrahedral, nature of the carbon atom, a concept proposed almost simultaneously in 1874 by Le Bel and van't Hoff, is conventionally written as shown. It is understood that C is the center of a regular tetrahedron

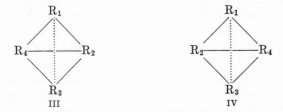

I   II

representing the carbon atom; the horizontal valences are considered as project-
ing forward from the plane of the paper, and the vertical valences project back
of the plane of the paper. Thus I and II are conventional projection formulas
for III and IV, respectively.[1] It will be observed that formulas III and IV, and

hence, also I and II, are mirror images of each other.[2] Since they are true mirror
images of each other they are spoken of more particularly as enantiomorphs.

Enantiomorphs, as isomers, are alike in most of their physical properties, such
as melting point, solubility in optically inactive solvents, crystalline habit
(except that in rare instances they may exhibit right-handed and left-handed
hemihedral facets), density, etc. They differ most in their effect on polarized
light, rotating in opposite directions, but under identical conditions of measurement, the magnitude of rotation is again equal.[3] In their chemical properties
they are also very similar, differing significantly chiefly when they react with
other stereoisomers, resulting in the formation of diastereoisomers, which are
discussed later.

[1] These conventions, as well as the rules of nomenclature of stereoisomeric compounds, enjoy
international acceptance. Adherence to them will minimize confusion and misunderstanding.
If one is not following these accepted practices, for which there may on occasion be excellent
justification, he is then obliged to explain adequately the system under consideration.

[2] It is recommended that stereoisomeric phenomena be studied with the aid of models; their
use will help considerably in clarifying the structures and reactions in three dimensions.

[3] Biot devised the formula now used to calculate specific rotation:

$$[\alpha] = \frac{\alpha}{ld}$$

or for solutions

$$[\alpha] = \frac{100\alpha}{lc}$$

$[\alpha]$ = specific rotation
α = observed angular rotation
l = length of liquid in decimeters
d = density
c = concentration in per cent

Factors Influencing Rotation. The observed rotation of plane polarized light is accounted for by the special properties of the absorption bands, and the direction of the rotation is a summation of the effects of the individual bands of the compound.[4] For example, two stereoisomers, such as illustrated in I and II, page 441, have identical groups and hence should show identical absorption; however, the summation of effects, although of equal magnitude, will be of opposite sign. This being true, any factor that influences the absorption of light will affect the experimentally observed values.

It was early observed that the rotatory power of a given substance varies approximately inversely with the square of the wavelength of the light employed; that is, the shorter the wavelength the greater the observed rotation. However, this is not always true, for, depending on the wavelength, some compounds not only show a decrease in rotation but may even show a reversal of sign. For example, *dextro*-camphor in hexane with 3200 A shows a maximum to the right, but measured at 2900 A shows almost as great levorotation. Other factors that have an effect on the observed rotation are temperature, character of the solvent, concentration, dissociation, association, etc. In order that the rotatory value may have meaning, all these factors must be specified. The spatial arrangement of the atoms within the molecule, however, is not affected.

Absolute Configuration

Knowledge of the *absolute* configuration of asymmetric molecules is still very meager and at best sketchy. From an interpretation of x-ray data from the measurements of the optical isomers of sodium rubidium tartrate,[5] and with the aid of quantum mechanics, it is concluded that Fischer was correct in his original assignment of relative configuration to D-glyceraldehyde.[6, 7, 8]

Relative Configuration

Early chemists, beginning with Fischer, unable to determine *absolute* configuration, resorted to the expediency of determining *relative* configuration, that is, establishing the stereostructure in terms of some arbitrarily selected reference compound. For this purpose the isomeric glyceraldehydes, the simplest sugars, aldotrioses, were chosen. For these, two conventional space models may be constructed, V and VI.

[4] Kühn, *Ber.*, **66,** 166 (1933).

[5] Bijvoet *et al.*, *Konikl. Ned. Akad. Wetenschap. Proc.*, **52,** 313 (1949); **B54,** 16 (1951).

[6] Waser, *J. Chem. Phys.*, **17,** 498 (1949).

[7] Klyne, *Progress in Stereochemistry*, Academic Press, New York, 1954, p. 178.

[8] Abernethy, *J. Chem. Educ.*, **33,** 88 (1956).

$$
\begin{array}{ccc}
\text{CHO} & \text{CHO} & \text{CHO} \quad 1 \\
| & | & | \\
\text{H}-\text{C}-\text{OH} & \text{HO}-\text{C}-\text{H} & \text{H}-\text{C}-\text{OH} \quad 2 \\
| & | & | \\
\text{CH}_2\text{OH} & \text{CH}_2\text{OH} & \text{HO}-\text{C}-\text{H} \quad 3 \\
& & | \\
& & \text{H}-\text{C}-\text{OH} \quad 4 \\
& & | \\
& & \text{H}-\text{C}-\text{OH} \quad 5 \\
& & | \\
& & \text{CH}_2\text{OH}
\end{array}
$$

V
D(+)-Glycer-
aldehyde

VI
L(−)-Glycer-
aldehyde

VII
D(+)-Glucose

Formula V has been arbitrarily assigned the tridimensional structure for the dextrorotating isomeride and given the name D(+)-glyceraldehyde, and VI then represents levorotating or L(−)-glyceraldehyde. This arbitrary assignment is based on carbon atom number 5 of natural glucose, for which Emil Fischer established structure VII.

Starting from the isomeric glyceraldehydes it now becomes possible to establish configurational relationships of many optically active compounds. All those configurationally related to dextrorotating glyceraldehyde are members of the D- series and, similarly, all related to the levoaldehyde belong to the L- series. For example, the aldehyde may be oxidized to carboxyl without affecting the asymmetric carbon atom, giving glyceric acids VIII and IX, respectively. The

$$
\begin{array}{cc}
\text{COOH} & \text{COOH} \\
| & | \\
\text{H}-\text{C}-\text{OH} & \text{HO}-\text{C}-\text{H} \\
| & | \\
\text{CH}_2\text{OH} & \text{CH}_2\text{OH}
\end{array}
$$

VIII
D(−)-Glyceric acid

IX
L(+)-Glyceric acid

actual specific rotation in aqueous solution of the acid from the D(+)-aldehyde, however, is counterclockwise, or to the left, 2°, that is −2°; yet because it is sterically similar to the standard aldehyde it is a member of the D- series. By the same token IX represents L-glyceric acid even though its aqueous solution rotates plane polarized light to the right. Thus it is seen that the prefixes D- and L- indicate configuration as related to the standard, whereas the symbols (+) and (−) show the direction in which the compound rotates plane polarized light.

These conventions are convenient in designating the configuration of hydroxy aldehydes and hydroxy ketones, i.e., carbohydrates and hydroxy acids. For amino acids it has been found advisable to have another reference, for which purpose serine has been selected. The tridimensional correlation between serine and lactic acid (and thus glyceric aldehyde) may be summarized in the accompanying equations.[9]

[9] Wolfram, Lemieux, and Olin, *J. Am. Chem. Soc.*, **71**, 2870 and 4057 (1949).

$$
\begin{array}{c}
\text{CHO} \\
| \\
\text{H—C—NHCOCH}_3 \\
| \\
\text{CH}_3\text{COO—C—H} \\
| \\
\text{H—C—OCOCH}_3 \\
| \\
\text{H—C—OCOCH}_3 \\
| \\
\text{CH}_2\text{OCOCH}_3
\end{array}
\qquad \xrightarrow{\;2\text{HSC}_2\text{H}_5\;}
$$

Pentaacetyl-D-glucoseamine

$$
\begin{array}{c}
\text{CH(SC}_2\text{H}_5)_2 \\
| \\
\text{H—C—NHCOCH}_3 \\
| \\
\text{CH}_3\text{COO—C—H} \\
| \\
\text{H—C—OCOCH}_3 \\
| \\
\text{H—C—OCOCH}_3 \\
| \\
\text{CH}_2\text{OCOCH}_3
\end{array}
\qquad \text{or} \qquad
\begin{array}{c}
\text{CH}_2\text{OCOCH}_3 \\
| \\
\text{CH}_3\text{COO—C—H} \\
| \\
\text{CH}_3\text{COO—C—H} \\
| \\
\text{H—C—OCOCH}_3 \\
| \\
\text{CH}_3\text{CONH—C—H} \\
| \\
\text{CH(SC}_2\text{H}_5)_2
\end{array}
\qquad \xrightarrow[\text{with Raney Ni}]{\text{desulfurization}}
$$

(Identical formulas for thioacetal)

$$
\begin{array}{c}
\text{CH}_2\text{OCOCH}_3 \\
| \\
\text{CH}_3\text{COO—C—H} \\
| \\
\text{CH}_3\text{COO—C—H} \\
| \\
\text{H—C—OCOCH}_3 \\
| \\
\text{CH}_3\text{CONH—C—H} \\
| \\
\text{CH}_3
\end{array}
\qquad \xrightarrow{\;\text{HOH}\;} \qquad
\begin{array}{c}
\text{CH}_2\text{OH} \\
| \\
\text{HO—C—H} \\
| \\
\text{HO—C—H} \\
| \\
\text{H—C—OH} \\
| \\
\text{CH}_3\text{CONH—C—H} \\
| \\
\text{CH}_3
\end{array}
\qquad \xrightarrow[\text{cleavage}]{\text{glycol}}
$$

Pentaacetyl-5-amino-5,6-didesoxy-L-gulitol   5-Acetamino-5,6-didesoxy-L-gulitol

$$
\begin{array}{c}
\text{COOH} \\
| \\
\text{CH}_3\text{CONH—C—H} \\
| \\
\text{CH}_3
\end{array}
\;\leftarrow\;
\begin{array}{c}
\text{COOH} \\
| \\
\text{NH}_2\text{—C—H} \\
| \\
\text{CH}_3
\end{array}
\;\leftarrow\;
\begin{array}{c}
\text{COOH} \\
| \\
\text{NH}_2\text{—C—H} \\
| \\
\text{CH}_2\text{OH}
\end{array}
$$

N-Acetyl-L-alanine   L(−)-Alanine (natural)   L(−)-Serine

The adoption of both glyceraldehyde and serine as references in assigning relative configuration opens the possibility for confusion, especially in naming hydroxy amino compounds. Considerable misunderstanding may be avoided, however, by adopting the designations D_s or D_g, the former indicating amino acid nomenclature and the latter carbohydrate nomenclature. Thus for (−)-ψ-ephedrine, page 451, the stereochemical name is given according to the carbohydrate convention; the amino acid designation would be L_s-(−)-threo-1-phenyl-2-methylamino-1-propanol.

The relative configuration of stereoisomeric compounds may be established by various methods. Chemical methods depend on conversion to the known glyceric aldehydes or the known serines, or to compounds which have already been established with respect to the references. Examples are: (+)-Tartaric acid may be converted into (+)-malic acid; this may be degraded to (+)-β-amino-α-hydroxypropionic acid; this, in turn, may be converted into D(−)-glyceric acid or into (−)-β-bromo-α-hydroxypropionic acid; the latter may be reduced to (−)-lactic acid. Since the relative configurations of D(−)-glyceric acid and D(+)-glyceraldehyde are reference standards, the configurations of the other compounds can be shown to be that of the D- series.

$$
\begin{array}{ccccc}
\text{CHO} & & \text{COOH} & & \text{COOH} \\
| & & | & & | \\
\text{H—C—OH} & \rightarrow & \text{H—C—OH} & \leftarrow & \text{H—C—OH} \\
| & & | & & | \\
\text{CH}_2\text{OH} & & \text{CH}_2\text{OH} & & \text{CH}_2\text{NH}_2
\end{array}
$$

D(+)-Glyceraldehyde   D(−)-Glyceric acid   D(+)

$$
\begin{array}{ccccccc}
\text{COOH} & & \text{COOH} & & \text{COOH} & & \text{COOH} \\
| & & | & & | & & | \\
\text{H—C—OH} & \rightarrow & \text{H—C—OH} & & \text{H—C—OH} & \rightarrow & \text{H—C—OH} \\
| & & | & & | & & | \\
\text{CHOHCOOH} & & \text{CH}_2\text{COOH} & & \text{CH}_2\text{Br} & & \text{CH}_3
\end{array}
$$

D(+)-Tartaric acid   D(+)-Malic acid   D(−)   D(−)-Lactic acid

The problem of determining relative configuration, difficult in itself, is complicated by the possibility of a shift in the groups when one group is replaced by another, such as replacing an amino by a hydroxyl group. For example, D-alanine may be converted into L-alanine through the reactions shown.

$$
\begin{array}{ccccc}
\text{COOH} & & \text{COOH} & & \text{COOH} \\
| & \xrightarrow{\text{NOBr}} & | & \rightarrow & | \\
\text{H—C—NH}_2 & & \text{Br—C—H} & & \text{NH}_2\text{—C—H} \\
| & & | & & | \\
\text{CH}_3 & & \text{CH}_3 & & \text{CH}_3
\end{array}
$$

D-Alanine   L-Bromopropionic acid   L-Alanine

The shift, from one series to another, is known as the Walden inversion. The Walden inversion, a reaction of considerable interest and importance, must always be considered as a possibility to be taken into account in instances where the bond to an asymmetric center is ruptured. A fuller understanding of such inversions may be employed for confirming and even establishing configurational relationships. For example, the following sequence of reactions confirms the correlation between hydroxy acids and amino acids.[10]

[10] Brewster et al., Nature, **166**, 178 (1950).

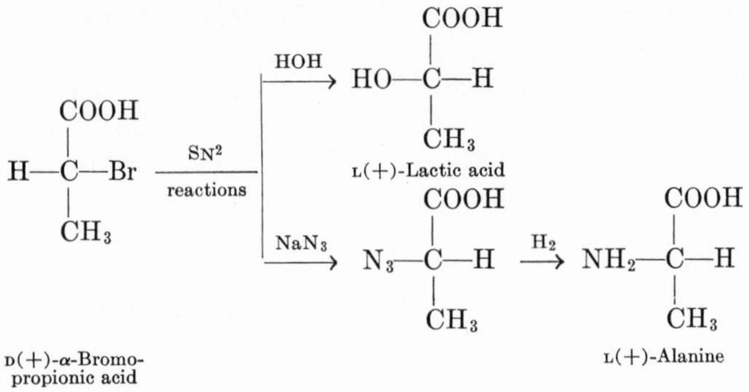

$$\text{H—C—Br} \xrightarrow[\text{reactions}]{\text{S}_N2}$$

COOH
|
H—C—Br
|
CH₃

D(+)-α-Bromo-
propionic acid

$\xrightarrow{\text{HOH}}$

COOH
|
HO—C—H
|
CH₃

L(+)-Lactic acid

$\xrightarrow{\text{NaN}_3}$

COOH
|
N₃—C—H
|
CH₃

$\xrightarrow{\text{H}_2}$

COOH
|
NH₂—C—H
|
CH₃

L(+)-Alanine

Optical rotation is no clue to relative configuration. This may be appreciated not only from what has been said but from many other facts. As an example, Levene and Rothen give an excellent summary of the effect of various substituents and of the relative point of attachment to an asymmetric carbon atom.[11] It is

TABLE XXVIII

ROTATION OF COMPOUNDS OF TYPE $CHR_1R_2R_3$

R_1	R_2	R_3	Maximum Rotation degrees
$-CH_3$	$-C_2H_5$	$-n\text{-}C_4H_9$	-11.4
$-CH_3$	$-n\text{-}C_3H_7$	$-n\text{-}C_4H_9$	-1.7
$-CH_3$	$-n\text{-}C_4H_9$	$-n\text{-}C_4H_9$	0
$-CH_3$	$-n\text{-}C_5H_{11}$	$-n\text{-}C_4H_9$	$+0.86$
$-C_2H_5$	$-OH$	$-CH_3$	-10.3
$-C_2H_5$	$-OH$	$-n\text{-}C_3H_7$	$+4.2$
$-C_2H_5$	$-OH$	$-n\text{-}C_4H_9$	$+9.4$
$-C_2H_5$	$-OH$	$-i\text{-}C_3H_7$	-16.7
$-n\text{-}C_3H_7$	$-OH$	$-i\text{-}C_3H_7$	-27.1
$-n\text{-}C_3H_7$	$-OH$	$-i\text{-}C_4H_9$	$+16.3$
$-C_2H_5$	$-OH$	$-C_6H_5$	-39.4
$-C_2H_5$	$-OH$	$-C_6H_{11}$ (cyclo)	-11.5
$-C_2H_5$	$-OH$	$-n\text{-}C_6H_{13}$	$+11.6$
$-CH_3$	$-COOH$	$-n\text{-}C_4H_9$	$+24.3$
$-CH_3$	$-CH_2COOH$	$-n\text{-}C_4H_9$	-6.1
$-CH_3$	$-CH_2CH_2COOH$	$-n\text{-}C_4H_9$	$+4.1$
$-CH_3$	$-CH_2CH_2CH_2COOH$	$-n\text{-}C_4H_9$	$+1.7$

found that in compounds of the structure indicated, all belonging to a single configurational series, the direction and magnitude of rotation changed as the size of one of the substituents was increased in a homologous manner. Part of their

[11] Levene and Rothen, *J. Org. Chem.*, **1**, 76 (1936).

results are summarized in Table XXVIII. This table is based on the assumed configuration, as shown.

$$
\begin{array}{c}
\text{H} \\
| \\
\text{R}_1\text{---C---R}_3 \\
| \\
\text{R}_2
\end{array}
$$

Physical Methods. To correlate further relative configurations, use has been made of certain regularities which have appeared; these have led to the formulation of certain rules which are of considerable assistance. The three most important rules may be briefly stated.[12]

Rule 1. Analogous compounds of similar configuration undergo like shift in rotation when similar substituents are introduced into the corresponding groups attached to the asymmetric molecule.

Rule 2. The rotatory effect of similarly constructed molecules of identical series varies in like manner on change in temperature, dilution, additions of neutral salts, etc.

Rule 3. If the rotation of an acid on conversion into its amide or phenylhydrazide is displaced toward the right, the acid belongs to the D- series. Conversely, if the displacement is toward the left, the acid belongs to the L- series.

These rules have proved very useful in correlating the amino acids with the corresponding hydroxy acids. Although it is simple to replace an amino group with a hydroxyl, it is difficult to know whether or not a Walden inversion occurs. By applying rule 1, however, evidence points to the fact that (+)-alanine has the same configuration as (+)-lactic acid. Hence, (+)-alanine, the one which occurs naturally, belongs to the L- series. The data on which this conclusion is based are given in Table XXIX.[13]

TABLE XXIX

DERIVATIVES OF (+)-ALANINE AND OF (+)-LACTIC ACID

Derivative	Molecular Rotation, degrees	
	(+)-Alanine	(+)-Lactic Acid
Amide of benzoyl derivative	−29	−36
Ethyl ester of benzoyl derivative	+ 3	+10.5
Methyl ester of benzoyl derivative	0	+ 7.5
Ethyl ester of hexahydrobenzoyl derivative	−19 (±4)	−15
Ethyl ester of acetyl derivative	−22	−25
Amide of toluenesulfonyl derivative	−26	−28 (±3)
Ethyl ester of toluenesulfonyl derivative	−26	−39

By applying a combination of the other rules, it has been possible to establish that all the natural amino acids, regardless of direction of rotation, belong to a

[12] Freudenberg, Brauns, and Siegel, *Ber.*, **56,** 193 (1923).
[13] Freudenberg and Rhino, *Ber.*, **57,** 1547 (1924).

single series. In the presence of strong acids and of strong alkalies, for example, the rotatory values of the amino acids vary markedly at that point where the zwitterion is converted into the alkali salt of the amino acid or into the substituted

TABLE XXX

THE EFFECT OF ACID AND OF ALKALI ON THE ROTATION OF
L(−)-ASPARAGINE AND OF L(+)-GLUTAMIC ACID

$M/10$ L-Asparagine with	$[\alpha]_D^{20}$	$M/10$ L-Glutamic Acid with	$[\alpha]_D^{18}$
0 eq. NaOH	− 5.3	0 eq. NaOH	+11.5
0.1 NaOH	− 5.3	0.33 NaOH	+ 5.7
0.5 NaOH	− 7.3	0.5 NaOH	+ 1.8
1 NaOH	− 9.3	1 NaOH	− 5.5
2 NaOH	− 9.3	2 NaOH	+10.4
4 NaOH	− 8.6	3 NaOH	+10.27
10 NaOH	− 7.3	10 NaOH	+10.96
30 NaOH	− 7.0	0.1 eq. HCl	+13.1
0.1 eq. HCl	− 2	1 HCl	+28.08
1 HCl	+20	2 HCl	+31.5
2 HCl	+25.3	3 HCl	+31.5
3 HCl	+27.3	10 HCl	+31.95
10 HCl	+28.3		
30 HCl	+30		

ammonium salt of the mineral acid. As a typical illustration, the experimental values with L(−)-asparagine and L(+)-glutamic acid are given in Table XXX. The same data are given graphically in Curve 1. It will be observed that in

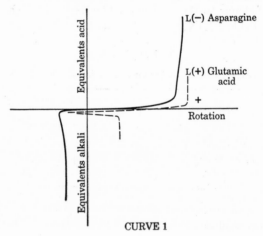

CURVE 1

general the curves are similar; that for L(+)-glutamic acid is shifted farther to the right. Analogous data from an acid of the D- series would give a similar curve but inverted, that is, as if the curve from the L- acids were being viewed in a mirror.[14]

[14] Lutz and Jirgensons, *Ber.*, **62**, 1916 (1929); **63**, 448 (1930).

By proceeding along the lines indicated and comparing the amino acids with each other it has been possible to establish that all of them are members of the L- series. Their general space formula then becomes that shown, in which R rep-

$$
\begin{array}{c}
\text{COOH} \\
| \\
\text{NH}_2-\text{C}-\text{H} \\
| \\
\text{R}
\end{array}
$$

Relative configuration of amino acids

resents the remainder of the molecule other than the carboxy and the α-carbon atom.

Racemic Modifications. If equal amounts of an enantiomorphic pair are present, it is obvious that no optical rotation will be possible. The rotatory effect of one isomeride in one direction will be neutralized by that of the other in the opposite direction. Such a system is called a racemic modification. In liquids, only one type of racemic modification is encountered, namely, a mixture of equal amounts of the two enantiomorphs. When the liquid solidifies, however, it may crystallize in one of three ways:

1. The enantiomorphs may unite to form a molecular compound with all crystals composed of equal amounts of each isomer. This is known as a racemic compound and its melting point is depressed by the addition of a small amount of either optically active component.

2. The enantiomorphs may form a mixture, the eutectic point requiring equal amounts of the two isomerides. This is known as a racemic mixture; its melting point rises when either isomer is added.

3. The enantiomorphs may be isomorphous and crystallize together as a solid solution without the formation of a solid compound.

The process of converting an optically active compound into its optically inactive modification, containing equal amounts of the optically active components, is called racemization. It involves the establishment of an equilibrium mixture between the stereoisomeric configurations and thereby effects external compensation. The mechanism by which racemization takes place is not always clear; but where tautomerism is possible it may be explained on the basis shown. Al-

$$
\begin{array}{ccccc}
\text{R}-\text{CO} & & \text{R}-\text{C}-\text{OH} & & \text{R}-\text{CO} \\
| & & || & & | \\
\text{R}_1-\text{C}-\text{H} & \leftrightarrows & \text{R}_1-\text{C} & \leftrightarrows & \text{H}-\text{C}-\text{R}_1 \\
| & & | & & | \\
\text{R}_2 & & \text{R}_2 & & \text{R}_2 \\
\text{X} & & \text{XI} & & \text{XII}
\end{array}
$$

though the enolic intermediate represented by XI may exist to only a very limited extent, it does enable equilibrium to be established, i.e., racemization, in a dynamic system.

Quasi-racemic compounds. Asymmetric compounds of similar structure, such as XIII and XIV, in which the groups x and y are similar or isosteric, when mixed in equimolar amounts may form an optically inactive racemic compound.[15] Thus (−)-thiol-

$$
\begin{array}{cccc}
\text{a} & \text{a} & \text{COOH} & \text{COOH} \\
| & | & | & | \\
\text{b---C---}x & y\text{---C---b} & \text{HS---C---H} & \text{H---C---CH}_3 \\
| & | & | & | \\
\text{c} & \text{c} & \text{CH}_2\text{COOH} & \text{CH}_2\text{COOH} \\
\text{XIII} & \text{XIV} & \text{XV} & \text{XVI}
\end{array}
$$

succinic acid, XV, and (+)-methylsuccinic acid, XVI, afford a quasi-racemic compound. This fact is interpreted as indicating that the two compounds are of opposite configuration.

Diastereoisomerism

It is possible on a purely theoretical basis for a compound to have more than one center of asymmetry. For a compound with two asymmetric carbon atoms, the accompanying general formulas come into consideration. XVII is the mirror

$$
\begin{array}{cccc}
\text{b} & \text{b} & \text{b} & \text{b} \\
| & | & | & | \\
\text{a---C---c} & \text{a---C---c} & \text{c---C---a} & \text{c---C---a} \\
| & | & | & | \\
\text{f---C---d} & \text{d---C---f} & \text{f---C---d} & \text{d---C---f} \\
| & | & | & | \\
\text{e} & \text{e} & \text{e} & \text{e} \\
\text{XVII} & \text{XVIII} & \text{XIX} & \text{XX}
\end{array}
$$

image of XX, and XVIII and XIX are likewise mirror images of each other; hence there are two pairs of enantiomorphs. The relationship of XVII, as of XX, to XVIII and XIX, though stereoisomeric, is not that of a full mirror image, and to distinguish it from enantiomorphous is called diastereoisomeric.

If it is assumed that in one of these, for example that represented by XVII, both carbon atoms rotate the plane of polarized light in the same direction, say to the right, then this configuration produces maximum dextrorotation. By the same token XX represents the configuration with the greatest levorotation, the magnitude for XVII and XX being equal.

If this argument is pursued further, then in the isomers represented by XVIII and XIX there is one center which produces levorotation and the other dextrorotation, but the experimentally observed value, both for magnitude and direction, will be determined by the algebraic summation of the two effects. Where the effect of the two is equal, the summation will be zero; such a compound is said to be internally compensated and is called a meso compound.

Diastereoisomers differ from each other in many respects. They may show different optical activities both as to magnitude and sometimes direction; they have different melting points, solubilities, densities, etc. Since they possess the same functional groups, it is to be expected that they will exhibit the same types of chemical reaction, but they may vary in their rates of reaction. In their

[15] Klyne, *Progress in Stereochemistry*, Academic Press, New York, 1954, Vol. I, p. 201.

physiological behavior, diastereoisomers frequently show considerable variation in quantitative responses and, as shown later, they may differ in their qualitative biological responses.

Nature abounds with examples of diastereoisomerism, the best known and most intensively studied being, perhaps, the simple sugars. Examples of such isomerism are given of the four aldotetroses, ephedrine, and tartaric acid.

1. Aldotetroses:

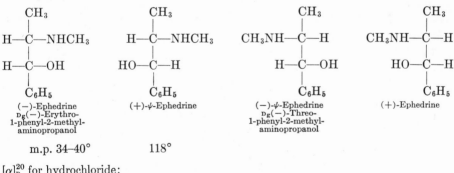

2. Tartaric acids:

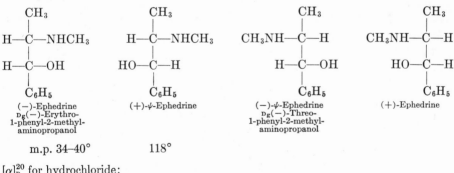

	L-Tartaric acid	meso-Tartaric acid	D-Tartaric acid
m.p.	170°	140°	170°
$[\alpha]_D^{20} =$	−15.06°	0	+15.06°

3. Ephedrines:

(−)-Ephedrine D_g(−)-Erythro-1-phenyl-2-methyl-aminopropanol   (+)-ψ-Ephedrine   (−)-ψ-Ephedrine D_g(−)-Threo-1-phenyl-2-methyl-aminopropanol   (+)-Ephedrine

m.p. 34–40°   118°

$[\alpha]_D^{20}$ for hydrochloride:

−35°   +62.5°   −62.5°   +35°

The relative configuration about the hydroxyl-bearing carbon atom was established by the synthesis of (−)-ephedrine from D(−)-mandelic acid and was placed in the D- series.[16]

The relative configuration about the methylamino-bearing carbon atom was established by the synthesis of some of the ephedrine isomers from optically active alanine.[17]

[16] Freudenberg, Schoeffel, and Braun, *J. Am. Chem. Soc.*, **54**, 234 (1932).

[17] Freudenberg and Nikolai, *Ann.*, **510**, 223 (1934).

The racemization of (−)-ephedrine results in the formation of an equilibrium mixture with the diastereoisomeric (+)-ψ-ephedrine; that is, there is an "Umklappen" (a shift around) of the hydroxyl group.

The conformation of the ephedrine isomers, that is, their actual shape in space (keeping in mind the relative configuration of the respective asymmetric centers) as established by ease of acyl migration,[18] by conversion into oxazoline,[19, 20] and reaction with urea,[21] is considered to be such that the CH_3— and the C_6H_5— groups are *transoid* in all isomers. Thus for (−)-ephedrine and for (+)-ψ-ephedrine the projection formulas become (it should be noted that the tetrahedron representing the phenyl-bearing carbon atom is not written in the conventionally accepted manner) as shown. It will be observed that this conformation makes the

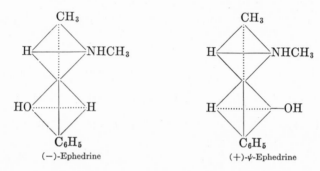

(−)-Ephedrine (+)-ψ-Ephedrine

distance between the polar hydroxyl and methylamino groups considerably greater in the ephedrine isomers than in the ψ-ephedrines, a factor which may contribute significantly to the difference in their biological properties.

The introduction of further centers of asymmetry increases the number of possible diastereoisomers. For example, with three asymmetric carbon atoms the accompanying possibilities appear.

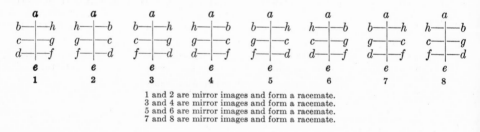

1 and 2 are mirror images and form a racemate.
3 and 4 are mirror images and form a racemate.
5 and 6 are mirror images and form a racemate.
7 and 8 are mirror images and form a racemate.

With 4 asymmetric carbon atoms in a molecule, 16 optically active isomers and 8 racemic mixtures are possible. As the number of asymmetric centers in the molecule increases, the number of optically active isomers possible is 2^n where n

[18] Welsh, *J. Am. Chem. Soc.*, **69**, 128 (1947); **71**, 3500 (1949).
[19] Fodor *et al.*, *J. Org. Chem.*, **14**, 337 (1949).
[20] Fodor and Koczka, *J. Chem. Soc.*, **1952**, 850.
[21] Close, *J. Org. Chem.*, **15**, 1131 (1950).

is the number of asymmetric carbon atoms. The number of racemic modifications is half that number. The aldoses are an excellent illustration of these considerations, as shown in Table XXXI.

TABLE XXXI

STRUCTURAL RELATIONSHIPS OF THE D-ALDOSES

```
                              CHO
                               |
                          H—C—OH
                               |
                             CH₂OH
                       D-Glyceric aldehyde
```

$[\alpha]_D^{20} = -21.5°$

```
        CHO                                              CHO
         |                                                |
    H—C—OH                                          HO—C—H
         |                                                |
    H—C—OH                                          H—C—OH
         |                                                |
       CH₂OH                                            CH₂OH
   D-Erythrose (syrup)                                D-Threose
```

```
    CHO            CHO              CHO             CHO
     |              |                |               |
H—C—OH         HO—C—H          HO—C—H          H—C—OH
     |              |                |               |
H—C—OH         H—C—OH          HO—C—H          HO—C—H
     |              |                |               |
H—C—OH         H—C—OH          H—C—OH          H—C—OH
     |              |                |               |
   CH₂OH          CH₂OH            CH₂OH           CH₂OH
 D-Ribose       D-Arabinose      D-Lyxose        D-Xylose
```

	D-Ribose	D-Arabinose	D-Lyxose	D-Xylose
$[\alpha]_D^{20} =$	−19.5°	−105.1°	−13.9°	+18.6°
m.p. =	86-7°	158.5°	99°	141.5°

```
  CHO      CHO    CHO     CHO     CHO      CHO    CHO      CHO
   |        |      |       |       |        |      |        |
H—C—OH  HO—C—H  HO—C—H  H—C—OH  H—C—OH  HO—C—H  H—C—OH  HO—C—H
   |        |      |       |       |        |      |        |
H—C—OH  H—C—OH  HO—C—H  HO—C—H  HO—C—H  HO—C—H  H—C—OH  H—C—OH
   |        |      |       |       |        |      |        |
H—C—OH  H—C—OH  H—C—OH  H—C—OH  HO—C—H  HO—C—H  HO—C—H  HO—C—H
   |        |      |       |       |        |      |        |
H—C—OH  H—C—OH  H—C—OH  H—C—OH  H—C—OH  H—C—OH  H—C—OH  H—C—OH
   |        |      |       |       |        |      |        |
 CH₂OH   CH₂OH  CH₂OH   CH₂OH   CH₂OH    CH₂OH  CH₂OH    CH₂OH
D-Allose D-Altrose D-Mannose D-Glucose D-Galactose D-Talose D-Gulose D-Idose
                                                  (syrup)  (syrup)  (syrup)
```

	D-Allose	D-Altrose	D-Mannose	D-Glucose	D-Galactose	D-Talose	D-Gulose	D-Idose
m.p.			132	146	165.5			
$[\alpha]_D^{20} =$			14.25	52.3	82	13.95	−20.4	−7.5

Specific Rotations of Equilibrium between α- and β- Isomer

In Table XXXI the indicated structures for the aldohexoses are those assigned according to the classical work of Emil Fischer. It should not be forgotten that these compounds may assume an inner, cyclic hemiacetal structure (page 105) with the formation of an additional asymmetric carbon atom, giving rise to the α- and β- sugars, especially in solution.

Using glucose as a typical example, the equilibrium between α- and β- sugars by virtue of internal hemiacetal formation, which is mutarotation, may be illustrated by the equation shown. The assignment of configuration to the hemi-

$$
\begin{array}{ccc}
\begin{array}{c}
\text{H—C—OH} \\
\text{H—C—OH} \\
\text{HO—C—H} \\
\text{H—C—OH} \\
\text{H—C} \\
\text{CH}_2\text{OH}
\end{array}
&
\rightleftharpoons
\begin{array}{c}
\text{CHO} \\
\text{H—C—OH} \\
\text{HO—C—H} \\
\text{H—C—OH} \\
\text{H—C—OH} \\
\text{CH}_2\text{OH}
\end{array}
\rightleftharpoons
&
\begin{array}{c}
\text{OH} \\
\text{H—C} \\
\text{H—C—OH} \\
\text{HO—C—H} \\
\text{H—C—OH} \\
\text{H—C} \\
\text{CH}_2\text{OH}
\end{array}
\\
\text{α-D-Glucose} & \text{D-Glucose} & \text{β-D-Glucose} \\
[\alpha] + 19.8° & & [\alpha] + 106°
\end{array}
$$

Equilibrium $[\alpha] + 53°$

acetal carbon atom is based, for example, on the knowledge that, with a cyclic 1,2-glycol, boric acid forms internal esters, resulting in increased conductivity, when the hydroxyl groups are *cis*.

It may be well to repeat at this point that structures in which the hemiacetal hydroxyl of sugars is converted into an ether, that is into —OR, are known as glycosides. Glycosides exist as α- and β- isomers. The enzymes for hydrolyzing glycosides are stereospecific; α-glycosidases react with α-glycosides and emulsin with β-glycosides.

The rotatory values given for the various aldoses in Table XXXI are for the equilibrium in solution of the α- and β- forms.

The spatial relationships indicated in Table XXXI find confirmation in the following observed facts.[22]

1. The configuration for D-glyceraldehyde is arbitrarily assigned as already indicated.

2. From D-glyceric aldehyde, L-tartaric acid may be synthesized:

$$
\begin{array}{ccccc}
\begin{array}{c}
\text{CHO} \\
\text{H—C—OH} \\
\text{CH}_2\text{OH}
\end{array}
& \rightarrow &
\begin{array}{c}
\text{CN} \\
\text{HO—C—H} \\
\text{H—C—OH} \\
\text{CH}_2\text{OH}
\end{array}
& \rightarrow &
\begin{array}{c}
\text{COOH} \\
\text{HO—C—H} \\
\text{H—C—OH} \\
\text{COOH}
\end{array}
\\
\text{D-Glyceraldehyde} & & & & \text{L-Tartaric acid}
\end{array}
$$

[22] For a concise, lucid, and enlightening history of the determination of configuration in the sugar series see Hudson, *J. Chem. Educ.*, **18**, 353 (1941).

3. D-Threose may be reduced to L-erythritol:

$$
\begin{array}{ccccc}
\text{CHO} & & \text{CH}_2\text{OH} & & \text{COOH} \\
| & & | & & | \\
\text{HO}-\text{C}-\text{H} & & \text{HO}-\text{C}-\text{H} & & \text{HO}-\text{C}-\text{H} \\
| & & | & & | \\
\text{H}-\text{C}-\text{OH} & \rightarrow & \text{H}-\text{C}-\text{OH} & \rightarrow & \text{H}-\text{C}-\text{OH} \\
| & & | & & | \\
\text{CH}_2\text{OH} & & \text{CH}_2\text{OH} & & \text{COOH} \\
\text{D-Threose} & & \text{L-Erythritol} & & \text{L-Tartaric acid}
\end{array}
$$

If in the tetrahydroxybutane, the two asymmetric carbon atoms do not rotate in the same direction, the molecule must be internally compensated, the meso form. Since L-erythritol may be oxidized to L-tartaric acid it is not meso.

4. The proof for the configurations of D- and L-erythrose depends on the degradation products of arabinose. These are given under item 11.

5. Aldopentoses, with three asymmetric carbon atoms, may exist in eight stereoisomeric configurations. Four belong to the D- series: D-ribose, D-arabinose, D-xylose, and D-lyxose.

6. D-Xylose may be degraded to D-threose; this establishes the relative configuration of two carbon atoms. D-Xylose may also be oxidized to a trihydroxyglutaric acid which is optically inactive, nonresolvable, and internally compensated. These facts can be reconciled with only one configuration:

$$
\begin{array}{ccccc}
\text{COOH} & & \text{CHO} & & \\
| & & | & & \text{CHO} \\
\text{H}-\text{C}-\text{OH} & & \text{H}-\text{C}-\text{OH} & & | \\
| & & | & & \text{H}-\text{C}-\text{OH} \\
\text{HO}-\text{C}-\text{H} & \leftarrow & \text{HO}-\text{C}-\text{H} & \rightarrow & \text{HO}-\text{C}-\text{H} \\
| & & | & & | \\
\text{H}-\text{C}-\text{OH} & & \text{H}-\text{C}-\text{OH} & & \text{H}-\text{C}-\text{OH} \\
| & & | & & | \\
\text{COOH} & & \text{CH}_2\text{OH} & & \text{CH}_2\text{OH} \\
\text{meso-Trihydroxyglutaric acid} & & \text{D-Xylose} & & \text{D-Threose} \\
\text{(optically inactive)} & & &
\end{array}
$$

The degradation of a sugar is effected as follows: The aldose oxime is heated with acetic anhydride, which acetylates the hydroxyl groups and converts the oxime into a nitrile; treatment with ammoniacal silver solutions removes the acetyl groups as acetamide and the nitrile group as ammonium cyanide, leaving a sugar with one less carbon atom.

7. D-Xylose and D-lyxose form the same osazone; hence, these two sugars are epimeric, i.e., they differ only in the configuration about the carbon atom alpha to the aldehyde group.

$$
\begin{array}{ccccc}
\text{CHO} & & \text{H}-\text{C}=\text{N}-\text{NHC}_6\text{H}_5 & & \text{CHO} \\
| & & | & & | \\
\text{HO}-\text{C}-\text{H} & & \text{C}=\text{N}-\text{NHC}_6\text{H}_5 & & \text{H}-\text{C}-\text{OH} \\
| & & | & & | \\
\text{HO}-\text{C}-\text{H} & \rightarrow & \text{HO}-\text{C}-\text{H} & \rightarrow & \text{HO}-\text{C}-\text{H} \\
| & & | & & | \\
\text{H}-\text{C}-\text{OH} & & \text{H}-\text{C}-\text{OH} & & \text{H}-\text{C}-\text{OH} \\
| & & | & & | \\
\text{CH}_2\text{OH} & & \text{CH}_2\text{OH} & & \text{CH}_2\text{OH} \\
\text{D-Lyxose} & & \text{Osazone} & & \text{D-Xylose}
\end{array}
$$

8. D-Lyxose on reduction forms D-arabitol, a pentahydroxypentane also obtained by the reduction of D-arabinose. In D-arabinose and D-lyxose, however, the —CH_2OH and the —CHO groups must be reversed.

```
      CHO              CH2OH             CHO
       |                |                 |
  HO—C—H           HO—C—H           HO—C—H
       |                |                 |
  HO—C—H   →       HO—C—H   ←       H—C—OH
       |                |                 |
  H—C—OH            H—C—OH            H—C—OH
       |                |                 |
     CH2OH            CH2OH             CH2OH
   D-Lyxose         D-Arabitol        D-Arabinose
```

9. L-Arabinose and L-ribose form identical osazones; D-ribose and D-arabinose also form the same osazone and are epimers.

```
      CHO            CH=N—NHC6H5           CHO
       |                |                   |
  HO—C—H            C=N—NHC6H5          H—C—OH
       |                |                   |
  H—C—OH   →        H—C—OH      ←      H—C—OH
       |                |                   |
  H—C—OH            H—C—OH              H—C—OH
       |                |                   |
     CH2OH            CH2OH               CH2OH
   D-Arabinose        Osazone           D-Ribose
```

10. Both D- and L-ribose on reduction form adonitol, optically inactive and nonresolvable; on oxidation they form the internally compensated ribotrihydroxyglutaric acid.

11. L-Arabinose may be degraded to L-erythrose; this establishes the configuration of these aldotetroses, since D-erythrose is the mirror image of the L-isomer.

```
    CHO            CHO
     |              |
 HO—C—H         H—C—OH            CHO            CHO
     |              |              |              |
 H—C—OH         HO—C—H        HO—C—H         H—C—OH
     |              |              |              |
 H—C—OH         HO—C—H        HO—C—H         H—C—OH
     |              |              |              |
   CH2OH          CH2OH          CH2OH          CH2OH
 D-Arabinose    L-Arabinose    L-Erythrose    D-Erythrose
```

12. In the aldohexoses, with 4 asymmetric carbon atoms, 16 stereoisomers are possible. The names and configurations of the D- series are given in Table XXXI; the L- series is also completely known.

13. D-Mannose and D-glucose may be degraded to D-arabinose. They also form the same osazone. Hence, D-glucose and D-mannose are epimeric.

14. L-Gulose and L-idose form identical osazones; therefore, they are epimeric. In like manner D-gulose and D-idose are epimeric.

15. The same dibasic tetrahydroxyadipic acid (D-saccharic acid) may be obtained from L-gulose and D-glucose. This indicates that in these two sugars, the positions of the terminal —CHO and —CH₂OH groups are reversed with respect to each other.

```
        CHO                                        CHO
         |                                          |
   HO—C—H                   CHO              H—C—OH
         |                    |                      |
   HO—C—H              HO—C—H             HO—C—H
         |                    |                      |
    H—C—OH             H—C—OH             H—C—OH
         |                    |                      |
    H—C—OH             H—C—OH             H—C—OH
         |                    |                      |
       CH₂OH              CH₂OH               CH₂OH
      D-Mannose          D-Arabinose          D-Glucose


        COOH                 CHO                CH₂OH
         |                    |                    |
    H—C—OH             HO—C—H             H—C—OH
         |                    |                    |
   HO—C—H              HO—C—H    or    HO—C—H
         |                    |                    |
    H—C—OH             H—C—OH             H—C—OH
         |                    |                    |
    H—C—OH             HO—C—H             H—C—OH
         |                    |                    |
        COOH               CH₂OH                CHO
     D-Saccharic         _____/
        acid                        L-Gulose
```

If the terminal groups in the structure of D-mannose were reversed, the configuration of the molecule as a whole would be unchanged.

16. It follows, then, that the structures for D-gulose and D-idose are as indicated in Table XXXI.

17. D-Galactose may be degraded to D-lyxose. On oxidation D-galactose forms mucic acid, a tetrahydroxyadipic acid, optically inactive and nonresolvable. Epimeric with D-galactose is D-talose, which may be oxidized to talomucic acid, an optically active tetrahydroxyadipic acid. These observations are explained on the basis of the assigned formulas.

```
    COOH            CHO                               CHO            COOH
     |               |                                 |               |
 H—C—OH          H—C—OH          CHO            HO—C—H          HO—C—H
     |               |             |                   |               |
HO—C—H          HO—C—H          HO—C—H          HO—C—H          HO—C—H
     |               |             |                   |               |
HO—C—H          HO—C—H          HO—C—H          HO—C—H          HO—C—H
     |               |             |                   |               |
 H—C—OH          H—C—OH          H—C—OH          H—C—OH          H—C—OH
     |               |             |                   |               |
    COOH           CH₂OH          CH₂OH            CH₂OH            COOH
  Mucic acid     D-Galactose      D-Lyxose         D-Talose      Talomucic acid
```

18. D-Allose and D-altrose are epimers. They may be built up from D-ribose by means of the cyanohydrin synthesis. D-Altrose forms the same tetrahydroxyadipic acid as that obtained from D-talose; hence, in D-altrose the four asymmetric centers have the same configuration as in D-talose, but the positions of the —CHO and —COOH groups are reversed. These relationships appear structurally as follows:

$$
\begin{array}{cccc}
\text{CHO} & & \text{CHO} & \text{COOH} \\
| & & | & | \\
\text{H—C—OH} & \text{CHO} & \text{HO—C—H} & \text{HO—C—H} \\
| & | & | & | \\
\text{H—C—OH} & \text{H—C—OH} & \text{H—C—OH} & \text{H—C—OH} \\
| & | & | & | \\
\text{H—C—OH} \leftarrow & \text{H—C—OH} \rightarrow & \text{H—C—OH} \rightarrow & \text{H—C—OH} \\
| & | & | & | \\
\text{H—C—OH} & \text{H—C—OH} & \text{H—C—OH} & \text{H—C—OH} \\
| & | & | & | \\
\text{CH}_2\text{OH} & \text{CH}_2\text{OH} & \text{CH}_2\text{OH} & \text{COOH} \\
\text{D-Allose} & \text{D-Ribose} & \text{D-Altrose} & \text{D-Talomucic acid}
\end{array}
$$

Physical and Chemical Differences between Diastereoisomers

Diastereoisomers, although composed of identical structural elements, are different chemical compounds. It is only natural therefore to expect variations in physiological responses, both qualitatively and quantitatively.

Evidence will be given showing the differences in physical and chemical properties of diastereoisomers. No proof is available yet to indicate how these properties may affect physiological activity and, consequently, the following information may at first glance appear heterogeneous and unrelated; it is given primarily to emphasize the fact that diastereoisomers are not identical compounds. Since structural isomers may show wide variations in biological behavior, it need not come as a total surprise to find analogous differences in space isomers.

Light Absorption. One would assume, *a priori*, that in diastereoisomers of the type formulas shown that the rotatory effect of the upper carbon atom in the two models would be identical in magnitude and of the same sign, and that the

$$
\begin{array}{cc}
b & b \\
| & | \\
a\text{—C—}d & a\text{—C—}d \\
| & | \\
g\text{—C—}e & e\text{—C—}g \\
| & | \\
f & f
\end{array}
$$

effect of the two lower carbon atoms would be of the same magnitude but of opposite sign. If this were true, then it should be possible to select groups of diastereoisomers for which the summation of rotatory effect should be zero. For example, with four asymmetric carbon atoms the system might be considered as shown. This system is found in the four hexonic acids shown. The summation

$$
\begin{array}{cccc}
+a & +a & -a & -a \\
-b & +b & +b & -b \\
+c & -c & +c & -c \\
+d & -d & -d & +d
\end{array}
$$

COOH	COOH	COOH	COOH
H—C—OH	H—C—OH	HO—C—H	HO—C—H
HO—C—H	H—C—OH	H—C—OH	HO—C—H
H—C—OH	HO—C—H	H—C—OH	HO—C—H
H—C—OH	HO—C—H	HO—C—H	H—C—OH
CH₂OH	CH₂OH	CH₂OH	CH₂OH

D-Gluconic acid	L-Mannonic acid	L-Galactonic acid	D-Talonic acid
$[\alpha]M/100\ -13°$	$+1°$	$+24°$	$+33°$

of rotation is $+45°$ and not $0°$ as might be expected. Hence, the assumption indicated is not valid. Instead, it appears that the configuration about one asymmetric carbon atom may be influenced by the asymmetry of a neighboring carbon atom. In agreement with this is the observed difference in the absorption bands between the active and the mesotartaric acids.[23, 24]

Adsorption. An optically active adsorbent may select preferentially one isomer from a racemic mixture; or an optically inactive adsorbent may show greater activity toward one diastereoisomer than toward another.

Wool will adsorb preferentially one isomer from a racemic mixture of dyes.[25] Wool and casein selectively adsorb (+)-mandelic acid and (+)-naphthylglycolic acid from racemic solutions.[26] From solutions of the same concentration aluminum hydroxide will adsorb approximately 50 per cent more of racemic tartaric acid than of the meso acid.[27]

Solubilities. So many examples of the differences in solubilities of diastereoisomers are known that it is impossible to call attention to all of them. One need only mention that this variation is most frequently employed in the resolution of racemic substances. For example, $(+)A(-)A$ may be a racemic modification; on reaction with $(+)B$, two diastereoisomers are formed:

$$(+)A(-)A + 2(+)B \rightarrow (+)A(+)B + (-)A(+)B$$

of which one is, as a general rule, more soluble in a given solvent than the other, thus allowing them to be separated by fractional crystallization or fractional

[23] For a more complete discussion of these phenomena see Kühn, Freudenberg, and Wolf, *Ber.*, **63**, 2367 (1930).

[24] For further evidence in cyclic compounds with three asymmetric carbon atoms see Read, *Trans. Faraday Soc.*, **26**, 441 (1930).

[25] Porter and Ihrig, *J. Am. Chem. Soc.*, **45**, 1990 (1923).

[26] Bradley and Easty, *J. Chem. Soc.*, **1951**, 499; **1953**, 1519.

[27] Dumanski and Jakolew, *Kolloid-Z.*, **48**, 155 (1929).

solution.   Pure (−)A and (+)A may then be recovered from these two fractions.[28]

Salts of the four isomeric ephedrines with optically active acids form an interesting series.   With (−)-mandelic acid, for example, the solubility of the salts increases in the following order:

(−)-ephedrine (−)-mandelate
(+)-ephedrine (−)-mandelate
(+)-pseudo-ephedrine (−)-mandelate
(−)-pseudo-ephedrine (−)-mandelate

The physiological activities of the ephedrine isomers, when measured by the rise produced in blood pressure, decreases in the same order.   Whether there is a mathematical parallelism between the two phenomena has not been established.

Crystalline Structure of Solids.   The first example is the mirror-image relationship of the sodium ammonium tartrates, studied by Pasteur, which marks the beginning of the scientific study of the optical activity of organic molecules. Another example, also reported by Pasteur,[29] is the tartaramide-malamide complexes.   (+)-Tartaramide combines rapidly with (−)-malamide, 1:1, to form large, transparent crystals, $[\alpha] = +43.02°$, soluble 18:100 in water.   (−)-Tartaramide-(−)-malamide, also 1:1, forms small, silky needles, $[\alpha] = -134.15°$, soluble more than 33:100 in water.   *Trans*-1,4-diacetoxycyclohexane forms fragile needles; the *cis*-isomer forms massive prisms.[30]

Density.   (−)-Benzedrine (−)-mandelate has specific gravity 1.27.   (−)-Benzedrine (+)-mandelate has specific gravity 1.19.[31]   *Cis-trans* isomers of decahydronaphthalene (page 475) also have different densities.

Dielectric Constants.   Winstein and Wood[32] have employed dielectric values to distinguish between pairs of *meso* and racemic isomers and between the racemic *erythro* and *threo* pairs of diastereoisomers.   They report the following values.

Substance	Isomer	ϵ at 25°
2,3-diacetoxybutane	*meso-*	6.644
	DL-	5.10
2,3-dibromobutane	*meso-*	6.245
	DL-	5.758
2-acetoxy-3-bromobutane	DL-*erythro-*	7.268
	DL-*threo-*	7.414

Electrical Properties.   The butylsulfonates of (−)- and (+)-phenylalanine at 0.02 molar concentration in 95 per cent acetone develop a glass electrode potential of +100 mv.; the salt of racemic phenylalanine, under identical conditions, develops a potential of less than +85 mv.[33]

[28] For a complete table on this method of resolution see Freudenberg, *Stereochemie*, p. 569 *et seq.*

[29] Pasteur, *Ann. chim. phys.*, (3) **38**, 465 (1853) through Freudenberg, p. 556.

[30] Perrine and White, *J. Am. Chem. Soc.*, **69**, 1542 (1947).

[31] Jarowski and Hartung, *J. Org. Chem.*, **8**, 564 (1943).

[32] Winstein and Wood, *J. Am. Chem. Soc.*, **62**, 548 (1940).

[33] Rask and Eckles, *Am. J. Hygiene*, **33**, 86 (1941).

Energy Content. Physical chemists and physicists apparently have not investigated the energy of formation, fugacities, entropies, etc., of diastereoisomers in which the asymmetric carbon atoms are in the open chain of the molecules. However, in the *cis-trans* isomers of cyclic compounds, as pointed out on page 471, different physical values of this nature have been observed. It should not prove unexpected to find differences also in diastereoisomers of the type discussed.

Vapor Pressures. Volatile diastereoisomers may exhibit differences in vapor pressures. Racemic acids have been resolved by the fractional distillation of esters formed with optically active alcohols; racemic alcohols, esterified with optically active acids, likewise have been resolved.

The (−)-menthyl esters of DL-2-methylbutanoic acid and of DL-2-methoxy-propanoic acid were vaporized through a 60-plate column. The esters of the dextrorotatory acids came over first. Accurate boiling-point determinations are still to be made, but it is estimated that the ester of the (+) acid boils at least 3° lower than the ester of the (−) acid. DL-Butanol-2 was partially resolved by fractionating the ester formed with active 2-acetoxypropanoic acid.[34, 35]

Solubilities in Optically Active Solvent. On shaking together (−)-carvone, water and DL-mandelic acid, the aqueous layer became dextrorotatory because of the unequal distribution of the (+)- and (−)-acids between the water and the optically active organic solvent.[36]

Rates of Reaction. One of the components of a racemic mixture may react with an optically active compound at a faster rate than its isomer. In a mixture of diastereoisomers one of them may react more rapidly than the other with an optically inactive compound. Or one component of a racemic mixture may react more rapidly than its isomeride with an optically inactive compound in the presence of an optically active catalyst.

Camphorcarboxylic acid in non-ionizing solvents undergoes decarboxylation. The addition of organic bases enhances the reaction. With symmetrical bases the velocity constants for decarboxylation are identical for the two enantiomorphous acids. With asymmetrical bases the velocity constants differ; those bases configurationally related to the L-amino acids, e.g., the esters of L-alanine, L-proline, etc., (−)-nicotine, for which the configurational relationship to the L-amino acids has been established,[37] all catalyze more rapidly the decarboxylation of (+)-camphorcarboxylic acid than that of the (−)-acid.[38]

During the esterification of DL-mandelic acid with (−)-menthol the dextrorotatory component of the acid reacts more rapidly; the esterification rate for the (−)-acid is 0.897 that for the (+) acid.

A mixture of (+)-neoisomenthol and (+)-neomenthol was separated into its component fractions by means of partial esterification with 3,5-dinitrobenzoyl chloride. (+)-Neoisomenthol reacted at a more rapid rate and could be separated as its ester.[39]

[34] Bailey and Hass, *J. Am. Chem. Soc.*, **63**, 1969 (1941).
[35] Hass, U. S. pat. 2,389,099; *C.A.*, **40**, 1539 (1946).
[36] Schröer, *Ber.*, **65**, 966 (1932).
[37] Hudson and Neuberger, *J. Org. Chem.*, **15**, 24 (1950).
[38] Pratesi, Arpesell, and La Manna, *J. Am. Chem. Soc.*, **75**, 5476 (1953).
[39] Hückel and Niggemeyer, *Ber.*, **72**, 1354 (1939).

Secondary alcohols, particularly in the phenylmethylcarbinol series, react with acid anhydrides or chlorides with what seems to be stereospecificity in the presence of brucine or strychnine.[40]

Reactions with Enzymes. Enzymes, it will be recalled, are organic biochemical catalysts. As the chemical structures of enzymes become more understood it becomes more certain that they are constructed from asymmetric components. Hence, enzymatic effects are special cases of kinetics and stereospecificity of reaction.

The first indication that enzymes distinguish between optical isomers was observed by Pasteur when he allowed a solution of racemic ammonium tartrate to ferment. The solution at first became levorotatory; when this had reached a maximum no (+)-acid was present; then rotation slowly decreased. The ferment reacted more rapidly with the (+)-acid, leaving the solution to rotate counterclockwise; the slow recession from maximum levorotation indicated a slower reaction with the (−)-acid.

Equally classic are the observations of Emil Fischer on the fermentation of sugars.[41] D-Glucose, but not L-glucose, is readily fermented by yeast. Emil Fischer also first distinguished between α- and β-glycosides by enzymic methods. The α-glycosides are hydrolyzed by α-glycosidase (present in hops), and the β-glycosides are hydrolyzed by β-glycosidase (found in emulsin).

A pure strain of *Penicillium glaucum* cultured on various racemic acids was found to metabolize preferentially (−)-lactic acid, (+)-ethoxypropionic acid, (−)-glyceric acid, (+)-malic acid, (+)-ethoxysuccinic acid, (+)-tartaric acid, and (+)-dimethoxysuccinic acid.[42] At the time there seemed to be little consistency, for it seemed that sometimes the organism preferred one direction of rotation and then the other. It is now known, however, that all these acids are configurationally related and belong to the D- series.[43]

Enzymes are active not only in degradation but also in synthetic reactions. If in syntheses an asymmetric center is formed, one configuration is frequently formed at the expense and even to the exclusion of its isomer.

o-Methylcyclohexanone is reduced by hops to a dextrorotating alcohol.[44] Benzoylformic acid, C_6H_5—CO—COOH, is reduced in the presence of milk, hops, or beef liver to L-mandelic acid.[45] Benzaldehyde and hydrogen cyanide in the presence of emulsion form optically active mandelonitrile.[46, 47]

The synthesis of (−)-phenylacetylcarbinol during the fermentation of glucose in the presence of benzaldehyde has been mentioned under the synthesis of (−)-ephedrine (see page 227).[48]

[40] Wegler, *Ann.*, **506**, 77 (1933); **510**, 72 (1934).
[41] Fischer, *Z. physiol. Chem.*, **26**, 60 (1898).
[42] McKenzie and Harden, *J. Chem. Soc.*, **83**, 424 (1903).
[43] Cf. Freudenberg, p. 684.
[44] Akamatsu, *Biochem. Z.*, **142**, 188 (1923).
[45] Freudenberg, p. 584.
[46] Rosenthaler, *Biochem. Z.*, **14**, 238 (1908).
[47] Krieble, *J. Am. Chem. Soc.*, **35**, 1643 (1913).
[48] Bockmühl, Stein, and Ehrhart, U. S. pat. 1,962,476; *C.A.*, **28**, 4834 (1934).

Even symmetrical molecules may react in an asymmetric manner in biochemical systems under the influence of enzymes. Ogston [49] first observed this with isotopically labeled citric acid, which he obtained by incubating radioactive carbon dioxide and pyruvate ion in the presence of liver tissue. The *in vivo*

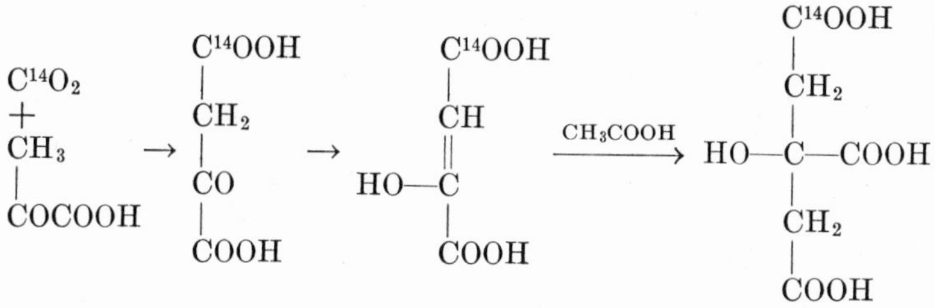

$$
\begin{array}{ccc}
C^{14}O_2 & C^{14}OOH & C^{14}OOH & C^{14}OOH \\
+ & | & | & | \\
CH_3 \rightarrow & CH_2 \rightarrow & CH & \xrightarrow{CH_3COOH} \quad CH_2 \\
| & | & \| & HO-C-COOH \\
COCOOH & CO & HO-C & | \\
& | & | & CH_2 \\
& COOH & COOH & | \\
& & & COOH
\end{array}
$$

Terminally labeled
citric acid

degradation of citric to succinic acid may be summarized as shown. It might be

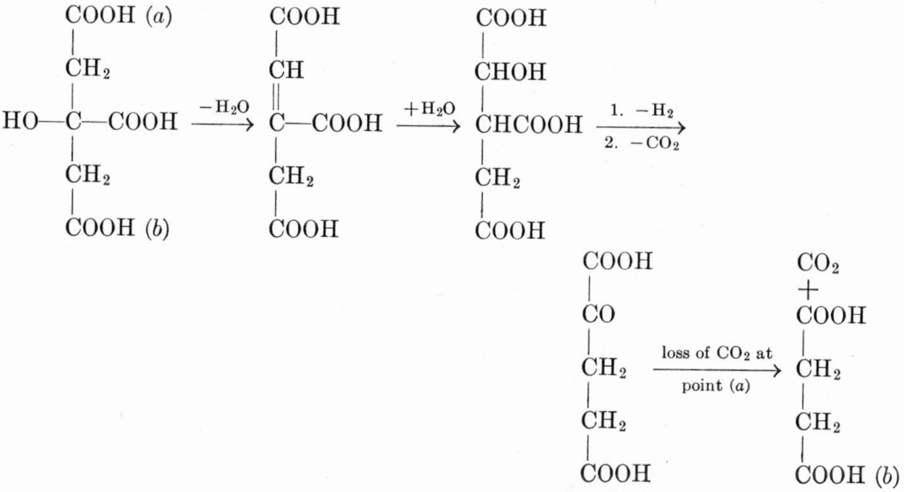

$$
\begin{array}{ccc}
COOH\ (a) & COOH & COOH \\
| & | & | \\
CH_2 & CH & CHOH \\
| & \xrightarrow{-H_2O} \ \| & \xrightarrow{+H_2O} \\
HO-C-COOH & C-COOH & CHCOOH \xrightarrow[2.\ -CO_2]{1.\ -H_2} \\
| & | & | \\
CH_2 & CH_2 & CH_2 \\
| & | & | \\
COOH\ (b) & COOH & COOH
\end{array}
$$

$$
\begin{array}{cc}
COOH & CO_2 \\
| & + \\
CO & COOH \\
| & \xrightarrow[\text{point }(a)]{\text{loss of }CO_2\text{ at}} \quad | \\
CH_2 & CH_2 \\
| & | \\
CH_2 & CH_2 \\
| & | \\
COOH & COOH\ (b)
\end{array}
$$

Ketoglutaric
acid

Succinic
acid

anticipated that citric acid, in its degradation, should lose with equal facility either terminal carboxyl (*a*) or (*b*), thus affording both radioactive carbon dioxide and radioactive succinic acid. But only $C^{14}O_2$ and no radioactive succinic acid was found. However, if, during the biosynthesis of citric acid, radioactive acetate, $CH_3C^{14}OOH$, was employed, then the enzymic degradation yielded only tagged succinic acid and no $C^{14}O_2$. These results indicate that symmetrical citric acid combines with the enzyme in an asymmetrical manner.

Equally interesting and analogous results are reported with deuterium-labeled ethanol.[50] In the presence of alcohol dehydrogenase, ADH, from yeast,

[49] Ogston, *Nature*, **162**, 963 (1948).
[50] Loweus, Westheimer, and Vennesland, *J. Am. Chem. Soc.*, **75**, 5018 (1953).

ethanol reacts with diphosphopyridine nucleotide, DPN^+, according to the equation

(i) $\qquad CH_3CD_2OH + DPN^+ \xrightleftharpoons{ADH} CH_3CDO + DPN\text{-}D + H^-$

By allowing deuterized, i.e., reduced with deuterium, diphosphopyridine nucleotide, DPN-D, to react with acetaldehyde, one stereoisomeride of monodeuteroethanol is formed thus,

(ii) $\qquad CH_3CHO + DPN\text{-}D + H^+ \xrightleftharpoons{ADH} CH_3CDHOH + DPN^+$

Deuteroacetaldehyde, CH_3CDO, in the presence of reduced diphosphopyridine nucleotide, affords the other enantiomorph of monodeuteroethanol, as in equation (iii).

(iii) $\qquad CH_3CDO + DPN\text{-}D + H^+ \xrightleftharpoons{ADH} CH_3CHDOH + DPN^+$

Acetaldehyde reduced with DPN-D formed an isomer which on reoxidation gave the original aldehyde; deuteroacetaldehyde reduced with DPN-H formed an isomer that was reoxidized only to CH_3CDO.

ASYMMETRIC SYNTHESIS

The synthesis of exclusively or even predominantly a single configuration from a symmetrical intermediate is called *total asymmetric synthesis*. The production of a new center of asymmetry in a molecule that is already optically active is known as *partial asymmetric synthesis*.

Attempts at total asymmetric synthesis have not been encouraging. This is not unexpected if the probabilities [51] are reckoned, as indicated. The starting

$$
\begin{array}{ccc}
R' & R' & Y \quad\quad R' & X\text{---}Y \\
\diagdown\quad & \diagdown\diagup & \diagdown\diagup \\
CX \xrightarrow{Y_2} & C & + \quad C \\
\diagup\quad & \diagup\diagdown & \diagup\diagdown \\
R & R \quad X\text{---}Y & R \quad\quad Y
\end{array}
$$

molecule is symmetrical and the mathematical probabilities favor equally the formation of both space modifications, that is, the racemic mixture of the two isomers.

Partial asymmetric syntheses, however, are well known, for the continuation of natural living processes depends on them. The enzymic syntheses mentioned may be taken as illustrations.

In the synthesis of optically active mandelonitrile, for example, it is postulated that emulsin and benzaldehyde form a complex in which the enzyme furnishes the asymmetric centers already present, and with which the hydrogen cyanide reacts to form optically active cyanohydrin.

Another example is seen in the Kiliani synthesis of the sugars. The addition of hydrogen cyanide to L-arabinose produced predominantly the nitrile of

[51] Cf. Freudenberg, p. 584; Gilman, p. 224.

L-mannonic acid and only a very small amount of the epimeric gluconic acid nitrile.[52, 53]

The formation of benzaldehyde cyanohydrin in the presence of quinine produces a (−)-nitrile; in the presence of quinidine, a stereoisomer of quinine, the nitrile becomes dextrorotatory.[54] Likewise, in the presence of diethylamine "anchored" on cotton fiber, e.g., in diethylaminocellulose, 61 per cent of the mandelonitrile formed is (+) and 39 per cent (−); but in the presence of the —$N(C_2H_5)_2$ group not in conjunction with an optically active carrier the racemic nitrile is obtained.[55] The hydrogenation of β-methylcinnamic ester with platinum oxide catalyst deposited on hydrocinchonidine salts formed 8–9 per cent (+)-β-methyl-β-phenylpropionic ester.[56]

α-Ketoacids esterified with an optically active alcohol may be reduced, at least in part, to optically active α-hydroxyacids. The (−)-menthyl ester of benzoylformic acid may be reduced to (−)-mandelic acid.[57] The (+)-bornyl ester of benzoylformic acid reacts with ethylmagnesium iodide to form (+)-phenylethylglycolic acid.[58]

PHYSIOLOGICAL ACTIVITY

In view of the differences in physical and chemical properties of diastereoisomers, a difference in physiological activity is not unexpected, especially if one keeps in mind the extreme sensitivity of the living organism.[59, 60] If a drug with but a single asymmetric carbon atom is administered, it is soon converted by means of "protoplasmic reaction" into a substance capable of existing in diastereoisomeric modifications. The physiological response may then be caused by either physical or chemical forces or even as a result of the two working together. This conception is expressed in another way by Easson and Stedman.[61]

It is considered that the different physiological activities of optical isomerides may frequently be ascribed to circumstances which are identical with those which cause different symmetrical molecules to exhibit different physiological activities; . . . that molecular dissymmetry is, of itself, without influence on physiological activity, and that both it and the optical activity with which it is associated are accidental accompaniments . . . of different molecular arrangements which differ in their ability to cause the development of a particular physiological effect for precisely the same reasons that two structural isomerides so differ.

[52] Kiliani, Ber., 20, 339 (1887).
[53] Fischer, Ber., 23, 2611 (1890).
[54] Bredig and Fiske, Biochem. Z., 46, 7 (1912).
[55] Bredig and Gerstner, Biochem. Z., 250, 414 (1932).
[56] Lipkin and Stewart, J. Am. Chem. Soc., 61, 3295 (1939).
[57] McKenzie, J. Chem. Soc., 91, 1215 (1907).
[58] McKenzie and Mitchell, Biochem. Z., 208, 471 (1920).
[59] An enlightening, short treatise on the physiological effects of isomers is that given by Cushny, Biological Relations of Optically Isomeric Substances, Williams and Wilkins Co., Baltimore, 1926.
[60] Another review is that by Ammon, "Die Bedeutung der Stereochemie in der Physiologie," Ergeb. Physiol. exptl. Pharmakol., 37, 366–405 (1935). This author gives numerous references to original literature. See also Beckett and Casy, J. Pharm. Pharmacol., 7, 433 (1955).
[61] Easson and Stedman, Biochem. J., 27, 1257 (1933).

The first recorded observation of differences in physiological properties of optical isomers is that of Piutti [62] who found that (+)-asparagine has a sweet taste but that the (−)-isomer is insipid.

It is of more than a little interest to find that Pasteur ascribed this difference to the presence of an optically active substance in the nervous mechanism of taste and likened it to the specific action of ferments.[63]

It has since been shown that the enantiomorphs of practically all the amino acids give different taste responses. The L- or natural amino acids are either tasteless or bitter; the members of the D- series are sweet.[64]

The difference in the taste and sweetness of the various stereoisomeric sugars is even better known, e.g., in the aldohexose group, D-glucose is sweet but D-galactose and D-mannose are much less so. Another striking difference in the tissue response to the sugars is seen in the permeability of the glomeruli of the frog kidney. Glucose is reported to be impermeable but mannose, fructose, and some of the disaccharides are allowed to pass completely.[65]

(−)-Secondary butyl alcohol shows greater narcotic effect toward tadpoles than does the (+)-isomer, although the oil-water partition coefficient is the same for both.[66]

The first optical isomers to be investigated pharmacologically were the hyoscyamines. These compounds are particularly interesting in that the center of asymmetry is found in the tropic acid component rather than in what might seem to be the more important tropanol fragment (see page 387). (−)-Hyoscyamine was generally found to be about twice as powerful a mydriatic as the racemic atropine and 20–25 times stronger than (+)-hyoscyamine.

Similar relations were found to exist for the hyoscines and homatropines.

DL-Malic acid is twice as toxic toward fish as is (−)-malic acid, indicating that the (+)-isomer is more toxic than the (−)-isomer.[67] (+)-Carnosine has no depressor effect even when administered in 20 times the dose at which (−)-carnosine is active.[68] Pigeons injected intramuscularly with DL- or D-alanine gave evidence of great distress, whereas L-alanine produced no such symptoms.[69] L-Ascorbic acid possesses antiscorbutic properties, but D-ascorbic acid is inactive. The specificity of the ribose fragment in riboflavin has been mentioned, page 423.

In feeding experiments it was observed that when D-lysine replaced the natural L-amino acid in the diet, the experimental animals failed to grow; and if D-tryptophan and D-histidine were substituted for their natural L-isomers, the animals developed at a slower rate.[70] In humans racemic tryptophan showed

[62] Piutti, *Compt. rend.*, **103**, 134 (1886).

[63] Pasteur, *Compt. rend.*, **103**, 138 (1886).

[64] Kaneko, *J. Chem. Soc. Japan*, **60**, 531 (1939); *C.A.*, **36**, 2874 (1942).

[65] Hamburger, *Ergeb. Physiol.*, **23**, 120 (1924).

[66] Hano, *Folia Pharmacol. Japon.*, **27**, 315 (1939); *C.A.*, **34**, 2069 (1940).

[67] Gauze and Smaragdove, *J. biol. méd. exptl. (U.S.S.R.)*, **7**, 105 and 107 (1939).

[68] du Vigneaud and Hunt, *J. Biol. Chem.*, **115**, 93 (1936); *C.A.*, **30**, 7217 (1936).

[69] Abderhalden and Tetzner, *Z. physiol. Chem.*, **232**, 79 (1935); *C.A.*, **29**, 3398 (1935).

[70] Totter and Berg, *J. Biol. Chem.*, **127**, 375 (1939); *C.A.*, **33**, 2188 (1939).

only half the activity of an equal amount of the natural or L-isomer.[71]
L-Thyroxine is twice as active as racemic thyroxine.[72] Racemic amino acids are
less efficacious in nutrition than are the L-isomers.[73, 74] Acetyl-L-tryptophan is
utilized by the experimental animal, but not acetyl-D-tryptophan.[75]

L-Thienylalanine is an active microbiological inhibitor, antagonized by phenylalanine. D-Thienylalanine is inactive.[76]

The pharmacological activities of the ephedrine isomers, according to Chen and
Schmidt,[77] are shown in Table XXXII.

TABLE XXXII

ACTIVITIES OF THE DIASTEREOISOMERIC EPHEDRINES

Isomer	Mydriasis	M.L.D. Intravenous to White Rabbits, mg./kg.	Ratio of Pressor Activity— l-ψ-ephedrine = 1	Pressor Action in Men per os	Per Cent Increase in Blood Pressure after Injection of 2 mg. into Pithed Cat, 2.5 kg.
(−)-pseudo	+	80	1:1	−	8
DL-pseudo	+++	70	1:4	+	28
(+)-pseudo	++++	75	1:6.8	+	37
(+)-	+++	80	1:11.9	−	68.5
DL-	+++++	60	1:26.5	+	211
(−)-	+++++	60	1:35.1	+	280

For epinephrine the ratio of pressor activities for the three isomers has been
found to be (−):DL:(+)::1:1/2:1/20. The (−)-isomer is also 6 to 20 times
more toxic than the (+)-isomer.[78, 79] It is reported that mice pretreated with
(+)-epinephrine develop a tolerance for 10 or more times the lethal dose of the
(−)-isomer, although such immunity is only temporary.[80, 81] It is also said that
intravenous administration of (+)-epinephrine to cats and dogs renders them
nonresponsive to the normal hormone.[82] The three isomers show characteristic
effects on the duration of the pressor response when administered in doses which
produce moderate but approximately equivalent elevations in blood pressure.
That produced by (−)-epinephrine lasts an average of 1.5 min.; that from DL-

[71] Albanese and Frankston, *J. Biol. Chem.*, **155**, 101 (1944).
[72] Reineke and Turner, *Endocrinology*, **36**, 200 (1945).
[73] Pilsum and Berg, *J. Biol. Chem.*, **183**, 279 (1950).
[74] Graham *et al.*, *ibid.*, **185**, 97 (1950).
[75] Baldwin and Berg, *J. Nutrition*, **39**, 203 (1949); *C.A.*, **44**, 1580 (1950).
[76] Ferger and du Vigneaud, *J. Biol. Chem.*, **174**, 241 (1948).
[77] *Medicine*, **9** 88, (1930).
[78] Tainter, *J. Pharmacol.*, **40**, 43 (1930).
[79] Launoy and Menguy, *Compt. rend. soc. biol.*, **87**, 1066 (1922).
[80] Abderhalden and Kautsch, *Z. physiol. Chem.*, **61**, 119 (1909).
[81] Waterman, *Z. physiol. Chem.*, **63**, 290 (1909).
[82] Fröhlich, *Zentr. Physiol.*, **23**, 254 (1909).

epinephrine extends to 2.5 min.; and the rise produced by (+)-epinephrine persists for 4.7 min.   These differences are ascribed to variations in "protoplasmic reaction." [83]

The pressor activities for the synephrine isomers vary in the following order, (−):DL:(+)::1:1/2:1/60.   The (+)-isomer also produces longer duration in blood pressure rise.   It is in the perfusion experiments, however, that a striking difference appears.   Doses of 0.5 to 2.0 mg. of the (−)-isomer produce prompt and prolonged vasoconstriction; the dextrorotatory isomer up to 10 mg. doses produces no effect or causes dilatation; the racemic mixture in doses ranging to 50 mg. never produces constriction.   Since 25 mg. of the (−) compound was administered along with an equal amount of the (+) isomeride, it appears that the dextrorotating substance is not only inactive but also antagonistic to the vasoconstricting (−)-isomer. [84]

A most interesting substance showing qualitative and quantitative differences between its optical isomers is seen in 3,4-dihydroxypropadrine (Cobefrin or norhomoepinephrine).   The ratio of pressor activities is (−):DL:(+)::1:1.6:160. The response obtained from the (−)-substance is substantially like that obtained from (−)-epinephrine; the response from the (+)-isomer is very much like that seen with (−)-ephedrine.   The fact that the racemic mixture is 1/1.6 as active as its most active component, instead of 1/2, suggests that the (+) half exerts a potentiating action on the epinephrinelike isomer.   On the isolated rabbit uterus the (−)-isomer is active but the (+)-isomer is practically inert.   In its ability to mobilize glycogen the (−)-component is active like epinephrine, but the (+)-fraction is quite inert like ephedrine.   Cocaine increases the activity of the (−)-isomer, as it does with (−)-epinephrine, but decreases the pressor response from the (+)-compound, as it does with ephedrine.   The levorotating isomer is 15 to 25 times more toxic.   Every indication, therefore, points to the fact that the two optically active isomers are distinct compounds when measured and evaluated in terms of their pharmacological response. [85]

Analgesics, such as methadon and probably also morphine, whose isomers are sterically related to D-(−)-alanine are presumed to react more favorably with specific receptor sites to produce their desired physiological effects. [86]

ASYMMETRIC CARBON ATOMS IN A CYCLE

Three-, four-, and five-membered cycles are planar.   Although the rigidity of these cycles does not permit the carbon atoms composing them to adopt a conformation or constellation which is most favorable thermodynamically as for the alicyclic series, the general considerations thus far discussed for the asymmetric carbon atom apply also when the carbon is part of a cycle.   However, because of the rigidity of the cycle, there is an added phenomenon which is seen in *cis*-

[83] Tainter, *J. Pharmacol.*, **40**, 43 (1930).
[84] Tainter and Seidenfeld, *J. Pharmacol.*, **40**, 23 (1930).
[85] Schaumann, I. G. Farbenindustrie Aktiengesellschaft, *Medizin und Chemie*, **3**, 383 (1936).
[86] Beckett and Casy, *J. Chem. Soc.*, **1955**, 900.

trans isomerism, which may or may not accompany optical isomerism. For the truxillic and truxinic acids, which are hydrolytic moieties from the truxillines, page 392, or may be synthesized by the irradiation of cinnamic acid,[87] the accepted structural formulas are indicated.[88]

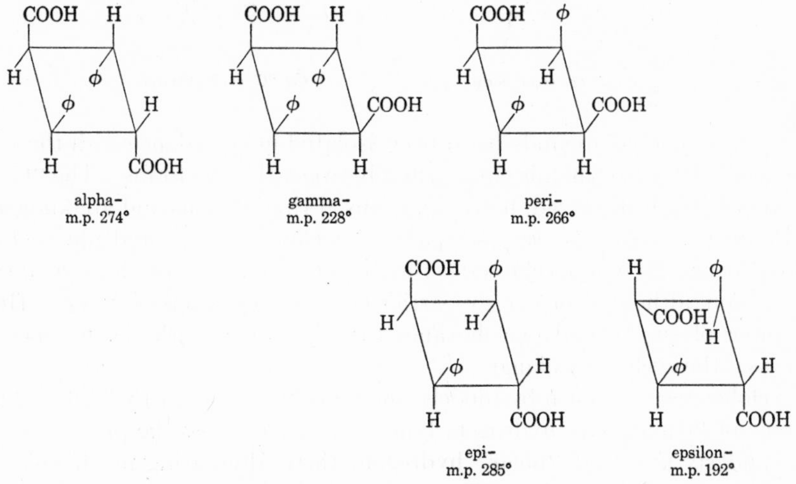

alpha-
m.p. 274°

gamma-
m.p. 228°

peri-
m.p. 266°

epi-
m.p. 285°

epsilon-
m.p. 192°

Truxillic acids, 1,3-dicarboxy-2,4-diphenylcyclobutanes

beta-

omega-

neo-

zeta-

mu-

delta-

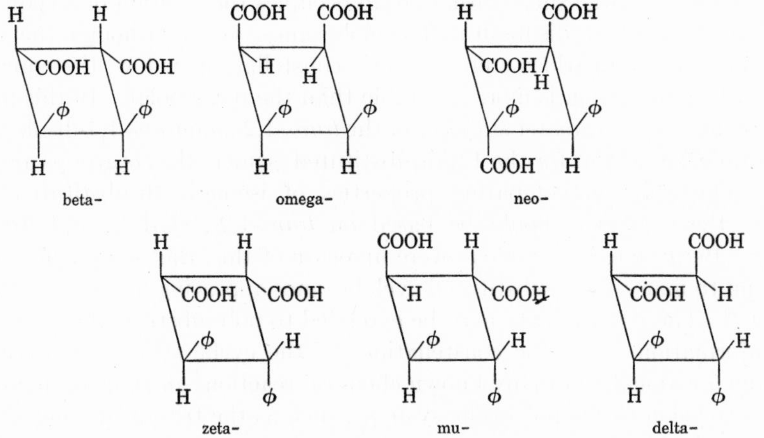

Truxinic acids, 1,2-dicarboxy-3,4-diphenylcyclobutanes

Six-membered cycles are not planar, but rather are three-dimensional; atoms numbered 1,2,4,5 lie in a plane and atoms numbered 3 and 6 above or below the

[87] Bernstein and Quimby, *J. Am. Chem. Soc.*, **65,** 1845 (1943).

[88] The conventions for writing and naming the *cis* and *trans* substituents are given in *Chem. Eng. News*, **28,** 1842 (1950). A substituent written downward from a cycle is *trans* to the one placed upward.

plane, theoretically giving rise to the two possible structures indicated.[89] Thus

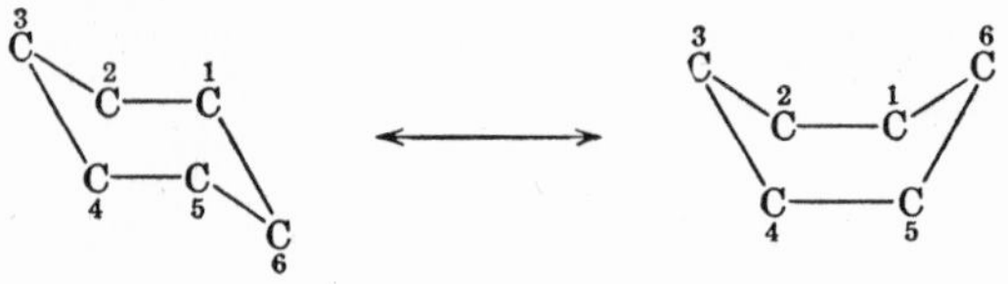

Trans, "Z" or "chair" form   *Cis,* "C" or "bed" form

far no monocyclic compounds have been isolated in accordance with these concepts, since there is a dynamic equilibrium between the two forms. The "C" and "Z" forms become stabilized, however, in fused ring systems and are known, for example, in the steroidal series, see page 52. Computations and physical data indicate that in the monocyclic series the "Z" or "chair" form is the more favored conformation, although the energy barrier between the two is very low. Hence, the number of substituted cyclohexanes isolated agrees with the number predicted, as if the cycle were planar.

In cyclohexane, as shown by models, there are two types of hydrogen, that is, six atoms of "equatorial" hydrogen, lying in a circle about the plane of carbon atoms, and six atoms of "polar" hydrogen, three alternating north polar and three alternating south polar. The equatorial hydrogens are statistically less hindered, and a substituent occupying an equatorial position is energetically more favorable; thus a monosubstituted monocyclohexane will prefer the conformation in which the substituting group occupies the position of an equatorial hydrogen atom. For disubstituted cyclohexanes, again although the energy barrier between the various stereoisomeric constellations is low, the equatorial-equatorial conformation is more favorable than the polar-polar. In this manner may be explained the greater stability of the *trans*-1,2- and *trans*-1,4-disubstituted cyclohexanes; however, for the 1,3-disubstituted isomers the *cis* groups are equatorial. Therefore, in comparing properties of isomeric disubstituted cyclohexanes, the analogies should be based on *trans*-1,2-, *cis*-1,3-, and *trans*-1,4-isomers. Because earlier workers were unaware of this, the assignments of configuration to many 1,3-disubstituted cyclohexanes appearing in the literature are in error.[90] These arguments may be extended to polysubstituted cyclohexenes. Such information about the constellations of the cyclic structures is useful in providing a rationale for many known chemical reactions and elucidating others, and its extension to the polycyclic systems, such as the triterpenes and steroids, has been valuable.

For the 1,2- and 1,3-disubstituted cyclohexanes the accompanying structures come into consideration.

---

[89] It is suggested that suitable models be employed here as a means of more clearly illustrating these phenomena.

[90] Rossini and Pitzer, *Science,* **105,** 647 (1947); Goering and Serres, *J. Am. Chem. Soc.,* **74,** 5908 (1952); Noyce and Denny, *ibid.,* **74,** 5912 (1952); Noyce and Nagle, *ibid.,* **75,** 127 (1953); Siegel, *ibid.,* **75,** 1317 (1953).

There are two enantiomorphic *cis* and two enantiomorphic *trans* isomers. When X = Y the *cis* isomers in each instance are internally compensated, hence, *meso*. For the 1,4-disubstituted cyclohexanes there are only *cis* and *trans* isomers, even when X = Y; they have no enantiomorphic forms.

The configurational relationships of many cyclohexane derivatives have been determined. Menthane is an example of 1,4-disubstituted cyclohexane. The isomers may be obtained, for example, by the hydrogenation of the monocyclic terpenes or by replacing the hydroxyl group of menthol with a hydrogen atom. From natural menthol is obtained *trans*-menthane and from isomenthol is obtained *cis*-menthane. The properties of the two are compared in Table XXXIII.

TABLE XXXIII

PROPERTIES OF MENTHANES

	b.p.	D_4^{20}	n_4^{20}
cis-Menthane	168.50	0.816	1.4575
trans-Menthane	161	0.792	1.4393

The assignment of configuration is based on a consideration of physical properties, e.g., dipole moment, and also on application of the rule of Auwers and Skita,[91] that is, the *cis*-isomer usually has greater density, higher refractive index, and lower molecular refraction than the *trans*-isomeride.

With the presence of a substituent on carbon atom number 3, carbons numbered 1 and 4 become asymmetric. Thus there are two *cis* and two *trans* menthones and four *cis* and four *trans* menthols, for which the steric relationships are summarized in Table XXXIV.

[91] Auwers and Skita, *Ann.*, **410**, 287 (1915); **420**, 91 (1920).

TABLE XXXIV

STERIC RELATIONSHIPS OF MENTHONES AND MENTHOLS

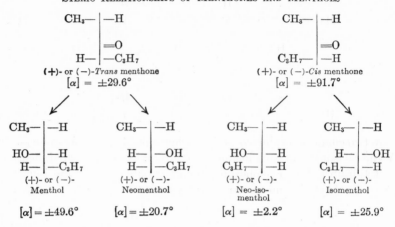

It is of interest to note that the esterification rate of the isomeric menthols with p-nitrobenzoyl chloride decreases in the following ratio:

(−)-menthol	16.3
(−)-isomenthol	12.3
(−)-neoisomenthol	3.1
(−)-neomenthol	1.0

The cyclic, pyranose structures of the aldohexoses are examples of six-membered cycles with five asymmetric carbon atoms. There are 2^5 or 32 possible isomers, including the α- and β- modifications.

The configurational correlation between these naturally occurring cyclic and the known alicyclic products is not yet completely solved, although much progress has already been attained.[92]

Polycyclic Compounds

Camphor and Borneol. The camphor molecule contains two asymmetric carbon atoms, C–1 and C–4. At first thought it might be expected to exist in four stereoisomeric modifications. This, however, is not true, for the bridge joining C–1 and C–4 makes these two carbon atoms act as a unit and at the same time permits only that configuration in which the methyl at C–1 and the hydrogen at C–4 are *cis;* a *trans* bridge would put an impossible strain on the molecule.

This fact will be much better appreciated if demonstrated with molecular models. Consequently the number of optical isomers is 2.[93] Both (+)- and (−)-camphor are known.

[92] Porath, *Arch. Kemi*, **1**, 385, 525 (1950); Fregda, *Acta Chem. Scand.*, **3**, 208 (1949); Noyce and Denny, *J. Am. Chem. Soc.*, **76**, 768 (1954).

[93] For a more detailed presentation, the interested student is referred to Gilman, *Organic Chemistry*, John Wiley & Sons, p. 401 *et seq.*, 1943.

It is suggested that, until the relative configuration of the natural terpenoids can be established in terms of the alicyclic reference points, camphor be employed for designating the relative configuration of these cyclic derivatives. Hückel [94] has proposed that the structure of camphor with the 1-to-4 bridge extending forward from the plane of the paper and the ketonic carbonyl group at the right be called D-camphor.

The reduction of camphor yields two corresponding alcohols, borneol and isoborneol.

D-Camphor   D-Borneol   D-Isoborneol

The indicated configurations are based on reactions which involve oxidation to carboxylic acids and lactone-formation or nonlactone-formation of the carboxyl groups with the hydroxyl group. [95]

Tropane Compounds.   Although it contains two asymmetric carbon atoms they are *meso* and thus tropane can exist in only one form as indicated.

Tropane

The=NMe bridge allows C–1 and C–5 to assume only the *cis* configuration. 3-Tropanol, tropine, is likewise internally compensated and optically inactive. The hydroxyl group at C–3 may, however, be *cis* or *trans* with respect to the =NMe bridge. On the basis of various reactions, including the ease of acyl migration from N to O, the *cisoid* structure is assigned to pseudotropanol, namely, that isomer obtained by the hydrolysis of tropacocaine and also formed by reducing 3-tropanone with sodium and alcohol. Tropanol, the isomer obtained by the hydrolysis of atropine or by catalytic reduction of tropanone, has the *transoid* structure. [96] Scopine, the basic moiety resulting from the hydroly-

[94] Hückel, *J. prakt. Chem.*, **157**, 225 (1941).

[95] Toivonen *et al.*, *Acta Chem. Scand.*, **3**, 991 (1949).

[96] Fodor and Nador, *Nature*, **169**, 462 (1952); Zenitz *et al.*, *J. Am. Chem. Soc.*, **74**, 5564 (1952); Nickon and Fieser, *J. Am. Chem. Soc.*, **74**, 5566 (1952).

sis of scopolamine, likewise has the hydroxyl *trans* to the N-methylbridge, as indicated by the ease with which it rearranges to scopoline.[97]

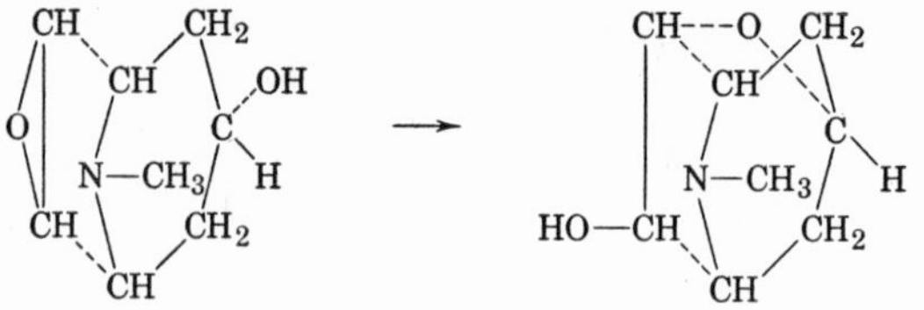

I
Scopine

II
Scopoline

Ecgonine, as its nor-derivative, readily undergoes benzoyl migration from the nitrogen atom to the oxygen atom, thus showing it to be a derivative of pseudotropanol.[98] The position of the carboxyl group follows from a reappraisal of reactions observed long ago in the light of what is now known about stereochemical mechanisms, such as *trans* elimination of water to form anhydroecgonine and the stereo-path of the Hofmann degradation; these place the —COOH *cis* to both the hydroxyl and to the nitrogen bridge.[99]

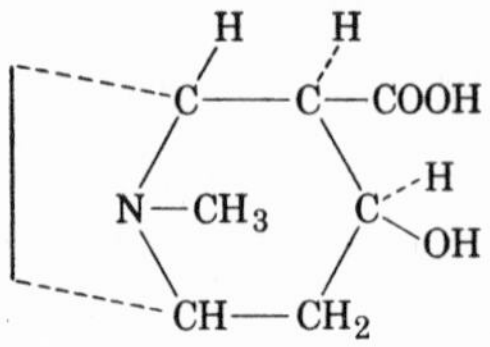

Ecgonine

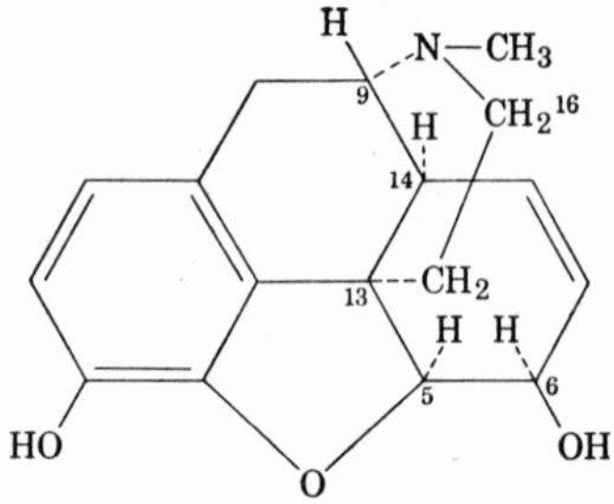

Morphine

Morphine. Stereochemical studies now make it possible to show the *cis-trans* relationships of the five asymmetric centers. The hydrogen atoms at C–5 and C–6 are *cis*, for, when the ether at C–5 is converted into a hydroxyl, the derivative shows the characteristic properties of a *cis*-glycol. The ethaneamine portion, that is, C–15, is attached to C–13 *cis* to the hydrogens at C–5 and C–6; for manipulation of C–16 in such manner as to permit lactone formation through C–6 does not result in the formation of the lactone. The nitrogen atom can be linked to C–9 only in such manner that the hydrogen atoms at C–9 and C–13 are *cis*. The hydrogen at C–14, it becomes apparent from involved reactions, is *trans* to the hydrogens at C–9 and C–13. Hence, except for relative configuration, the formula for morphine may be written as indicated.[100]

[97] Smith and Hartung, *J. Am. Chem. Soc.*, **75**, 3859 (1953).

[98] Findlay, *J. Am. Chem. Soc.*, **75**, 4624 (1953).

[99] Findlay, *J. Am. Chem. Soc.*, **76**, 2855 (1954).

[100] Rapoport and co-workers, *J. Am. Chem. Soc.*, **74**, 2630 (1952); **75**, 5329 (1953); *J. Org. Chem.*, **15**, 1093 (1950).

Decahydronaphthalene. When two cycles are fused, as in decahydronaphthalene, a factor of greater rigidity appears.[101] This rigidity becomes more pro-

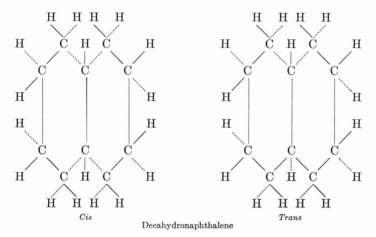

Cis   *Trans*

Decahydronaphthalene

nounced as the number of fused cycles in the molecules increase, e.g., in the steroid
compounds. Decahydronaphthalene, as seen from the formulas, exists in the
cis and the *trans* forms. Physical data for the two isomers are given in Table
XXXV.[102, 103, 104] These data are not, in themselves, important to the phar-

TABLE XXXV

Cis AND *Trans* DECAHYDRONAPTHALENES

	Cis	*Trans*
B.p. at 760 mm.	194.6°	185.5°
M.p.	−43.26°	−31.47°
d_4^{20}	0.8963	0.8699
n_D^{20}	1.48113	1.46968
Cal. per gram	10851.3	10836.0
Viscosity at 20° centipoises	3.381	2.128

maceutical chemist, but they do give emphasis to the very strong possibility
that similar differences will be found in the case of physiologically active, polycyclic stereoisomers, for example, in the cyclopentenophenanthrene derivatives,
and that these differences may conceivably explain the variations in biological
responses observed in such isomers.

Sterols. The complexity of the stereochemistry in these compounds may be
appreciated from a contemplation of the structure of cholesterol. In the hydrogenated molecule carbon atoms numbered 3, 5, 8, 9, 10, 13, 14, 17, and 20 are

[101] For a more detailed and complete exposition of the theoretical aspects of the problem see
Gilman, p. 320 *et seq.*

[102] Seyer and Walker, *J. Am. Chem. Soc.*, **60,** 2125 (1938).

[103] Davies and Gilbert, *J. Am. Chem. Soc.*, **63,** 1585 (1941).

[104] Seyer and Leslie, *J. Am. Chem. Soc.*, **64,** 1912 (1942).

asymmetric. This permits 2^9 or 512 theoretically possible stereoisomers. In cholesterol, carbon atom 5 is doubly linked to 6; and for this structure 256 isomers are possible. Since the stereochemical riddle of these compounds has not been completely solved, only a few general conclusions will be given here. The unraveling of the problem presented by sterol chemistry is proceeding at such a rapid rate that comprehensive treatises which were excellent at the time of their publication are quickly becoming out of date. The number of original publications in this field runs into several hundreds annually.

Evidence from several sources, both chemical and physical, points to the fact that the four cycles are "flat," that is, not bowed-in, except in rare instances such as pyrocalciferol. This suggests that cycles B and C are *trans*. D, a five-membered ring, occurs naturally in as near a plane as circumstances permit. Most, if not all, of the members of this group belong to one of two main series, the cholestane or the coprostane series. In coprostane the rings A and B are of the *cis*-decalin type; in cholestane they are the *trans*-decalin type or *trans*.

Cholesterol

The configuration about C–3 is of great importance. In the sex hormones and, perhaps, in the cardiac glycosides, a change in the configuration about this carbon atom may reduce very substantially, and in some instances even cause a reversal of, the physiological activity. If the hydroxyl at C–3 is *cis* with respect

Cholestane configuration   Coprostane configuration

to the angular methyl at C–10, the compound usually forms an insoluble digitonide, a property which may be used to separate diastereoisomers and may frequently be employed to give preliminary indication of the configuration in the investigation of new compounds.

For the experimental data and arguments on which the accepted stereochemical formulas are based, the student is advised to consult comprehensive texts and reviews. These are not developed here. However, in the preceding discussion of the sterols, the hormones of the adrenal cortex and of the sex glands, and the bile acids, an effort has been made to show the accepted relative configurational structures.

cis-trans-ISOMERISM ABOUT THE ETHYLENIC BOND

In 1838 Liebig observed that maleic and fumaric acids have the same empirical formula. The explanation for this phenomenon became clear when Le Bel and van't Hoff advanced their theory for the tetrahedral nature of the carbon atom. Two carbon atoms linked with a double bond are no longer free to rotate but become fixed with respect to each other, as indicated in Figure 1:

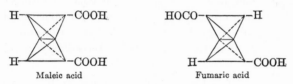

Maleic acid   Fumaric acid

Figure 1

These space relationships are much better seen from a study of atomic models. For convenience the space model diagrams of Figure 1 are commonly written as in the accompanying diagram, or more simply as in the second diagram. The

$$
\begin{array}{ccc}
\text{H}\quad\text{COOH} & & \text{HOOC}\quad\text{H}\\
\diagdown\diagup & & \diagdown\diagup\\
\text{C} & & \text{C}\\
\| & & \|\\
\text{C} & & \text{C}\\
\diagup\diagdown & & \diagup\diagdown\\
\text{H}\quad\text{COOH} & & \text{H}\quad\text{COOH}
\end{array}
$$

H—C—COOH   and   HOOC—C—H
 ‖   ‖
H—C—COOH   H—C—COOH

four substituents of ethylene lie in a plane; their relative positions are not interchangeable, and there is a plane of symmetry, making optical isomerism about the double bond impossible.

Two ethylenedicarboxylic acids are possible, as the space models indicate. Two are known. One of them, maleic acid, readily forms an anhydride. Fumaric anhydride is unknown. Examination of the space models shows that of the two possible structures the one with the two carboxyl groups in *cis* position explains the easy loss of water with the formation of a cyclic anhydride. This is difficult for the *trans* structure. This is not a question therefore of relative configuration, as in optical isomerism, but of absolute configuration.

This type of geometric or *cis-trans* isomerism is found if each of the two ethylenic carbon atoms is substituted by two unlike groups.

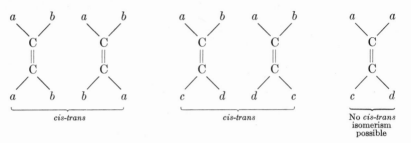

The determination of which is the *cis* and which the *trans* configuration is comparatively easy in the maleic and fumaric acids, or where the formation of cycles is employed. Geraniol and nerol both cyclize to form dipentene (page 11) but nerol does so more readily; examination of the space models shows that the *trans* member of this pair of isomers should lose water and form a six-membered cycle more easily than the *cis* member. Accordingly, nerol must be *trans* and geraniol must be *cis*.

The higher melting form of crotonic acid, m.p. 72°, is shown to be *trans* by the accompanying relationships:

$$\underset{\text{Fumaric acid}}{\overset{\displaystyle H—C—COOH}{\underset{\displaystyle HOOC—C—H}{\|}}} \quad \xleftarrow{\text{HOH}} \quad \underset{\text{Trichlorocrotonic acid}}{\overset{\displaystyle H—C—CCl_3}{\underset{\displaystyle HOOC—C—H}{\|}}} \quad \xrightarrow{\text{H}_2} \quad \underset{\text{Crotonic acid}}{\overset{\displaystyle H—C—CH_3}{\underset{\displaystyle HOOC—C—H}{\|}}}$$

Sometimes chemical methods are difficult to apply, and resort must be had to physical measurements, which are not infallible and must be used with caution. In the acids a surprising regularity appears in the differences between the *cis* and the *trans* isomers. The *cis* compound usually has the lower melting point, the higher degree of ionization, the greater heat of combustion, and shows the greater solubility in inert solvents. Some of these characteristics are shown in Table XXXVI.

Differences in the physical properties of the *cis* and the *trans* dichloroethylenes are summarized in Table XXXVII.

Usually one isomer of a *cis-trans* pair is less stable and may be quite easily converted into the more stable form. Such conversion is frequently promoted by heat, sunlight, acids, traces of iodine, etc. It appears that the *trans* isomer usually is the more stable, e.g., maleic acid on changing into fumaric acid liberates 6 kg.-cal. of energy per molecule; at 29° the heats of addition of hydrogen to ethyl maleate and ethyl fumarate are 33.6 and 29.3 kg.-cal. per molecule, respectively.[105] Conversely, increasing the energy, e.g., by irradiation with ultra-violet light, isomerizes fumaric into maleic acid. If the two isomers possess approximately equal stability, conversion from one form to the other is rarely complete.

TABLE XXXVI

Cis-trans ACIDS

Acid	Melting Point ° C.	K_a	Heat of Combustion, kg.-cal./mol.	Solubility in Water at 25° g./100 ml.
Maleic	130	1.17	326	78.8
Fumaric	286	0.093	320	0.7
cis-Crotonic	15.5	3.6×10^{-5}	486	40
trans-Crotonic	72	2×10^{-5}	478	8.3
cis-Cinnamic	68	1.38×10^{-4}	1047	14.4
trans-Cinnamic	133	0.035×10^{-4}	1041	0.1
Angelic	45	4.9×10^{-5}	634.8	—
Tiglic	64	0.95×10^{-5}	627.4	—

TABLE XXXVII

Cis AND *Trans* DICHLOROETHYLENES

	H—C—Cl ‖ H—C—Cl	H—C—Cl ‖ Cl—C—H
Melting point	$-80.5°$	$-50.5°$
Boiling point at 760 mm.	48.35°	60.25°
Specific gravity	1.2498	1.2743
Dipole moment	1.85×10^{-18} e.s.u.	—
Dissolves *cis*-β-chloro-crotonic acid	32.2	37.3
Dissolves *trans*-β-chloro-crotonic acid	5.75	2.36

Additional examples might be included but those given suffice to show that *cis* and *trans* isomers are, in fact, distinct chemical compounds. It is not un-expected, therefore, that they should show differences also in physiological properties. However, present knowledge of the effect of *cis-trans* isomerism on biological and medicinal action is limited.

Two grams of maleic acid per kilogram was fatal to a dog, but the same dose of fumaric acid produced no damage. At 20° maleic acid is reported to be the more toxic toward bacteria; at 37° fumaric acid is the more toxic. Fumaric acid, al-though it has a lower dissociation constant, inhibits more strongly than maleic the action of diastase, pepsin, and lipase, and it precipitates proteins. Fumaric acid has the characteristic sour taste of acids; maleic acid has an irritating taste.

[105] Williams, *J. Am. Chem. Soc.*, **64**, 1395 (1942).

The ethyl ester of angelica acid is sweet; the ester of tiglic acid is pungent. The higher melting of the two isomers having the structure shown is tasteless; the

$$CH_3—C=CH—COOC_2H_5$$
$$|$$
$$NH—CH_2C_6H_5$$

lower-melting isomer is sweet.

Oleic acid, m.p. 14°, is *cis*, as shown. Whether its *trans* isomer, elaidic acid,

$$H—C—(CH_2)_7—COOH$$
$$||$$
$$H—C—(CH_2)_7—COOH$$
Oleic acid

m.p. 45°, is equally metabolized apparently has not been established.

Considerable interest attaches to the multiple unsaturated C_{18} acids, especially to linoleic and linolenic acids, because of their "vitagenic" properties. They relieve the symptoms once attributed to deficiency of vitamin F. The spatial configuration of these acids has not been established.

The polyenes of carotenoid structure theoretically may exist in many geometric forms. Fortunately nature avoids structural complexity, for chemical and roentgenographic studies show that nearly all of them exist in the more stable *trans* form. A notable exception is crocin, a pigment isolated from the stigma of the crocus. This pigment is especially interesting because of the part it and its degradation products, including geometric isomers, presumably play in sex processes of certain living substances. This has been demonstrated by Kühn and his co-workers for algae of the Chlamydomonas group.[106] A single molecule activates one gamete (the experimentally determined ratio is six molecules for five cells), either male or female. The degradation of crocin produces the *cis*-crocetin dimethyl ether, which stimulates the feminine characteristics of the isogamous organisms. Irradiation with blue or ultraviolet light converts the *cis* into the *trans* dimethyl ester, which activates the male gametes to copulative activity. Structurally, these manifestations have been summarized by Kühn as shown.

[106] Kühn, *Angew. Chem.*, **53**, 1 (1940).

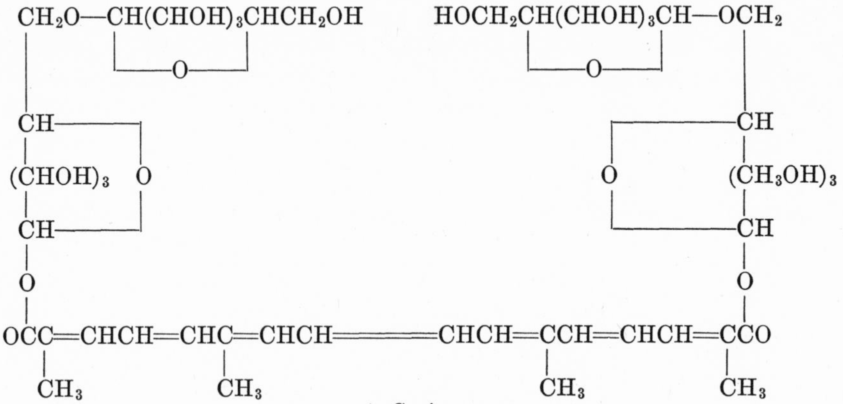

CH$_2$O—CH(CHOH)$_3$CHCH$_2$OH   HOCH$_2$CH(CHOH)$_3$CH—OCH$_2$

CH—

(CHOH)$_3$ O

CH—

O

CH

(CH$_3$OH)$_3$

CH

O

OCC=CHCH=CHC=CHCH══════CHCH=CCH=CHCH=CCO

CH$_3$ CH$_3$ CH$_3$ CH$_3$

Crocin

Under anaerobic conditions activates cells of both sexes—limit of activity 1 molecule per cell.

↓

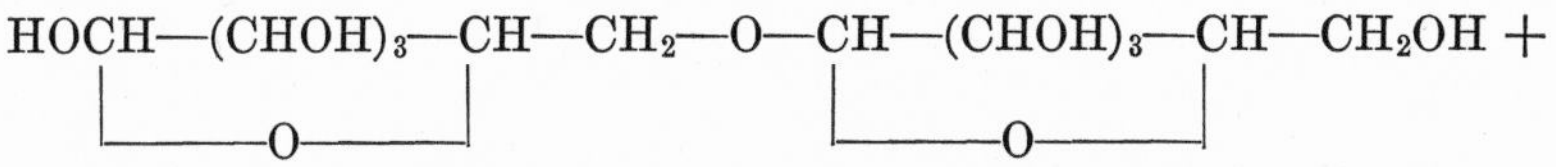

HOCH—(CHOH)$_3$—CH—CH$_2$—O—CH—(CHOH)$_3$—CH—CH$_2$OH +

Gentiobiose (2 molecules)—under anaerobic conditions activates both male and female cells
(chemotaxis)—100 times more active than glucose.

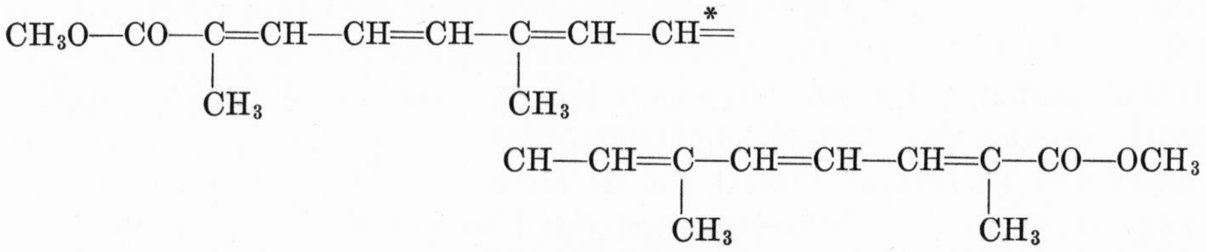

CH$_3$O—CO—C=CH—CH=CH—C=CH—CH═

CH$_3$ CH$_3$

CH—CH=C—CH=CH—CH=C—CO—OCH$_3$

CH$_3$ CH$_3$

Crocetin dimethyl ester

Responsible for the attraction between the male and female gametes leading to copulation—limit
of sensitivity 10,000 molecules per gamete.

* Double bond probably involved in *cis-trans* isomerization.

CHAPTER 14

Antibiotics

An antibiotic is a chemical that is produced by a living organism and that, in a relatively high dilution, will inhibit the growth or reproduction of some other organism. Though quite broad, this definition excludes all synthetics that are not natural products. The important fact to remember is that *antibiotics are chemicals*. As such, they do not differ *fundamentally* from the hundreds of synthetics, such as the sulfa drugs, antimalarials, etc., which have been used for many years for the treatment of the same infections for which the antibiotics are so widely used today. When the glamor of recent years has been forgotten, antibiotics will not be considered as a class of drugs, but will be described in the groups to which they belong—fumagillin as an amebicide, streptomycin as a tuberculostat, penicillin for the treatment of infections caused by Gram-positive bacteria.

The only difference between the antibiotics and other chemicals used for the same purposes is their method of production—and even this difference is not hard and fast. Whereas quinine is extracted from the bark of a tree, and chloramphenicol is now produced entirely by synthesis, most of the antibiotics are produced by culturing microorganisms (bacteria, actinomycetes, molds) in large tanks under specialized conditions. These processes are expensive and difficult to operate, and require highly trained personnel. The development of these technics has made possible the great advances in the treatment of infectious diseases since 1940, when the first clinical results with penicillin became known.

The crucial advantage of the development of the antibiotic field is that the artificial culturing of microorganisms has made available to us certain very valuable chemicals that are too difficult or even impossible to synthesize. There are even antibiotics available whose structure we do not know; yet they are of extremely high value to the medical practitioner. Another great advantage that has accrued is the widening of our horizon pertaining to the types of structures that have value as therapeutic agents. Who would ever have thought—or could have afforded—to develop syntheses for penicillin, streptomycin, or the tetracyclines without first having a knowledge of their great therapeutic value? There certainly is nothing in their structures that would have led one to predict their high antibiotic activities. Finally, another great advantage of research in the antibiotic field is that, by screening against predetermined organisms, one can search for these highly active molecules without a previous knowledge of what they are. One is automatically directed into new fields of chemicals having high biological activity.

The modern history of antibiotics goes back to 1899 when Emmerich and Low used an antibiotic prepared from *B. pyocyaneus* for the treatment of streptococcal and other infections. It proved to be too toxic, however, and its use ceased. After this, one finds many references in the literature to phenomena that are now recognized to have been caused by antibiotics. This was more clearly brought into focus by the publication in 1929 of Fleming's now famous paper on penicillin. Waksman described actinomycin in 1940 but it was too toxic to be useful. The possibilities of the antibiotic field never received full recognition until Florey and his colleagues at Oxford University demonstrated (1940) the highly successful results of using penicillin in the treatment of septic conditions. During the ensuing five years, technics were developed for penicillin production by fermentation, and, at the same time, the intense search for new antibiotics was undertaken on all sides. Many thousands of papers have been published since then, and many hundreds of new antibiotics have been described. Of these, however, only about a dozen have proved to be useful, the rest having been found wanting on the basis of too high toxicity, too low stability, or lack of effectiveness when used *in vivo*. The possibilities are, however, by no means exhausted, and one may look forward with confidence to the development of many more therapeutically effective antibiotics.

The antibiotics find use not only as therapeutic agents, but the prospect of even greater use in agriculture looks bright.[1] They are employed to suppress pathogenic microorganisms that are too mild to be recognizable yet decrease the animal's rate of growth; and they encourage benign organisms that produce vitamins in the intestinal tract, thus modifying favorably the intestinal flora. They seem to affect favorably the intestinal walls to permit better absorption of vitamins and other nutrients. In plants they are absorbed directly into the vascular system from the leaves and stems and thus help the plant fight disease and, perhaps, accelerate the plant's metabolism. Antibiotics can be used by the geneticist to produce mutations in molds.

[1] *Chem. Eng. News*, **33**, 4643 (1955).

THE PENICILLINS

Penicillin is a generic term which refers to a class of compounds produced by various strains of *Penicillium notatum, Penicillium chrysogenum,* and various other molds. The penicillins have the same basic structure; they vary only in the acid portion of the molecule as indicated by R in the structure illustrated below.

Chemical studies of penicillin revealed that the initial product was a mixture of several different and closely related compounds. The constitution of the penicillins was elucidated as the result of collaborative research carried out in many laboratories in the United States and Great Britain in the period 1943–1945.[2] The amounts of a given species produced vary according to the strain of fungi used and the cultural conditions. It has been shown that the yields of penicillin can be increased and that new penicillins may be biosynthesized by the addition of certain precursors to the fermentative media.[3]

The structure of the common penicillins is indicated, and the degradation reactions which served to elucidate these structures are summarized.[4]

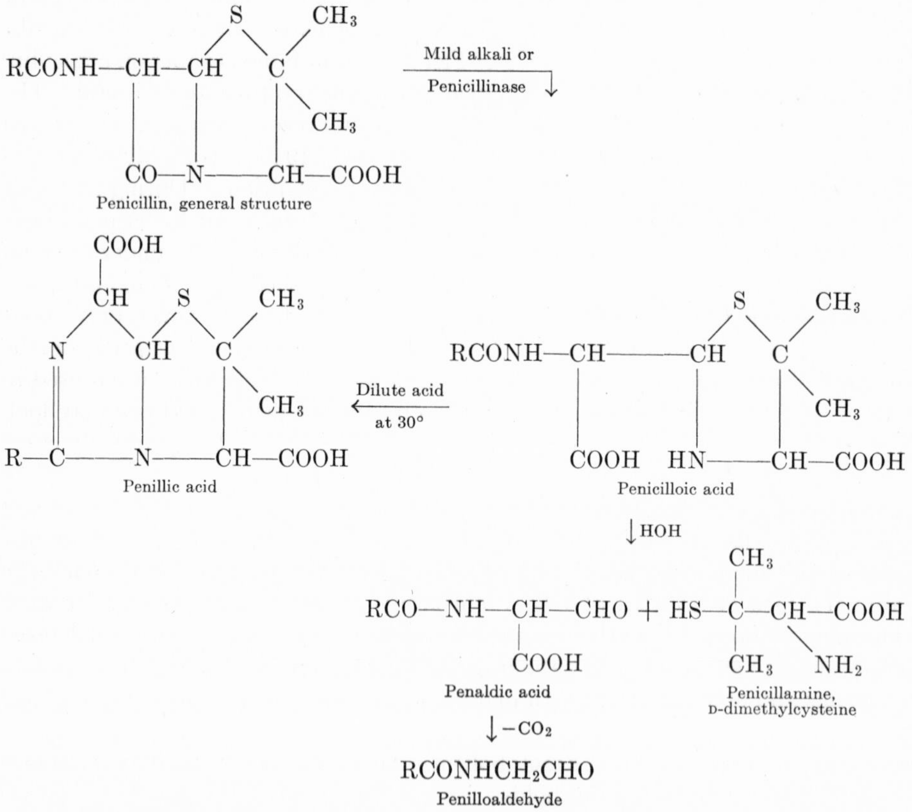

Penicillin, general structure

Penillic acid

Penicilloic acid

Penaldic acid

Penicillamine, D-dimethylcysteine

$$RCO—NH—CH—CHO + HS—C—CH—COOH$$

$$RCONHCH_2CHO$$

Penilloaldehyde

[2] Clarke, H. T., *The Chemistry of Penicillin,* Princeton University Press, Princeton, 1949.
[3] *Science,* **106,** 503 (1947).
[4] *Science,* **102,** 627 (1945).

Because of its availability, stability, and physical properties, most of these degradative studies were carried out on benzylpenicillin, the member of the family most widely used at present.

The common penicillins known to be produced by fermentation are listed with their names and structures in Table XXXVIII.

TABLE XXXVIII

THE NATURAL PENICILLINS

$$
\begin{array}{c}
\qquad\qquad S \\
\qquad\quad /\ \backslash \\
RCONHCH\text{—}CH\qquad C(CH_3)_2 \\
\quad|\qquad\quad|\qquad\quad| \\
\quad CO\text{—}N\text{———}CH\text{—}COOH
\end{array}
$$

R	Chemical Name	American Trade Name	British Trade Name
$CH_3CH_2CH{=}CHCH_2{-}$	2-Pentenylpenicillin	Penicillin F	Penicillin I
$CH_3(CH_2)_4{-}$	n-Amylpenicillin	Dihydropenicillin F	Dihydropenicillin I
$C_6H_5CH_2{-}$	Benzylpenicillin	Penicillin G	Penicillin II
$p\text{-}HOC_6H_4CH_2{-}$	p-Hydroxybenzylpenicillin	Penicillin X	Penicillin III
$CH_3(CH_2)_6{-}$	n-Heptylpenicillin	Penicillin K	Penicillin IV

In addition to the natural penicillins, there is a host of "biosynthetic" penicillins possible. For example, when phenylacetic acid derivatives are present, the mold utilizes such precursors [5] directly, resulting in a greatly increased yield of benzylpenicillin. The addition of other precursors to the fermentation broth has resulted in a wide variety of new penicillins, some of which have therapeutic advantages over the natural forms.

Commercial penicillin may contain one or more of the penicillins in varying proportions. Since the different species of penicillin have different activities, the introduction of pure crystalline penicillin [6] marked a great advancement. Crystalline penicillin in the dry state is stable, but solutions of the crystals lose potency rapidly at ordinary temperatures. The crystalline purified amorphous salts are free from many toxic impurities that occurred often in products when penicillin was first introduced. Consequently, massive doses may be given without danger, other than systemic reactions encountered in susceptible individuals. Other advantages of the purified crystalline penicillin over less pure amorphous mixtures are less irritation, absence of local pain or reaction at the site of injection, certainty of full therapeutic effect, and greater stability of preparations.

The potency of penicillin is expressed in terms of units per milligram of drug. The unit is defined as the activity present in 0.6 microgram of the penicillin master standard consisting of crystalline sodium penicillin established by the

[5] Clarke, Johnson, and Robinson, *The Chemistry of Penicillin*, Princeton University Press, Princeton, 1949.

[6] Schmidt, Ward, and Coghill, *J. Bact.*, **49**, 11 (1945). Also see *Science*, **106**, 504 (1947) for other values.

U. S. Food and Drug Administration.[7] One mg. of crystalline penicillin is equivalent to 1667 Oxford units.

The use of penicillin has passed through the stage of uncertainty concerning the indications, dosage, and methods of administration. Technics for accurate bacteriological diagnosis, measurement of the degree of susceptibility of organisms, and determination of the blood level of penicillin have been devised. Most susceptible organisms are controlled by a blood level of about 0.15 unit of penicillin per cubic centimeter of serum. The choice of method of treatment, duration of treatment, and adjuvant therapy depend on the individual case. The difficulty of maintaining effective blood levels of penicillin have been overcome by the introduction of products that suppress the excretion of the antibiotic through the renal tubules. Examples of such agents are Caronamide (page 292) and Probenicid (page 292).

Penicillin is active in general against Gram-positive microorganisms, and inactive, with certain exceptions, against Gram-negative forms. It acts on a culture of *S. aureus* to liberate glutamic acid, aspartic acid, alanine, and serine into the medium; the loss of these amino acids by the organism might explain the activity of penicillin.[8] Organisms rich in sulfhydryl groups are more resistant than those poorer in that group.[9] A partial list of conditions and diseases that respond to adequate penicillin therapy include anthrax, tetanus, diphtheria, pneumonia, meningitis, gonorrhea, syphilis, septicemias, actinomycosis, and bacterial endocarditis.

The antibiotic may be used topically, orally, or parenterally. When used parenterally, the intramuscular route is the method of choice; in oral therapy, the dosage must be much larger (at least fivefold) because of destruction in the digestive tract as well as incomplete and variable absorption.

Penicillin is the least toxic of all the antibacterial drugs. Enormous doses can be administered without adverse effects. However, there is mounting concern over the high incidence of sensitization caused by penicillin therapy. Approximately 5 per cent of those receiving the drug may suffer from some degree of allergic response varying from skin manifestations to anaphylactic shock and death.

A second major problem encountered is the large number of penicillin-resistant organisms that are found regularly. This drawback is being overcome with the advent of newer "broad-spectrum" antibiotics and therapy designed to alternate the antibiotics used against a given organism.

Penicillin, being an acid, forms soluble salts including those of sodium, potassium, and calcium. The dry sodium and potassium salts are available in ampules for sterile injections or inhalations. The dry calcium salt may be applied topi-

---

[7] Defined in the *Federal Register*, November, 1946, Chapter 1, Food and Drug Administration, Part 146: "Crystalline Penicillin G is crystalline penicillin which contains not less than 90 per cent of the sodium salt of penicillin G."

[8] Kubo and Yamamoto, *Symposium on Enzyme Chem. (Japan)*, **5**, 100 (1950); *C.A.*, **46**, 2124 (1952).

[9] Ishui, Igakuto, *Seibutsugaka*, **21**, 120 (1951); *C.A.*, **46**, 10294 (1952).

cally as a powder or in an ointment. Other dosage forms include a sterile suspension of a salt in oil and wax for intramuscular injection, buffered oral tablets, and lozenges or troches. The use of depot or repository preparations has helped to overcome the rapid excretion of the drug. This dosage form accompanied by the use of very insoluble salts of penicillin has permitted the attainment of high blood levels over long periods of time.

Potassium Penicillin, U.S.P. (Benzyl Penicillin Potassium, Penicillin G Potassium), is the crystalline potassium salt of benzylpenicillin. It is the cheapest and most widely distributed of all the penicillins. It is a soluble form of the antibiotic and is available in tablets for oral use.

Procaine Penicillin G, U.S.P. (Benzyl Penicillin Procaine, Penicillin G Procaine), is the insoluble salt formed by the reaction of procaine with an equimolecular quantity of benzylpenicillin. This form of the antibiotic has achieved great popularity in repository dosage forms which permit the injection of penicillin at much less frequent intervals.

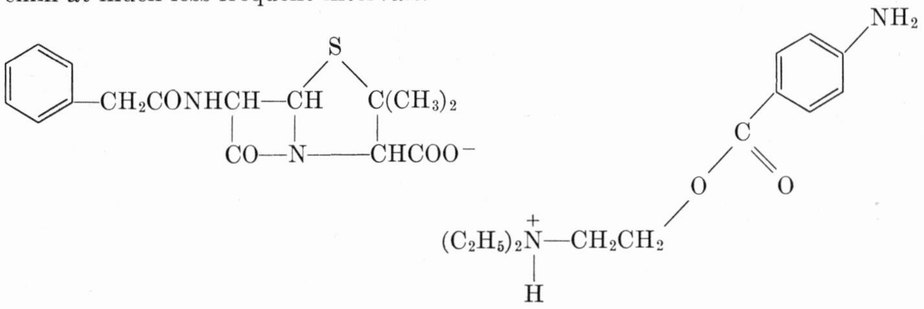

Procaine penicillin

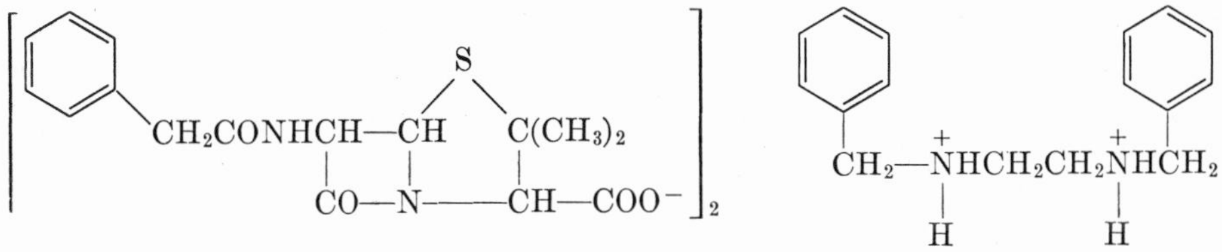

Benzathine penicillin

Benzathine Penicillin G, U.S.P. (Dibenzyl Penicillin, Bicillin), is the salt formed by the reaction of two moles of benzylpenicillin with one mole of N,N'-dibenzylethylenediamine. It is an essentially tasteless compound having a solubility in water of only 0.02 per cent. In a single dose of 300,000 units it is said [10] to give detectable blood levels of penicillin over periods of up to 17 days.

Potassium Penicillin O, N.N.R. (Cer-O-Cillin Potassium), is a biosynthetic penicillin resulting from the addition of S-allylmercaptoacetic acid to the fermentation broth. It is said to produce no allergic reactions in penicillin-sensitive patients. Penicillin O is also available as the 2-chloroprocaine salt, an insoluble form of this antibiotic.

[10] Welch, Randall, and Hendricks, *Antibiotics and Chemotherapy*, **1**, 491 (1951).

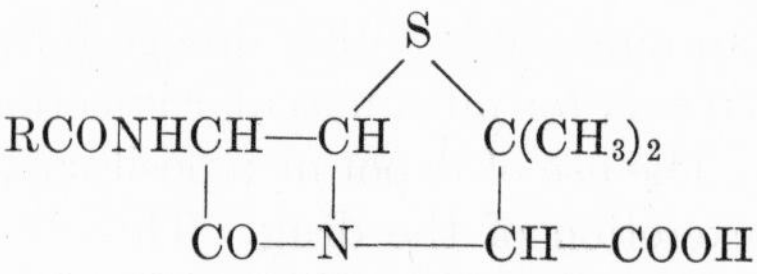

$$
\begin{array}{ccc}
& & S \\
& & / \backslash \\
\text{RCONHCH}-\text{CH} & & \text{C(CH}_3)_2 \\
| & | & | \\
\text{CO}-\text{N}-& & \text{CH}-\text{COOH}
\end{array}
$$

R = CH$_2$=CHCH$_2$SCH$_2$—, Penicillin O
  = C$_6$H$_5$OCH$_2$—, Penicillin V

Penicillin V (Phenoxymethylpenicillin, V-Cillin) is prepared biosynthetically by the addition of phenoxyacetic acid to the fermentation broth as a precursor. It is unusually stable in solution, making possible its therapeutic use in oral form. The greater availability of Penicillin V for absorption leads to higher blood levels than those obtained with other oral penicillin preparations.[11]

STREPTOMYCIN

Streptomycin, from *Streptomyces griseus* was discovered by Waksman in 1944. The manufacture consists of four main processes, namely, fermentation, recovery, purification, and finishing.[12] It may be obtained as pure crystals in the form of streptomycin calcium chloride complex, $C_{21}H_{39}O_{12}N_7 \cdot 3HCl \cdot \frac{1}{2}CaCl_2$.[13] On hydrolysis streptomycin yields streptidine, a natural guanidine derivative which has been identified as the meso form of 1,3-diguanidine-2,4,5,6-tetrahydroxycyclohexane, and streptobiosamine which is linked to streptidine through the 4 position.[14,15,16] The structures of streptomycin and its hydrolytic products may be indicated as shown.

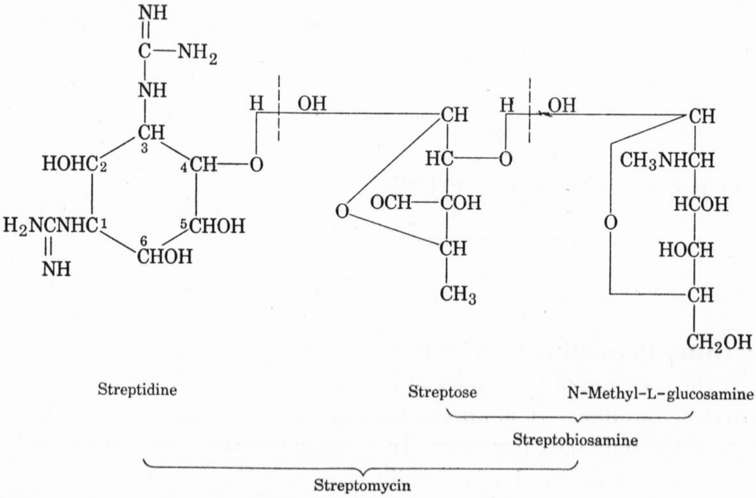

Streptidine   Streptose   N-Methyl-L-glucosamine

Streptobiosamine

Streptomycin

---

[11] Welch, *Antibiotic Med.*, **2,** 11 (1956).

[12] Porter, *Chem. Eng.*, **53,** 94 (Oct. 1946).

[13] Porter, *The Merck Report*, **56,** 4 (1947).

[14] Peck, Hoffhine, Peel, Graber, Holly, Mozingo, and Folkers, *J. Am. Chem. Soc.*, **68,** 776 (1946).

[15] Kuehl, Peck, Hoffhine, Peel, and Folkers, *J. Am. Chem. Soc.*, **69,** 1234 (1947).

[16] Kuehl, Peck, Hoffhine, and Folkers, *J. Am. Chem. Soc.*, **70,** 2325 (1948).

Streptomycin is an organic base, forming salts which are relatively stable in solution over a pH range of 4 to 7. It is rapidly inactivated by 0.1 N NaOH or 0.1 N HCl. Streptomycin calcium chloride complex can be stored at temperatures not exceeding 30° for periods up to one year without significant loss of potency. Solutions are less stable, and when intended for parenteral administration, they should be freshly prepared. The sulfate and hydrochloride salts are soluble in water and slightly soluble or insoluble in most organic solvents.

Streptomycin is effective in many Gram-negative bacillary infections,[17] including: tularemia, influenzal meningitis and pneumonia, meningitis, plague, Shigella dysentery, and infections of the urinary tract, wounds and bacteremias caused by *Escherichia coli, Bacillus proteus, Pseudomonas aeruginosa,* and *Aerobacter aerogenes.* It is often effective against Gram-positive organisms causing diseases that are resistant to penicillin and the sulfonamides, such as septicemia due to hemolytic streptococci, *Staphylococcus aureus* and *Staphylococcus albus* infections, anthrax, and diphtheria. For the treatment of tuberculosis streptomycin is used alone or in combination with p-aminosalicylic acid or isoniazid.

Streptomycin is of low toxicity, but repeated large doses over longer periods of time may lead to toxic reactions. It is usually administered by injection in concentration of 10 to 25 per cent.

Dihydrostreptomycin, U.S.P., is produced by reduction of the aldehyde group of the streptose moiety to a primary alcohol. It is not available as the base but is dispensed as the hydrochloride or sulfate salt.

The hydrochloride or sulfate salts occur as white or faintly yellow granules or white powder which are soluble in water but in general insoluble in organic solvents. They are not affected by air or light.

Its action and uses are very similar to streptomycin. It is reported to cause less neural damage, thus permitting continuous and adequate therapy with less toxic reactions to the eighth cranial nerve. It is also claimed to have fewer allergic reactions than streptomycin.

THE TETRACYCLINE GROUP

Three very important closely related antibiotics contain the naphthacene skeleton. These are **Tetracycline, Chlortetracycline,** and **Oxytetracycline,** all of which are produced by actinomycetes. Chlortetracycline (Aureomycin) is a product of the fermentation of *Streptomyces aureofaciens* and oxytetracycline (Terramycin) is isolated from *Streptomyces rimosus.* Tetracycline is also produced by *Streptomyces aureofaciens* as well as other *Streptomyces* organisms. Unraveling the structures of chlortetracycline and oxytetracycline resulted from the work of two independent groups of chemists on the respective antibiotics. That their paths were converging and that tetracycline was common to both soon became obvious. The chemical relationship between the three antibiotics can be seen from their structural formulation.

[17] *J. Am. Med. Assoc.,* **135,** 839 (1947).

The tetracyclines

Tetracycline, R_1 = H; R_2 = H.
Chlortetracycline, R_1 = Cl; R_2 = H.
Oxytetracycline, R_1 = H; R_2 = OH.

The proof of structure of oxytetracycline and chlortetracycline was the object of very intensive research. Space does not permit a complete description of all the work involved since each major degradation product in turn required further degradation as well as synthetic studies for its own proof of structure. The puzzle for oxytetracycline was solved first; the complete chemistry of its structure proof was described by Hochstein and his co-workers [18] in 1953.

Oxytetracycline, U.S.P. (Terramycin), is a yellow, crystalline amphoteric substance, forming well-defined salts with acids or bases and having a molecular formula of $C_{22}H_{24}N_2O_9$. Spectrographic and titration evidence early indicated that of the eight active hydrogens present, two could be indentified as phenolic or enolic. Through the action of acetic anhydride two alcoholic hydroxyls were identified and treatment with alkali liberated dimethylamine and ammonia. The principal degradation reactions are summarized briefly on the next page.

Chlortetracycline, U.S.P. (Aureomycin), is a golden yellow, crystalline compound having an empirical formula of $C_{22}H_{23}N_2O_8Cl$; like oxytetracycline, it too is amphoteric and forms salts with acids or bases. Comparison of the chemical, biological, and physical data for chlortetracycline and oxytetracycline suggested at an early date the close structural relationship between the two antibiotics. The alkaline degradation of chlortetracycline gave rise to dimethylamine, ammonia, and *5-chlorosalicylic acid.* Speculation on this evidence alone indicated that chlortetracycline was a 7-chloro-5-desoxyterramycin. The degradation studies on chlortetracycline were reported in a series of papers by Waller, Hutchings, and their co-workers [19] and additional proof of structure was provided by Stephens and his co-workers.[20] These degradation studies are summarized on page 492.

Tetracycline, U.S.P. (Achromycin, Polycycline, Stecline, Tetracyn), chemically the most stable of the series, is a crystalline base having a molecular formula of $C_{22}H_{24}N_2O_8$; it has essentially the chemical features of both oxytetracycline and chlortetracycline. It is unique in that its biological activity was first discovered during the chemical investigation of the structures of the parent

[18] Hochstein, Stephens, Conover, Regna, Pasternack, Gordon, Pilgrim, Brunings, and Woodward, *J. Am. Chem. Soc.*, **75**, 5455 (1953).

[19] Waller, Hutchings, *et al.*, *J. Am. Chem. Soc.*, **74**, 3710, 4978, 4979, 4980, 4981 (1952).

[20] Stephens *et al.*, *J. Am. Chem. Soc.*, **76**, 3568 (1954).

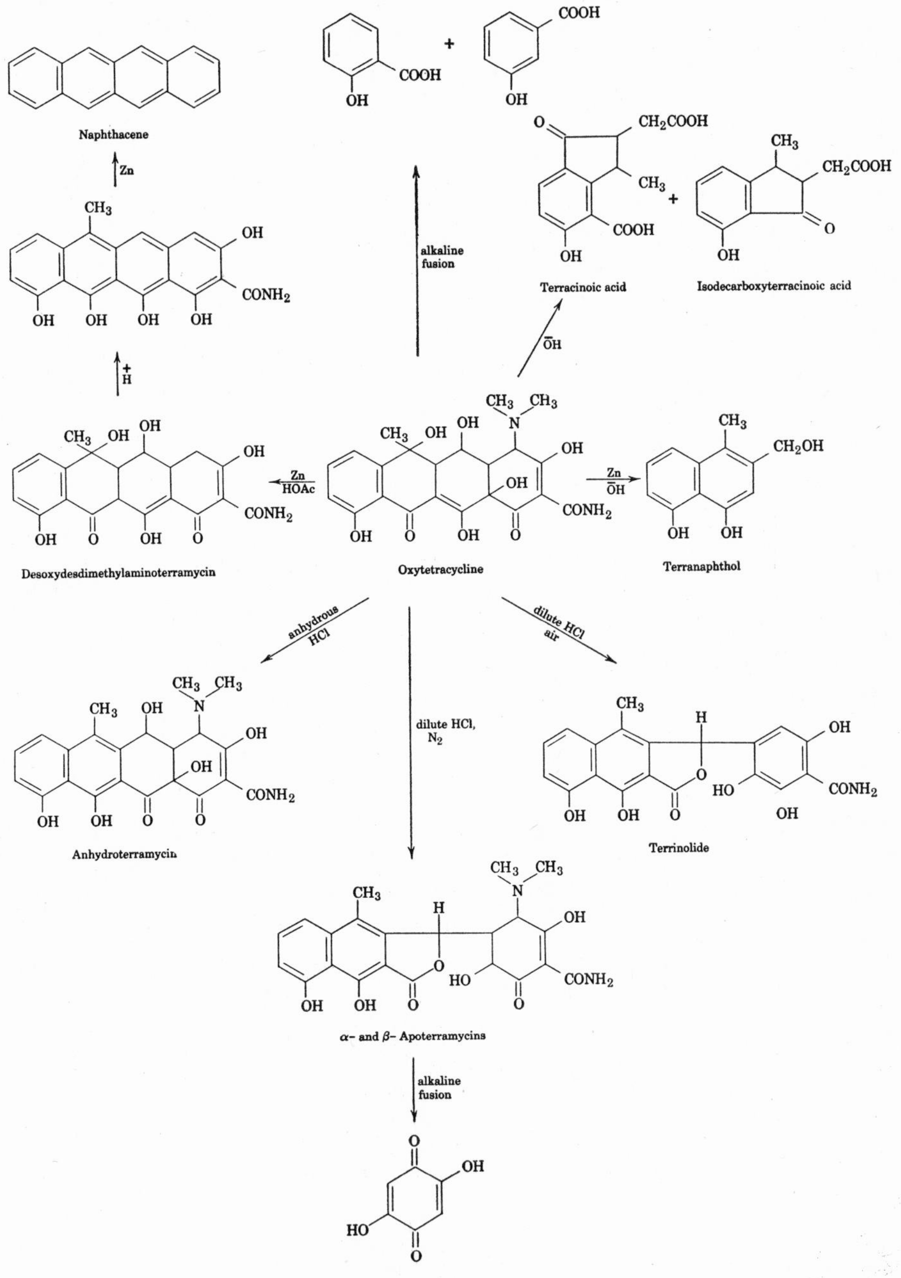
Naphthacene
Zn
alkaline fusion
Terracinoic acid
Isodecarboxyterracinoic acid
Desoxydesdimethylaminoterramycin
Zn HOAc
Oxytetracycline
Zn OH
Terranaphthol
anhydrous HCl
dilute HCl, N2
dilute HCl air
Anhydroterramycin
Terrinolide
α- and β- Apoterramycins
alkaline fusion

Degradation reactions of oxytetracycline

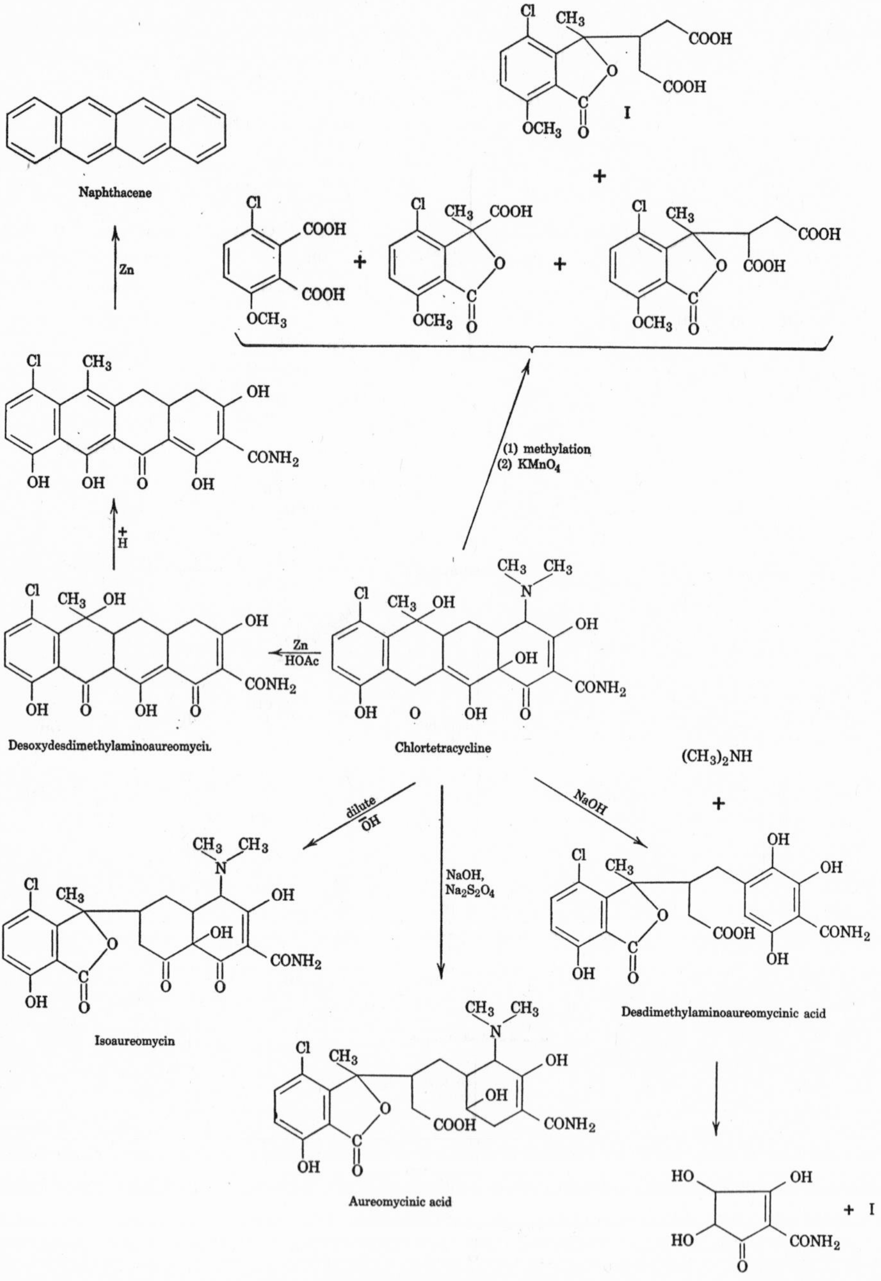
I
Naphthacene
Zn
(1) methylation
(2) KMnO4
Zn
HOAc
Desoxydesdimethylaminoaureomycin
Chlortetracycline
(CH3)2NH
dilute
OH
NaOH,
Na2S2O4
NaOH
Isoaureomycin
Desdimethylaminoaureomycinic acid
Aureomycinic acid
+ I

Degradation reactions of chlortetracycline

antibiotics. Although it can be obtained by fermentation methods, it is readily synthesized by the catalytic hydrogenation of chlortetracycline. The chemical conversion of chlortetracycline to tetracycline, simultaneously announced by two groups of investigators,[21] is illustrated below:

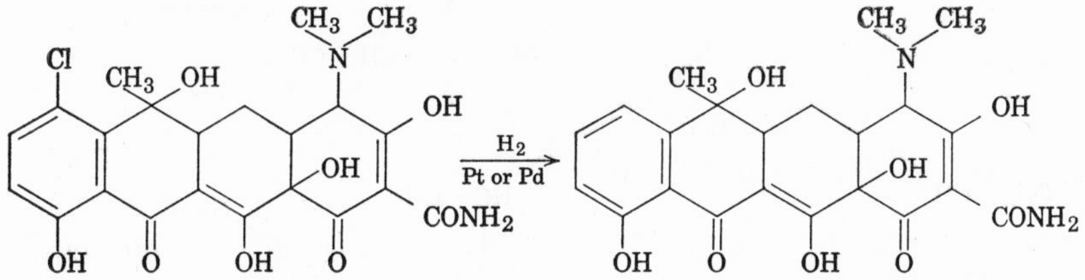

Chlortetracycline   Tetracycline

Biological Activity. The antibiotics of the tetracycline group are highly active against numerous Gram-positive and Gram-negative organisms as well as rickettsiae and certain viruses and are therefore called broad-spectrum antibiotics. They have proved to be especially valuable against penicillin-resistant Gram-positive bacteria. However, once resistance to one of the tetracycline group has developed by a particular organism, that organism develops cross-resistance to the other tetracyclines.

These antibiotics are orally effective and are generally nontoxic; the side reactions are rarely serious and consist of nausea, vomiting, and diarrhea. Tetracycline is thought to be less toxic and to cause less gastrointestinal side effects. The members of the tetracycline group of antibiotics are recommended for the treatment of a variety of infections including pneumonia, actinomycosis, brucellosis, urinary infections, Rocky Mountain spotted fever, and typhus fever.

The wide antibacterial activity of the members of this group on prolonged ingestion may cause complete sterility of the gut which may lead to the development of secondary fungal infections in the mouth and gastrointestinal tract. The risk of the growth of *Monilia* such as *Candida albicans* is serious.

Another serious complication, antibiotic enterocolitis, may be caused owing to the replacement of the normal intestinal flora by strains of organisms not susceptible to the antibiotics. The indiscriminate use of these compounds as prophylactics is to be guarded against.

ERYTHROMYCIN

Erythromycin, U.S.P. (Erythrocin, Ilotycin), is a crystalline antibiotic produced by *Streptomyces erythreus* fermentation.[22] It is a basic compound soluble in most organic solvents but only sparingly soluble in water. Its accepted structure is indicated.[23]

[21] Booth, Morton, Petisi, Wilkinson, and Williams, *J. Am. Chem. Soc.*, **75**, 4621 (1953). Conover, Moreland, English, Stephens, and Pilgrim, *J. Am. Chem. Soc.*, **75**, 4622 (1953).

[22] McGuire, *Antibiotics and Chemotherapy*, **2**, 281 (1952).

[23] Wiley *et al.*, *J. Am. Chem. Soc.*, **77**, 3677 (1955); **78**, 388, 808 (1956).

CH₃   CH₃
N
CH
HOCH   CH₂   Desosamine
CH₃   CH₂   CH   CH—CH₃
CH   CH   O
C=O   HO
CH₃—CH   O   CH
O   HC—CH₃
HC—OH   OH   O   CH   CH—CH₃
C   H   CH   CH₂   CHOH
CH₃   CH   C   CH₃   C
CH₂   O   C=O   CH₃   OCH₃
CH₃   Cladinose

Erythromycin

Erythromycin is active against Gram-positive bacteria and to some extent against Gram-negative organisms. It has potency against mycobacteria, typhus, rickettsiae, and some of the larger viruses. It is active against many of the organisms that have become resistant to penicillin, streptomycin, and the tetracycline group. Although various organisms have become resistant to erythromycin, no cross-resistance has developed with any of the other antibiotics in common use with the exception of carbomycin.

Clinically erythromycin is useful for the treatment of staphylococcal and streptococcal infections, pneumonia, and scarlet fever. It is quite nontoxic and the side effects encountered in its use are rare. Erythromycin is available in various forms for topical, oral, and parenteral administration. Its bitter taste has been masked by the use of coated tablets or through the formation of tasteless derivatives such as the stearate salt or the ethyl carbonate ester.

A second crystalline antibiotic, designated as Erythromycin B, has been isolated [24] from *Streptomyces erythreus*. It is considerably more stable to acid than erythromycin. Early degradative studies [25] indicate a structural resemblance between the two Erythromycins. Although Erythromycin B is only 75 per cent as active as erythromycin, the bacterial spectra of the two antibiotics are esssentially identical.[26]

Neomycin Sulfate, N.N.R. (Mycifradin Sulfate), is a polybasic compound whose structure has not been elucidated and which is obtained by deep fermentation of *Streptomyces fradiae* in a suitable media. It is a water-soluble compound which differs from other antibiotics in that it is extremely stable, retaining its potency for as much as 2 years in the dry state at room temperature. It is very

[24] Pettinga, Stark, and VanAbeela, *J. Am. Chem. Soc.*, **76**, 569 (1954).
[25] Clark and Taterka, *Antibiotics and Chemotherapy*, **5**, 206 (1955).
[26] Grundy *et al.*, *ibid.*, **5**, 212 (1955).

active in alkaline solutions and retains its activity in the presence of exudates, enzymes, gastrointestinal secretions, digestive products, and bacterial growth.

Neomycin Sulfate exhibits activity against both Gram-positive and Gram-negative bacteria, and it is claimed to have a broader antibacterial spectrum than bacitracin, penicillin, or streptomycin.

It is useful topically in solutions or ointments for the treatment or prevention of skin and eye infections by susceptible organisms. Orally, it finds value in surgery as an intestinal antiseptic for suppression of the common bacterial flora of the colon, large bowel, and anus. It is well tolerated and relatively non-irritating.

Carbomycin, N.N.R. (Magnamycin), is a monobasic antibiotic whose structure has not been elucidated and which is obtained by deep fermentation of *Streptomyces halstedii* in a suitable media. It is a white powder very slightly soluble in water.

It possesses a strong inhibitory activity against certain Gram-positive organisms. It may be used in the treatment of infections caused by staphylococci, pneumococci, and hemolytic streptococci. It exhibits a low order of toxicity in experimental animals.

It is administered orally in the treatment of infections caused by organisms indicated above in such conditions as pneumonia, urinary tract infections, abscesses, and tonsillitis.

CHLORAMPHENICOL

Chloramphenicol, U.S.P. (Chloromycetin, $D(-)$-*Threo*-1-p-nitrophenyl-2-dichloroacetamido-1,3-propandiol), is an antibiotic that may be prepared either by fermentation or synthesis. It is synthesized commerically from p-nitro-ω-bromoacetophenone by the accompanying sequence of reactions.

Chloramphenicol

When pure the product is a white, needlelike crystal or elongated plate which is neutral in reaction. It is slightly soluble in water, 1:400, but freely soluble in alcohol and propylene glycol. It is fairly stable in a neutral or in a moderately acid solution and unstable in dilute alkali, being inactivated to the extent of 87 per cent at pH 10.8. The dry form is stable at room temperature. It is more stable in solution than are penicillin or streptomycin.

Chloromycetin has a bitter taste which is difficult to mask. The bitter taste makes oral administration less desirable. In an effort to prepare tasteless derivatives the palmintic acid ester has been chosen for oral administration for children and adults who must have a more palatable product.

Chloromycetin is an antibiotic with a broad spectrum, being effective against diseases caused by spirochetes, Gram-negative bacteria, rickettsiae, and large viruses such as atypical pneumonia. It is not effective against fungal and protozoan infection. Thus, it is effective in the management of relapsing fever, syphilis, undulant fever, whooping cough, gonorrhea, typhoid fever, Rocky Mountain spotted fever, scrub typhus, murine typhus, and Q fever. It appears to be the drug of choice for typhoid fever.[27]

The use of Chloromycetin therapy has raised some concern in view of the development of aplastic anemia by a few patients on prolonged medication with this antibiotic. Statistical evidence indicates that the incidence of aplastic anemia has not increased since the use of this drug began. It is possible that the disease existed in these patients prior to the administration of the drug or could have been caused by other drugs administered concurrently with chloromycetin.

PUROMYCIN

Puromycin   [6-Dimethylamino-9-(3'-p-methoxy-L-phenylalanylamino-3'-deoxy-β-D-ribofuranosyl)purine] is an antibiotic obtained from the fermentation of *Streptomyces alboniger*. It has been reported [28] active against certain Gram-positive and Gram-negative organisms and more interestingly against experimental trypanosomiasis [28] and experimental tumors.[29] In addition, it has shown promising activity against *Endamoeba histolytica* infections in the rat and guinea pig.[30]

As indicated by its structure, Puromycin contains a purine, an amino sugar

Puromycin

[27] Olive, *Chem. Eng.*, **56**, No. 10, 107–113, 172–175 (1949).

[28] Porter *et al.*, *Antibiotics and Chemotherapy*, **2**, 409 (1952).

[29] Troy *et al.*, *Antibiotics Annual 1953–1954*, p. 186, Medical Encyclopedia, Inc., New York, 1953.

[30] Taylor, Bond, and Sherman, *Antibiotics Annual 1954–1955*, p. 745, Medical Encyclopedia, Inc., New York, 1955.

and an amino acid portion. Cleavage of the p-methoxyphenylalanine portion of the molecule with methanolic sodium methoxide affords an "aminonucleoside" in which the trypanocidal activity and activity against tumors resides.[31] The total synthesis of Puromycin from D-xylose has been described.[32]

CYCLOSERINE

Cycloserine, Oxamycin (Seromycin) is D-4-amino-3-isoxazolidone, an antibiotic elaborated by the organisms *Streptomyces orchidaceous* and *garyphalus*. This antibiotic exists in aqueous solution as a dipolar ion and has been synthesized as indicated.[33] It is a crystalline material unstable in acidic and neutral solutions but stable to treatment with base.

D-4-Amino-3-isoxazolidone
(Cycloserine, Oxamycin)

Cycloserine is considered a broad-spectrum antibiotic being active *in vitro* and *in vivo* against Gram-positive and Gram-negative bacteria and against rickettsial infections and certain Protozoa.[34] It appears to have some synergistic effects in combination with other antibiotics.

Early results of its clinical trial indicate [35] that cycloserine will have some usefulness in the treatment of infectious diseases caused by penicillin-resistant organisms and may have a place in tuberculosis therapy in combination with dihydrostreptomycin.

[31] Baker, Joseph, and Williams, *J. Am. Chem. Soc.*, **76**, 2838 (1954).
[32] Baker, Schaub, Joseph, and Williams, *J. Am. Chem. Soc.*, **76**, 4044 (1954).
[33] Stammer, Wilson, Holly, and Folkers, *J. Am. Chem. Soc.*, **77**, 2346 (1955).
[34] Cuckler, Frost, McClelland, and Solotorovsky, *Antibiotics and Chemotherapy*, **5**, 191 (1955).
[35] Robinson *et al.*, *Antibiotics and Chemotherapy*, **6**, 35 (1955).

TYROTHRICIN

Tyrothricin, U.S.P., is a mixture of antibacterial substances elaborated by *Bacillus brevis* Dubos (Fam. Bacteriaceae). The mixture consists principally of the tyrocidines and gramicidins, and it is effective primarily against Gram-positive microorganisms.

Tyrocidine is a mixture of three major components, of which tyrocidine A and tyrocidine B have been established as cyclic decapeptides, as shown.[36]

$$CH_2-NH_2(L) \quad CH_3 \quad CH_3(L)$$

$$
\begin{array}{ccccccc}
CH_3 \quad CH_3(L) & CH_2 & CH & C_6H_5(D) & CH_2 \\
CH & CH_2 & CH_2 & CH_2 & CH_2 \quad CH_2(L) \\
CH-CO-NH-CH-CO-NH-CH-CO-NH-CH-CO-N----CH-CO \\
NH & & & & NH \\
CO-CH-NH-CO-CH-NH-CO-CH-NH-CO-CH-NH-CO-CH \\
CH_2 & CH_2 & CH_2 & CH_2 & R(L) \\
C_6H_4OH(L) & CH_2 & COOH(L) & C_6H_5(D) \\
& COOH(L)
\end{array}
$$

Tyrocidine A, R = $-CH_2$ [indole ring structure]

Tyrocidine B, R = $-CH_2C_6H_5$

Gramicidin is a group of heteromeric polypeptides characterized by the presence of ethanolamine. It is a mixture of at least four substances, of which three have been isolated and the fractions given the letters A, B, and C, respectively. Chemical evidence suggests that the molecular weights are about 8700, and crystallographic data suggest a molecule perhaps half that large. The composition of gramicidins A and B has been established to be as shown.[37]

Fragment	Number in Gramicidin A	Gramicidin B
Glycine	5	5
Alanine	9	10
Valine	17	17
Leucine	20	21
Phenylalanine	0	5
Tryptophan	20	18
Ethanolamine	4	4

Gramicidin S, elaborated by a related strain of *B. brevis*, is a cyclic decapeptide in which the sequence of components has been determined as L-valyl-L-ornithyl-L-leucyl-D-phenylalanyl-1-prolyl-.[38]

[36] King and Craig, *J. Am. Chem. Soc.*, **77**, 6627 (1955).

[37] Bricas and Fromageot, *Advances in Protein Chemistry*, Vol. VIII, p. 62, Academic Press, New York, 1953.

[38] Abbott and Ambrose, *Proc. Roy. Soc. (London)*, **A219**, 17 (1953); *C.A.*, **47**, 11989 (1953).

NOVOBIOCIN

Novobiocin Sodium, N.N.R., of indicated structure, is derived from *Strep-*

Novobiocin sodium

tomyces niveus. It inhibits the growth *in vitro* of many Gram-positive organisms, but has little or no activity against Gram-negative bacilli. It is reported to be particularly active against *Micrococcus pyogenes*, var. *aureus*.

ANTIBIOTICS OF UNSOLVED STRUCTURE

Bacitracin, N.N.R., produced by *Bacillus subtilis*, is a water-, glycerol- and propylene-glycol-soluble, neutral polypeptide. It is stable in the dry state and in acid solution but unstable in strong alkaline solutions. It is not digested by proteolytic enzymes or inactivated by penicillinase. It is inactivated by oxidizing agents. It is active chiefly against Gram-positive organisms and inactive against most Gram-negative bacteria. However, it is ineffective against most aerobic Gram-negative bacilli.

Bacitracin is indicated in the treatment and prevention of infections caused by susceptible organisms. It is administered intramuscularly for the treatment of systemic infections and for localized infections by local injections. It may be used topically by incorporating it in either water-soluble or petrolatum bases for saline solutions for the treatment of infections of the skin, eye, nose, etc. It may be used by inhalation for respiratory infections. Bacitracin does not develop sensitiveness for most patients after repeated use. Bacteria are very slow to develop resistance.

Care must be exercised in its use in that large doses may produce renal tubular swelling; albuminuria occurs after the second or third day but falls back to normal with continued use, and other toxic manifestation may result. Before injections the urine should be examined for albumin, casts, and other cellular materials, and during its use the fluid intake should be measured and the output measured and examined to observe kidney function. With an output of 1000 ml. of urine the fear of toxicity is nil.

Polymyxin B Sulfate, N.N.R. (Aerosporin Sulfate), is a basic polypeptide which contains leucine, threonine, phenylalanine, α,γ-diaminobutyric acid and a fatty acid, $C_9H_{18}O_2$, the structure of which is unknown. It is a white, or slightly colored, scalelike material which is soluble in water and isotonic sodium chloride. The product is derived from *Bacillus polymyxa*.

It is injected intramuscularly for the treatment of pseudomonal bacteremia, meningitis, and urinary tract infections. It is used orally in the nonsystemic treatment of intestinal infections such as Shigella or Pseudomonas enteritis. It is used topically for the treatment of certain local infections responding to Polymyxin B sulfate, especially *Pseudomonas aeruginosa*. It is used in ophthalmic ointments for the treatment or preoperative prophylaxis of eye infections.

Fumagillin (Fumidil) is a rather unusual antibiotic produced by the mold, *Aspergillus fumigatus*, and having the approximate molecular formula $C_{26}H_{34}O_7$. It is a weak crystalline acid, melting at 189–194°. Preliminary data [39] indicate that fumagillin is a monobasic acid having a conjugated system of four double bonds. Schenck and his co-workers [40] reported the results of mild alkaline degradation as indicated.

$$\text{Fumagillin} \quad \xrightarrow{\text{NaOH}} \quad C_{16}H_{26}O_4 + \underset{\text{Alcohol I}}{\text{HOOC---(CH=CH)}_4\text{---COOH}}$$

$$\downarrow \text{Pt, H}_2$$

$$\text{Decahydrofumagillin} \quad \xrightarrow{\text{NaOH}} \quad \underset{\substack{\text{Dihydro-}\\\text{alcohol I}}}{C_{16}H_{28}O_4} + \underset{\text{Sebacic acid}}{\text{HOOC---(CH}_2)_8\text{COOH}}$$

Alcohol I has now been obtained in crystalline form, m.p. 55.5–56°, $[\alpha]_D^{23}$ −68°, and shown to contain an epoxide function.[40a]

The remaining structural features of fumagillin are incomplete; the presently established formulation may be summarized as shown.

$$\left[\begin{array}{c} C_9H_{11}O_2 \\ \text{(3-rings)} \end{array}\right] \begin{array}{l} \text{---CH}_3 \\ \text{---OCH}_3 \\ \text{---O---CO(CH=CH)}_4\text{COOH} \\ \diagdown \\ \quad \text{CHCH=C---CH}_3 \\ \diagup \qquad \qquad | \\ \qquad \qquad \quad \text{CH}_3 \end{array}$$

The biological importance of fumagillin is limited. It is inactive against most organisms of all types but is unique in being a potent amebicide. It is orally active and is available in 10 mg. capsules for the treatment of intestinal amebiasis caused by the parasite, *Endamoeba histolytica*.

Bicyclohexylammonium Fumagillin (Fumidil B) is the soluble dicyclohexylamine salt of fumagillin. The antibiotic has a high specific action against *Nosema apis*, the protozoan parasite that causes *nosema* disease in honeybees.[41]

[39] Eble and Hanson, *Antibiotics and Chemotherapy*, **1**, 54 (1951).

[40] Schenck, Hargie, Tarbell, and Hoffman, *J. Am. Chem. Soc.*, **75**, 2274 (1953); *ibid.*, *Abstracts Am. Chem. Soc.*, 126th meeting, New York, 17N (1954).

[40a] Ross, Tarbell, Lovett, and Cross, *J. Am. Chem. Soc.*, **78**, 4675 (1956).

[41] Bailey, *Nature*, **171**, 212 (1953).

Nystatin, N.N.R. (Mycostatin), of as yet undetermined chemical identity, is produced by *Streptomyces noursei* and is used to treat moniliasis, that is, infections caused by *Candida albicans*.

Neomycin was first isolated as a complex of three components, neomycin A, B, and C, from cultures of *Streptomyces fradiae*, in 1949 by Waksman and Lechevalier. Produced simultaneously is an antifungal substance fracidin, $C_{30}H_{34}N_4O_4$.

Commercial neomycin (contains 90 per cent neomycin B) possesses *in vitro* activity against a variety of Gram-positive, Gram-negative, and acid-fast organisms, but not against fungi or viruses. It occasionally synergizes the activity of penicillin, streptomycin, or bacitracin.[42]

The structure of the neomycins have not been determined, but it appears that they contain a streptidine moiety.

Carbomycin is produced by several strains of *Actinomyces* and is isolated as white, blunt-end, needle-shaped crystals, dec. 199.5–200.5°. It is principally active against Gram-positive organisms, and it is active against rickettsiae and some viruses. It synergizes the tetracyclines against *Endameba histolytica*.[43]

[42] Jawetz, *Antibiotics Monographs No. 5*, Medical Encyclopedia, Inc., New York, 1955, p. 36.
[43] Herrel, *Intern. Record of Med.*, **168**, 469 (1955).

CHAPTER 15

Organometallic Compounds
and Metal Salts

ORGANOMETALLIC COMPOUNDS

In true organometallic compounds the metal is attached directly to a carbon atom. Such compounds are important in the field of chemistry.[1,2] Except for the mercury compounds (unless arsenic and antimony are also considered to be metals) none is used directly in medicine or for medicinal purposes. Organolead compounds have been tried in the treatment of cancer.[3] Organogold compounds have been proposed and tried for the treatment of tuberculosis.[4] Up to the present time, neither lead nor gold compounds have given any particular encouragement to their advocates. As a general rule, all organometallic compounds are extremely toxic; even the therapeutically valuable mercurials are toxic to microorganisms and may be used as disinfectants only because of their greater relative toxicity to these parasitic organisms than to the host.

Aside from the bactericidal use of several organomercurials and the technical use of tetraethyllead as an antiknock in motor fuels, the organometallic compounds are most useful in syntheses.

The alkylmagnesium halides, general formula R—Mg—X, have shown themselves of considerable value in the synthesis of many physiologically active compounds. Such organomagnesium compounds are universally known as Grignard

[1] See the excellent chapter on this class of compounds in Gilman's *Organic Chemistry*, 489–580, John Wiley & Sons, New York, 1943.

[2] See also Gilman, *Science*, **93**, 47 (1941).

[3] Bischoff *et al.*, *J. Pharmacol.*, **34**, 85 (1928).

[4] Fischl u. Schlossberger, *Handbuch der Chemotherapie*, Fischers, Leipzig, 1934.

reagents after Victor Grignard whose investigations first described their usefulness as synthetic intermediates. Grignard reagents [5] where R can be either alkyl or aryl have been used to synthesize many different classes of organic compounds including hydrocarbons, alcohols, ketones, esters, and ethers.

Gold Compounds

Gold, as one of the precious metals, was highly regarded as a medicinal agent in early times. It was used in the treatment of syphilis at the time of Paracelsus. Later, gold compounds were introduced for the treatment of tuberculosis because gold salts were bactericidal to the tubercle bacillus when tested *in vitro*. It was found that effective concentrations of gold could not be maintained in the body with safety and that the results that could be obtained were disappointing. The literature relative to the use of gold salts for the treatment of tuberculosis, chronic arthritis, cancer, and other diseases is very extensive.

The gold salts are now used to treat rheumatoid arthritis, and, despite the successful use of cortisone, hydrocortisone, and phenylbutazone, gold is still considered to have an important therapeutic effect against the disease. The efficacy of gold therapy in nondisseminated lupus erythematosus is well established with about one-third of the cases being cured.

Various colloidal gold preparations have been used in these indications but are of questionable value. The inorganic salt, **Gold Sodium Thiosulfate, N.F.,** has been one of the most effective agents but is being replaced by gold preparations having lower toxicity. Organic derivatives that have been used include:

Aurothioglucose, N.F. (Solganal), is a water-soluble gold derivative of thioglucose containing 50 per cent gold. It is administered by intramuscular injection of a suspension in oil for use against lupus erythematosus and rheumatoid arthritis. It is considered to be much less toxic than gold sodium thiomalate.[6]

$$
\begin{array}{cc}
\text{HOCH}_2\text{—CH} & \text{HC—S—Au} \\
\text{HO—CH} & \text{CH—OH} \\
& \text{CH} \\
& \text{OH}
\end{array}
\qquad
\begin{array}{c}
\text{CH}_2\text{COONa} \\
\text{Au—S—CH—COONa} \cdot \text{H}_2\text{O}
\end{array}
$$

Aurothioglucose   Gold sodium thiomalate

Gold Sodium Thiomalate, N.F. (Myochrysine), is a water-soluble compound containing about 50 per cent gold. It is used by intramuscular injection to secure the antibacterial and antiarthritic effects of gold which is believed to be enhanced by the Au—S— linkage.

[5] Kharasch and Reinmuth, *Grignard Reactions of Nonmetallic Substances*, Prentice-Hall, New York, 1954.
[6] Lawrence, *Am. Rheumatic Diseases*, **12,** 129 (1953); *C.A.*, **47,** 10743 (1953).

Aurothioglycanide, N.N.R. (Auromercaptoacetanilid, Lauron), is a water-soluble gold compound used for the treatment of rheumatoid arthritis. Since it is apparently absorbed more slowly from the tissues, it produces fewer side reactions than other gold compounds.

Aurothioglycanide

Triphal

Triphal (Sodium Aurothiobenzimidazolecarboxylate) is a light yellow powder, readily soluble in water forming a slightly alkaline solution. It contains about 44 per cent gold. It is claimed to be effective in the treatment of lupus erythematosus. It is administered intravenously in sterile solution. Solutions of the salt are stable but readily decomposed by heat.

Silver Compounds

Silver was one of the first metals known in the pure state. Consequently, it is not surprising that it was used in very early times. The use of silver compounds was greatly expanded after Paracelsus advocated them in the treatment of diseases of the nervous system. A definite relationship was believed to exist between the moon and silver, and the moon goddess (Luna) was thought to control insane individuals (lunatics). Hence, lunar caustic (silver nitrate) came into use for the treatment of epilepsy, etc.

The compounds of silver are now used primarily for their activity as antiseptics and germicides. Inorganic salts such as silver nitrate yield silver ions which precipitate protein.

Efforts to produce organic compounds of silver that would be less caustic than the ionizable salts have resulted in numerous preparations. These consist for the most part of products of unknown chemical constitution formed from protein substances by precipitation with soluble silver salts. They are usually classed as strong or mild types.

Strong silver proteinates are intermediate in activity between the ionizable salts of silver and the colloidal silver halides. They consist of silver-protein complexes which probably yield a part or most of their silver as ions in contact with serous fluids. They contain a lower percentage of silver than the mild silver protein-type compounds and are called strong because they liberate the highest concentration of silver ions.

Strong Protein Silver, N.F. (Strong Silver Proteinate, Strong Protargin), is a brown powder, readily soluble in water but insoluble in alcohol, containing about 8 per cent of silver. Products of this type are made by treating a purified protein with a silver salt such as silver nitrate and dissolving the precipitate, after washing with more of the protein in aqueous solution, and evaporating the product to dryness under reduced pressure.

Protargol, according to the English patent 18478 (1897), is prepared by adding a concentrated aqueous solution of protalbumose to silver nitrate solution, collecting and washing the precipitate, and dissolving it in a solution of deuteroalbumose in water, heating until clear, and evaporating to dryness under reduced pressure.

Mild Protein Silver, N.F. (Mild Silver Proteinate, Mild Protargin), and a number of trademarked preparations, e.g., Argyn, is a colloidal preparation of silver oxide and serum albumin; Cargentos is a colloidal silver preparation made from silver oxide and a modified casein; Silvol consists of colloidal silver with an alkaline proteid; and Solargentum is a colloidal form of silver and gelatin. All of these are brands of the official product except Argyrol. They contain about 19 to 25 per cent silver. They consist of yellow to brown scales, soluble in water, with the formation of a low concentration of silver ions, and are called mild to differentiate them from the strong type. Argyrol (silver vitellin) is a colloidal silver, held in suspension by a protective colloid (protein), containing about 20 per cent of silver.

The silver proteinate preparations are used as antiseptics. In general, the strong proteinate type is more strongly germicidal and more irritant than the mild type. Solutions should be prepared freshly since, on standing, the concentration of silver ions may increase and cause increased irritation. Some of the uses and forms of application of these products are summarized in Table XXXIX.

TABLE XXXIX

SILVER PROTEINATE PRODUCTS AND THEIR USES

Uses	Strong Protein Silver, Per Cent	Mild Protein Silver, Per Cent
Solutions		
Eye, nose, and throat	0.5–10	10–50
Gynecological practice	2–10	—
Irrigations, urethral	1 : 2000–1 : 1000	1 : 1000
Sprays, nose and throat	0.5–10	10–20
Swabs and tampons	1–2	20–30
Suppositories, urethral	5–10	15–25
vaginal	5	15–25
rectal	5–10	15–20
Ointments, ophthalmic	—	25–50
gynecological	5	—

It will be noted that the protein silver compounds, when useful, are employed almost exclusively for application to the mucous membranes of the eye, nose, throat, urethra, bladder, and colon. They are used to treat numerous infections. Excessive use may lead to argyria.

Mercury Compounds

Mercury has been used as a therapeutic agent since ancient times. Until the discovery of arsphenamine in 1905, it was the only effective agent available for the treatment of syphilis. Inorganic compounds, such as red mercuric oxide, mercuric chloride, yellow mercurous iodide, and various preparations such as mercury with chalk, were administered orally. These have been abandoned because of the gastrointestinal symptoms which they cause. In recent years, several organic compounds of mercury have been introduced. They have been found to have a limited usefulness in the treatment of syphilis, but a number of them have proved of value as diuretics and as general antiseptics and disinfectants.

Mercurial Diuretics

The use of mercury as a diuretic has a long history, reference having been made in the sixteenth century to its use for this purpose by Paracelsus. The first organic mercurial employed to induce diuresis was Merbaphen (Novasurol), introduced originally as an antisyphilitic agent in 1917. Since then many organic mercurials have been synthesized, and as a group they are regarded as the most effective substances available for the treatment of edema in congestive heart failure.

Although considerable effort has been expended in this direction, the exact mechanism by which mercury acts upon the kidney is unknown. Most evidence points to the direct action of the organic mercurials on the kidney,[7] possibly blocking the reabsorption of water and electrolytes by the renal tubules. It has been suggested by many workers that this tubular action is cellular in nature, the mercury combining with the sulfhydryl enzyme systems within the tissue cells. The action of BAL or 2,3-dimercaptopropanol not only inhibits mercurial diuresis but protects animals against acute mercurial poisoning. The addition of a compound having only one sulfhydryl group apparently decreases the toxic effects of the mercurial on the heart while not altering the diuretic effect.

Most of the commonly accepted mercurial diuretics are synthesized by the general reaction sequence shown. The addition of mercuric salts to olefins is

$$RCO—NHCH_2CH=CH_2 + Hg(OCOCH_3)_2 \xrightarrow[0-95°]{R'OH}$$

$$RCONHCH_2CH—CH_2HgOCOCH_3$$
$$|$$
$$OR'$$

$$R' = H, CH_3, C_2H_5$$

usually carried out at room temperature or at the reflux temperature of the alcohol used as solvent.[8] Although the yields are high, the compounds are difficult to recrystallize and their solutions are unstable. Evidence [9] has been presented

[7] Pitts and Sartorius, *J. Pharmacol. Exptl. Therap.*, **98**, 161 (1950).

[8] Chatt, *Chem. Revs.*, **48**, 7 (1951).

[9] Pearson and Sigal, Jr., *J. Org. Chem.*, **15**, 1055 (1950).

indicating that the mercury atom is located in the γ position. The acetoxy group is readily replaced by other anions, and the most common derivative is that of theophylline or 1,3-dimethylxanthine, itself a diuretic.

Merbaphen (Novasurol) is a white, crystalline powder, containing about 33.5 per cent Hg, soluble in water, forming slightly alkaline solutions. It is usually administered by intramuscular or intravenous injection in 10 per cent solution.

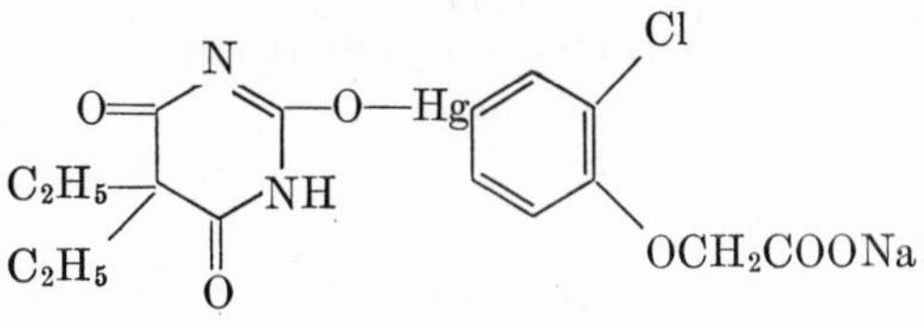

Merbaphen

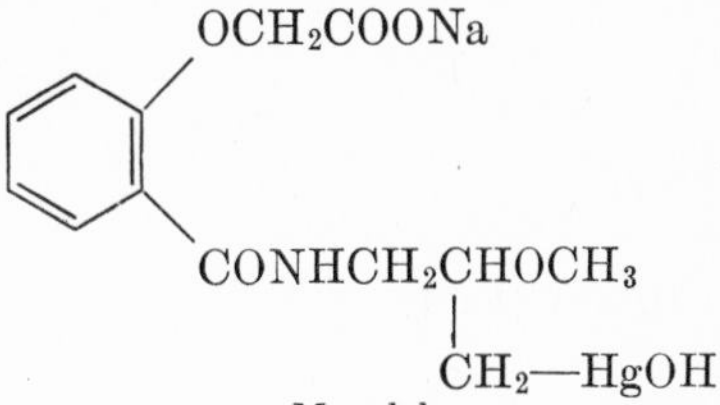

Mersalyl

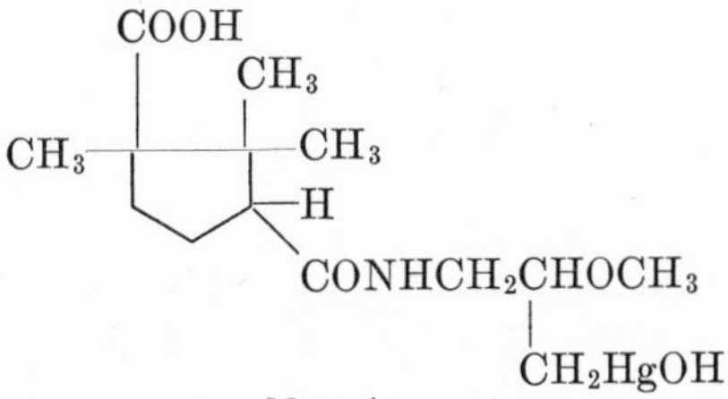

Mercurin

Mersalyl, U.S.P. (Salyrgan), contains about 40 per cent Hg. It is used like merbaphen as a diuretic to treat cardiac edemas, etc. *Mersalyl and Theophylline Injection, U.S.P.*, is used for the same purpose as salyrgan.

Mercurin, the β-methoxy-γ-hydroxymercuripropylamide of 1,2,2-trimethyl-cyclopentane-1,3-dicarboxylic acid, is used as a diuretic in the form of rectal suppositories. Replacement of the hydroxyl ion attached to the mercury by theophylline results in **Mercupurin;** the sodium salt of Mercupurin is **Mercurophylline Sodium, U.S.P.** (Mercuzanthin). If the hydroxyl anion of Mercurin is substituted by mercaptoacetic acid, the resulting compound is **Mercaptomerin, N.N.R.** (Thiomerin). It is claimed to be much less irritating on injection and less toxic to the heart than other organomercurials by virtue of the detoxifying action of the mercapto group.

Meralluride, U.S.P. (Mercuhydrin), is 1-(3′-hydroxymercuri-2′-methoxypropyl)-3-succinylurea and theophylline. It is used as such for rectal adminis-

$$\text{HOHg---CH}_2\text{---CH(OCH}_3)\text{CH}_2\text{NHCONHCOCH}_2\text{CH}_2\text{COOH}$$
Meralluride

tration as a suppository or by intramuscular or intravenous injection as the sodium salt.

Mercumatilin, N.N.R. (Cumertilin), 8-(2′-methoxy-3′-hydroxymercuripropyl)-coumarin-3-carboxylic acid and theophylline, is used orally as a diuretic in conjunction with parenteral injections of its sodium salt.

Meragidone, N-(β-methoxy-γ-hydroxymercuri)-2-pyridone-5-carboxylic acid, is a mercurial diuretic and has been used in combination with theophylline.

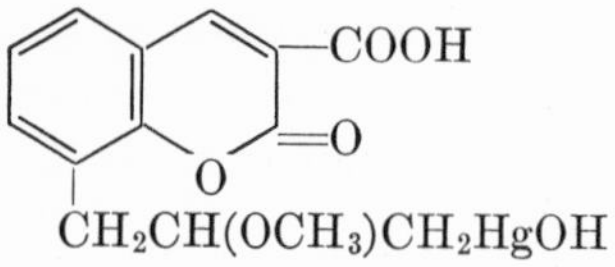

$$CH_2CH(OCH_3)CH_2HgOH$$

Mercumatilin

$$CH_2CH(OCH_3)CH_2HgOH$$

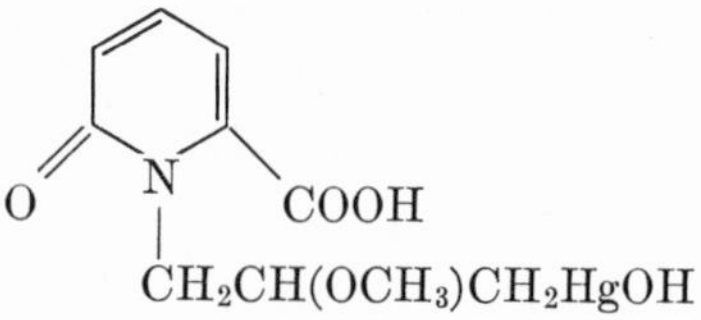

Meragidone

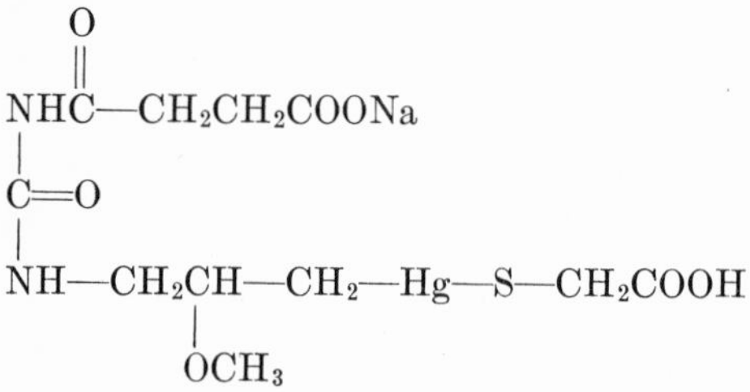

Diurgin

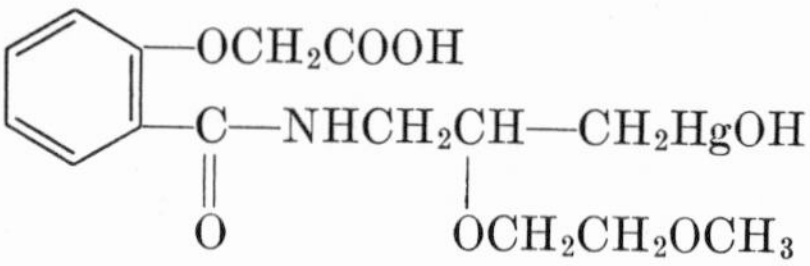

Merethoxylline

Diurgin, the disodium salt of N-succinyl-N'-(γ-carboxymethylmercapto-mercuri-β-methoxypropyl)urea, is reported [10] as being an effective diuretic of much lower toxicity than meralluride and is recommended for subcutaneous self-administration.

Merethoxylline (Dicurin), o-[N-(γ-hydroxymercuri-β-methoxypropyl)carba-moyl]-phenoxyacetic acid, has been reported [11] as a mercurial diuretic having an efficiency comparable with Mercaptomerin. It is used as the procaine salt to-gether with 5 per cent theophylline.

Chlormerodrin, N.N.R. [3-(Chloromercuri)-2-methoxypropylurea, Neohy-drin], $Cl—Hg—CH_2CH(OCH_3)CH_2NH—\overset{\overset{\textstyle O}{\textstyle \|}}{C}—NH_2$, is a mercurial diuretic reported to have unusual effectiveness when administered orally. It is par-ticularly useful against cardiac and nephrotic edemas.

Mercurial Antiseptics

It is generally believed that mercury compounds owe their antiseptic proper-ties to the reaction of liberated mercuric ions with the sulfhydryl groups of bacterial proteins, thereby interfering with the normal metabolism of the para-sites. The more readily the mercury compounds ionize, however, the more toxic and irritating is their effect on the tissues of the host. Thus, inorganic mercurials such as mercuric chloride are no longer used extensively as antiseptics. Other mercury salts including mercuric cyanide and mercuric oxycyanide have been used as substitutes for mercuric chloride but are also toxic and corrosive. In

[10] Frisk, Werkö, Wrange, *Acta Med. Scand.*, **144**, 85 (1952); *C.A.*, **47**, 2365 (1953).
[11] Frank, Nunez, Bellet, *J. Phila. Gen. Hosp.*, **4**, 39 (1953); *C.A.*, **47**, 8247 (1953).

addition, a variety of mercuric salts of organic acids have had use principally as antisyphilitics.

By far the most useful application of mercury as an antiseptic has been in the form of an organic compound. These organomercurials are less toxic and less irritating than the typical mercury salts and have a particular value in skin antisepsis. In general, they are bacteriostatic, having limited bactericidal and sporicidal properties.

The antiseptic power of an organomercurial depends upon its ability to ionize to an organomercuri ion and more particularly to the phenylmercuri ion, $C_6H_5Hg^+$. Although ionization of organic mercurials occurs slowly, the combination of the organomercuri ion with the sulfhydryl groups essential to the bacteria is considered the explanation of the activity of such compounds. Thus, the presence of sulfhydryl groups in serum serves to immobilize the organomercuri ions, rendering the compound impotent as an antiseptic for open wounds or mucous membranes.

In general, the synthesis of organomercurial antiseptics depends upon the addition of mercuric salts such as mercuric acetate to benzene or substituted benzenes. The synthesis of Merbromin (page 510) serves as an illustration. Use is also made of the reaction of mercuric chloride with Grignard reagents or aryldiazonium salts.

Mercuric Benzoate, $(C_6H_5COO)_2Hg \cdot H_2O$, is used locally for the irrigation of the urethra in gonorrhea in solutions of $1:2000$ to $1:1000$ concentration and by intramuscular injection in 2 per cent solution for the treatment of syphilis. Sodium chloride or ammonium benzoate is often used to increase the solubility of the salt.

Mercuric succinimide

Mercuric salicylate

Mercuric Salicylate contains about 57 per cent Hg. It is a white or slightly yellow powder, insoluble in water and in alcohol, possibly of the structure indicated. It can be prepared by heating freshly precipitated mercuric oxide with salicylic acid in the presence of a little acetic acid. It dissolves readily in alkalies and is precipitated from the alkaline solution by acids. It was used in suspension in bland vegetable oils for intramuscular injection in the treatment of syphilis, other substances such as ethyl aminobenzoate, quinine and urea hydrochloride, and chlorobutanol often being added to reduce the pain at the site of injection.

Mercuric Succinimide structurally is the salt of an ammono acid. It is the mercuric salt of succinic acid imide, is a white, crystalline powder, soluble about $1:20$ in water, stable in air but darkening on exposure to light, and containing about 50 per cent Hg. It is reported to be nonirritant. It is administered intramuscularly in aqueous solution.

A group of phenylmercuric salts including **Phenylmercuric Nitrate, N.F.,** phenylmercuric chloride, phenylmercuric acetate, phenylmercuric borate, and phenylmercuric picrate have been used as bacteriostatic agents. These compounds in buffered solutions are fairly stable, produce little irritation, and are colorless and stainless to the skin. They show relatively high activity against a variety of pathogenic organisms but are not effective against bacterial spores.

Acetomeroctol, N.N.R. [2-Acetoxymercuri-4-(1,1,3,3-tetramethylbutyl) phenol, Merbak], is used as a topical antiseptic in a 1:1000 solution containing alcohol and acetone.

Merbromin, N.F. (Mercurochrome Soluble, 2,7-Dibromo-4-hydroxymercurifluorescein), was the first of the organic mercurials to be introduced as a general antiseptic. It was prepared in 1918 with the specific idea that its blandness, bactericidal value, and especially its penetrating power would make it suitable for the treatment of gonorrhea. First it was used in infections of the urethra only, then in the bladder, then in the kidney, then in ophthalmology and laryngology, surgery, and then as a general antiseptic. The synthesis from dibromofluorescein is indicated.

Merbromin

It is used in the form of tablets for oral administration, 2 to 10 per cent solutions for local applications, a 5 per cent starch paste as a wet dressing, 2 per cent in suppositories, powder, applicator sticks, and sterile solution in ampules for parenteral administration.

It is a nonirritant antiseptic extensively used for disinfection of the skin and mucous surfaces and wounds as well as against infections of the genitourinary tract. It is a dye, coloring fabric red. Stains from Mercurochrome can be removed by washing with a solution of sodium hypochlorite.

Merthiolate (Sodium Ethylmercurithiosalicylate) is a cream-colored powder containing about 49 per cent Hg, soluble in water and physiological salt solution. It forms stable solutions miscible with alcohol and soaps. It does not stain tissues or fabric. It is a rapid and effective antiseptic and germicide used as a general antiseptic and for the disinfection of instruments, etc. It is employed in various forms as follows:

1:1000 solution in wound, nose, and throat infections; 2:1000 for instrument disinfection; 1:5000 for eye instillation; 1:10,000 to 1:5000 for bladder and urethral irrigation; 1:1000 tincture for skin disinfection. Other forms for its administration and application include: 1:1000 jelly, suppositories, and cream, and a 1:5000 ophthalmic ointment.

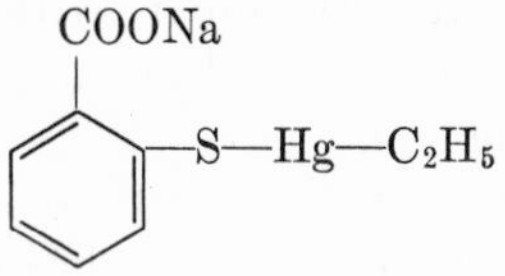

COONa

—S—Hg—C_2H_5

Merthiolate

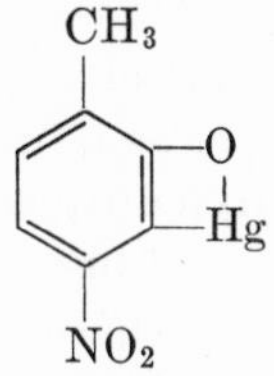

CH₃

—O
—Hg

NO₂

Metaphen

Nitromersol, N.F. (Metaphen, The Anhydride of 4-Nitro-3-hydroxymercuri-o-cresol), is a yellow powder, insoluble in water, containing about 56.5 per cent Hg. It is a relatively nonirritating and effective germicide used to disinfect the skin, for applications to mucous membranes, etc., like the other mercurial antiseptics. It is available in the following forms for application and administration: 1:5000 to 1:1000 solution in oil for irrigation of eye, ear, nose, throat, ureters, etc.; 1:2500 solution in alkaline water for the disinfection of instruments, rubber, etc., and treating skin infections; 1:1000 ampuled solution for intravenous administration; 1:500 ointment for scabies, ringworm, and parasitic skin diseases; 1:3000 ophthalmic ointment; 1:2000 vaginal suppositories; 1:1000 liquid soap; 1:500 bar soap; 1:5000 with 1 per cent ephedrine for colds, sinus, and nasal infections, etc.; 1:2500 with ephedrine 1 per cent and mineral oil as a nasal spray.

Mercocresols, N.N.R. (a mixture of the sec-Amyl tricresols and o-Hydroxyphenylmercuric Chloride, Mercresin), is an antiseptic for superficial wounds and infections. It is available as a tinted or stainless tincture as well as a cream.

BISMUTH COMPOUNDS

Certain bismuth compounds, such as the subcarbonate and subgallate, have been mentioned previously as useful in the treatment of diarrhea, dysentery and especially as an opaque substance in radiology. Other bismuth compounds have come into use in comparatively recent years (since about 1920) for the treatment of syphilis. To a large extent they have replaced the mercurials which, in turn, have given way to antibiotic therapy. The bismuth compounds are regarded as inferior to the arsenicals, but they are of value especially when used in conjunction with the latter.

A very large number of bismuth compounds have been prepared and suggested for use. Chemically, they are difficult to classify since the structures are not definitely known. They can be classified according to their solubilities and the nature of the preparation in which they are used.

Water-soluble Compounds

Bismosol is a pale yellow solution containing 10 per cent of potassium sodium bismuthotartrate in a sterile solution of glucose with 0.3 per cent piperazine. Potassium sodium bismuthotartrate contains about 35 per cent of bismuth.

Bismuth Sodium Tartrate is a white powder containing about 73 per cent of bismuth. It is usually administered in an aqueous sucrose solution with a small amount of benzyl alcohol.

Bismuth and Potassium Tartrate, N.F., is similar to the sodium compound. It contains about 69 per cent of bismuth. It is administered as an aqueous solution or as a suspension in a fixed oil.

Bismuth Ethylcamphorate is prepared by the reaction between sodium ethylcamphorate and bismuth nitrate in aqueous glycerol solution. It contains about 22 per cent bismuth. It is usually employed in the form of a solution in oil with added camphor and benzyl alcohol.

Bismuth Sodium Triglycollamate, N.N.R. (Sodium Bismuth Complex of Nitrilotriacetic Acid, Bistrinate), is an orally effective antisyphilitic containing

$$
\begin{array}{cc}
CH_2COOBiO & CH_2COONa \\
| & | \\
{}^+NHCH_2COONa \cdot 3 & {}^+NHCH_2COONa \\
| \quad {}^- & | \quad {}^- \\
CH_2COO & CH_2COO
\end{array}
$$

Bismuth sodium triglycollamate

approximately 18.3 per cent of bismuth. It is also indicated for some skin diseases.

Propylene Glycol-soluble Compounds

Sobisminol Solution is a solution of the products of the interaction of sodium bismuthate, triisopropanolamine, and propylene glycol. It contains 20 mg. of bismuth in each cubic centimeter.

Oil-soluble Compounds

Bismocymol is the basic bismuth salt of camphorcarboxylic acid dissolved in olive oil; the salt contains about 38 per cent bismuth.

Quiniobine (Quinine Bismuth Iodide) contains about 19 per cent bismuth; it is rendered soluble in olive oil by the use of lecithin.

Thiobismol (Bismuth Sodium Thioglycollate), $Bi(SCH_2CO_2Na)_3$, is prepared by the reaction between sodium thioglycollate and bismuth hydroxide. It contains about 38 per cent bismuth.

Insoluble Compounds

Bismuth Subsalicylate, U.S.P., is administered as a suspension containing 10 per cent of basic bismuth subsalicylate in peanut oil. Bismuth subsalicylate contains about 64 per cent of bismuth.

Mesurol is a basic bismuth methoxyhydroxybenzoate containing 20 per cent bismuth suspended in sesame oil.

Tartroquiniobine is a suspension of quinine bismuth iodide and sodium potassium bismuth tartrate in olive oil.

The water-soluble, oil-soluble, and oil suspensions of the bismuth-containing compounds are usually administered by intramuscular injection. In general, the water-soluble compounds are absorbed and excreted more rapidly than the oil-soluble and insoluble compounds. A preparation known as Sobisminol Mass has been introduced for oral use. It is administered in capsules, each capsule representing 150 mg. of bismuth.

Practically all the preparations of bismuth contain the metal in the electropositive form (cation), but iodobismitol and sobisminol are reported to contain the metal in the electronegative form (anion).

METAL CHELATES

When a metal ion combines with an electron-donating compound having two or more donor groups so as to form one or more rings, the resulting structure is known as a *chelate* compound or a *metal chelate*. The significance of the cyclic structures of such complexes was first recognized by Ley [12] who investigated the unusual properties of copper glycinate.

Copper glycinate

The importance of metal chelates in most branches of chemistry and particularly medicinal chemistry is now well recognized. Naturally occurring chelates such as chlorophyll and hemoglobin have important functions in biological systems. The heme proteins which contain iron bound to a porphine derivative function primarily in the storage and transport of oxygen in living organisms. They also have catalytic effects on oxidation-reduction reactions. Hemoglobin

[12] Ley, *Z. Electrochem.*, **10**, 954 (1904).

in oxygen transport, peroxidases for the oxidation of enzyme substrates, cytochrome, and catalase are important heme proteins.

Copper enzymes such as the various oxidases are involved in oxidation-reduction systems, and the cupric ion is believed to form a chelate with ascorbic acid in the catalytic autoxidation of the vitamin.

The role of chelation in the action of proteolytic enzymes has been described by Smith,[13] and the decarboxylation of some biologically important β-keto acids is catalyzed by metallo-enzymes.

Since the natural metal chelates play a vital role in biological systems, it is not unusual to find that certain unnatural chelating agents will alter these systems. Such a chelating agent can compete with the enzyme for the metal in a metal-enzyme function so as to kill the organism.

The uses of unnatural chelating agents in biological systems have been classified [14] as follows:

1. Destruction of the organism by chelation of essential metals—bactericidal and fungicidal action, e.g., 8-hydroxyquinolines.

2. Inhibition of certain metals and metal enzymes for the purposes of studying functions of metals and enzymes in biological media, e.g., cyanide ion, carbon monoxide, amino acids.

3. Removal of harmful metals from living organisms, e.g., ethylenediamine tetracetic acid, ion exchange resins.

SILICONES [15]

Silicones, comparative newcomers in industrial chemistry, are polymers of general structure $R_3Si[O—SiR_2]_n—OSiR_3$. Their unusual properties, influenced by the character of the alkyl substituents and by the degree of polymerization, make these compounds, more particularly those in which $R = CH_3$ and with a viscosity range between 0.65 to 1×10^5 centistokes, pharmaceutically useful. They are clear, sparkling, oily liquids, odorless, tasteless, insoluble in water, and stable at high temperature; they are water repellent, and their viscosity varies but little with change in temperature. They appear to be generally nontoxic; but because they produce a transitory conjunctival irritation they are not recommended for use in ophthalmic preparations.[16]

Silicones are finding use, for example, in the formulation of vehicles and in coating tablets and capsules to render them resistant to moisture. They show but slight diminishing action on antibacterial agents with which they may be incorporated.[17] Hair sprayed with a suitable formulation of silicones and then combed at about 150° takes on a "permanent wave" which is less sensitive to

[13] Smith, *Federation Proc.*, **8**, 581 (1949).

[14] Martell and Calvin, *Chemistry of the Metal Chelate Compounds*, p. 499, Prentice-Hall, New York, 1953.

[15] Cf. E. G. Rochow, *The Chemistry of the Silicones*, 2d ed., John Wiley & Sons, New York, 1951.

[16] Plein and Plein, *J. Am. Pharm. Assoc., Sci., Ed.*, **42**, 79 (1953).

[17] Burlage *et al.*, *Drug Standards*, **22**, 7 (1954).

atmospheric humidity. Silicones are finding wide use as ingredients in protective creams to prevent contact dermatitis.

The antifoaming properties, widely exploited in industry, have been used in pulmonary edema to liquefy fluid in the lungs [18] and for the treatment of "bloat" in animals.[19]

Dimethicone, N.N.R., $(CH_3)_3SiO \left[\begin{array}{c} CH_3 \\ | \\ -Si-O- \\ | \\ CH_3 \end{array} \right]_n Si(CH_3)_3$, is used as an ointment base and an agent for protecting the skin.

SALTS OF ORGANIC ACIDS WITH MEDICINAL METALLIC CATION

Lead Acetate, N.F., and **Lead Subacetate Solution, N.F.,** are used to secure the astringent action of lead.

Aluminum Acetate Solution, U.S.P., and **Aluminum Subacetate, U.S.P.,** are used as astringent washes.

Calcium Lactate, N.F., $(CH_3CHOHCOO)_2Ca \cdot 5H_2O$, is a white powder, soluble about 1:20 in water. It is used to restore to normal a low calcium content of the blood. The salt is less irritant than calcium chloride and more irritant than calcium gluconate and calcium levulinate. It is usually administered as the powder in milk, in capsules, or in tablets.

Calcium Gluconate, U.S.P., $[CH_2OH(CHOH)_4COO]_2Ca \cdot 2H_2O$, is the normal calcium salt of gluconic acid. It is prepared by the fermentation of glucose in the presence of lime by various bacilli such as *Bacillus oxydans*, or *B. aceti*. By careful control of the organism, the temperature, and the pH of the fermentation mixture, very high yields can be obtained. It is a crystalline or granular salt, soluble about 1:30 in water and insoluble in organic solvents. It is stable in air. Acids that are stronger than gluconic acid decompose the salt. It is incompatible with such salts as soluble sulfates, carbonates, bicarbonates, citrates, tartrates, salicylates, etc.

It is one of the most generally used calcium compounds for supplying any deficiency of this element in the normal blood. It is usually administered intravenously in sterile solution (*Calcium Gluconate Injection, U.S.P.*) or orally in the form of tablets, capsules, or as the powder stirred in milk, etc. Since the salt is not very soluble in water, various means have been used to secure stable supersaturated solutions, such as the addition of boric acid, soluble calcium salts of saccharic acids, and soluble calcium salts of sulfonic acids.[20] These supersaturated solutions are very important in veterinary therapy for the treatment of milk fever in cows, when it is often necessary to inject into the jugular vein as much as 50 to 75 g. of the gluconate in a single dose. Calcium gluconate is less

---

[18] *Chem. Eng. News*, **31**, 975 (1953).
[19] Lesser, *Drug and Cosmetic Industry*, **72**, 616 (1953).
[20] *J. Am. Pharm. Assoc.*, **27**, 484 (1938).

irritant and caustic than the chloride or the lactate. The levulinate is more expensive.

The importance of calcium in therapy is now quite well understood. It is known that the calcium plays an important part in metabolism. In the human body, it performs valuable functions in bone structure, colloidal aggregation, cell permeability, normal coagulation of the blood, transformation of energy derived from foods into muscular contraction, and in the regulation of nervous, muscular, and glandular activity. Human blood serum in temperate climates varies between about 9 and 10 mg. per 100 cc. in calcium content. The daily human requirements have been estimated to be about 1 g. for every 100 g. of protein. Milk is one of the best food sources. Deficiency in calcium may lead to disease conditions such as rachitis, osteomalacia, and tetany; these conditions are usually caused by failure to utilize calcium rather than by insufficient intake. Calcium salts are then given with vitamin D or parathyroid extracts, the calcium salts being merely adjuvants. Other conditions such as nervous twitching, allergy, inflammatory edema, and toxemias, have been reported to be benefited by the administration of calcium salts.

Calcium Levulinate, N.F., $(CH_3COCH_2CH_2CO_2)_2Ca \cdot 2H_2O$, is the hydrated calcium salt of levulinic acid. The acid is produced by heating hexose or polyhexoses with hydrochloric acid or from furfuryl alcohol and very dilute hydrochloric acid.

$$(C_6H_{12}O_6)_x + HCl \xrightarrow{\text{heat}}$$

$$\underset{O}{\text{furfuryl}}CH_2OH + HCl \xrightarrow{\text{very dilute}}$$

$$CH_3-\overset{O}{\overset{\|}{C}}-CH_2-CH_2COOH$$

Calcium levulinate occurs as a white, crystalline or amorphous powder which has a salty, bitter taste. It is freely soluble in water and slightly soluble in alcohol.

It is used for the same purposes as calcium gluconate. It has the advantage that solutions containing as much as 30 per cent can be prepared which are stable when heated as in sterilization. It is relatively nonirritant. This is a highly desirable property in salts intended for injection by the intravenous route since irritant salts like calcium chloride cause necrosis and sloughing if injected outside the vein. Calcium levulinate is generally administered intravenously in the form of a sterile 10 per cent solution. It has the same effect as other calcium salts. It may also be given orally.

Silver Lactate, prepared by dissolving silver carbonate or freshly precipitated silver oxide in lactic acid with the aid of heat and in the dark, is a crystalline powder, soluble about 1:15 in water. It is less caustic than silver nitrate. It is used in diluted solutions, 1:100 to 1:2500, as an antiseptic and astringent.

Ferrous Lactate is a crystalline or scale salt which largely masks the disagreeable taste of iron salts. It is used as an iron tonic, usually being administered in syrup solution.

Ferrous Gluconate, U.S.P., $[CH_2OH(CHOH)_4COO]_2Fe \cdot H_2O$, contains about 15 per cent iron. It occurs as a fine, yellowish-gray or pale greenish-yellow powder. It is soluble in water but insoluble in alcohol. It is used in tablets or an elixir to provide a readily assimilable, nonirritating ferrous iron in the treatment of anemia.

Ferric Ammonium Citrate, N.F., is a readily soluble, scale salt used for the administration of iron.

Antimony Potassium Tartrate, U.S.P. (Tartar Emetic, Antimonyl Potassium Tartrate, Tartrated Antimony), OSbOOC—CHOH—CHOH—COOK, consists of a white powder or colorless crystals, soluble in water about 1:12. It is administered orally in solution as an emetic and as a nauseant, the effect depending on the dose. Administered intravenously, it is used to treat a number of tropical diseases caused by protozoan infections, such as kala-azar, granuloma inguinale, Leishmaniasis, and sleeping sickness.

Bismuth Sodium Tartrate and **Bismuth Potassium Tartrate, N.F.,** are white powders of indefinite molecular formula, soluble about 1:2.5 in water. They are used to secure the systemic effect of bismuth in the treatment of syphilis, usually being administered parenterally in sterile solution.

Mercury Oleate, N.F., is prepared from yellow mercuric oxide and oleic acid. It is an ingredient of *Strong Mercurial Ointment, N.F.*

CHAPTER 16

Some Physicochemical
Properties
of Medicinal Products

It is natural in considering medicinal and related substances to place emphasis on chemical properties and, where available information permits, to attempt a correlation between structure and physiological activity. The difficulties encountered in making such correlations, however, are complicated by the fact that so little is understood of the "protoplasmic" reaction between the drug and the heterogeneous components of the tissue, e.g., the carbohydrates, fats, proteins, sterols, and metallic constituents, which in themselves are not uniform and may be highly sensitive to modification by the drug.[1]

As little understood as these intricate biological processes may be, there are, nevertheless, many responses which are not the direct result of chemical forces but may be primarily attributed to physicochemical properties. It has been suggested, in fact, that every pharmacological effect must ultimately result either from the physical properties of the drug or from the product formed when the drug reacts with the tissue. Accordingly it has been proposed that modifications in the chemical structure of an active molecule are of significance only to the extent that they influence its physical properties. This may be specious reasoning, for obviously the physical and chemical properties of a molecule are inseparable and both are a function of the chemical structure.

One difficulty certainly is the inadequacy of the conventional method of writing structural formulas. The customary depiction of the valence bond does not give adequate representation. Whether electronic formulas can remedy the deficiency by providing an appreciation of the finer molecular architecture remains

---

[1] Starkenstein, *Klin. Wochschr.*, **51**, 1865 (1936).

to be ascertained.[2] Until questions like this are settled it may not be out of place to call attention to some physicochemical properties or factors which contribute either in part or in whole to the therapeutic action of drugs, remembering that ultimately even these are dependent on chemical structure.

That physical properties should be important is not difficult to understand. Life, particularly as exemplified by the human being, exists in a delicately balanced physical environment. Only a few examples need be given to illustrate this fact. Known temperatures range from $-273°$ to about $6000°$, but man lives within a very narrow range between these extremes; deviations of only 2 to 5 degrees within the body from a normal of $37°$ ($98.6°$ F.) indicate serious disorders. The human ear perceives neither the longest nor the shortest sound waves which physical science has revealed. The eye responds to an extremely limited region of the known electromagnetic wave spectrum. Nerves are highly sensitive to small changes in electromotive force, as one can testify who has dashed cold water against a gold-filled molar. A delicate change in the potential and frequency of the normal brain waves may lead to convulsions.

Drugs operate, as do all biochemical processes, according to infallible physical and chemical laws.[3] The complex interplay of various forces makes the mechanism and the mode of drug action difficult to comprehend. The modes of drug action are numerous. They may act by osmotic properties; or they may act as acids or alkalies; they may increase the permeability of surfaces; they may precipitate proteins; some may act specifically on enzymes.[4]

It is to be regretted that the study of the physicochemical factors associated with or responsible for drug action has not received the attention it deserves. Some progress has been made, however, and it is the purpose of the following pages to call attention to some of the explanations, hypotheses, or theories that have been proposed. A critical review and discussion of all theories and hypotheses is beyond the scope of this book. These concepts are called to the attention of the student of today in the hope that as the investigator of tomorrow he may be stimulated to aid in solving the problems.

COLLOID SCIENCE

The whole realm of colloid science comes into play in drug action, but only reference can be made to it here. Solution, dispersion, particle size, permeability, diffusion, adsorption, desorption, osmosis, etc., all contribute their part. Obviously there can be no action unless the drug reaches the site where it is effective. To do this the molecules or particles must be neither too large to pass through the

---

[2] Schulemann, *Arch. exptl. Path. Pharmakol.*, **181**, 37 (1936).

[3] The interested student is referred to the excellent and thought-provoking treatise by Beutner, *Physical Chemistry of Living Tissues and Life Processes*, Williams and Wilkins Co., Baltimore, 1933, and to a brief paper by Herrera, "A New Theory of the Origin and Nature of Life," *Science*, **96**, 14 (1942).

[4] Many of these factors are discussed at length in special papers published in *Transactions of the Faraday Society* in 1937 and in 1943.

living membranes, nor must they be otherwise impermeable. Sulfates, for example, are not absorbed through the intestinal wall, and their presence in the intestines causes water to diffuse by osmotic processes from the blood into the bowel so that the gut becomes loaded and the characteristic peristalsis is induced. Chlorides, on the other hand, readily diffuse, and their elimination through the urinary tract sets up osmotic forces to produce diuresis. Similar phenomena at work throughout the various tissues, although on a smaller scale, may contribute to, if not completely account for, many distinct physiological effects.

That it may reach the site of action the drug molecule is transported by the blood or lymph, whence it is taken up by the appropriate tissues. Drug adsorption may then follow as a result of any one or several of various forces. For example, it may depend on ion-exchange, as in the amberlite resins,[5] by hydrogen bonding,[6] by covalent bond,[7] or by other processes. After exerting its effect, unless it is metabolized, the molecule is again taken up into the blood stream for elimination. It is by such mechanisms that iodophthalein reaches the gall bladder, that sulfanilamide enters the urine, and that digitalis finds its way to a specific lipoid in the heart.[8, 9] It is apparent that very delicately balanced forces of selective adsorption and desorption are involved which play their part in such varied and physiologically important processes as agglutination, sensitization, and lysis. It is not unlikely that the interplay of such forces also accounts for the preferential toxicity of some drugs for an invading parasite rather than for the host.

THE MEYER AND OVERTON THEORY OF NARCOSIS

H. Meyer and Overton in 1901, first independently and later in co-operation, advanced the theory that the narcotic potency of a drug is proportional to its partition or distribution coefficient between the lipoids and water. Useful and stimulating as this hypothesis has proved to be, it has not been completely satisfactory for it does not account for many of the observed discrepancies. K. H. Meyer (son of H. Meyer) and Hemmi have restated the theory as follows: Narcosis appears if a chemically indifferent substance has penetrated into the cell lipoids, more correctly the lipoid alcohols of the cell substances, to reach a definite molar concentration. This concentration is a function of the animal or of the cell but is independent of the narcotic.[10]

Part of the data on which this restatement of the original theory is based are summarized in Tables XL and XLI. Examination of these data, along with others not given, shows that this is a more satisfactory theory and that it reconciles inconsistencies heretofore unexplainable. Thus the partition coefficient as such is of importance primarily in making it possible for the narcotic drug to reach the necessary molar concentration in the cell lipoids.

[5] Gaddum, *Trans. Faraday Soc.*, **39**, 323 (1943).

[6] Rideal, *Trans. Faraday Soc.*, **39**, 368 (1943).

[7] Eley, *Trans. Faraday Soc.*, **39**, 381 (1943).

[8] Hecht, *Angew. Chem.*, **48**, 14 (1935).

[9] Albert, *Pharm. J.*, **145**, 84 (1940).

[10] Meyer and Hemmi, *Biochem. Z.*, **277**, 59 (1935).

TABLE XL

NONVOLATILE NARCOTICS

Substance	Narcotic Concentration in Water for Tadpoles, moles/liter	Partition Coefficient between Oleyl Alcohol and Water	Concentration in the Lipoid, moles/liter
Ethanol	0.33	0.10	0.033
n-Propanol	0.11	0.35	0.038
n-Butanol	0.03	0.65	0.02
Valeramide	0.07	0.30	0.021
Antipyrin	0.07	0.30	0.021
Pyramidon	0.03	1.30	0.039
Benzamide	0.013	2.50	0.033
Dial	0.01	2.4	0.024
Salicylamide	0.0033	5.9	0.021
Luminal	0.008	5.9	0.048
Adalin	0.002	6.5	0.013
o-Nitroaniline	0.0025	14	0.035
Thymol	0.000047	950	0.045
Veronal	0.03	1.38	0.041

TABLE XLI

VOLATILE NARCOTICS

Substance	Narcotic Concentration in Volume, Per Cent	Solubility Coefficient, Oil to Gas Phase	Concentration of Narcotic in Lipoid, moles/liter
Methane	370	0.54	0.08
Ethylene	80	1.3	0.04
Nitrous oxide	100	1.4	0.06
Acetylene	65	1.8	0.05
Dimethyl ether	12	11.6	0.06
Methyl chloride	6.5	14	0.07
Ethylene oxide	5.8	31	0.07
Ethyl chloride	5	40.5	0.08
Diethly ether	3.4	50	0.07
Amylene	4	65	0.10
Dimethyl formal	2.8	75	0.08
Ethyl bromide	1.9	95	0.07
Dimethyl acetal	1.9	100	0.06
Diethyl formal	1	120	0.05
Dichloroethylene	0.95	130	0.05
Carbon disulfide	1.1	160	0.07
Chloroform	0.5	265	0.05

The theories [11,12,13,14] attempting to link surface phenomena, adsorption, and cell respiration, or solubility in water with narcosis should be reexamined to determine what role the forces in question play in aiding the narcotic to build up to the requisite concentration in the lipoids.

The structures of various compounds determine the nature of their physical properties, including the partition coefficient. Thus, it is suggested that strongly heteropolar compounds, with high dielectric values, are generally insoluble in solvents with low dielectric constants (oils, fats, lipoids), and that apolar substances are practically insoluble in water but readily soluble in fats.[15] However, this view requires amendment in the light of the much greater effect of hydrogen bonding on solubilities as shown by azeotrope studies. Another view divides the substituents that are bound to a basic organic skeleton into hydrophobic and hydrophilic groups. The hydrophobic substituents are—SCN, —Br, —NO$_3$, —Cl, —NO$_2$ and —CH$_3$; the hydrophilic members include —OH, —NH$_2$, —COOH, —SO$_3$H, etc.[16]

TABLE XLII

ISONARCOTIC CONCENTRATIONS OF GASES AND VAPORS FOR MICE AT 37°

Substance	Narcotic Conc., % by Volume	Activity, p_t/p_s
Nitrous oxide	100	0.01
Acetylene	65	.01
Methyl ether	12	.02
Methyl chloride	14	.01
Ethylene oxide	5.8	.02
Ethyl chloride	5.0	.02
Ethyl ether	3.4	.03
Methylal	2.8	.03
Ethyl bromide	1.9	.02
Diethylacetal	1.9	.05
Diethylformal	1.0	.07
Dichloroethylene	0.95	.02
Carbon disulfide	1.1	.02
Chloroform	0.5	.01

It is postulated [17] that the narcotic dissolved in the cell lipoids reversibly increases the surface tension at the oil-water interphase, and in complete anesthesia there is assumed to be complete cessation of protoplasmic motion.[18]

Ferguson,[19] discussing non-specific toxic substances, including narcotics, points

[11] Traube, *Biochem. Z.*, **119**, 177 (1921).
[12] Gardner and Semb, *J. Pharmacol.*, **54**, 309 (1935).
[13] Warburg, *Biochem. Z.*, **119**, 134 (1921).
[14] Cone, Forman, and Krantz, *Proc. Soc. Exptl. Biol. Med.*, **48**, 461 (1941).
[15] Breyer, *Biochem. Z.*, **301**, 65 (1939).
[16] Schüller, *Arch. exptl. Path. Pharmakol.*, **167**, 70 (1932).
[17] Seelich, *Arch. ges. Physiol. (Pflügers)*, **243**, 283 (1940); *C.A.*, **35**, 1514 (1941).
[18] Seifriz, *Anesthesiology*, **2**, 300 (1941); *C.A.*, **35**, 4843 (1941).
[19] Ferguson, *Proc. Royal Soc. (London)*, **127B**, 387 (1939).
Albert, *Selective Toxicity*, Methuen & Co., Ltd., London, 1951, p. 28.

to a correlation between their biological potency and chemical potential. Table XLII,[20] shows considerable constancy for the p_t/p_s values of narcotic gases, where p_t is the partial pressure of the gas and p_s the saturated vapor pressure of the gas at the temperature of the experiment.

MOLECULAR SIZE AND SURFACE AREA

Transport from the site of administration to the site of action requires the drug to pass through the various membranes in its path. It cannot do so if the molecule or particle is too large. Thus salvarsan and neosalvarsan are less effective because of their colloidal nature, for they cannot penetrate tissues readily. This is not true for the more effective oxyphenarsine.[21]

In the estrogens, e.g., stilbestrol and its analogs, it appears that optimum activity is found in those compounds having the phenolic hydroxyl groups separated from each other by a distance of 8.55 A; as this distance is increased or decreased, the estrogenic activity becomes correspondingly less. It is suggested that estrogenic activity is associated with strong hydrogen bond-forming groups separated by this optimum distance. If the strength of the bond-forming group is diminished (by the hydrogenation of the aromatic nucleus, for example) and the distance is increased, the compound takes on the properties of a male hormone.[22]

It is suggested that in many drugs the distance between two functional groups is about 5.5 A, or about the same as the distance between two turns of the α-protein helix. These functional groups, such as hydroxyl or amine, are capable of bonding to the protein, thus modifying the hydrogen bonding arrangement and shape of the protein molecule. The other structural features of the drug molecule, such as aromatic nuclei, acyl groups, or alkyl side chains, then confer on the molecule the specific property of biological action which can be recognized by its response.[23]

It has been established that in colloidal systems surface area is of great significance. The role that the surface area of a drug molecule plays in therapy is a field difficult to explore and remains quite untouched. It is postulated, however, that the narcotic potency in any given homologous series is approximately proportional to the surface area of the drug molecule.[24]

MOLECULAR SHAPE

That the shape of a molecule is highly important in drug action has long been appreciated. Many of the differences in the physiological activity of position, optical, and geometrical isomers, to which attention has been called in Chapter 13, come into consideration. To give additional emphasis to the point, one simple

[20] Taken from Ferguson, *loc. cit.*, p. 399.
[21] Binz, *Ber.*, **70A**, 127 (1937).
[22] Schueler, *Science*, **103**, 221 (1946).
[23] Gero and Reese, *Science*, **123**, 100 (1956).
[24] King, Hall, Andrews, and Cole, *J. Pharmacol.*, **40**, 275 (1930).

example will be given, namely, the position isomers obtained by introducing a methyl group into various positions of the simple molecule propadrine, and the space isomers of the N-methyl derivatives. With respect to the functional chemi-

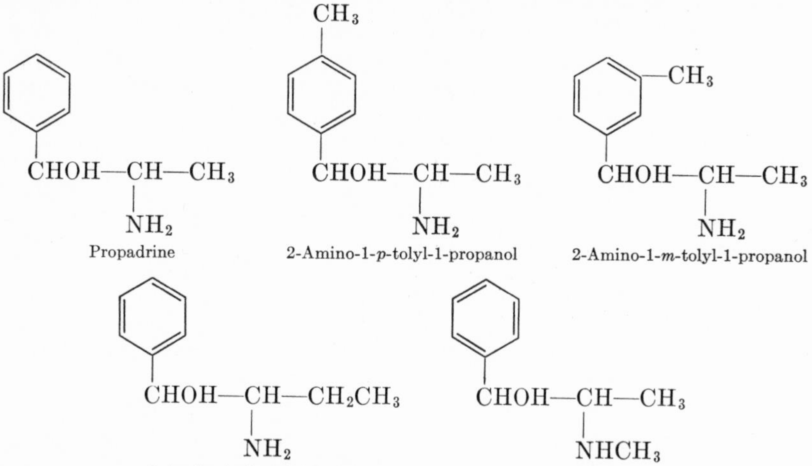

Propadrine — 2-Amino-1-*p*-tolyl-1-propanol — 2-Amino-1-*m*-tolyl-1-propanol

2-Amino-1-phenyl-1-butane — Ephedrine

cal groups these substances differ only in that ephedrine is a secondary amine; the other three are primary amines. It is not the secondary amine, however, that is responsible for the physiological activity which characterizes these compounds, for DL-propadrine, a primary amine, possesses slightly greater activity than DL-ephedrine. On the other hand, the presence of the methyl group in other positions of the molecule, on the side chain or in the nucleus, where it presumably affects no functional groups, has a most unfavorable effect on the pressor and toxic properties of the molecule (see page 220). The qualitative and quantitative differences between the optically active isomers of ephedrine have been discussed, page 467.

A more striking example is seen in the isomers of epinephrine.[25] Depending on

$$\begin{array}{c} CH_2NHCH_3 \\ | \\ H—C—H \\ | \\ C_6H_3(OH)_2 \end{array}$$

Epinine, 1/12 pressor activity of (−)-epinephrine

↙ ↘

$$\begin{array}{c} CH_2NHCH_3 \\ | \\ HO—C—H \\ | \\ C_6H_3(OH)_2 \end{array} \qquad\qquad \begin{array}{c} CH_2NHCH_3 \\ | \\ H—C—OH \\ | \\ C_6H_3(OH)_2 \end{array}$$

(+)-Epinephrine, 1/20 pressor activity of (−) epinephrine

(−)-Epinephrine [Relative configuration subject to confirmation]

[25] For assignment of relative configuration, see Drell, *J. Am. Chem. Soc.*, **77**, 5429 (1955).

the position taken in the molecule by the alcoholic hydroxyl group, even on the same carbon atom, the activity may be increased or decreased.

On the other hand occasional evidence appears that the similarity in shape of active molecules may be more significant than composition.[26] Thus 4-dimethyl-aminoantipyrine and 4-isopropylantipyrine possess similar activity. Also it is assumed that cocaine and procaine types of anesthetics possess certain structural similarities to choline and produce their effect by competing for the nerve endings.[27]

It is postulated that in synthetic analgesics the isomer exhibiting the greater activity is related to D($-$)-alanine, which fits better the suggested receptor surface. 6-Methylmethadon, even with the correct configurational arrangement of the three essential analgesic groupings, is inert because the methyl group is incorrectly positioned and prevents correct combination between the drug and receptor surface.[28]

The structure-toxicity relationships of the various isomers of hexachlorocyclo-hexane provide an interesting problem. The γ-isomer, which is insecticidal, is found to have the configuration *pppeee*,[29] and the calculated diameter of the molecule is 8.5 A and the thickness is 7.2 A, i.e., it is quite spherical, and as an insecticide it is a strong excitant. The β-isomer, which is *eeeeee*, has a molecular diameter of 9.5 A and a thickness of 5.4 A; that is, it is quite planar, and it exerts an inert or weak depressant action. It is not surprising that the two isomers evoke unlike responses when taken up by lipoprotein, especially if the relative thermodynamic activities of the isomers are also taken into consideration.[30]

It is quite likely that the conformation of substituted cyclohexane compounds also influences biological reactions. It is known, for example, that *in vitro* a hydroxyl in equatorial conformation is more readily acetylated than one in polar conformation; similarly an equatorial acetoxy group is more readily hydrolyzed.

Conformation of a drug, in addition to stereoconfiguration, may also influence significantly the nature of a physiological or biochemical response. The calculated distance between the polar oxygen and nitrogen atoms of choline, for example, varies from 2.51 A for the *cisoid* to 3.73 A for the *transoid* conformation;

transoid   cisoid

for tropanol the distances are 3.08 A for the Z-form to 3.93 A for the C-form; for pseudo-tropanol the distances are, respectively, 4.10 and 2.08 A. It will be noted that the tropic acid ester of that configuration and conformation of tro-

[26] Pauling, *Ind. Eng. News*, **24**, 1377 (1946).

[27] Schueler, *J. Chem. Ed.*, **22**, 585 (1945).

[28] Beckett and Casy, *J. Pharm. Pharmacol.*, **6**, 986, 999 (1954).

[29] With reference to the *chair* or "Z" form of cyclohexane; *p* means the substituent is polar, and *e*, that it is equatorial.

[30] Mullins, *Science*, **122**, 118 (1955).

panol which approximates the dimension of the choline ester is antagonistic in its physiological action to acetylcholine.[31]

If modification in molecular shape can produce such profound changes in physiological activity in so comparatively simple a series of isomers, it may be of greater importance in complex compounds.

Tropanol
Z-form

Tropanol
C-form

Homologous, polymeric series of sulfated hexosans, pentosans and polyvinyl alcohols depend for their anticoagulant properties not only on the size of the molecule but on the shape as well; threadlike molecules are more effective than spherocolloids.[32]

It is appropriate to call attention to the announcement that antibodies are formed by modifying the shape and structure of certain large blood protein molecules.

It is postulated that the perception of odor results when a suitable "odoriphore," possessing the configuration complementary to the olfactory system, lodges on the receptor; the energy changes in the receptors, whether caused by oxidation-reduction or other means, cause discrete impulses to pass up the olfactory nerve, and their reception in the brain is the basis for the sense of smell.[33]

OXIDATION-REDUCTION POTENTIAL

The significance of this factor may be appreciated from the fact that the body is well supplied with systems for oxidation-reduction, including such compounds as ascorbic acid, glutathione, and cysteine. Their interaction with drugs of higher or lower potential may, depending on circumstances, modify the drug, i.e., inactivate it or perhaps activate it. Pentavalent arsenic, e.g., is inactive toward spirochetes, but after biological reduction to the trivalent state it becomes active. Fuadin, as mentioned, page 309, is stable toward oxidizing agents and does not liberate the antimony prematurely; if the sulfonic acid groups are removed from the co-ordination compound, the catechol is too easily oxidized and antimony does not reach the site of action.

It is possible that many antibiotics, especially those derived structurally from quinone, are effective because of their oxidation-reduction possibilities.[34]

[31] Hoy, Thesis, University of North Carolina, 1955.

[32] von Kualla and Husemann, *Experimenta*, **2**, 222 (1946); *C.A.*, **40**, 6165 (1946).

[33] Erb, *Am. Perfumer Essent. Oil Rev.*, **50**, 561 (1947); Moncrieff, *Perfumery Essent. Oil Record*, **40**, 279 (1949).

[34] Marini-Bettolo and Del Pianto, *Commentationes Pontif. Acad. Sci.*, **10**, 87 (1946); *C.A.*, **41**, 1728 (1947).

IONIC MECHANISMS

Many reactions of a drug with tissue may be conceived as mechanisms of the drug ion with the tissue ion. Protoplasm is an ampholyte, and it is explained that a physiologically active agent may join with the protoplasm to form a poorly dissociated and poorly soluble complex. A response may be inhibited or thwarted by a redistribution of the agent by the interposition of a stronger cation or anion, as the case may require.[35]

HYDROGEN ION CONCENTRATION

The effect of hydrogen ion concentration encompasses a wide range of physiological chemistry. Its importance may be appreciated from many points of view, e.g., effect on proteins, the isoelectric point of amino acids, influence on oxidation-reduction processes, buffer systems, enzymes, and electronic configuration. The *in vivo* pH range, however, is very narrow, being confined to about 7.25, and since the tissues and body fluids generally provide an excellent buffer system the cautious student will not automatically interpret *in vitro* experimental results obtained at other than biological pH as practically applicable. This is particularly true for substances such as acids, bases, or salts; for, depending on the hydrogen ion concentration, they may exist as undissociated molecules, or partially ionized, and the effects of the total molecule may be different from that of its component ions. Many of the amino-substituted acridines, for example, exhibit bacteriostatic activity by virtue of ion formation, which is favored by suitable hydrogen ion concentration.[36]

DIELECTRIC POLARIZATION

The introduction of certain substituents into an otherwise symmetrical molecule causes dipoles to be set up. Thus, butane, which is nonpolar, becomes polar when the hydroxyl group is introduced. The negative —OH induces in the adjacent carbon atom a positive charge with alternations and weakening of charges along the chain with remoteness from the oxygen atom. This theoretical assumption may explain the alternating toxicities of the homologous nitriles. The polar

$$
\begin{array}{c}
\text{H} \quad \text{H} \quad \text{H} \quad \text{H} \\
| \quad\; | \quad\; | \quad\; | \\
\overset{-}{\text{HC}}\!-\!\overset{+}{\text{C}}\!-\!\overset{-}{\text{C}}\!-\!\overset{+}{\text{C}}\!-\!\overset{-}{\text{OH}} \\
| \quad\; | \quad\; | \quad\; | \\
\text{H} \quad \text{H} \quad \text{H} \quad \text{H}
\end{array}
$$

structures and relative toxicities of hydrogen cyanide and the alkyl cyanides are approximately as follows:[37]

[35] A comprehensive exposition of this concept is found in the book *Ionic Interpretation of Drug Action in Chemotherapeutic Research* by A. V. Tolstoouhov, Chemical Publishing Co., New York, 1955.

[36] Albert, *Selective Toxicity*, Methuen & Co., Ltd., London, 1951, p. 85.

[37] Mameli, *Boll. chim. farm.*, **68**, 491 (1929).

Hydrogen cyanide 1 (most toxic)		$H\!\!-\!\!\overset{+}{C}\!\!\equiv\!\!\overset{-}{N}$
Methyl cyanide	92.2	$\overset{-}{C}H_3\!\!-\!\!\overset{+}{C}\!\!\equiv\!\!\overset{-}{N}$
Ethyl cyanide	3.56	$\overset{+}{C}H_3\!\!-\!\!CH_2\!\!-\!\!\overset{+}{C}\!\!\equiv\!\!\overset{-}{N}$
Propyl cyanide	1.17	$\overset{-}{C}H_3\!\!-\!\!\overset{+}{C}H_2\!\!-\!\!\overset{-}{C}H_2\!\!-\!\!\overset{+}{C}\!\!\equiv\!\!\overset{-}{N}$
Butyl cyanide	14.3	$\overset{+}{C}H_3\!\!-\!\!\overset{-}{C}H_2\!\!-\!\!\overset{+}{C}H_2\!\!-\!\!\overset{-}{C}H_2\!\!-\!\!\overset{+}{C}\!\!\equiv\!\!\overset{-}{N}$

It is difficult to fit into this conception another peculiar "alternating" effect. Dicarboxylic acids of the general structure $COOH\!\!-\!\!(CH_2CH_2)_n\!\!-\!\!COOH$ have the power to destroy carcinomatous cells if n is 1, 3, or 5, but are inactive if n is fractional or an even number.[38]

Rosenmund reports that the lactone of γ-(3-methyl-4-methoxyphenyl)-γ-hydroxybutyric acid possesses stronger ascaricidal properties than santonin, whereas the isomeric lactone of γ-(2-methyl-4-methoxyphenyl)-γ-hydroxybutyric acid is inactive.[39]

A diagrammatic distribution of the charges induced by the various polar substituents in the two lactones reveals that the active compound is more polar. Rosenmund attributes the difference in activity to differences in polarity. By

Lactone from o-cresol,
active

Lactone from m-cresol,
inactive

extending Rosenmund's theory of dipole effect, Muller explains odor.[40] Unbalanced molecules reacting with the "osmoceptors" of the olfactory senses set in motion forces that are perceived as odors.

HOMOLOGY

The full significance of homology in pharmacodynamic activity is not yet understood, perhaps because in medicinal chemistry it is the unusual property that is useful and sought rather than the most characteristic property of a given homologous series. It is suggested, however, that within limits there is a relationship between the logarithm of the thermodynamic activity required for equi-effective biological activity and the length of the carbon chain. This is

[38] Freund and Kaminer, *Wien. klin. Wochschr.*, **32**, 1105 (1919), through Mameli, *loc. cit.*
[39] Rosenmund, *Angew. Chem.*, **48**, 701 (1935).
[40] Muller, *Perfumery Essent. Oil Record*, **27**, 202 (1936).

demonstrated especially for the hemolytic effect of alkyl acetates on ox blood; for the bactericidal action of homologous alcohols on *S. aureus;* for the paraffin hydrocarbons in their narcotic effect on mice; for alcohols in their inhibition of the development of the sea-urchin egg; and for alcohols in their narcotic effect on tadpoles. The average increase in the logarithm of the thermodynamic activity for each —CH_2— increase is 0.10.[41]

RAMAN SPECTRUM

Dyson advances the attractive hypothesis that odors may be scientifically explained on the basis of vibrational movements of molecules, namely, the Raman shift.[42] If molecules with Raman frequencies within the range of "osmic sensation" come in contact with the olfactory apparatus, the sensation is that of odor, and the type of odor depends on the magnitude of the Raman shift. According to this hypothesis the olfactory sensation, like that of vision and hearing, depends on a form of wavelength and vibration. Dyson's classification of odors is shown.

Raman shift	*Type of odor*
1700	Aldehydes and ketones
1800	Esters, terpene aldehydes
1900	Acyl chlorides (excluding chemical effect)
2000	——
2100	Acetylenes
2200	——
2300	Chlorinated aromatic hydrocarbons
2400	——
2500	Mercaptans
2700	Ether types
2800	Higher aliphatic hydrocarbons
3000	Aromatic hydrocarbons
3200	Heterocycles and amine bases
3300	Pyridine, pyrrole, etc.

TAUTOMERISM AND RESONANCE

Schönhöfer [43] suggested that the antimalarial activity of quinacrine is associated with the possibility of resonance, such as that between structures A and B. This appeared inadequate to Curd, Davey, and Rose [44] because it does not account for the profound effect resulting from the presence of the chlorine atom in the molecule; accordingly they advance the theory that the unusual properties of quinacrine are due to an electronic shift within the molecule, as indicated between structures B and C. Development of this hypothesis led Curd and

[41] Badger, *Nature,* **158,** 585 (1946).

[42] Dyson, *Chemistry & Industry,* **57,** 647 (1938). For further discussion of this phenomenon see Wright, Reid, and Evans, *ibid.,* **1956,** 973.

[43] *Z. physiol. Chem.,* **274,** 1 (1942).

[44] *Ann. Trop. Med. Parasitol.,* **39,** 157 (1945).

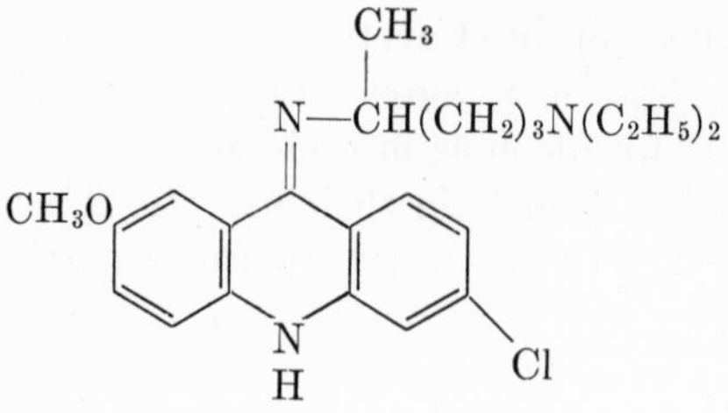

A

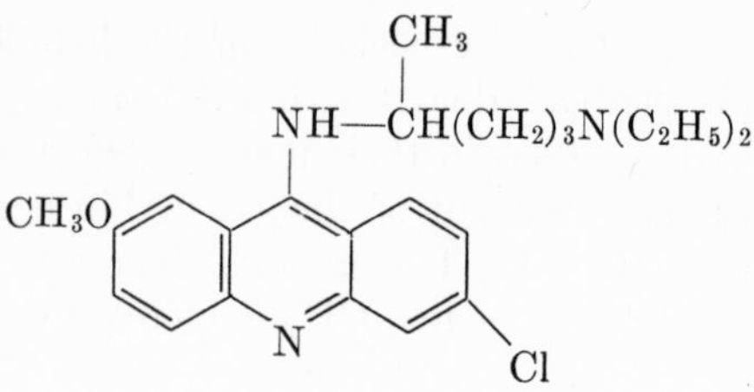

B

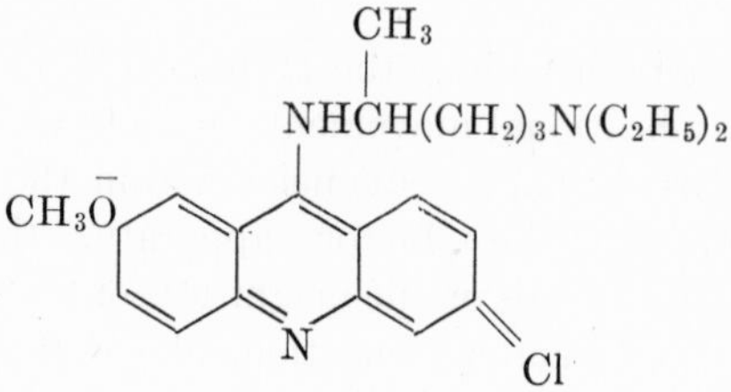

C

his co-workers to investigate chlorophenylaminopyrimidines and eventually to an "open chain" pyrimidine, that is, the biguanidino derivatives, of which paludrine, N_1-*p*-chlorophenyl-N_5-biguanide, is especially active.[45]

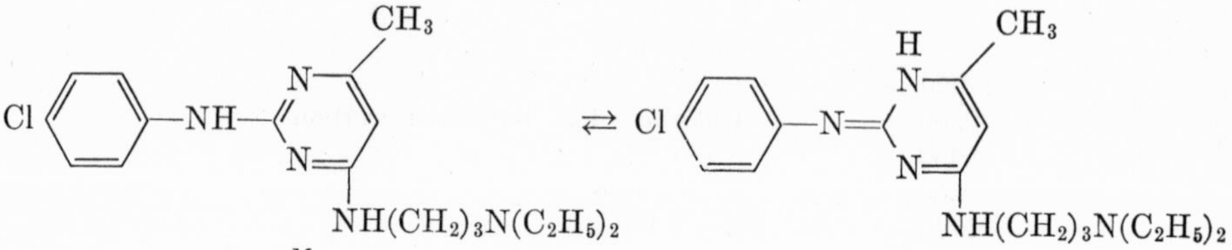

M $\rightleftharpoons$ *N*

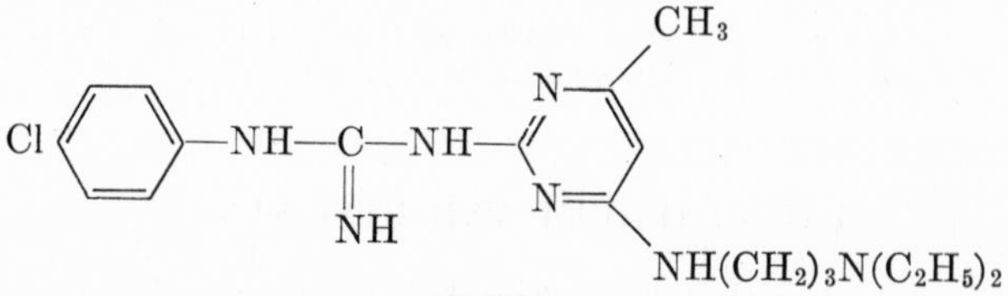

"3349"
P

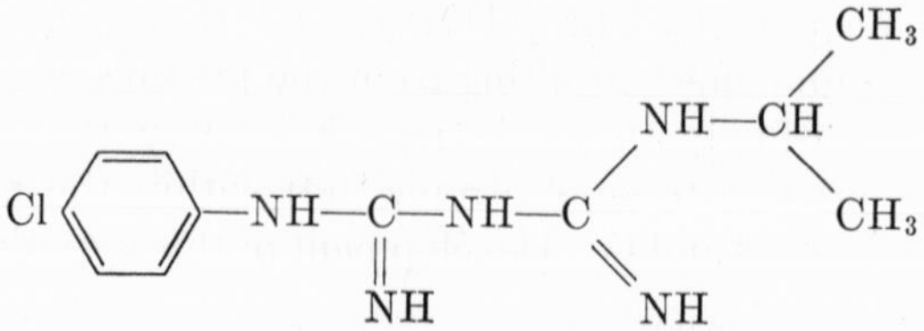

Paludrine
Q

[45] *Ibid.*, 208.

ELECTROMOTIVE FORCE

Substances that influence electropotential difference stimulate the tissues in the smallest doses. It is this thought which leads to the conclusion that perhaps the action of some highly toxic substances may be caused by electrical changes. In line with this reasoning the effect of varying concentration of alkaloids on the electromotive force of a model cell was observed.[46] The model cell was set up as

$-$ Hg	KCl solution saturated with HgCl	Nitrobenzene and 10% oleic acid	Physiological saline with 0.02% sodium oleate. Alkaloid added here	KCl solution saturated with HgCl	$+$ Hg

shown. The normal electromotive force of this cell, without any alkaloid added, is approximately 85 mv. The change in electromotive force produced by adding the indicated amounts of alkaloids is given.

Substance	mg./100 cc.	Decrease in e.m.f., mv.
Pilocarpine	1	33
	2	43
	5	57
	10	69
Atropine sulfate	0.2	7
	1	25
	2	40
	5	57
	10	71
Strychnine sulfate	0.1	4
	0.2	9
	0.5	18
	1.0	31
Cocaine hydrochloride	0.2	10
	1	49
	5	94
Quinine hydrochloride	0.5	4
	1.0	11
	2	17
Morphine sulfate	1	0
	2	6
	5	11
	10	18
Caffeine	0.5	1
	2	2
	10	4

It appears that these highly active, toxic substances, in amounts that are found medicinally active, produce an appreciable variation in the model cell, and the

[46] Beutner, *J. Pharmacol.*, **31**, 305 (1927).

assumption does not seem unwarranted that this artificial system may respond, at least as far as change in electromotive force is concerned, much like living tissue.

A solution of acetylcholine also produces electronegativity when in contact with oils or lipoids, or when in contact with the skin. In a cell similar to that described it was found that 0.03 per cent mecholyl and nitrobenzene in saline solution produced a negative potential of 200 mv. The lowest effective concentration of acetylcholine chloride gave a negative potential of 5 mv. in a concentration of $1:10^{-8}$. Whatever theory of acetylcholine innervation may finally be accepted, the electromotive activity of this substance in such high dilutions is impressive to say the least.[47]

Prostigmine, in such a model cell, has much greater activity than acetylcholine. This may aid in explaining why it exhibits properties in addition to its anticholinesterase toxicity.[48]

It has long been known that clinically effective anticonvulsant drugs are also effective against electrically induced convulsions. It was by testing against such convulsions that diphenylhydantoin was discovered.[49]

Beutner explains the action of many drugs on the basis of electromotive variation.[50]

Electrical potential differences in tissues have a vital function, and naturally any foreign chemical that modifies the normal potential difference, or rectifies an abnormal electromotive force, is bound to show drug action.

Complete inhibition of all these forces is a general property of all narcotic substances.[51]

By electrophoretic methods mammalian sperm has been separated into anodic and cathodic fragments. Artificial insemination, in rabbits, showed that sperm migrating toward the anode resulted in the birth chiefly of females and toward the cathode chiefly in males. These differences are associated with the presence of X or Y chromosomes.[52]

The measurement of electrokinetic potential serves as a means of predicting the susceptibility of bacteria to antibiotics. For example, the addition of bacteriophage to *E. coli* results in an immediate rise in electric potential, reaching a maximum in 5 to 15 min. With inactive bacteriophage, or if dead organisms are used, no rise occurs. Bacteriostatic substances, such as penicillin, give a rise of longer duration. It is suggested that the drug is adsorbed on the surface of the organisms which then dissociate into charged particles.[53]

[47] Beutner and Barnes, *Science*, **95**, 212 (1942).

[48] Barnes and Mauer, *Arch. internat. pharmacodynamie*, **73**, 386 (1947).

[49] Barany and Stein-Jensen, *Arch. internat. pharmacodynamie*, **73**, 1 (1946).

[50] Beutner, *Z. physik. Chem.*, **139**, 107 (1928).

[51] Beecher, *J. Neurophysiol.*, **3**, 347 (1940).

[52] Schreder, *Z. Tierzücht. Zücht ungsbiol.*, **50**, 1 (1941); *C.A.*, **39**, 2792 (1945).

[53] Dorfman *et al.*, *Biokhimiya*, **10**, 407 (1946); *C.A.*, **40**, 3156 (1946).

THE PERIODIC TABLE

Of inestimable value to the inorganic and physical chemist, the periodic table has not been used to any appreciable extent by the medicinal chemist. Except hydrogen and a few metals (used in the synthesis of organometallic compounds such as the mercurials) practically all the elements that are used in the construction of medicinal molecules are found in the upper right-hand corner of the old Mendeleeff table.

IV	V	VI	VII
C	N	O	F
	P	S	Cl
	As	Se	Br
	Sb		I

The chemist is always impressed with the families of the elements. In group VII the three halogens, chlorine, bromine, and iodine, are very similar, with gradual change in properties as the weight increases. In organic compounds there is an analogous relationship between the corresponding halogenated derivatives, whether they are chlorides, bromides, or iodides, and again a regular shift in properties appears with increase in the weight of the halogen atom. It is not surprising, therefore, to find considerable similarity in drug properties. These have been indicated in earlier chapters. Fluorine has not been properly classified with respect to its sister halogens.

An effort has been made to classify the biological functions of the elements according to their position in the periodic table; in group V*b* are found the chemotherapeutic elements; in VI*b* the catabolic elements; and in VIII those that modify violent reactions.[54]

Certain analogies between the organic compounds of arsenic and antimony are well recognized. Considerable similarity is seen in the work of Welch and Roepke [55] between phosphorus and arsenic analogs of choline. They found that

$$[(CH_3)_3\overset{+}{N}CH_2CH_2OH]OH$$
Choline

$$[(CH_3)_3\overset{+}{P}CH_2CH_2OH]OH$$
Phosphocholine

$$[(CH_3)_3\overset{+}{As}CH_2CH_2OH]OH$$
Arsenocholine

phosphocholine chloride and arsenocholine chloride possess qualitatively the same type of action as choline chloride; quantitatively phosphocholine was 77 per cent and arsenocholine was 3.5 per cent as active as choline. The three acetyl derivatives were also qualitatively identical; acetylphosphocholine was approximately 8 per cent and acetylarsenocholine little more than 1 per cent as active as acetylcholine.

Oxygen and sulfur show similarities only when S^{-2} is considered. Otherwise there is appreciable divergence.

[54] Valcarel, *Med. españ.*, **16**, 558 (1945); *C.A.*, **40**, 5076 (1946).
[55] Welch and Roepke, *J. Pharmacol.*, **55**, 118 (1935).

All these analogies, it will be seen, deal with relationships within the same families of the periodic table. It is also possible to cross from one group to another. Pyridine, C_5H_5N, m.w. 79, is very much like benzene, C_6H_6, m.w. 78. Thiophene, C_4H_4S, m.w. 84, in many ways is more aromatic even than pyridine. Since none of these unsubstituted cycles has drug properties, a comparison of medicinal virtues cannot be made. Corresponding derivatives of such isosters, however, frequently show unusual parallelisms. An excellent illustration of this is that of the sulfanilamide derivatives, e.g., sulfanilanilide, sulfathiazole, sulfapyridine, sulfapyrazine, etc.

Ethers may be looked upon as isosters of hydrocarbons, page 75. A parallelism exists between oxygen and nitrogen compounds, page 322.

A further extension of these ideas would include the comparison of the physiological activities of a molecule, M—X, in which X represents the first elements (joined by a single bond, the other valences being satisfied with hydrogen) of groups IV, V, VI, and VII of the periodic table; an example is shown. All of these

$$M—CH_3 \qquad M—NH_2 \qquad M—OH \qquad M—F$$
$$(15) \qquad\qquad (16) \qquad\qquad (17) \qquad\qquad (19)$$

have approximately the same molecular weight, the electronic structures should be quite similar, and the variation in molecular size should not be great. Such series are rare, but as an illustration the accompanying compounds may be cited.

All these compounds are known, but unfortunately adequate pharmacological data are not available to permit full comparison. Certain similarities, however, are apparent. All four compounds are pressors. II, III, and IV are reported not to show tachyphylaxis, which is characteristic of the unsubstituted parent compound; I has not been examined for this property.

Another hypothetical series is structurally derived from β-phenylethylamine, as shown. Of these, V and VII are known. Both are very much less toxic than

C_6H_5

CH—CH_2—NH_2

CH_3

V

C_6H_5

CH—CH_2—NH_2

NH_2

VI

C_6H_5

CH—CH_2—NH_2

OH

VII

C_6H_5

CH—CH_2—NH_2

F

VIII

the unsubstituted compound and show a more dependable pressor action than β-phenylethylamine. Salts of the two compounds show remarkably similar behavior in melting point and solubility.

ISOTOPES AND RADIOACTIVE TRACERS

The discovery of isotopes was in no way associated with the development of medicinal chemistry, and there is considerable risk in the careless handling of those isotopes that are radioactive. Notwithstanding, atomic science, the youngest of the philosophical disciplines, promises immeasurably to contribute to an understanding of the mechanisms of drug action, and some of the isotopes are finding use in their own right as therapeutic materials. It is estimated that except for cobalt three-fourths of the radioisotopes produced are now being used medicinally, many of them in more than 1300 hospitals and clinics in the United States.

Among the clinically useful inorganic products are radioiodine, as U.S.P. XV NaI^{131}, radiophosphorus, as U.S.P. XV $Na_2HP^{32}O_4$, and radiogold, Au^{198}. Deuterium oxide, D_2O, is finding use in determining total body water. By employing $C^{14}O_2$ in experiments on photosynthesis that process is revealing its secrets (cf. page 143).

The medicinal use of organic compounds "tagged" with radioactive components still awaits development. Already the clinical value of such labeling is foreshadowed. For example, radioiodinated human serum, IHSA, is a versatile substance, finding use in determining blood and plasma volume by the dilution principle, for studying cardiac output and blood circulation, and for the localization of blood tumors. I^{131} is in the phenolic nucleus of the tyrosine component of the albumen and is present in not more than one atom of I^{131} per 60,000 molecular weight. Globulins tagged with Fe^{59} are contributing to a better understanding of immunological reactions. Radioiodinated oils and fatty acids may prove useful in the study of lipids.

Sodium Radio-Chromate, N.N.R., $Na_2Cr^{51}O_4$, is used as a biological tracer. The chromium is reduced to Cr^{+3}, which firmly associates itself with the globin in the blood stream, tagging erythrocytes. It thus becomes useful for determining circulating blood volume and survival time of the red cells.

The technics for the synthesis of many pharmacologically active compounds labeled with C^{14} are well developed. But until more is known about the biological consequences following the administration of this radioactive carbon isotope there is a justifiable hesitancy to employ such substances as medicinal agents, except perhaps in some cases of terminal illness. This reluctance is natural in view of the long half-life of C^{14}, which is 5700 years, for there is no known method by which this active isotope may be selectively removed once it has become mingled with the body tissues. It may be expected, nevertheless, that it will be possible, by the use of C^{14}-tagged reagents, to study better the various chemical reactions of life. Examples of such studies are already described in the examination of the biosynthetic mechanism of squalene, starting with $C^{14}H_3COOH$ and $CH_3C^{14}OOH$, and its conversion into cholesterol.[56]

[56] Woodward and Bloch, *J. Am. Chem. Soc.*, **75**, 2023 (1953); Dauben and Takemura, *ibid.*, **75**, 6302 (1953).

Index

537